Modern Algebra
with
Trigonometry

A Mathematics Text

Under the Editorship of

Carl B. Allendoerfer

Modern Algebra
with
Trigonometry

SECOND EDITION

JOHN T. MOORE
The University of Western Ontario
The University of Florida

THE MACMILLAN COMPANY
COLLIER-MACMILLAN LIMITED, LONDON

The Macmillan Company
Collier-Macmillan Canada, Ltd., Toronto, Ontario

Printed in the United States of America

To
MARY DEBORAH

Preface

The primary purpose of this text is to provide an adequate foundation for an intensive study of analytic geometry and the calculus, but it can also be used as the basis of a terminal course for students who are not planning any further study of mathematics. Although most of the material in the text can be covered in one academic term, the first six chapters can be used as a self-contained unit for an introduction to analysis—the pace of such a course being naturally much more leisurely. The idea of a function, the unifying concept in Chapters 1 to 6, ties together—with the help of sets—the elementary polynomial, exponential, logarithmic, and circular functions.

There are three important respects in which this edition differs from the earlier edition with the same title. For the benefit of those who are familiar with the earlier edition, I shall describe these differences before any further comments on other matters of a more general nature.

1. *The number of problems in each of the problems sets has been greatly increased*—at least doubled in most instances. Moreover, although I cannot promise that Problem $n + 1$ is always more difficult than Problem n, I have tried to make the first few problems in each set very simple with either the degree of difficulty or abstraction increasing as one proceeds through the set.

2. In this edition, *I have followed what I believe is now generally the custom of placing analytic trigonometry before the trigonometry of angles and triangles.* There seem to be two important reasons for this ordering in trigonometry: One is the current emphasis on the circular functions in analysis—a matter that is discussed more thoroughly in the Historical Interlude between Chapter 5 and Chapter 6; the other is the fact (for better or for worse!) that elementary trigonometry is now being introduced this way in the high schools. It is desirable to continue and expand on this viewpoint—and show later how the older view of trigonometry appears as a corollary to the new. In the first edition, I attempted to justify

the placement of "angle" trigonometry first, because it was my considered opinion at *that* time of writing that whatever trigonometry appeared in the high school curriculum was for the most part of this variety. However, times have changed, and it may seem curious that I am now using in part what is essentially the same reason to justify the reverse ordering found in this book: It is better to review and further build on what has gone before than to confuse the students (who have been exposed to trigonometry before) with an approach that is entirely new to them.

3. From the point of view of cold logic, whatever one wishes to say about number systems in a book on algebra should be said at the beginning, because numbers are the ingredients of the foundation of algebra. However, *instead of including all number-theoretic topics in Chapter 1, I have put them at those points where some important use is to be made of them.* The very desirable effect is that the first chapter is relatively simple, instead of being what very well might have been—and possibly was in the first edition—the most difficult one in the entire book.

To quote what continues to be valid from the Preface to the first edition:

The underlying philosophy of the text is to give a careful and logical foundation for any topic discussed, if this seems feasible, but not to disdain the use of intuition for the sake of clarification. It is the firm opinion of the author that, while the material of the book could be framed in a straitjacket of formal logic, the result would be to reduce it to an extremely dull and insipid study of "dry bones." This is not to discount the value of logic in mathematics, because all mathematics is based on it and mathematical propositions must depend ultimately on it. However, at an elementary level, it seems healthier to demand something less than complete rigor (if complete rigor is even possible!) and to let the student gradually acquire a respect and an appreciation of the need for higher levels of rigor as he proceeds with his mathematical education.

In general, the subject matter of the book is much the same as any other book on algebra and trigonometry. However, an attempt has been made to introduce modern concepts, methods, and notations whenever this appears feasible. Moreover, it is my fond hope that, while there may be some omissions, there are no ideas in this book which the student will have to "unlearn" at a later time. In connection with omissions, it may be well to point out that the text contains no discussion whatever of probability and statistics. It has been my experience throughout my teaching career that these topics—although appearing in many books on algebra and trigonometry—are regularly omitted in courses similar to the one I have in mind. This is not because they are unimportant but, rather, because they are usually covered separately in other more specialized courses.

There are several features of the text (for the most part common to both editions) to which it might be appropriate to call attention. In Chapter 3 there is a discussion of inequalities that is somewhat more extensive than usual, including a brief introduction to convex sets and—in the problems—to the modern topic of linear programming. It is in this chapter that I have also found it appropriate to include the topics of "order" and "completeness" of the system of real numbers. The matrix solution of systems of linear equations, as given in Chapter 2, is more detailed than in most books of a similar nature; in addition, Appendix B contains a discussion of methods of matrix inversion with applications to linear systems. A study of the algebra of functions is given in Chapter 4, including a general discussion of inverse functions. The student is then able to appreciate the fact that logarithmic functions are inverse to exponential functions, and inverse circular functions are inverse to certain circular functions with restricted domains. In most textbooks at this level, the introduction of inverse functions is made solely to obtain the definitions of the inverse circular functions. Opinions vary considerably on how much material of a computational nature should be included in a book such as this one. There are those who feel that, with modern computers available, there is no real need for drill in hand computation. However, my personal feeling is that while computers are "available," it is not the case that everybody has one! Moreover, even if everybody had access to a computer, there is still the problem of programming—and this requires at least a theoretical skill in the art of computation. For these reasons, I have included some computational problems—principally in the context of logarithms and trigonometry. At the same time, since I agree that the importance of hand computation has diminished, I have severely limited the material of this kind. For the convenience of those instructors who prefer to exclude computation, the sections of the book have been so arranged that this can be easily done. Finally, it has been suggested by some people that induction should be introduced and used as early as possible in a book such as this, because of the importance of this type of proof in mathematics. Although there is some validity to this viewpoint, there are two more important arguments against it: Induction is a difficult topic for students at the maturity level of this book, and it would be unwise to present it too early; in the ordering of this book, there are very few places in the early chapters where one *could* use inductive proofs—and the student would very likely have forgotten about induction when the time does come for a meaningful use of this method of proof. It is for these reasons that it is located in Chapter 8 in this edition—which is, however, earlier than in the first edition.

Answers have been given at the end of the book to all odd-numbered problems with a numerical or very brief verbal answer; answers to even-numbered problems of a similar nature are available to instructors in a separate booklet on request to the publisher. In some instances where proofs are requested, useful hints are provided in one or the other of these two locations. A review of high school algebra is given in Appendix A for the benefit of those students whose backgrounds in elementary algebra are deficient. Because it is assumed that this section will be used by students, generally without the aid of an instructor, *all* answers to the problems in this Appendix have been included in the answer section of the book. There are a number of personal acknowledg-

ments that I would like to make. Initial reviews and commentaries on the first
edition of *Modern Algebra with Trigonometry* were provided me by three people:
Professor C. B. Allendoerfer (the editor of this series of texts) of the University
of Washington, Professor Edwin Comfort of Ripon College, and Professor
Marion B. Walker of Kent State University. Their comments were of great benefit to me and, even though I was unable to agree or act with respect to every
point they raised, the present book is much better because of what they said.
Professor Howard Eves of the University of Maine was very kind in allowing me
to use his various writings on the history of mathematics in the preparation of
the Historical Interlude between Chapter 5 and Chapter 6. Particularly useful
was the material credited to Professor Eves in the book by Clayton W. Dodge
(*The Circular Functions:* Prentice-Hall, Englewood Cliffs, N.J., 1966). My long-
time friend, Professor W. S. Cannon of Presbyterian College (Clinton, S.C.),
assisted me at various points in the writing; and four students at the University
of Western Ontario helped me to obtain answers to the problems in the text—
Messrs. George Conn and Anton Fieder for those with odd numbers and
Messrs. Nathan Friedman and Soon Sim for those with even numbers (contained in the separate answer booklet). Another student, Mr. Harry Panjer, was
very generous with his time, during a busy period, for some useful last-minute
rechecking of answers. To each and every one of these people I wish to express
my grateful and most cordial thanks. However, it is to Professor Edwin Comfort
—of whom mention was made above—that I must reserve a very special allot-
ment of thanks, because he has been of continuing assistance to me throughout
the writing of the complete book, being most generous of his time on my
behalf at every "beck and call." Although the remaining defects of the book
must be blamed on me alone, a great deal of the credit for its good qualities
must go to Professor Comfort. I would be most appreciative of being informed
as soon as convenient of any errors that do in fact remain in either the text
or answer booklet, so that they may be eliminated from future printings.
Finally, to the staff of The Macmillan Company and in particular to the mathematics editor, Mr. Harry R. Conn, I would like to express my sincere thanks for
continuing a very pleasant relationship that began some years ago with
Mr. A. H. McLeod.

J. T. M.

Contents

Modern Algebra
with
Trigonometry

1

Our Number Systems

1.1 The Nature and Symbolism of Sets

One of the most basic concepts in mathematics is that of a *set* or *collection* of entities (concrete or abstract), although it may be surprising at first to discover that the concept is even mathematical in nature. It is, in fact, so basic that no satisfactory definition for it has been found, and so we accept the concept as *undefined* but *familiar*. It is customary to refer to the entities contained in a set as its *elements* or *members*. In many instances in mathematics the question of the "existence" of a mathematical concept arises, and its resolution usually has philosophical overtones. In any serious study of sets this question arises, but we shall not be concerned with it here: The description of *any set to be discussed in this book* will be sufficiently sharp so that the membership of the set will be easily understood by everyone—even though at times there may be difficulties (possibly unsurmountable) in an explicit determination of this membership. If it is known that the only members of a set are *a*, *b*, *c*, the set is often designated {*a*, *b*, *c*} ; on the other hand, if there are possibly other untabulated members, the set may be designated {*a*, *b*, *c*, . . .}. It is much more common, however, to describe a set by referring to some property or characteristic that is possessed by all of its members. For example, we may speak of the set of dogs in the city of Chicago, the set of resident aliens in the United States, or the set of stars in the constellation Orion. The members of a set may be tangible objects like dogs, men, and oranges, or they may be intangible things like colors, virtues, and senses. It is even possible—and this is a common occurrence—for the members of a set to be themselves sets. For example, the set known as the New York Yankees is a set of baseball players, but it is also a member of a set of teams known as the American League. It is also useful for some purposes to introduce a set with no members and to refer to it as the *empty set*. This rather peculiar set will be considered unique, and it will be denoted by $\emptyset$. For example, the set of persons named Zzpfh listed in your telephone directory, the set of six-legged horses, and the set of four-sided triangles are all illustrations of the empty set $\emptyset$!

The individual members of a set must be carefully distinguished from the set itself, and the properties of the two may be quite different. For example, a bushel of apples and the individual apples in the bushel may differ in many ways: The bushel can be split into two half-bushels, while each apple remains unchanged; the bushel may be heavy, while one apple is quite light; one or two apples in the bushel may be overripe or wormy, while the bushel as a whole is in good condition. Even a set with one single member should not be identified with that member, although the distinction here is somewhat more subtle. H. M. Tomlinson writes in *Old Junk* [New York, Knopf, 1920]: "His shop has its native smell. It was of coffee, spices, rockwool, cheese, bundles of wood, biscuits, and jute bags, and yet none of these things; for their separate essences were so blended by old association that they made one indivisible smell, peculiar but not unpleasing when you were used to it."

Whenever symbols or names are used to denote entities, there is always a danger that the symbols or names will be confused with the entities, although the context should make the meaning clear. For example, the statements "Bob has red hair" and "Bob is a three-letter word" are both clear in their meanings, although "Bob" in the first statement refers to some particular person, while "Bob" is merely a name in the second statement. If a set is described by using names to list its membership, it is *possible* to consider the set as either a collection of names or the set of objects identified by the names. For example, the set {John, James, Harry} could be either a set of three names or the set of three people identified by the names John, James, and Harry. Both interpretations will be used at various times, but in order to avoid ambiguity and repeated explanations, we shall make the following assumption in the sequel:

> *The members of a set* $\{a, b, c, \ldots\}$ *are the entities of which* $a, b, c, \ldots$ *are names, except when stated otherwise or when the context makes it clear that the symbols or names are themselves to be regarded as the members of the set.*

Thus, without further explanation, we would regard {John, James, Harry} as a set of people, while $\{*, ?, +\}$ would be regarded as a set of symbols.

The most important relationship between a set and an entity is that of possible membership in the set: The entity either *is* or *is not* a member. Moreover, for the sets to be discussed here, it will usually be possible to make this decision from the description of the set—regardless of whether a tabulation of the set membership is possible. For example, it is clear that your dog Fido is a member of the set of all living animals, even though a complete tabulation of this set is not feasible. On the other hand, your eligibility to vote in the next election can be verified by an actual inspection of the tabulated list of registered voters in your precinct. In general, if x is a member of a set S, we shall indicate this fact by writing $x \in S$; the denial of this—meaning that x is not a member of S— will be indicated by $x \notin S$. The symbol $\in$ is a "membership epsilon" and will be used frequently throughout the course of this book. The symbolic statement "$x \in S$" may be read "x is a member of S", "x is an element of S" or, in some contexts, simply "x in S".

One of the most familiar symbols in mathematics is that of *equality* $(=)$, used to express the fact that two quantities are *equal*. Although the meaning of "equality" may vary somewhat in its colloquial usage, its meaning in mathematics remains quite constant and the following definition will seem quite natural in the context of sets.

Definition. *The two sets A and B are* equal, *and we write* $A = B$, *provided they contain precisely the same elements. In the symbolism just introduced, this means that* $A = B$ *provided* $x \in A$ *if and only if* $x \in B$.

Note. The phrase "if and only if" is of frequent occurrence in mathematics; it is used to abbreviate a statement and its converse. In the case of the above definition, the condition as symbolized is an abbreviation for the following two statements:

1. *If* $x \in A$, *then* $x \in B$.
2. *If* $x \in B$, *then* $x \in A$.

It follows from an earlier remark that, if $A = B$, then A and B are merely different names for the same set. The sign of equality may also be used in the actual naming of a set. For example, if we wish to give the set $\{a, b, c\}$ the name A, it would be appropriate to write $A = \{a, b, c\}$. If A and B are sets that are *not* equal, we write $A \neq B$; this implies that one of the sets contains at least one element that is not a member of the other set.

Definition. *A set A is a* subset *of a set B if every member of A is also a member of B. We express this fact with the symbolism* $A \subset B$.

For example, if B is the set of all men in your county and A is the set of all of them who weigh over 200 pounds, then $A \subset B$. As another example of the "subset" concept, let Y be the set of all animals in the United States. Then, if X is the set of all dogs in the United States, we may write $X \subset Y$. The denial of $A \subset B$, for sets A and B, is, of course, $A \not\subset B$. If A and B are sets such that both $A \subset B$ and $B \subset A$, it is clear that A and B have the same members and so $A = B$. This could be considered an alternative definition of the notion of equality for sets. If $A \subset B$ and $A \neq B$, we say that A is a *proper* subset of B, but we shall not distinguish this type of subset notationally. With reference to our first example above of a subset, if it is known that there are men in your county who weigh less than 200 pounds, then A is a proper subset of B—a relationship which is most surely true for your county! It is clear that the empty set $\varnothing$ is a subset of any set, because every element of $\varnothing$ (there are none!) is an element of an arbitrary set. Because any set is clearly a subset of itself, the following relations of set inclusion are true for any set S: $\varnothing \subset S$ and $S \subset S$.

The symbolism $\{x| \quad \}$, known as a *set builder*, is often very useful in the description of a set. For example, the set of all dogs in the world could be described in this symbolism as $\{x| \ x \text{ is a dog}\}$; the set of all trees would be $\{x| \ x \text{ is a tree}\}$. The description of the first of these sets would be read "the set of all x such that x is a dog," and the second description would be "the set of all x such that x is a tree," the vertical bar having the verbal meaning of "such that." A very slight modification of this symbolism is used to denote a *subset* of a given set, and this occurs more often than that for a basic set. For example, let D be the set of all dogs. Then the subset of dogs in Chicago could be denoted as $\{x \in D| \ x \text{ is in Chicago}\}$. If B is the set of all books, the subset of books in the Harvard library could be described as $\{x \in B| \ x \text{ is in the Harvard library}\}$. This symbolism of the set builder and its modification will keep recurring in the sequel, so the student should familiarize himself with it.

The two most common operations on sets are described by the following definitions, in each of which we have used the notation just introduced.

Definition.   *The* union *of two sets A and B is $\{x| \ x \in A \text{ or } x \in B\}$ and is denoted by $A \cup B$. This latter symbolic statement is often read "A union B."*

In this definition, the word "or" should be understood to mean that x may be in A alone, in B alone, or possibly in both A and B.

Definition.   *The* intersection *of two sets A and B is $\{x| \ x \in A \text{ and } x \in B\}$ and is denoted by $A \cap B$. The symbolism $A \cap B$ is often read "A intersect B."*

In words, the *union* of two sets is the *combined* membership of the sets, whereas the *intersection* is the collection of elements that both sets have in common. If the sets A and B have no elements in common, it follows from the definition of $\varnothing$ that $A \cap B = \varnothing$, and the sets A and B are then said to be *disjoint*.

It is easy to think of examples of the union and intersection of sets. If A is the set of all cows and B is the set of all horses, then $A \cup B$ is the combined collection of all cows and horses. If S is the set of all three-letter English words and T is the set of all four-letter English words, $S \cup T$ is the collection of all English words with either three or four constituent letters. If V is the set of all stone buildings and W is the set of all cathedrals, the set $V \cup W$ is the set of all buildings each of which is either made of stone or is a cathedral—possibly both. As an illustration of intersection, we may use the last example and denote the set of stone cathedrals as $V \cap W$. If P is the set of all English nouns and Q is the set of all five-letter words, the set $P \cap Q$ is the collection of all English nouns with five constituent letters.

One very convenient way to illustrate sets and their operations is by means of *Venn diagrams*, in which each element of a set is identified with a point within or on some geometric plane figure—often a circle. In Figure 1, two sets A and B are represented by the points of overlapping circles, whereas $A \cap B$ and $A \cup B$ are the indicated shaded portions.

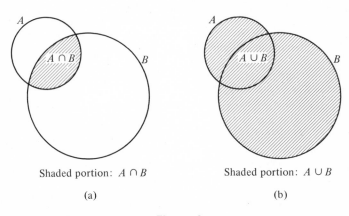

Shaded portion: $A \cap B$ Shaded portion: $A \cup B$

(a)   (b)

Figure 1

If all sets involved in a given discussion are considered to be subsets of some all-encompassing set (usually designated U), this latter set is called the *universal set* or *universe* of the subsets. In many instances, there is a very natural identification for a universal set: for subsets of plane points, it is the plane itself; for subsets of real numbers, it is the set of all real numbers. However, the universe for a given discussion may be taken to be a subset of what one might consider the "natural" one! There is a third set operation whose definition makes use of the concept of a universal set, but, since we shall make no use of it beyond the next section, the definition is given in a note preceding Problem 24 in the problem set.

It may have been noticed that the discussion in this introductory section has been phrased in a language that does not have the usual "mathematical" sound. We have done this intentionally to emphasize the very general nature of the basic notion of a set, but, beginning with §1.2, our concern will be with sets of *numbers* as they occur in more traditional mathematics. We realize that a large number of distinct ideas has been introduced in a few pages, but this has been done in the belief that most—if not all—of what we have said will be familiar to the reader.

Problems 1.1

1. If S is the set of Boy Scout virtues, decide which of the following are true statements: (a) Rudeness $\in S$; (b) bravery $\notin S$; (c) loyalty $\in S$; (d) uncleanliness $\notin S$; (e) cheerfulness $\in S$.

2. Make a list of the members of the following sets:
   (a) $\{x \mid x$ is a city in your state with a population over 100,000$\}$
   (b) $\{x \mid x$ is the catalogue designation of a course you are taking$\}$
   (c) $\{t \mid t$ is a planet in our solar system$\}$
   (d) $\{y \mid y$ is a country in continental North America$\}$

3. If A is the set of universities comprising the Big Ten football conference, decide which of the following are members of A: (a) the University of Illinois; (b) the head coach of the football team of Ohio State University; (c) the football team of the University of Wisconsin; (d) Purdue University; (e) the University of Chicago.

4. Supply an example of a set that has (a) only one member; (b) exactly two members; (c) exactly three members.

5. If A is the set of equilateral plane triangles and B is the set of plane triangles with all interior angles equal, state a theorem from Plane Geometry that has the effect of asserting that $A = B$.

6. If S is the set of people in your state, identify two subsets of S that (a) have no elements in common; (b) are distinct but have at least one common element.

7. Try to think of a set S that is adequately described—and so exists—but for which the truth of "$x \in S$" cannot be decided for every entity x.

8. In each of the following cases, decide whether the indicated set can be conveniently tabulated: (a) $\{x \mid x$ is a bird$\}$; (b) $\{t \mid t$ is a man over 6 feet tall$\}$; (c) $\{y \mid y$ is a regular solid$\}$; (d) $\{x \mid x$ is a living organism$\}$; (e) $\{z \mid z$ is a New England state$\}$.

9. According to the understanding in this book, decide which of the following are not satisfactory descriptions of sets: (a) the five greatest living Americans; (b) the ten most beautiful girls in your college; (c) the letters of the Greek alphabet; (d) the words spoken in your city between midnight and 6 A.M. on July 4 of last year; (e) the months of the year.

10. (a) If A is the set of fruit varieties grown in the United States, list three members of the subset $\{x \in A \mid x$ is sweet$\}$.
    (b) If B is the set of known gases, list three members of the subset $\{x \in B \mid x$ is combustible$\}$.
    (c) If S is the set of polygon types, list three members of the subset $\{s \in S \mid s$ has four sides$\}$.

11. Decide which of the following sets have the property that each of its members can be considered to be a set of people with more than one member: (a) the Ivy League football conference; (b) the basketball team of your college; (c) the American Baseball League; (d) the national ΦBK organization; (e) the chapter of ΦBK at your college.

12. If T is the set of former Presidents of the United States, indicate the truth or falsity of each of the following statements: (a) John Hancock $\notin T$; (b) Woodrow Wilson $\notin T$; (c) Oliver Wendell Holmes $\in T$; (d) Benjamin Franklin $\in T$; (e) Washington Irving $\notin T$; (f) Patrick Henry $\in T$.

13. Check that the following are immediate consequences of the definition of equality, for any sets A, B, C: (a) $A = A$; (b) if $A = B$, then $B = A$; (c) if $A = B$ and $B = C$, then $A = C$.

14. If A, B, C denote plane triangles, list some other relations used in Euclidean geometry which could replace equality in the three statements in Problem 13.

15. Make a complete list of the subsets of $\{a, b, c, d\}$.

16. If $S = \{a, ?, *, \pi\}$, list all nonempty proper subsets of S.

17. If A, B, C, D, E, F denote, respectively, the set of plane quadrilaterals, trapezoids, parallelograms, rectangles, rhombuses, squares, indicate the correct inclusion relation ($\subset$) between the following pairs of sets: (a) A, B; (b) E, F; (c) C, E; (d) B, E; (e) D, F; (f) A, E.

18. If $A = \{a\}$ and $B = \{b\}$, what can be said about a and b if (a) $A \subset B$; (b) $A \cap B = \varnothing$; (c) $A \cap B \neq \varnothing$?

19. Let A, B, C, D represent the sets of points within or on the indicated circles. Redraw the diagram for each part of the problem, and crosshatch the region described as:
(a) $\{x \mid x \in A \text{ and } x \notin B\}$
(b) $\{x \mid x \in A, x \notin B, \text{ and } x \in C\}$
(c) $\{x \mid x \in A \text{ and } x \in B\}$
(d) $\{x \mid x \in B, x \notin C, \text{ and } x \in D\}$

20. If $A = \{a, b, c, d\}$ and $B = \{a, x, y, c, f\}$, list the members of (a) $A \cup B$; (b) $A \cap B$.

21. If S is the set of coeds in your college and T is the set of majors in mathematics, what is the physical interpretation of (a) $S \cup T$; (b) $S \cap T$?

22. Explain why the following are true relations between arbitrary sets A, B, C, and use Venn diagrams to clarify your argument:
(a) $A \cup (B \cup C) = (A \cup B) \cup C$; (b) $A \cap (B \cap C) = (A \cap B) \cap C$.

23. If A is the subset of football players, B is the subset of boys under 5 feet in height, and C is the subset of boys with red hair in your college, give a verbal description of each of the following sets:
(a) $A \cap B$;   (b) $A \cap (B \cap C)$;   (c) $(A \cap B) \cup C$;   (d) $B \cap C$.

Note: For some of the following problems we need the definition of the third set operation referred to in the text. If U is a given universal set, the elements of U that are *not* members of a subset A constitute a subset A' called the *complement* of A (in U). In the diagram below, we have shown the complement of the set of points in or on the circle A (relative to the rectangular universe U) as the crosshatched region. It is clear that $A \cap A' = \varnothing$ and $A \cup A' = U$.

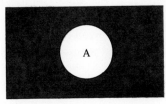

24. (a) If U is the universe of letters in the word BABOON, what is the complement A' if $A = \{A, O\}$?

(b) If $U = \{A, B, C, D, E, F\}$ is the universal set, with the member subsets of U defined as in Problem 17, list the membership of S' where $S = \{A, C, D\}$?

(c) If the universal set U is the set of 50 states in the United States, how many members does the set S' have where $S = \{\text{California, Florida, New York}\}$?

25. Use relevant definitions to establish the truth of the following "De Morgan laws" for arbitrary subsets A, B, C of a universe U, and check them with Venn diagrams: (a) $(A \cap B)' = A' \cup B'$; (b) $(A \cup B)' = A' \cap B'$.

26. Use the De Morgan laws (see Problem 25) to prove each of the following: (a) $A' \subset (A \cap B)'$ and $B' \subset (A \cap B)'$; (b) $(A \cup B)' \subset A'$ and $(A \cup B)' \subset B'$; (c) $A \cap (A \cup B)' = \varnothing$; (d) $A \cup (A \cap B)' = U$; (e) $[(A \cup B) \cap C]' = (A' \cap B') \cup C'$.

27. With A and B subsets of a universe U identify each of the following compound expressions as representations of U, $\varnothing$, or neither: (a) $(A \cap U) \cup \varnothing$; (b) $A' \cup (A \cap B)$; (c) $U \cap \varnothing$; (d) $A \cap A'$; (e) $(A \cap B) \cap (B \cap A')$; (f) $(A \cap B) \cup (A' \cap B')$.

28. If $P = \{A, B, C, D\}$, $Q = \{B, E, F, G\}$, and $R = \{A, G, H, J\}$ are considered subsets of the universe U, where U is the set of the first ten letters of the alphabet, list the membership of each of the following sets: (a) $(P \cap Q)' \cup R$; (b) $(P' \cup Q')$; (c) $(P \cup Q)' \cap (Q \cup R)'$.

29. With reference to Problem 28, list the members of each of the following sets: (a) $\{x \mid x \in (P' \cap Q)\}$; (b) $\{x \mid x \in (P \cup Q)'\}$; (c) $\{x \mid x \in P \cap (Q \cup R)'\}$.

30. The *power set* of a set is the collection of all of its subsets.

(a) Show that the power set of $\{a, b, c\}$ has eight members.

(b) Generalize the result in (a) to a set with n members.

(c) If A is considered a subset of some universal set U, what can be said about (i) the power sets of A and A'; (ii) a subset of U which is in neither the power set of A nor the power set of A'?

1.2 The Real Numbers

The number systems used in arithmetic and algebra are, for the most part, familiar to everyone since the early grades of elementary school. By this remark we mean that the student, in his grade school environment, has learned to work with these numbers and to get numerical answers to problems, but very likely with little or no thought about the essential nature of the abstract number *concept*. In fact, it is quite possible (or probable!) that the elementary student does not even distinguish a number from the symbol used to denote it. The early Greek mathematicians chose the point and line as the basic elements for their mathematical systems, but, in more modern times, an attempt was made to put numbers in the central position and to reduce all mathematical statements to statements about numbers—and ultimately about natural numbers. This thesis was proclaimed by Kronecker (1823–1891) in his famous remark that "God created the natural numbers; all else is the work of man." However, mathematicians were not content to stop even here in their search for a basis for mathematics, and Cantor (1845–1918) initiated the theory of sets as a foundation on which to build all of mathematics—including even the natural numbers. This foundation is generally accepted today as satisfactory, and in §1.1 we presented a brief outline of the nature and symbolism of sets—but with no attempt to develop any theory thereof. The transition from sets or collections to the abstract concept of number is highly philosophical; but very fortunately for the working mathematician, he need not be concerned with it. Neither will it concern us here, but we shall make free use of the symbols and language of sets—as introduced in the preceding section. In the present section, it is our objective to give a brief descriptive and intuitive survey of real numbers as they are used by the mathematician and scientist.

The natural or "counting" numbers 1, 2, 3, . . . are the most basic kind in mathematics, their primitive use being to obtain a measure of size for a set or collection of objects.

We shall always use the symbol **N** *to denote the set* $\{1, 2, 3, . . .\}$ *of natural numbers.*

In line with our understanding concerning symbolism stated in §1.1, the symbols or *numerals* 1, 2, 3, . . . are names that identify the numbers in **N**, but we shall see later in this section that it is sometimes convenient to use more than one symbol to denote the same number.

Two sets are said to be (*cardinally*) *equivalent* or to *have the same number of elements* if it is possible to pair off their members so that every element of both sets is paired with an element of the other set and so that no element of either set is used twice. A pairing of this kind is said to establish a *one-to-one correspondence* between the elements of the two sets. This notion is actually a more primitive one than counting: for, if such a one-to-one correspondence can be actually effected, the two sets have the *same number* of elements—and we are able to make this assertion without any attempt at counting to find out what this number is. For example, if an instructor tells his class to be seated and observes afterward that there are no empty chairs and no student is standing, he knows immediately that the number of chairs in the room is the same as the number of students. Expressed in more mathematical language, he has made the observation that the set of chairs in the room and the set of students are cardinally equivalent. On the other hand, if the instructor wishes to know how many students there are in the room, he "counts" them, which means that he sets up a one-to-one correspondence between the set of students and a certain subset of natural numbers. If the subset of natural numbers used in this correspondence is $\{1, 2, 3, . . . , k\}$, we know there are k students in the room—or the *cardinal number* of the set of students is k. Any set whose cardinal number is one of the natural numbers is said to be *finite*. A nonempty set that is not finite is *infinite*, and an infinite set that is cardinally equivalent to the set of *all* natural numbers is *denumerable*. Probably the simplest example of a denumerable set—distinct from the set of all natural numbers—is the subset of all even natural numbers, the correspondence between the elements of this subset and **N** being illustrated in Figure 2 below.

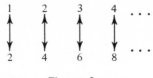

Figure 2

The natural numbers are quite adequate for the job of *counting* any *finite* set, but how suitable are they for making other kinds of measurements? It is a trite remark that "two and two make four," but is it true?! If you take two steps from where you are and follow this with two more steps, are you necessarily four steps from your original position? The answer, of course, is NO—if you have distance in mind—because this distance may be less than four steps. It is four *only if* the steps were all taken in the *same direction*. It is this int uitive notion of direction that now leads us to our next type of number—the (signed) *integer*. The *integers* are the numbers designated . . . , −3, −2, −1, 0, 1, 2, 3, . . . , where we note the presence of "negative" integers and zero, along with the natural numbers or "positive" integers. With the use of integers, we are able to attach a *sign* (+ or −) to a number and so indicate measurements in each of two *opposite* directions—one designated *positive* and the other *negative*. Unless the positive sign (+) is needed for emphasis, however, it is regularly omitted from the numeral for a positive integer. The positive integers—*so identified with the natural numbers*—are now seen to comprise a subset of the set of integers.

We shall always use the symbol **Z** *to denote the set*

$$\{\ldots, -3, -2, -1, 0, 1, 2, 3, \ldots\}$$

of integers.

Perhaps it should be pointed out that there are other reasons (which are more mathematically sophisticated) for extending the set **N** of natural numbers to the set **Z** of integers, but in this section we are pitching our remarks at a very intuitive level. Some of these other reasons will become apparent in later sections of this chapter, but for the present we shall be content merely with noting that **N** ⊂ **Z**. In the sequel we shall rarely ever refer to natural numbers— for they are "natural" only in a primitive sense—and it will be our preference to use the equivalent name of "positive integers." If 0 is included, the enlarged set will be called the set of *nonnegative* integers.

As we continue our intuitive development of numbers, motivated by measurements of various kinds, we are soon aware that, with nothing but integers available, our measurements often fail to come out "even." If, for example, we measure the length of a table, this length may be close to 4 feet but not exactly 4 feet. With the introduction of *fractions* or *rational numbers* all such measurements can be made more precise. The idea, of course, is to divide our unit of measure into n equal subunits, for any n (> 0) $\in$ **Z**, and to make the desired measurement by counting the number of these subunits contained in the object measured. Each of these subunits of measure is denoted by $1/n$, and if the measurement shows m of these, the desired measurement is $m(1/n)$. If we agree to identify $m(1/n)$ with m/n, we have obtained the familiar form of a positive fraction or rational number. Of course, the need for negative numbers still exists, and so a general rational number has the form m/n, for arbitrary m, n ($\neq 0$) $\in$ **Z**. We remark, without any attempt at proof, that the numbers $-(m/n)$, $(-m)/n$, and $m/(-n)$ are always considered identical. Of course, if $n = 1$ in the preceding discussion, it is clear that we are working with the original *integral* units, and so the integer m and the rational number $m/1$ are not to be distinguished for any $m \in$ **Z**. In this sense then, the integers form a subset of the set of rational numbers.

We shall always use the symbol **Q** *to denote the set*

$$\{m/n \,|\, m, n(\neq 0) \in \mathbf{Z}\}$$

of rational numbers.

It follows from the foregoing that **Q** is an extension of **Z**, and we see that the following relations of set inclusion hold: $\mathbf{N} \subset \mathbf{Z} \subset \mathbf{Q}$.

With the advent of rational numbers, all measurements of any practical importance (involving either of two opposite directions) can be made, but the number system is still deficient—even apart from considerations of other directions. It was known to the early Greeks that the length of the hypotenuse of a right triangle with sides of length 1 is not a rational number. The argument may be made by the method of *reductio ad absurdum*. Let us assume that x in Figure 3 is the rational number m/n. Then, by the Pythagorean Theorem,

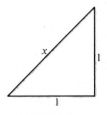

Figure 3

$x^2 = m^2/n^2 = 1^2 + 1^2 = 2$ and so $m^2 = 2n^2$. It is clear that any prime number must occur as a factor of the square of an integer with an even (possibly 0) multiplicity. Hence, we see that the multiplicity of 2 as a factor of the left member of $m^2 = 2n^2$ is even, but its multiplicity as a factor of the right member is necessarily odd from the form of this member. Since this deduction is absurd, our assumption that $x = m/n$ is untenable. Hence, if we wish to measure the length of the above hypotenuse, it is necessary to use numbers still more comprehensive than rational numbers, and this will lead us to the so-called *irrational* numbers. However, before we introduce them, let us return to the matter—promised earlier—of different names or symbols for the same number.

It is likely that the student learned how to add and multiply integers and fractions at approximately the same time that he first heard of these numbers. The rules pertaining to these operations, along with those connected with positive integral exponents, are reviewed in Appendix A. In this study of arithmetic, it may have been pointed out that the system regularly used to designate numbers is the *decimal* system—because of the prominent part played by the number 10. The sequence of digits used to denote any given integer is, in fact, merely the ordered set of coefficients if the number is expressed in an orderly fashion as a sum of multiples of powers of 10, the final digit or "coefficient" denoting the remainder that is less than 10. For example, in this decimal system, the numeral 345 is merely an abbreviation for the sum $3(10^2) + 4(10) + 5$; and the numeral 5067 is a similar abbreviated form for the sum $5(10^3) + 0(10^2) + 6(10) + 7$. The number 10 is called the *base* for the decimal system, but it is clear that any positive integer greater than 1 could serve as a base.

Example 1. Let us suppose that we wish to represent the "decimal" number 32 in base 5 numeration. We observe easily that $32 = 1(5^2) + 1(5) + 2$, and so the desired numeral is 112. To reemphasize, we are stating that 112 *in base* 5 denotes the same number as 32 *in base* 10.

There are certain advantages in some systems other than the decimal—in spite of our familiarity with the latter—and the *binary* system using 2 as the base is one of them. Although we cannot go into details here, we shall simply remark that the binary base is very useful in the operation of digital computers. This system, incidentally, was also a favorite of the great mathematician Leibniz (1646–1716), as pointed out by another famous mathematician Laplace: "Leibniz saw in his binary arithmetic the image of creation. He imagined that Unity represented God, and zero the void, just as unity and zero express all numbers in his system of numeration." As noted in the quotation, the only digits needed to represent any number are 0 and 1, since these are the only nonnegative integers less than 2.

Example 2. To illustrate the binary system, consider the representation of the "decimal" number 11. Since $11 = 1(2^3) + 0(2^2) + 1(2) + 1$, the desired binary representation is 1011. That is, the numeral 1011 in the binary system denotes the same number as 11 in the decimal system.

Example 3. As a "reverse" illustration, we find the decimal representation of the "binary" number 1111. Since 1111 is an abbreviation for the "decimal" number $1(2^3) + 1(2^2) + 1(2) + 1$, the desired numeral in the decimal system is 15.

However, although there are some advantages in the use of bases other than 10, *it will always be assumed in the sequel*—unless otherwise stated—that the decimal system of numeration is being used. With the completion of this slight digression on symbolism, we now return to the problem of finding a type of number that is suitable for the most sophisticated linear measurement.

The key to the solution of this problem is provided partly by the discussion in the preceding paragraph and partly by the geometric representation of numbers on a scale. The basis for an idealized measuring device or *number scale* is a straight line of infinite length, one point of which (the *origin*) is associated with the number 0, and another point to its right (the *unit point*) is associated with the number 1, the distance between these two points being the unit of measurement for the scale. Every point to the right of the origin is now associated with a positive "number," and every point to the left with a negative "number," in such a way that the "number"—apart from sign—is the measure of distance

Figure 4

of the point from the origin. In Figure 4, we have shown a portion of such a scale, with a few of the integers and rational numbers recorded on it. Even though the notions of "point" and "number" are intrinsically different, we often find it convenient to use the same language and speak of, say, the "point" 3 on the scale. We have already noticed that not all measurements of length are rational numbers, and so there must be points on a number scale that are not associated with numbers of this kind. It is (intuitively!) not difficult, however, to see how these "gaps" can be filled with numbers of a different type, and this type will complete our system of real numbers. In the numeral, representing one of these numbers, we shall use the familiar "decimal point," with digits to its right denoting successively higher powers of 1/10. For example, the numeral 325.14 is a numeral that abbreviates the sum $3(10^2) + 2(10) + 5 + 1(1/10) + 4(1/10^2)$. An example will illustrate the construction of our new numbers.

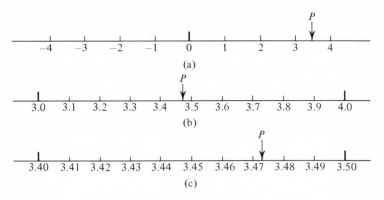

Figure 5

In Figure 5*a*, we have shown a portion of a number scale, and we wish to associate with the point *P* a number that will denote its distance and direction from the origin. We observe at once that the number must be between 3 and 4. In Figure 5*b*, the section of the scale between 3 and 4 is shown, expanded and subdivided into ten equal subdivisions—each of length 1/10 or 0.1. From this figure, it is clear that the number associated with *P* must be between 3.4 and 3.5. In Figure 5*c*, we have shown the portion of the scale between 3.4 and 3.5, expanded and further subdivided into ten equal subdivisions—each of length $1/10^2$ or 0.01. A glance at the figure shows that the number sought is between 3.47 and 3.48, while another stage (which we have not shown) might show it to be between 3.472 and 3.473. It is clear that this process of expanding and subdividing into ten equal subdivisions can be continued indefinitely—at least in theory—and one of two things must ultimately happen: The point *P* coincides with one of the points of subdivision; the point *P* never coincides with one of these subdivision points. In the former case, the number associated with *P* is a "terminating decimal," with a finite number of nonzero digits after the decimal point—but which may be followed by an endless succession of zero digits. In the latter case, even though the exact distance of *P* from the origin is not given by any of the numbers 3, 3.4, 3.47, 3.472, . . . , it is approximated arbitrarily close if enough digits are computed, and we *define the unending decimal 3.472* · · · *, obtained by the geometric process described, to be the number associated with P.* We have thus shown that there may be associated with each point of a number scale an unending decimal, and it is not difficult to see intuitively that the converse is also true. Inasmuch as distinct points of a number scale would be associated with numbers that have different digits at some stage of the geometric process just described, it follows that distinct points are associated with distinct numbers. A number so represented that every digit following some digit c is 9 cannot be distinguished from the number represented by replacing c by $c + 1$ and all subsequent digits by 0, and so we equate any two such numbers. For example, $3.146999 \cdots = 3.147000 \cdots = 3.147$. With this understanding, there is then a one-to-one correspondence between the points of a number scale and unending decimal numbers.

The discussion in the above example assumed that P was on the positive portion of the number scale, but it is clear that a similar argument can be made if P is to the left of the origin and so associated with a negative number. We are now led by this example to the following important definition.

Definition. *A* real number *is an unending decimal expression of the form* $\pm r.r_1 r_2 r_3 \cdots$, *where r is a nonnegative integer and $r_1, r_2, r_3, \ldots$ are digits from the set* $\{0, 1, 2, \ldots, 9\}$. *The set of all real numbers will be denoted by* **R**.

There remains the matter of identifying the rational numbers as a subset of **R**. We observe first that the decimal equivalent of a rational number in fractional form may be obtained in a direct arithmetic manner by the familiar process of long division. If we apply this process to the rational number m/n, there can be at most n distinct remainders; and, if the division is continued past the decimal point in m, the quotient digits must begin an orderly repetition with the reappearance of an earlier remainder in this stage. If 0 never occurs as a remainder, we obtain what is usually called a "repeating decimal." However, if 0 does occur as a remainder, the division process is essentially at an end and the resulting decimal number is terminating—but there is no harm in assuming an endless succession of repeated zeros, even in this case. The important point is that *any rational number* has a decimal expansion *with one or more digits being repeated endlessly in some fixed pattern*. As illustrations of this, we may cite the following: $\frac{6}{5} = 1.2000 \cdots$, $\frac{2}{3} = 0.666 \cdots$, $\frac{4}{33} = .121212 \cdots$. The rational numbers —*as endless repeating decimals*—then comprise a subset of the real numbers, and so the following inclusion relations are valid: $\mathbf{N} \subset \mathbf{Z} \subset \mathbf{Q} \subset \mathbf{R}$. In Chapter 8, we shall give a further extension of our number system, but, until that point is reached in the text, *all numbers will be considered real*.

The number scale may now be considered a sort of "picture" of the real numbers, with a one-to-one correspondence between the geometric points of the scale and the real numbers. The real numbers that are not rational—and so have nonrepeating decimal expansions—are the *irrational* numbers to which we made earlier reference. All numbers that are usually expressed as radicals (like $\sqrt[3]{2}$, $\sqrt{3}$, $\sqrt[5]{7}$) are irrational, but there are many others (such as the familiar π and e) that also belong to the same collection. The rational and irrational numbers together make up the set **R** of real numbers.

The real numbers have been associated with points on the number scale in such a way that any number x less than ($<$) a number y appears on the scale to the left of y. This is an extension of the ordering of the natural numbers in which $1 < 2 < 3 < \cdots$. Of course, $y > x$ is equivalent to $x < y$, whereas $x \leq y$ or $y \geq x$ means that either $x = y$ or $x < y$. This ordering of the real numbers—referred to as the *natural ordering*—implies, in particular, that $x < y\,(y > x)$ for *any* negative number x and *any* positive number y. A further discussion of ordering will be found in Chapter 3.

Example 4.   If $A = \{x \in \mathbf{R}|\; -1 \leq x \leq 3\}$ and $B = \{x \in \mathbf{R}|\; 0 \leq x \leq 4\}$, describe the sets $A \cup B$ and $A \cap B$.

SOLUTION.   It is an immediate consequence of the definitions of union and intersection that

$$A \cup B = \{x \in \mathbf{R}|\; -1 \leq x \leq 4\} \quad \text{and} \quad A \cap B = \{x \in \mathbf{R}|\; 0 \leq x \leq 3\}.$$

Problems 1.2

1. Identify the subsets of natural numbers, integers, rational numbers, and irrational numbers in each of the following sets of numbers:
   (a) $\{2,\; -\frac{1}{2},\; \sqrt{3},\; \frac{1}{5},\; 0.272727\cdots\}$; (b) $\{-\sqrt{2}/2,\; \frac{1}{2},\; \sqrt[3]{5},\; 1.571571571\cdots,\; -6, 0\}$; (c) $\{2/\sqrt{5},\; -2,\; \sqrt[7]{2},\; 3,\; \frac{5}{6},\; \sqrt{2}/\sqrt{2}\}$.

2. On a number scale, show the approximate location of the numbers listed in all parts of Problem 1.

3. Use an argument similar to that used in the text for $\sqrt{2}$ to show that the diagonal of a cube of unit side cannot be measured by a rational number. Then deduce that $\sqrt{3}$ is irrational.

4. Use long division to illustrate the "repeating" nature of the decimal expansion of each of the following rational numbers: (a) $\frac{11}{13}$; (b) $\frac{27}{37}$.

5. On a number scale, what number is located (a) half way between 2 and 3; (b) half way between 2.1 and 2.2; (c) one third of the way from $\frac{1}{2}$ to $\frac{5}{4}$; (d) one fifth of the way from -2 to 1?

6. What would be the simplest way—without counting—to determine if there are the same number of ladies as gentlemen at a party?

7. Explain how you could decide—without counting—whether there are the same number of oranges as there are grapefruit in a certain basket of fruit.

8. What is meant by the statement that π is not a rational number? Give a rational *approximation* of π in (a) fractional form; (b) decimal form.

9. Is there a smallest (a) nonzero positive integer; (b) nonzero positive rational number; (c) rational number in the set $\{x \in \mathbf{R}|\; 1 \leq x \leq 2\}$; (d) rational number in the set $\{x \in \mathbf{R}|\; 1 < x < 2\}$?

10. Use a geometric construction to find as many digits as you can of the decimal representation of $\sqrt{2}$.

11. Use a one-to-one correspondence to show that the set of natural numbers that terminate in the digit 3 and the set of natural numbers that terminate in the digit 7 are cardinally equivalent.

12. Decide whether (a) the sum of two arbitrary rational numbers is a rational number; (b) the sum of two irrational numbers is necessarily an irrational number; (c) the sum of an arbitrary rational number and an arbitrary irrational number is an irrational number.

13. From your past acquaintance with the "operations" of addition, subtraction, multiplication, and division, identify one (if possible) that can always be performed within (a) $\mathbf{Z}$ but not always within $\mathbf{N}$; (b) the subset of nonzero rational numbers, but not always within $\mathbf{Z}$; (c) $\mathbf{R}$ but not always within $\mathbf{Q}$.

14. Explain why the process of long division produces the "decimal" expansion of a rational number as a sum of powers of 10, a nonnegative number less than the divisor, and powers of $\frac{1}{10}$. Illustrate your reasoning with the number $\frac{231}{5}$.

15. Write the Roman numeral for each of the numbers, shown represented below in our "Hindu-Arabic" numeration: 2, 5, 6, 10, 14, 20, 50, 100, 1000.

16. Express each of the following numbers in base 2 numeration: (a) 12; (b) 17; (c) 24; (d) 36.

17. Express each of the following numbers in base 8 numeration: (a) 64; (b) 100; (c) 226.

18. Express each of the following numbers, understood to be written in base 2 numeration, in our familiar decimal numeration: (a) 110; (b) 10101; (c) 111011; (d) 1111111.

19. There are only a finite number of reduced fractions m/n, with m and n positive integers, such that $m + n = k$, for any fixed positive $k \in \mathbf{Z}$. (A fraction m/n is *reduced* if the only common integral factors of m and n are ± 1). Use this fact, and, with k ranging over all positive integers, prove that the positive rational numbers form a denumerable set.

20. If $x = 0.273273273 \cdots$, then $1000x = 273.273273273 \cdots = 273 + x$, so that $x = \frac{273}{999} = \frac{91}{333}$. Use this method to find the reduced fraction (see Problem 19) equivalent to (a) $0.181818 \cdots$; (b) $0.141141141 \cdots$; (c) $2.212121 \cdots$; (d) $1.23161616 \cdots$.

21. Use the symbolism of the (modified) set builder to denote the subset of real numbers x such that (a) $x > 2$ and $x \leq 4$; (b) $x \geq -1$ and $x < 5$; (c) $x > -2$ and $x > 1$; (d) $x > -2$ or $x > 1$; (e) $x < 1$ or $x > -2$.

22. If $A = \{1, 2, 5, 6\}$, $B = \{2, 5, 7, 9, 11\}$, $C = \{1, 3, 5, 7, 9, 12\}$, describe each of the following sets: (a) $A \cap B$; (b) $A \cap C$; (c) $A \cup C$; (d) $A \cup B$; (e) $A \cup C$.

23. Using the sets in Problem 22, determine
(a) $(A \cap B) \cup (A \cap C)$; (b) $(A \cup B) \cap (A \cup C)$.

24. Using the sets in Problem 22, determine (a) $A \cap (B \cup C)$; (b) $A \cup (B \cap C)$. Can you conjecture a general law of set theory from the results in Problems 22 and 23?

25. If A, B, C are defined so that $A = \{x \in \mathbf{R} \mid 1 \leq x \leq 3\}$, $B = \{x \in \mathbf{R} \mid -1 \leq x \leq 2\}$, $C = \{x \in \mathbf{R} \mid x < 0\} \cup \{x \in \mathbf{R} \mid x > 1\}$, determine (a) $A \cap B$; (b) $B \cap C$; (c) $A \cap C$; (d) $(A \cap B) \cup (B \cap C)$.

26. Explain why it is reasonable to equate the unending decimal $1.999 \cdots$ with the number 2.

27. Try to prove that the set $\mathbf{R}$ is not denumerable. If unsuccessful, look up a proof in some more advanced book [for example, Moore: *Elements of Abstract Algebra*, 2nd ed.; New York, Macmillan (1967), page 5].

See note preceding Problem 24 in §1.1 for symbolism used in the following problems.

28. If $U = \mathbf{Z}$, $A = \{x \in \mathbf{Z} \mid x > 2\}$, and $B = \{x \in \mathbf{Z} \mid x < -1\}$, find
   (a) A'; (b) B'; (c) $(A \cup B)'$; (d) $(A \cap B)'$.
29. If $U = \mathbf{R}$, $A = \{x \in \mathbf{R} \mid -2 \leq x \leq 5\}$, and $B = \{x \in \mathbf{R} \mid x < -5\}$, find
   (a) $A \cap B'$; (b) $A' \cup B$; (c) $(A \cap B)'$.
30. With U, A, and B as in Problem 29, and $C = \{x \in \mathbf{R} \mid x > 2\}$, find
   (a) $(A \cap B)' \cup C'$; (b) $(A' \cup B') \cap C$; (c) $(A \cup B)' \cap (B \cup C)'$.

1.3 The Real Numbers as an Additive System

Ever since the time of Euclid, geometry has been the subject of an axiomatic development—albeit the approach has been somewhat less than satisfactory during much of the period. By this we mean that certain entities—points, lines, and planes—were taken to be essentially undefined, and on them the edifice of geometry was built with the help of additional definitions. The content of Euclidean geometry was accordingly the composite of theorems proved on the basis of these undefined and defined concepts. Until quite recently, there has been no corresponding treatment of arithmetic and algebra, because these subjects were considered to be less worthy of study, having their roots more in matters of utilitarian importance. There was an attempt by the followers of Pythagoras (*circa* 500 B.C.) to attach mystical significance to (natural) numbers, but this did not lead to any logical development of our number system. Through the centuries, rules such as $x + y = y + x$ and $xy = yx$, for any numbers x and y, were considered to be obviously true and accepted—just like the familiar "two apples plus two apples equals four apples." Intuition was thus at the center of arithmetic and algebra in earlier times, and it is by no means our intention now to downgrade the importance of intuition—because it is at the heart of all new mathematics. However, in recent years it has been discovered that arithmetic and algebra do not have to be as disorganized as they have been in the past and that they can be axiomatized in a manner much like that of geometry. Of course, our axioms are chosen in such a way that our results still make good "practical sense," but the axioms—now called *rules*—that provide the foundation for our structure are now clearly in evidence. In this and the two subsequent sections, we shall make a very brief study of the system of real numbers—which were described intuitively in §1.2—from an axiomatic point of view.

It may be well to point out first that an algebraic *system* is usually understood to be a set to which a certain algebraic structure has been assigned. By this we mean that certain "relations" and "operations" have been defined in the underlying set of elements that form the membership of the system. There is no doubt that the operations of *addition* and *multiplication*, in the context of real numbers, are familiar to the student, and although there may very well be some doubt as to what a relation actually *is*, he will have had some practical experience with some of the common relations. In a very intuitive sense, we say that a *relation* $\Re$ has been defined in a set of numbers if it is possible to decide whether "*a* is in the relation $\Re$ to *b*" (written $a \, \Re \, b$) is true or false for arbitrary numbers a and b of the set. The relation of *equality* ($=$) is probably the most common of all relations, and it is this relation that concerns us very briefly now. If $\Re$ is this relation, we would then write $a \, \Re \, b$ as $a = b$, and, in view of our remarks in §1.1, we know that the equality $a = b$ means that a and b are merely *different names or representations of the same number.* For example, $2 + 5 = 4 + 3$ states that both $2 + 5$ and $4 + 3$ denote the same number—which in this case happens to be 7. We shall use **R** indifferently to denote either the system of real numbers or its underlying set, and it is clear (in fact, trivial!) that, in **R**, the relation of equality obeys the following three laws (cf. Problem 13, §1.1):

E_1: $a = a$ [reflexive law]

E_2: If $a = b$, then $b = a$ [symmetric law]

E_3: If $a = b$ and $b = c$, then $a = c$ [transitive law]

These laws may be considered the basic rules—corresponding to axioms in geometry—that govern the equality relation.

In practice we very seldom need refer to E_1, but even though E_2 and E_3 are used a great deal, it is convenient to replace them by equivalent but more useful formulations. We shall refer to these newer rules as E_2^* and E_3^*.

E_2^*: The two members of an equality may be interchanged.

E_3^*: If $a_1 = a_2 = \cdots = a_n$ for some natural number n, it follows that $a_1 = a_n$.

It is clear that E_2^* is merely a rephrasing of E_2, whereas E_3^* is the result of successive applications of E_3. Both of these "starred" rules also follow immediately, of course, from our meaning of equality, and E_3^* may be seen to be an algebraic formulation of Euclid's familiar axiom that "things equal to the same thing are equal to each other." It is doubtless true that the student has applied these rules without any question of their validity since his first encounter with arithmetic in grade school.

Example 1.   If we know that $3 = a$, for some real number a, an application of E_2 or E_2^* will allow us to write $a = 3$.

Example 2.   If we know that $a = b$, $c = b$, and $c = 5$, for real numbers a, b, c, we may use E_2^* to write $a = b = c = 5$. An application of E_3^* now implies that $a = 5$.

In our system **R** of real numbers, we have already referred to the two basic—and familiar—operations of *addition* and *multiplication*, which are indicated, respectively, by $+$ and either $\cdot$ or the mere juxtaposition of elements. The rules for addition—the operation of primary interest in this section—may be listed as follows:

A_1: For arbitrary $a, b \in \mathbf{R}$, the *sum* $a + b$ is a unique real number. (Because $a + b$ is real, as well as a and b, we say that $\mathbf{R}$ is *closed* under addition.)

A_2: $(a + b) + c = a + (b + c)$, for arbitrary $a, b, c \in \mathbf{R}$. This is the *associative* law of addition.

A_3: There exists a real number 0 (the additive *identity* of $\mathbf{R}$) with the property that $a + 0 = 0 + a = a$, for arbitrary $a \in \mathbf{R}$.

A_4: With each real number a, there is associated a real number $-a$ (the additive *inverse* of a), such that $a + (-a) = 0$.

A_5: $a + b = b + a$, for arbitrary $a, b \in \mathbf{R}$. This is the *commutative* law of addition.

The five rules, which we have just listed, will be very familiar to the student, but our reason for reviewing them is to point out that *all* the additive properties of $\mathbf{R}$ can be derived from them. In other words, these are the "axiomatic" rules pertaining to the operation of addition. It may be appropriate at this time to translate into algebraic language one of Euclid's axioms that is concerned with addition. This axiom states rather loosely that "if equals are added to equals, the results are equal," and its algebraic formulation in our present context may be given as F below.

F: If a, b, c are real numbers with $a = b$, then $a + c = b + c$.

The validity of this rule—which will be used without comment on countless occasions in the sequel—follows, of course, from the fact that a and b denote the same number and so its sum with c is independent of how the number is represented.

There is often associated with an operation another operation that, in some sense, is "inverse" to the original. If the basic operation is addition, the associated inverse operation is *subtraction*. Let us suppose that three numbers a, b, c are so related that $a = b + c$. If we now add $-b$ to both members of this equality, being mindful of the commutative and associative laws, we obtain

$$a + (-b) = -b + (b + c) = (-b + b) + c = 0 + c = c$$

It is customary to replace $a + (-b)$ by $a - b$ and to say that we have obtained c or $a - b$ by *subtracting* b from a. That is, *by definition of subtraction*, the subtraction of a number a may be effected by the addition of $-a$. This "rule of subtraction" is often memorized in elementary arithmetic.

The intuitive effect of an inverse operation—if it exists—is to undo the result of the primary operation. In the case of subtraction, this means that the subtraction of a number b from some given number annuls the effect of a conceived prior addition of b. This is true because, by definition of subtraction, $(a + b) - b = (a + b) + (-b) = a + [b + (-b)] = a + 0 = a$. Similarly, it may be seen that the addition of b annuls the effect of a conceived prior subtraction of b, so that each operation is the inverse of the other.

Although there is probably no great confusion about the matter, it may be well to point out that we are aware of the double usage of the $+$ and $-$ signs: They have been used to denote both the sign of a number and an operation. In the case of the $+$ sign, it almost always denotes a sign of operation, because— as we have noted earlier—it is rarely attached to a number, and the context should make the exceptional usage clear. As for the $-$ sign, we have *defined* $a - b$ to be the same as $a + (-b)$, and so it really makes no difference whether the $-$ sign in $a - b$ is associated with b or is regarded as a symbol for sub- traction. Hence, the apparent ambiguity is of no practical consequence, even though the sign of a number and the symbol of an operation are entirely different notions.

Example 3.   Prove that $a + (b + c) = (b + a) + c$, for $a, b, c \in \mathbf{R}$; in- dicate the justification at each step of the proof.

PROOF. $\qquad\qquad a + (b + c) = (a + b) + c \qquad\qquad$ [A$_2$]

$\qquad\qquad\qquad\qquad (a + b) + c = (b + a) + c \qquad\qquad$ [A$_5$]

Hence,

$\qquad\qquad\qquad\qquad a + (b + c) = (b + a) + c \qquad\qquad$ [E$_3^*$]

Problems 1.3

1. Simplify the following expressions as real numbers:
   (a) $2 - [3 + (2 - 5)]$ $\qquad\qquad$ (b) $1 - [2 - (1 - 4)] + 2$
   (c) $(3 - 4) - [1 - (2 - 3)] + 1$
2. Find $-x$, if (a) $x = -2$; (b) $x = -(-3)$; (c) $x = -2^2$.
3. If a, b, c are assumed to be real numbers, find $-x$ where (a) $x = -(-a)$;
   (b) $x = -a^2$; (c) $x = a - (b - c)$.

   Use the additive properties of real numbers (without any evaluation) to verify the equalities in Problems 4–6; include the proper justification for each step in the verifications.

4. $2 + (3 + 1) = (2 + 3) + 1$
5. $(2 - 4) + (1 - 3) = (1 + 2) - (3 + 4)$
6. $(1 + 2) - (6 - 4) = (1 + 4) + (2 - 6)$

   In Problems 7–11, use the same directions as those for Problems 4–6; assume a, b, c, d are arbitrary real numbers.

7. $a + (b - a) = b$
8. $a + (-b) + b + (-a) = 0$
9. $(a + 1) + (1 + b) = a + b + 2$
10. $(a + b) + (c + d) = (d + a) + (c + b)$
11. $(b + a + 1) + [(-a) + (-b) + 2] = 3$

12. What is the "rule of subtraction" referred to in the text?

13. Verify that $(a - b) - c \neq a - (b - c)$, for arbitrary a, b, $c \in \mathbf{R}$; that is, show that subtraction is not an associative operation. Under what general condition would this inequality become an equality? Can it be an equality for other particular values of a, b, c?

14. If $x \in \mathbf{Z}$, for what values of x does the following expression denote a non-negative integer?
    (a) $2 + x$ (b) $3x - 2 + x$ (c) $3 - (2x + 5)$

15. Identify the real-number properties that are used to validate the assertion that $-(a + 0 + b) + (b + a) = 0$, for a, $b \in \mathbf{R}$.

16. Would it be appropriate to consider a set with no operations and only the trivial equality ($=$) relation defined in it to be a special case of an algebraic system? If so, explain.

17. Would you consider "is more clever than" an appropriate relation in the set of students at your school? If not, why not?

18. We have shown in the text that subtraction is an operation that annuls addition. Give the similar argument to show that addition also annuls subtraction.

19. If an operation, denoted by $*$, is defined in $\mathbf{R}$ so that $x * y = 0$, for arbitrary x, $y \in \mathbf{R}$, explain why there can be no operation which is inverse to $*$ (that is, which annuls $*$ as subtraction annuls addition).

20. Examine the laws E_1, E_2, E_3 and point out one basic difference between the *form* of E_1 and that of E_2 and E_3.

21. Prove that the real numbers, asserted to exist by A_3 and A_4, are unique. That is, if a, $t \in \mathbf{R}$, show that (a) $a + t = a$ implies that $t = 0$; (b) $a + t = 0$ implies that $t = -a$.

22. As a generalization of the parenthetical remark in A_1, if $*$ denotes an operation defined in a system, we say that a subset S of the system is *closed* under $*$ provided $x * y \in S$ whenever x, $y \in S$. Decide which of the following subsets of $\mathbf{R}$ are closed under ordinary addition: (a) the set of odd integers; (b) the set of even integers; (c) the set of prime integers; (d) the set of integers divisible by 3; (e) the set of irrational numbers.

Note: A relation $\mathfrak{R}$ in a set S is said to be an *equivalence* relation if it satisfies three *abstract* conditions analogous to E_1, E_2, E_3 as listed in the text for equality. Such a relation is usually denoted by $\sim$.

23. Write out the three conditions to be satisfied by a general equivalence relation $\sim$.

24. Check that the geometric notion of similarity is an equivalence relation in any set of plane triangles. Can you think of another example of an equivalence relation in a geometric context? Consider $\leq$ and $<$ in $\mathbf{R}$.

25. Show that "is divisible by" is not an equivalence relation in $\mathbf{Z}$.

26. If we replace c by a in the *abstract* law E_3, it would appear (!) that the associated laws E_2 and E_3 together imply the abstract law E_1. Explain the fallacy in this argument.

27. If $\sim$ is an equivalence relation defined in a set S, prove that S is partitioned by $\sim$ into subsets of equivalent elements (that is, $a \sim b$ for arbitrary a, b in the same subset), with no element common to any two subsets.

28. If we define the relation $\mathfrak{R}$ in $\mathbf{Z}$ so that $a\mathfrak{R}b$ provided a and b are both even or both odd, show that $\mathfrak{R}$ is an equivalence relation. How many subsets of $\mathbf{Z}$ would there be in the resulting partition? (See Problem 27.)

29. If a subset S is partitioned into nonoverlapping subsets, show how this partition can be used to define an equivalence relation in S. If $\sim$ is the equivalence relation defined in $S = \{1, 2, 3, 4, 5, 6, 7\}$ by the subsets $\{1, 3, 4\}$, $\{2, 7\}$, $\{5, 6\}$, what are the possible values of x if (a) $x \sim 3$; (b) $x \nsim 3$?

30. Give an example of a relation in some set, such that the relation is (a) reflexive and symmetric but not transitive; (b) reflexive and transitive but not symmetric; (c) symmetric and transitive but not reflexive.

1.4 The Real Number System as a Field

In the set of real numbers we also define the operation of multiplication, and the familiar multiplicative properties are analogous to those for addition. In the following list of properties, we use the juxtaposition of symbols to denote multiplication:

M_1: For arbitrary $a, b \in \mathbf{R}$, the *product* ab is a unique real number, and—by analogy with addition—we say that $\mathbf{R}$ is closed under multiplication.

M_2: $(ab)c = a(bc)$, for arbitrary $a, b, c \in \mathbf{R}$. This is the *associative* law of multiplication.

M_3: There exists a real number 1 (the multiplicative *identity* of $\mathbf{R}$) with the property that $a(1) = (1)a = a$, for arbitrary $a \in \mathbf{R}$.

M_4: With each real number $a \neq 0$, there is associated a real number a^{-1} (the multiplicative *inverse* of a) such that $aa^{-1} = a^{-1}a = 1$.

M_5: $ab = ba$, for arbitrary $a, b \in \mathbf{R}$. This is the *commutative* law of multiplication.

These five rules play the role of axioms insofar as the operation of multiplication is involved in $\mathbf{R}$, and all multiplicative properties of $\mathbf{R}$ can be derived from them.

In addition to those rules pertaining to the two operations in $\mathbf{R}$, we have two other rules—called the *left* and *right distributive* laws—which connect these operations. We shall denote either or both of these rules by D.

D: For arbitrary $a, b, c \in \mathbf{R}$, $a(b + c) = ab + ac$ and $(a + b)c = ac + bc$.

Definition. *A set of elements, with the usual trivial equality relation and in which two operations have been defined so that requirements analogous to A_1, A_2, A_3, A_4, A_5, M_1, M_2, M_3, M_4, M_5, D are satisfied, is called a field.*

It is then an immediate consequence of our definition that the system $\mathbf{R}$ of real numbers forms a field.

Just as subtraction is inverse to addition, so is *division* an operation that may be considered inverse to multiplication. The division or quotient of a by b, denoted by a/b, is *defined* to be the product ab^{-1} for any $a, b \ (\neq 0) \in \mathbf{R}$. If $b = 0$, the symbol a/b becomes $a/0$ and is without meaning, so that *division by 0 is undefined*. The identification of a/b (if $b \neq 0$) with ab^{-1} in the multiplicative system of $\mathbf{R}$ may be seen to parallel the identification of $a - b$ with $a + (-b)$ in the additive system.

Example 1.   Prove that $(a + b)(c + d) = (ac + bc) + (ad + bd)$, for $a, b, c, d \in \mathbf{R}$; include the justification of each step in the proof.

SOLUTION

$$
\begin{aligned}
(a + b)(c + d) &= a(c + d) + b(c + d) & \text{[D]}\\
&= (ac + ad) + (bc + bd) & \text{[D]}\\
&= ac + [ad + (bc + bd)] & [\mathrm{A}_2]\\
&= ac + [(bc + bd) + ad] & [\mathrm{A}_5]\\
&= [ac + (bc + bd)] + ad & [\mathrm{A}_2]\\
&= [(ac + bc) + bd] + ad & [\mathrm{A}_2]\\
&= (ac + bc) + (bd + ad) & [\mathrm{A}_2]\\
&= (ac + bc) + (ad + bd). & [\mathrm{A}_5]
\end{aligned}
$$

Hence,

$$(a + b)(c + d) = (ac + bc) + (ad + bd). \qquad [\mathrm{E}_3^*]$$

Example 2.   Prove that $ab + (a + b)c = (a + c)b + ac$, for $a, b, c, d \in \mathbf{R}$; include the justification of each step in the proof.

SOLUTION

$$
\begin{aligned}
ab + (a + b)c &= ab + (ac + bc) & \text{[D]}\\
&= ab + (bc + ac) & [\mathrm{A}_5]\\
&= ab + (cb + ac) & [\mathrm{M}_5]\\
&= (ab + cb) + ac & [\mathrm{A}_2]\\
&= (a + c)b + ac. & \text{[D]}
\end{aligned}
$$

Hence,

$$ab + (a + b)c = (a + c)b + ac. \qquad [\mathrm{E}_3^*]$$

Problems 1.4

Without evaluating either member, verify each of the equalities in Problems 1–3; include the justifications.

1. (a) $(-2)(3 - 7) = (-2)3 + (-2)(-7)$
    (b) $(-2)(5 - 4) - 3(3 - 2) = (-2)5 + (-2)(-4) - 3(3) + (-3)(-2)$
2. (a) $(\frac{2}{3})(\frac{1}{2} - \frac{1}{5}) - \frac{1}{3} = (\frac{2}{3})(\frac{1}{2}) + [(\frac{2}{3})(-\frac{1}{5}) + (-\frac{1}{3})]$
    (b) $(\frac{2}{3})/(\frac{1}{2}) - (\frac{1}{2})/(-\frac{2}{5}) = (\frac{2}{3})(\frac{2}{1}) - (\frac{1}{2})(-\frac{5}{2})$
3. (a) $\sqrt{2}[\sqrt{3} + (2\sqrt{2} + \sqrt{7})] = \sqrt{2}\sqrt{3} + \sqrt{2}\sqrt{7} + 4$
    (b) $(\sqrt{2}/\sqrt{3})/(\sqrt{3}/\sqrt{5}) + \sqrt{3}/\sqrt{3} = (\sqrt{2}\sqrt{5})/3 + 1$

In Problems 4–10, without evaluating either member, verify each of the equalities, for $a, b, c, d \in \mathbf{R}$; include the justifications.

4. $(a + b)c + ab = b(c + a) + ac$
5. $(a + 1)(b + 2) = ab + (b + 2a + 2)$
6. $b(a + 1) + [(-b) + a] = a(b + 1)$
7. $(a + b + c)d = d(a + b) + cd$

8. $(ab)(cd) = (cb)(ad)$
9. $(a - b) + (c - d) = (a + c) + [(-b) + (-d)]$
10. (a) $(a - b)c = ac + (-b)c$
    (b) $(a - b)(c - d) = ac + (-b)c + a(-d) + (-b)(-d)$

11. Simplify, for arbitrary $x \in \mathbf{R}$:
    (a) $2(x + 1) + 2[x + (2x + 1)]$ (b) $3(2x + 1) + 4[2x + (1 + 3x)]$
12. Simplify, for arbitrary $x \in \mathbf{R}$:
    (a) $1 + [1 + (1 + x)]$
    (b) $-[3x + 2(x + 1)]$
13. Assuming $a, b \in \mathbf{R}$, perform the indicated multiplications and simplify the result as much as possible.
    (a) $(a + b)(a^2 + ab + b^2)$ (b) $(a + 1)(a + 2)(a + 3)$
14. If we were to state a "rule of division" that would be analogous to the "rule of subtraction" in §1.3, what would be the statement of the rule?
15. We have noted that $a/0$ is undefined for any number a. Does $0/a$ denote a number?
16. The system $\mathbf{Z}$ of integers, with the equality relation and the usual operations of addition and multiplication, fails to be a field because it lacks one property. Identify this property.
17. Decide which of the subsets of $\mathbf{R}$ described in Problem 22 of §1.3 are closed under multiplication.
18. One sometimes hears of the "rule of substitution" which states that it is permissible to replace any element in an algebraic expression by an equal element without affecting the value of the expression. Explain why this rule is trivial in our treatment of algebraic systems.
19. Use an example to show that the operation of division is neither commutative nor associative in $\mathbf{R}$.
20. Show that division is the inverse of multiplication in the sense that dividing and multiplying by the same nonzero number are operations that annul each other.
21. Show that either of the distributive laws implies the other, assuming the properties of $\mathbf{R}$ listed prior to D.
22. If the operations of addition and multiplication are interchanged in the statements of D, are two new valid equalities obtained?
23. Explain why $-(a + b) = -a - b$, for arbitrary $a, b \in \mathbf{R}$. (See Problem 21 of §1.3.)
24. If $a, b (\neq 0) \in \mathbf{R}$, show that $ab = b$ implies that $a = 1$, thereby proving that the real number 1 is uniquely defined by the property M_3.
25. Examine the system $\mathbf{Q}$ of rational numbers and decide whether it satisfies all the requirements of a field.
26. Use two new symbols, say $*$ and $\odot$, to denote two new operations which are analogous, respectively, to addition and multiplication in $\mathbf{R}$, and list the field properties in this notation.
27. Examine the 11 properties that make $\mathbf{R}$ a field, and decide which of them are no longer valid if addition and multiplication are interchanged.
28. Let us construct an algebraic system out of the set $\{0, 1\}$ by defining addition and multiplication as follows: $0 + a = a + 0 = a$, $0a = a0 = 0$, $(1)a = a(1) = a$, $1 + 1 = 0$, with a denoting either element of the system. Prove that this two-element system is a field.

Note: The following important properties of real numbers will be derived in §1.5, but try to establish them independently.

29. $a(-b) = (-a)b = -ab$, for arbitrary $a, b \in \mathbf{R}$.
30. $(-a)(-b) = ab$, for arbitrary $a, b \in \mathbf{R}$. In particular, $(-1)(-1) = 1$.

1.5 Important Properties of Real Numbers

In the two sections immediately preceding this one, we have listed the basic rules, or axioms, that are the foundation of our system **R** of real numbers. It is the purpose of this section to show how these rules can be used to derive other familiar properties of real numbers. The diligent and observant student will note that several of the results, which we call theorems in this section, have been suggested earlier in the problems! It may be well to point out that these properties are probably as well known as the 11 basic rules, but it is our intention to show *why* they are consequences of these rules, rather than merely to obtain them. This is the spirit that characterizes the modern axiomatic method in algebra and that parallels that of geometry. We ask the student to keep this purpose in mind as we develop the present discussion; without this understanding, the study of this section may appear to be quite pointless.

■ **THEOREM 5.1.**   (*Cancellation Laws of Addition and Multiplication*).
(a) *If* $a + b = a + c$, *for arbitrary* $a, b, c \in \mathbf{R}$, *then* $b = c$.
(b) *If* $ab = ac$, *for arbitrary* $a \, (\neq 0), b, c \in \mathbf{R}$, *then* $b = c$.

PROOF.   (a)
$$a + b = a + c$$
$$-a + (a + b) = -a + (a + c)$$
$$(-a + a) + b = (-a + a) + c \qquad [A_2]$$
$$0 + b = 0 + c \qquad [A_4]$$
$$b = c \qquad [A_3]$$

(b) This proof is left to the student in Problem 29.

■ **THEOREM 5.2.**   *The number* $x = 0$ *is the* only *real number such that* $a + x = a$, *for arbitrary* $a \in \mathbf{R}$.

PROOF.   Suppose x is any real number such that $a + x = a$, for arbitrary $a \in \mathbf{R}$. Then, by the property of 0,

$$a + x = a + 0.$$
Hence, $$x = 0 \qquad [\text{Theorem } 5.1a]$$
as asserted.

■ **THEOREM 5.3.**   *For an arbitrary* $a \in \mathbf{R}$, *the number* $x = -a$ *is the* only *real number such that* $a + x = 0$.

PROOF.   With a an arbitrary element of $\mathbf{R}$, suppose x is any real number such that $a + x = 0$. Then, by the basic property of $-a$,

$$a + x = a + (-a) \qquad\qquad [\text{E}_3^*]$$

Hence, $\qquad\qquad\qquad x = -a \qquad\qquad\qquad$ [Theorem 5.1a]

as asserted.

■ **THEOREM 5.4.**   *The number* $x = 1$ *is the* only *real number such that* $ax = a$, *for arbitrary* $a\ (\neq 0) \in \mathbf{R}$.

PROOF.   Let x be any real number such that $ax = a$, for aribtrary $a \in \mathbf{R}$. The basic property of 1 then requires that $ax = a(1)$, whence

$$a^{-1}(ax) = a^{-1}[a(1)]$$
$$(a^{-1}a)x = (a^{-1}a)1 \qquad\qquad [\text{M}_2]$$
$$(1)x = (1)1 \qquad\qquad [\text{M}_4]$$

Hence, $\qquad\qquad\qquad x = 1 \qquad\qquad\qquad [\text{M}_3]$

as asserted.

■ **THEOREM 5.5.**   *For arbitrary* $a\ (\neq 0) \in \mathbf{R}$, *the number* $x = a^{-1}$ *is the* only *real number such that* $ax = 1$.

PROOF.   Suppose x is any real number such that $ax = 1$, for arbitrary $a \in \mathbf{R}$. Then, the basic property of a^{-1} requires that

$$a^{-1}(ax) = a^{-1}(1)$$
$$(a^{-1}a)x = a^{-1} \qquad\qquad [\text{M}_2, \text{M}_3]$$
$$(1)x = a^{-1} \qquad\qquad [\text{M}_3]$$

Hence, $\qquad\qquad\qquad x = a^{-1}$

as asserted.

■ **THEOREM 5.6.** $a0 = 0$, *for arbitrary* $a \in \mathbf{R}$.

PROOF. $\qquad\qquad aa + a0 = a(a + 0) \qquad\qquad [\text{D}]$
$$= aa \qquad\qquad [\text{A}_3]$$
$$= aa + 0 \qquad\qquad [\text{A}_3]$$

Hence, $\qquad\qquad\qquad a0 = 0 \qquad\qquad$ [Theorem 5.1a]

■ **THEOREM 5.7.** $a(-b) = (-a)b = -ab$, *for arbitrary* $a, b \in \mathbf{R}$.

PROOF. $\qquad\qquad ab + a(-b) = a[b + (-b)] \qquad\qquad [\text{D}]$
$$= a0 \qquad\qquad [\text{A}_4]$$
$$= 0 \qquad\qquad [\text{Theorem 5.6}]$$

Hence, $\qquad\qquad\qquad a(-b) = -ab \qquad\qquad$ [A_4, Theorem 5.3]

The proof that $(-a)b = -ab$ is quite similar.

■**THEOREM 5.8.** *For arbitrary* $a \in \mathbf{R}$, $-(-a) = a$; *if* $a \neq 0$, $(a^{-1})^{-1} = a$.

PROOF. Since $-a + a = 0$, an application of Theorem 5.3 shows that $a = -(-a)$. A similar application of Theorem 5.5 to the equality $a^{-1}a = 1$ shows that $a = (a^{-1})^{-1}$.

■**THEOREM 5.9.** $(-a)(-b) = ab$, *for arbitrary* $a, b \in \mathbf{R}$.

PROOF.
$$\begin{aligned}
-ab + (-a)(-b) &= (-a)b + (-a)(-b) && \text{[Theorem 5.7]} \\
&= -a[b + (-b)] && \text{[D]} \\
&= (-a)0 && \text{[A}_4\text{]} \\
&= 0 && \text{[Theorem 5.6]}
\end{aligned}$$

Hence, $\quad\quad\quad (-a)(-b) = -(-ab) = ab \quad\quad$ [Theorem 5.8]
as asserted.

■**THEOREM 5.10.** *If* $ab = 0$, *with* $a, b \in \mathbf{R}$, *then either* $a = 0$, $b = 0$, *or* $a = b = 0$.

PROOF. If $a = 0$ or $a = b = 0$, there is nothing to prove; so let us assume that $a \neq 0$. Then

$$\begin{aligned}
a^{-1}(ab) &= a^{-1}(0) && \text{[M}_4\text{]} \\
(a^{-1}a)b &= 0 && \text{[Theorem 5.6, M}_2\text{]} \\
(1)b &= 0 && \text{[M}_4\text{]} \\
b &= 0 && \text{[M}_3\text{]}
\end{aligned}$$

Hence,
and the proof is complete.

It is Theorem 5.10 that is so invaluable in the solving of equations. For example, if x is a real number such that $(x - 2)(x + 3) = 0$, it is a consequence of this theorem that either $x - 2 = 0$ or $x + 3 = 0$. It then follows that $x = 2$ and $x = -3$ are the two solutions of the equation.

Problems 1.5

1. Evaluate the following expressions:
   (a) $2 - 5(3 - 1) - (2 - 1)(4 - 5)$
   (b) $-[1 - 3(1 - 2)(4 - 7) - 3]$
2. Find $-x$ if (a) $x = -(2 - 7)$; (b) $x = (-3)^2$; (c) $x = a - (b - c)$ for $a, b, c \in \mathbf{R}$; (d) $x = -t^2$ for $t \in \mathbf{R}$.

3. Is it possible that $-x > 0$, for $x \in \mathbf{R}$? Explain.

4. Is it possible that $x^2 = -1$, for $x \in \mathbf{R}$?

5. Simplify the following expressions:

    (a) $(\frac{2}{3})(\frac{1}{2} - \frac{1}{4}) - (\frac{1}{3})(2 - \frac{3}{5})$

    (b) $(\frac{2}{3} - \frac{1}{5})(\frac{1}{2} - \frac{1}{3}) - (\frac{2}{3})(1 - \frac{1}{2})$

6. Simplify, for $x \in \mathbf{R}$:

    (a) $-2(x - 4) - [3x - (1 - x)]$

    (b) $(2x - 1)(x + 1) - (x - 2)(x - 3)$

7. Simplify, for $x, y \in \mathbf{R}$:

    (a) $(0.1x - 0.2y)^2$;   (b) $0.01x(x - 0.2y)^2$

8. Simplify $1 - [1 - (1 - x)]$, for arbitrary $x \in \mathbf{R}$.

9. Simplify, for arbitrary $x, y \in \mathbf{R}$:

    (a) $2x - [2 - 3x(1 - x)]$

    (b) $(x + 2y)(x - 2y)(x^2 + 4y^2)$

10. Is $(x^2 - 4)/(x - 2)$ equal to $x + 2$ for all $x \in \mathbf{R}$?

11. Show that

    (a) $\{x \in \mathbf{R} \mid x - 1 = 0\} \cup \{x \in \mathbf{R} \mid x - 2 = 0\}$

$$= \{x \in \mathbf{R} \mid (x - 1)(x - 2) = 0\} = \{1, 2\};$$

    (b) $\{x \in \mathbf{R} \mid x^2 - 2x + 1 = 0\} \cup \{x \in \mathbf{R} \mid (x - 1)(x - 2) = 0\}$

$$= \{x \in \mathbf{R} \mid (x - 1)(x - 2) = 0\} = \{1, 2\}.$$

12. Show that

    (a) $\{x \in \mathbf{R} \mid (x - 1)(x - 2) = 0\} \cap \{x \in \mathbf{R} \mid (x - 2)(x - 3) = 0\} = \{2\}$;

    (b) $\{x \in \mathbf{R} \mid (x - 1)(x - 3) = 0\} \cap \{x \in \mathbf{R} \mid (x - 1)(x - 3)^2 = 0\} = \{1, 3\}$.

13. Prove, for arbitrary $a, b, c \in \mathbf{R}$, that $(a - b)(a - c) - bc = a(a - b - c)$ and include the justification for each step of the proof.

14. Prove, for arbitrary $a, b, c \in \mathbf{R}$, that $a(b - c) + b(c - a) + c(a - b) = 0$ and include the justification for each step of the proof.

15. Prove that $(a + b)(a - b) = a^2 - b^2$ and include the justification for each step of the proof.

16. Without using M_5, prove that $x = 1$ is the only real number with the property that $xa = a$, for arbitrary $a \in \mathbf{R}$.

17. Without using M_5, prove that $x = a^{-1}$ is the only real number associated with $a \; (\neq 0) \in \mathbf{R}$ such that $xa = 1$.

18. Imitate the *proof* in Theorem 5.9—but without using its result—to prove that $(-1)(-1) = 1$.

19. Refer to Theorem 5.1 and explain the principle of "transposition," by means of which elements are transposed from one member of an equality to the other.

20. If $a, b \; (\neq 0) \in \mathbf{Z}$, the symbolism a/b suggests that rational numbers may be obtained from integers by formal division. Is there an analogous formal relationship between the (signed) integers and natural numbers? Explain.

21. Give a proof similar to that of Theorem 5.7 to prove that $(-a)b = -ab$.

22. If x is a real number such that $(x + 1)(x - 2)(x - 1) = 0$, why can we conclude that $x = -1$, $x = 2$, or $x = 1$?

23. Give the steps of the argument, implied in the proof of Theorem 5.8, that $(a^{-1})^{-1} = a$, for $a \; (\neq 0) \in \mathbf{R}$.

24. Prove that (a) $(-1)a = -a$, for aribtrary $a \in \mathbf{R}$; (b) $-(a - b) = b - a$, for arbitrary $a, b \in \mathbf{R}$.

25. If $a = b$, for $a, b \in \mathbf{R}$, why can we conclude that $-a = -b$?

26. Use the concept of division to show that $a/b = 1$, for $a, b \in \mathbf{R}$ implies that $a = b$.

27. Use the concept of division to explain why $(a + b)/c = a/c + b/c$ for $a, b, c \, (\neq 0) \in \mathbf{R}$.

28. Explain why $-(a/b) = (-a)/b = a/(-b)$, for arbitrary $a, b \, (\neq 0) \in \mathbf{R}$.

29. Use a proof similar to that of Theorem 5.1a to show that if $ab = ac$, with $a \, (\neq 0), b, c \in \mathbf{R}$, then $b = c$. This is the *Cancellation Law of Multiplication.*)

30. Use the concept of division to justify the following cancellation process: $a(b/a) = b$, for arbitrary $a \, (\neq 0), b \in \mathbf{R}$.

2

Systems of
Equations

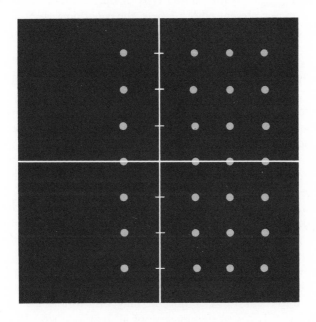

2.1 Truth or Solution Sets

In its somewhat restricted usage by a
mathematician, a *statement* or *sentence* is
a declaration that is either true or false.
For example, the sentence "Florida is
south of New York" is true, whereas
"Chicago is in the State of Ohio" is false.
Each statement may then be said to have
a *truth value: true* if the statement is true,
and *false* if the statement is false. It is
clear that "x was the first President of the
United States" and "x is the capital of
Michigan" are not statements or sentences
of this restrictive kind, but they are
illustrative of the following more general
concept.

Definition.   *An* open *sentence is a formal statement involving symbols, the truth value of which becomes known when the symbols are replaced by the elements of some appropriate set.*

If x is replaced by "George Washington" in the first illustrative open sentence just before the definition, the resulting statement is true; if x is replaced by "Flint" in the second, the result is a false statement.

In mathematics, the most common type of open sentence is an *equation* or *inequality.* From our present point of view, the equation $x + 6 = 5$ is an open sentence, which is true if x is replaced by -1 and false for any other replacement. The symbols—such as this x—that appear in an equation or inequality are usually called *variables*; its *truth set* or *solution set* is the set of replacements for the variables that transform the equation into a true statement. Of course, it is assumed that we know what sort of replacements are appropriate or eligible for consideration. For example, we must understand whether x in an equation is to be replaced by an integer or merely a real number. The set of eligible replacements for a variable is called the *universal set* or *universe U* of the variable (quite analogous to the universal set associated with subsets, discussed in Chap. 1). If U is the set of positive integers, the solution set of the equation $x + 6 = 5$ is the empty set $\varnothing$, but if U is the set of integers, the solution set is $\{-1\}$. It is important to realize that the solution set of an equation depends on the universe of the variable as well as on the structure of the formal equation. A determination of the solution set of an equation is known as *solving* the equation.

Although we are postponing any major discussion of inequalities until Chapter 3, we may point out that the remarks in the preceding paragraph are also applicable to them. For example, we may wish to find the solution set of the inequality $x - 1 < 4$ in the universe of all real numbers. The solution set comprises all real numbers less than 5, which, in our familiar symbolism, may be expressed as $\{x \in \mathbf{R} \mid x < 5\}$.

It is possible, of course, that an open sentence contains more than one variable in its construction. Equations such as $y = x + 2$ and inequalities such as $x + y < z$ are of common occurrence and illustrate the use of more than one variable in an open sentence. Although the universes of the variables in a given equation or inequality may be different, this is usually not the case. Without an explicit statement to the contrary, we shall always assume a common universe for such variables in the sequel. Before discussing solution sets of open sentences that contain more than one variable, however, it is desirable to introduce the notion of the *Cartesian product* of sets.

It was implicit in our discussion of sets in §1.1 that the order in which the members of a set may be listed is of no importance. For example, $\{1, 3, 5, 7\} = \{3, 5, 1, 7\} = \{7, 1, 5, 3\}$. However, there are times when it *is* important to take notice of the listed order of the elements of a set, and the set is then said to be *ordered.* If the names of the six prize winners of a contest are listed, the order in which the names occur usually makes quite a difference to the prize winners.

It has been said that a recipe for success is "work, play," whereas the arrangement "play, work" often leads to disastrous results! If the latitude and longitude of a ship in distress are recorded as (45, 65), it is important for a rescue ship to know which of the two numbers denotes latitude and which denotes longitude. Such a pair of elements in prescribed order is called an *ordered pair*, and the two elements are the *components* of the pair. We shall always distinguish an ordered pair notationally from an unordered set by the use of parentheses instead of braces. It is only natural, of course, that two ordered sets are *equal* (=) if their respective components are equal. Thus, for example, $(2, 3) \neq (3, 2)$, but $(2, 3) = (1 + 1, 4 - 1)$. If there are three (or n) components of an ordered set, the set is called an *ordered triple* (or *ordered n-tuple*). We are now able to give the desired definition.

Definition. *If A and B are any two sets, the* Cartesian product *A × B of A and B is the collection of all ordered pairs* (a, b), *with a* ∈ *A and b* ∈ *B. That is, A × B = {(a, b)| a* ∈ *A, b* ∈ *B}. The special case A × A is frequently called simply the* Cartesian *set of A.*

By way of illustration, let $A = \{1, 2, 3\}$ and $B = \{-1, 1\}$. Then, $A \times B = \{(1, -1), (2, -1), (3, -1), (1, 1), (2, 1), (3, 1)\}$, and $B \times B = \{(-1, -1), (-1, 1), (1, -1), (1, 1)\}$. There is a very simple way to give a plane graphical

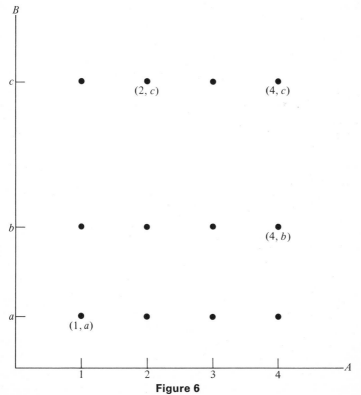

Figure 6

representation of a Cartesian product set $A \times B$. First, we associate the elements of A with distinct points on a horizontal line, and the elements of B with distinct points on an intersecting vertical line in the plane. If we then draw vertical lines through all points associated with elements of A and horizontal lines through all points associated with elements of B, the points of intersection of these lines may be considered to represent the elements of $A \times B$. To be explicit, the vertical line through $a \in A$ and the horizontal line through $b \in B$ intersect in a point that represents the ordered pair $(a, b) \in A \times B$. In Figure 6, we have given a graphical representation (or we have *drawn a graph*) of $A \times B$, where $A = \{1, 2, 3, 4\}$ and $B = \{a, b, c\}$.

The case of most interest to us here is that in which both A and B are subsets of real numbers, so that the original horizontal line and vertical line can be regarded as algebraic scales that intersect at their common zero point. We recall that each point of an algebraic scale is associated with a unique real number, and each real number is associated with a unique point on an algebraic scale—a fact sometimes referred to as the *Fundamental Postulate of Analytic Geometry*. A pair of algebraic scales (called *axes*) positioned as just described, constitutes a *rectangular*, or *Cartesian*, coordinate system in the plane. If $A = B = \mathbf{R}$, the graph of the Cartesian set $A \times B$ (that is, $\mathbf{R} \times \mathbf{R}$) is the set of all points of the plane, and the ordered pair (a, b) associated with a point is called its *coordinate pair*, the numbers a and b being its *coordinates*. We can

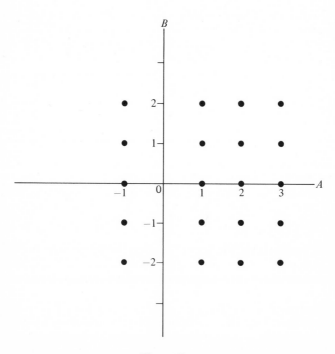

Figure 7

illustrate a more restrictive case by letting $A = \{-1, 1, 2, 3\}$ and $B = \{-2, -1, 0, 1, 2\}$; the graph of the Cartesian product $A \times B$ is shown in Figure 7.

Returning now to the matter of solution sets, let us consider the equation $y = x + 4$, with x and y variables in the universe $\mathbf{R}$. The equation becomes a true statement if x is replaced by 1 and y is replaced by 5, and so it is convenient to say that the ordered pair $(1, 5)$ is a solution of the equation. There are, of course, many other solutions, and the complete solution set may be designated formally as $\{(x, y) \in \mathbf{R} \times \mathbf{R} \mid y = x + 4\}$. In stating that $(1, 5)$ is a solution of $y = x + 4$, it is important to understand that 1 is a replacement for x and 5 is a replacement for y. In general, if we denote an n-tuple as a solution of an equation in n variables, it is necessary to order the variables and to understand that the components of the n-tuple solution are associated with the variables in the *same ordered position*.

The usual methods of solving linear and quadratic equations are reviewed in §6 of Appendix A, and we consider this problem for more general polynomial equations in Chapter 9. Most of the present chapter is devoted to methods of solving *systems* of linear equations, a subject that we introduce in the next section.

Problems 2.1

1. Paraphrase each of the following statements in a form that does not involve the symbol x:
   (a) For some integer x, x is divisible by 5; (b) For every x, if x is an orange, then x is a fruit; (c) There exists x such that x is a dog and x is dangerous; (d) If x is a student who studies hard, then x will pass his examinations.
2. Paraphrase each of the following statements in a form that does not involve the symbol x:
   (a) For some integer x, the number 5 is not divisible by x; (b) For every x, if x is a bear then x is an animal; (c) If x is a person who walks in the rain, then x will get wet; (d) There exists x such that x is a student at your school and x is lazy.
3. Decide which of the following are open sentences:
   (a) Abraham Lincoln was a President of the United States; (b) The number of prime factors of 12 is x; (c) x is an integer less than 10; (d) 3 is an integral factor of 12.
4. Decide which of the following are open sentences:
   (a) t is an even integer; (b) x is a prime integer between 4 and 18; (c) $3 + 5 = 8$; (d) For every $x \in \mathbf{Z}$, x is either even or odd; (e) $2 + 3 < 10$; (f) $x + y = z$, with $x, y, z \in \mathbf{Z}$.
5. If the universe of x is assumed to be $\mathbf{Q}$, decide whether the solution set of each of the following open sentences is $\varnothing$, $\mathbf{Q}$, or some finite subset of $\mathbf{Q}$—in which case tabulate it:
   (a) $x^2 - 25 = (x - 5)(x + 5)$; (b) $2x - 5 = 7$; (c) $x^2 - 5x + 6 = 0$; (d) $x^2 = 5$; (e) $x^2 > -2$; (f) $x^2 + 2x = x(x + 2)$.

6. List the members of $A \times B$, where (a) $A = \{1, 2, 3\}$, $B = \{1, 2\}$; (b) $A = \{a, b\}$, $B = \{2, 4, 6\}$; (c) $A = \{1, a, c\}$, $B = \{3, x, a\}$; (d) $A = \{1\}$, $B = \{2, 3\}$.

7. List all members of $A \times B$, where (a) $A = \{1, -1\}$, $B = \{2, 3\}$; (b) $A = \{1, a, -1\}$, $B = \{0, 1\}$; (c) $A = \{2\}$, $B = \{1\}$; (d) $A = B = \emptyset$.

8. List the complete membership of $A \times A$, where $A = \{2, 4, 6\}$.

9. List the complete membership of $A \times A$, where $A = \{0, -1\}$.

10. In what respect in this section are we restricting the concept of a statement or sentence from its colloquial usage?

11. Criticize the use of the word "variable" for the symbol x of an equation.

12. If A and B are sets with 5 and 10 members, respectively, how many elements are there in (a) $A \times B$; (b) $A \times A$; (c) $B \times B$?

13. Identify a, b, c if (a) $(a, b, c) = (1, -1, 2)$; (b) $(a, b, c) = (2, 1, -3)$.

14. Draw one or more conclusions from each of the following equalities:
    (a) $(2, x) = (2, y)$; (b) $(x, 1) = (3, y)$; (c) $(x, y) = (y, x)$.

15. Identify x if (a) $\{1, x, 2\} = \{4, 2, 1\}$; (b) $\{x, -3, 1\} = \{1, -3, 5\}$.

16. List the possible values of x and y if (a) $(x, y, 1) = (2, -3, 1)$; (b) $\{x, y, 1\} = \{2, -3, 1\}$.

17. Determine the maximum number of ordered pairs that can be formed by using the elements of $\{a, b, c, d\}$ as components.

18. If $A = \{1, 2, 3\}$, determine (a) all two-element subsets of A; (b) the Cartesian set of A.

19. Construct a graph of $A \times B$, where (a) $A = \{1, 2\}$, $B = \{1, 2, 3\}$; (b) $A = \{1, 3\}$, $B = \{2, 3\}$; (c) $A = \{2\}$, $B = \{3\}$.

20. Construct a graph of $A \times B$, where (a) $A = \{-1, 0, 1\}$, $B = \{1, 2\}$; (b) $A = \{1, 2, 3, 4\}$, $B = \{-1, 0, 1\}$; (c) $A = \{-1, 1, 3\}$, $B = \{1, 3\}$.

21. Explain why an open sentence involving a variable x always partitions the universe of x into two subsets with no common elements.

22. What is the generalization of the assertion in Problem 21 for the case of an open sentence involving two or more variables?

23. What must one conclude if the truth set of an open sentence is $\emptyset$?

24. What is the effect on the solution set of an equation if both members of the equation are multiplied by $k (\neq 0) \in \mathbf{R}$?

25. If the universe of x is assumed to be $\mathbf{R}$, find the solution set of each of the following equations:
    (a) $x^2 - 9 = 0$; (b) $x^2 + 6 = 0$; (c) $x^2 - 4x + 4 = 0$.

26. If the universe of x is assumed to be $\mathbf{R}$, find the solution set of each of the following equations or inequalities:
    (a) $x(x - 2)(x - 3) = 0$; (b) $x + 1 < 6$; (c) $x^2 < 4$.

Note: The following terminology is introduced for use in the remaining problems: A *tautology* is an open statement that is true for all substitutions made from the universes of the variables; if the resulting statements are false for all such substitutions, the open statement is said to be an *absurdity*. An equation, which is a tautology, is often called an *identity*.

27. Decide which of the following open sentences are tautologies and which are absurdities:
    (a) x is a living man who breathes; (b) The number of prime factors of x is 5; (c) x is a triangle with four sides; (d) The temperature is $x°$, where $x > 60$ and x is an integral divisor of 50.

28. Give two examples each of a tautology and an absurdity, none of which are algebraic equations or inequalities.

29. Assuming that the universe of x is $\mathbf{R}$, determine the solution set of each of the following:
(a) $x + 2 \neq 5$; (b) $x + x = 2x$; (c) $x - 2 \not< 4$;
(d) $x + 4x = 6x$; (e) $x \neq x$.

30. Let p, q, r be open statements, with p a tautology and r an absurdity. Then, using $\vee$, a symbol meaning "or (possibly both)," and $\wedge$, a symbol meaning "and," examine the truth value of each of the following:
(a) $p \vee q$; (b) $p \wedge r$; (c) $q \vee r$; (d) $p \wedge q$.

2.2 Simple Linear Systems

A *compound* statement is a composite or *conjunction* of two or more statements that are *simple* in the sense that each makes but one assertion. For example, "George Washington was the first President of the United States and Albany is the capital of the State of New York" is a compound statement, made up of the conjunction of two statements that are easily identified. Since each of these two simple statements is true, the compound statement is also true. It is easy to think of compound statements that are the conjunction of any number of simple statements, some of which may be false and some true. Of course, each statement has its own truth value, and a compound statement is false if any of its component statements is false. For example, the statement "A circle is round and a man has never orbited the earth" is false, because the second component of this compound (double) statement is false.

Just as we have compound statements, so also do we have compound open sentences that involve one or more variables. An example of this, with one variable, is "x is a capital city and x is a city in the State of California"; the occurrence of two variables is illustrated by "x is a capital city and y is a city in the State of California." The universe of x, in either sentence, is the set of 50 capital cities, and the universe of y is the set of all cities in California. It is clear that there is only one replacement for x that will make the first open sentence true, and this replacement is "Sacramento." The truth set of this sentence then contains this city as its unique member. On the other hand, there are many elements in the truth set of the other compound open sentence: 50 suitable choices exist for x, whereas any city in California may be used to replace y.

More generally, suppose T is a compound sentence made up of the conjunction of m open sentences, each involving the same one variable. Then, if $S_1, S_2, \ldots, S_m$ are the truth sets of the m component sentences, the truth set of T is the intersection $S_1 \cap S_2 \cap \cdots \cap S_m$. If there are n variables $x_1, x_2, \ldots, x_n$ in a compound open sentence, the truth set of the sentence (as suggested near the end of §2.1) consists of all those n-tuples $(c_1, c_2, \ldots, c_n)$ such that the sentence is true when $c_1, c_2, \ldots, c_n$ are substituted, respectively, for $x_1, x_2, \ldots, x_n$. It is clear that we have the same result as above for this multivariate case: The truth set of a compound sentence is the intersection of the truth sets of the component sentences.

The type of open sentence that occurs most frequently in mathematics is the equation, and the associated type of compound open sentence is a *system* of equations. In this chapter, for the most part, our interest will be in systems of linear equations—or *linear systems*—and their solution sets. A typical linear equation in n variables, or "unknowns," $x_1, x_2, \ldots, x_n$ has the form

$$a_1 x_1 + a_2 x_2 + \cdots + a_n x_n = b$$

where $a_1, a_2, \ldots, a_n$ and b are real numbers; any collection of such equations constitutes a *linear system*. The solution set of such a system is the set of n-tuples $(c_1, c_2, \ldots, c_n)$ such that the respective replacements of $x_1, x_2, \ldots, x_n$ by $c_1, c_2, \ldots, c_n \in \mathbf{R}$ transform each equation of the system into a true equality. *In this chapter, unless an explicit statement is made to the contrary or the context implies otherwise, we shall always assume that the universe of each variable of any system of equations is* $\mathbf{R}$. It should be clear that, although a nonempty solution set may exist for each equation of a system, it is quite possible for the solution set of the system—which, as we noted above, is the intersection of these solution sets—to be $\varnothing$. If this is the case, the equations of the system are said to be *inconsistent*.

We now come to the problem of actually determining the solution set of a system of linear equations. The general procedure is to make successive replacements of equations of the system by other equations such that the various new systems of equations have the same solution set as the original system. After a finite number of such replacements, we obtain a system of equations whose solution set is evident by mere inspection. One of three possibilities must occur: The solution set is $\varnothing$, so that the equations are inconsistent; the solution set contains only one element, so that the system has a *unique* solution; the solution set has more than one element so that the system has more than one solution. In this section we shall confine our discussion to systems of two equations in two unknowns.

Two equations or systems of equations are said to be *equivalent* if their solution sets are the same. Any operation that we can perform on the equations of a system without any resulting change in its solution set is known as an *elementary operation*. There are four elementary operations in common use:

1. Interchange the positions of two equations of the system.
2. Multiply both members of an equation by the same nonzero number.
3. Add any real multiple of the members of one equation to the corresponding members of another equation of the system.
4. Eliminate any "zero" equation (i.e., one with constant term and coefficients of all unknowns 0).

Any one of these operations on the equations of a system transforms the system into an equivalent system, as does any sequence of such operations. These are the operations that we use to convert a system of equations into its simplest form from which we can obtain the solutions. We illustrate this "elimination" procedure with an example.

Example 1.   Solve the linear system

$$3x - 2y = 1$$
$$6x + y = 7$$

SOLUTION.   If we multiply both members of the second equation by 2, the resulting system is

$$3x - 2y = 1$$
$$12x + 2y = 14$$

On adding the members of the second equation to the corresponding members of the first equation, we obtain

$$15x = 15$$
$$12x + 2y = 14$$

From the first equation it follows that $x = 1$, and the second equation gives $y = 1$. The desired unique solution of the given system of equations is then

$$(x, y) = (1, 1)$$

Let us now apply the above procedure to the more general pair of equations

$$a_1 x + b_1 y = c_1$$
$$a_2 x + b_2 y = c_2$$

where we assume, for the sake of generality, that $a_1 a_2 \neq 0$ and $b_1 b_2 \neq 0$. On multiplying the members of the first equation by b_2 and those of the second by b_1, the result is the equivalent system

$$a_1 b_2 x + b_1 b_2 y = c_1 b_2$$
$$a_2 b_1 x + b_2 b_1 y = c_2 b_1$$

If we subtract the members of the second equation from the corresponding members of the first equation, we obtain

$$(a_1 b_2 - a_2 b_1) x = c_1 b_2 - c_2 b_1$$
$$a_2 b_1 x + b_2 b_1 y = c_2 b_1$$

The first equation of this system now yields $x = (c_1 b_2 - c_2 b_1)/(a_1 b_2 - a_2 b_1)$, provided $a_1 b_2 - a_2 b_1 \neq 0$. If we substitute this solution for x in the second equation and solve the resulting linear equation for y, the result is $y = (a_1c_2 - a_2c_1)/(a_1b_2 - a_2b_1)$, and our system of equations has been solved.

We now introduce what we shall call for the present a mnemonic device to remember the form of the above solution. If we define the symbol $\begin{vmatrix} a & b \\ c & d \end{vmatrix}$ to represent the number $ad - bc$ (the difference of the products of the diagonal elements in the square array), the solution of the general system above is then (x, y) where

$$x = \frac{\begin{vmatrix} c_1 & b_1 \\ c_2 & b_2 \end{vmatrix}}{\begin{vmatrix} a_1 & b_1 \\ a_2 & b_2 \end{vmatrix}} \quad \text{and} \quad y = \frac{\begin{vmatrix} a_1 & c_1 \\ a_2 & c_2 \end{vmatrix}}{\begin{vmatrix} a_1 & b_1 \\ a_2 & b_2 \end{vmatrix}}$$

Three things should be noted about the above symbolic solution:

1. The denominator, in both cases, involves the array of coefficients of the unknowns as they appear in the left members of the original equations.
2. The numerator, in each case, may be obtained from the denominator by replacing the coefficients of the unknown being determined by the right (constant) members of the equations.
3. The method fails to give a solution if $a_1b_2 - a_2b_1 = 0$.

If it happens that $a_1b_2 - a_2b_1 = 0$, the system either is inconsistent (with an empty solution set) or has infinitely many solutions. These cases will be treated later in more general circumstances, but we shall give a few illuminating examples in this section.

Example 2. Solve the linear system

$$x - 3y = 1$$
$$2x - 3y = 5$$

SOLUTION. An application of the above mnemonic device gives us the following results:

$$x = \frac{\begin{vmatrix} 1 & -3 \\ 5 & -3 \end{vmatrix}}{\begin{vmatrix} 1 & -3 \\ 2 & -3 \end{vmatrix}} = \frac{1(-3) - 5(-3)}{1(-3) - 2(-3)} = \frac{-3 + 15}{-3 + 6} = \frac{12}{3} = 4$$

$$y = \frac{\begin{vmatrix} 1 & 1 \\ 2 & 5 \end{vmatrix}}{\begin{vmatrix} 1 & -3 \\ 2 & -3 \end{vmatrix}} = \frac{1(5) - 2(1)}{3} = \frac{5 - 2}{3} = \frac{3}{3} = 1$$

The solution of the system is then $(x, y) = (4, 1)$.

Example 3. If we consider the equations

$$x - 2y = 5$$
$$2x - 4y = 10$$

we discover that $a_1b_2 - a_2b_1 = 0$. The above method is then inapplicable, but we observe that the second equation is obtainable from the first by merely doubling each of its members. Hence the two equations are equivalent as a system to the single equation $x - 2y = 5$. This equation—and so the original pair of equations—has infinitely many solutions for (x, y). For example, $(7, 1)$ and $(3, -1)$ are easily seen to be solutions.

Example 4. If we consider the system

$$x - 2y = 5$$
$$2x - 4y = 3$$

we again note that $a_1b_2 - a_2b_1 = 0$. However, although the left member of the second equation is twice the left member of the first equation, it is not true(!) that 3 is twice 5. Hence no simultaneous solution of these equations is possible, and the system is inconsistent.

Problems 2.2

1. Let p, q, r, s be the indicated statements:
     p: Today is warm q: It is cloudy
     r: The air is humid s: A breeze is blowing
   Write down the statement that is the conjunction of (a) p and q; (b) q and r; (c) p, q, and r; (d) p, q, and s.
2. Use the directions given in Problem 1, but with p, q, r, and s defined as follows:
     p: Roses are red q: Violets are blue
     r: Roses are sweet smelling s: Violets grow best in the shade
3. Explain why the following sentences are not the conjunction of two more simple statements:
   (a) John and Bill are good friends; (b) The sum of 5 and 2 is 7; (c) Work and play should be accomplished in that order; (d) Wisconsin and Illinois have a common border.
4. Write each of the following compound sentences as the conjunction of two or more simple statements:
   (a) x and y are even integers; (b) The problem can be solved by both algebra and arithmetic; (c) t is an odd integer which exceeds 10; (d) Mary and I had a date and we went to a movie; (e) The sum of x and y is 15, and the product xy is 36; (f) The room was hot and crowded, and nobody opened a window.
5. Write each of the following compound sentences as the conjunction of two or more simple statements:
   (a) Jack and Jill went up the hill; (b) It is snowing and the streets are slippery; (c) My car has snow tires and I arrive at work on time; (d) The oranges are large, sweet, and juicy.

6. Decide which of the following are not compound sentences:
   (a) The product of x and y is 12; (b) The weather is hot and dry; (c) John and Mary make a perfect match; (d) A cool but sunny day is perfect for walking.
7. Construct a sentence that is the conjunction of (a) three simple statements; (b) four simple statements.
8. Verify that $(x, y) = (1, 1)$ is a solution of each of the following equations:
   (a) $x + y = 2$; (b) $3x - 2y = 1$; (c) $4x + 3y = 7$.
9. Verify that $(x, y, z) = (1, 0, -2)$ is a solution of each of the following equations:
   (a) $2x - 5y + 4z = -6$;   (b) $x + 2y - 3z = 7$;   (c) $4x + 0y - 2z = 8$;
   (d) $0x + 0y - z = 2$.
10. Verify that $(x, y) = (-1, 2)$ is a solution of each of the following systems of equations:

(a)	(b)	(c)
$x + y = 1$	$3x - 2y = -7$	$x - y = -3$
$2x + y = 0$	$2x + y = 0$	$3x + 2y = 1$
	$3x + 4y = 5$	$4x - y = -6$

11. Verify that $(x, y, z) = (1, 0, -1)$ is a solution of each of the following systems of equations:

(a)	(b)
$2x - 3y + z = 1$	$x + y + z = 0$
$x + 2y - z = 2$	$3x + 2y - 2z = 5$
	$x - 5y + 3z = -2$

12. Find a pair of equations in two unknowns which has (a) no solution; (b) a unique solution; (c) infinitely many solutions.
13. (a) Check that $(3, -4, 0)$ and $(4, 3, 5)$ are solutions of the following system of equations:

$$2x - y + z = 10$$
$$3x + y - 2z = 5$$

(b) Show that $(3 + t, -4 + 7t, 5t)$ is a solution of the system in (a) for any $t \in \mathbf{R}$.
(c) If (a, b, c) and (d, e, f) are solutions of the system in (a), show that $(a - d, b - e, c - f)$ is a solution of the system that results when the right members of the given system are replaced by 0.
14. Explain why the solution set of a system of linear equations is unchanged by an application of any of the elementary operations to the system.

Use the method developed in this section to investigate the solution set of each of the linear systems in Problems 15–24. If a unique solution is found, check this solution by substitution in the system.

15. $2x + 5y = 12$	16. $3x - y = -7$	17. $x - 2y = 2$
$x + 3y = 7$	$2x + 3y = 10$	$3x - 6y = 6$
18. $x - 2y = 2$	19. $2x + 3y = 1$	20. $x + \frac{2}{3}y = 3$
$3x - 3y = 9$	$8x + 12y = 3$	$2x + y = 5$
21. $x/2 + y/3 = 6$	22. $1.2x + 0.4y = 1.24$	
$x/4 + y/5 = \frac{7}{2}$	$0.2x - 2.2y + 0.02 = 0$	
23. $2/x - 3/y = 3$	(*Hint:* Solve first for $1/x$ and $1/y$)	
$3/x + 6/y = 8$		
24. $4/x - 3/y = 3$	(cf. Problem 23)	
$2/x + 9/y = -2$		

25. If $L_1(x, y) = 0$, $L_2(x, y) = 0$ denotes a system of equations in x and y, explain why an equivalent system is obtained if either equation is replaced by $aL_1(x, y) + bL_2(x, y) = 0$, with a, b nonzero real numbers.

26. The sum of the digits of a two-digit number is 14, whereas the number formed by reversing the digits is 18 less than the original number. Determine the number.

27. Determine the amounts of a 5 per cent acid solution and a 20 per cent acid solution that must be mixed in order to produce 2 gallons of a solution that is 15 per cent acid.

28. An airplane flies 1386 miles with a tail wind in $4\frac{1}{2}$ hours. On the return trip, and against the same wind, the time of flight is $5\frac{1}{2}$ hours. Determine the velocity of the wind.

29. Four times the present age of Mike is 3 more than five times Spike's age 3 years from now. Three times Spike's present age is 3 more than the age of Mike 4 years ago. Find the present ages of Mike and Spike.

30. Two cyclists are known to be 15 miles apart at a certain moment and traveling in the same direction. In 6 hours, the faster cyclist overtakes the slower. If they had traveled toward each other at the same rates of speed and met in 2 hours, determine what these rates must have been.

2.3   Matrices and Determinants

A *matrix* is a rectangular array of numbers, usually enclosed by parentheses or brackets, the numbers being called the *elements* or *entries* of the matrix. The following is an illustration of a matrix with integral entries:

$$\begin{bmatrix} 2 & -1 & 4 & 1 \\ 2 & 0 & 3 & 2 \\ -1 & 1 & 2 & 1 \end{bmatrix}$$

The individual horizontal and vertical arrays of numbers are called, respectively, the *rows* and *columns* of the matrix. If a matrix has m rows and n columns, it is called an "m by n" (written $m \times n$) matrix. The illustration above, then, is of a 3 by 4 matrix. If $m = 1$, an $m \times n$ matrix is often called a *row matrix*; an $m \times n$ matrix is often called a *column matrix* if $n = 1$. In case $m = n$, the matrix is said to be *square of order n*, and it is usually not necessary to distinguish a square matrix of order 1 from its one entry. For the remainder of this section, we shall be concerned only with square matrices.

If we designate a matrix by A, it is convenient to indicate the element at the intersection of the ith row and jth column by a_{ij}. The matrix may then also be designated as $A = [a_{ij}]$, and, in the 3 by 3 case, A takes the following form:

$$\begin{bmatrix} a_{11} & a_{12} & a_{13} \\ a_{21} & a_{22} & a_{23} \\ a_{31} & a_{32} & a_{33} \end{bmatrix}$$

There is associated with every *square* matrix $A = [a_{ij}]$ a number, called the *determinant* of A, which is designated by $|A|$ or det A. We also write

$$|A| = \begin{vmatrix} a_{11} & a_{12} & a_{13} \\ a_{21} & a_{22} & a_{23} \\ a_{31} & a_{32} & a_{33} \end{vmatrix}$$

to illustrate the 3 by 3 case, and refer to the number so indicated as an *evaluation* or *expansion* of the determinant. We shall make a ("recursive") definition of the determinant of a matrix of order n in terms of determinants of matrices of order $n - 1$. Then, *if we agree to identify the determinant of a 1×1 matrix $A = [a]$ with the number a*, our recursive definition will completely describe how to evaluate any determinant. We first develop some preliminary terminology in anticipation of this definition.

If one row and column of a square matrix are deleted, the resulting array of numbers is a *submatrix* whose determinant is a *minor* of A. (It is possible to give more general definitions of "submatrix" and "minor," but this restricted definition takes care of our present needs.) We label a minor as M_{ij} if it arises from the deletion of the ith row and jth column of A. The element a_{ij} is at the intersection of the deleted row and column, and $(-1)^{i+j}M_{ij} = A_{ij}$ is a number called the *cofactor* of a_{ij}. If we multiply the elements of any row or column of a matrix by their respective cofactors and add these products, *the resulting sum can be shown to be independent of which row or column was selected.* We shall assume this result and make the following definition for a matrix A of order n.

Definition.   *If $A = [a_{ij}]$, det $A = |A| = a_{i1}A_{i1} + a_{i2}A_{i2} + \cdots + a_{in}A_{in} = a_{1j}A_{1j} + a_{2j}A_{2j} + \cdots + a_{nj}A_{nj}$, for any i or j between 1 and n, inclusive.*

In practice, in the applications of this definition, it is customary to select either $i = 1$ or $j = 1$ and thereby evaluate the determinant "in terms of" the first row or column of the matrix. An exception to this practice occurs, however, whenever zeros are more numerous in some other row or column; then this row or column is selected for reasons of simplicity of the computation.

Example 1.   Show that

$$\begin{vmatrix} a_{11} & a_{12} \\ a_{21} & a_{22} \end{vmatrix} = a_{11}a_{22} - a_{12}a_{21}$$

PROOF.   We evaluate the determinant in terms of the elements of the first row. Because $A_{11} = (-1)^2M_{11} = M_{11} = \det [a_{22}] = a_{22}$ and $A_{12} = (-1)^3M_{12} = -M_{12} = -a_{21}$, an application of the above definition gives $|A| = a_{11}a_{22} - a_{12}a_{21}$, where we have designated the original matrix by A.

We now see from the result of Example 1 that the "mnemonic device" introduced in the preceding section was in reality a formula for the evaluation of the determinant of a 2×2 matrix.

Example 2.   Evaluate

$$\begin{vmatrix} 1 & 2 \\ -1 & 3 \end{vmatrix}$$

SOLUTION.   By the result of Example 1, we see that the desired determinant is $1(3) - (-1)2 = 3 + 2 = 5$.

Example 3.   If $A = [a_{ij}] = \begin{bmatrix} 2 & -1 & 1 \\ 1 & 2 & 2 \\ -3 & 2 & 1 \end{bmatrix}$, determine A_{12} and A_{23}.

SOLUTION.   If we delete the first row and second column of A, we see that

$$M_{12} = \begin{vmatrix} 1 & 2 \\ -3 & 1 \end{vmatrix} = 1 + 6 = 7$$

Hence,

$$A_{12} = (-1)^3 M_{12} = -7$$

Similarly, if we delete the second row and third column of A, we find that

$$M_{23} = \begin{vmatrix} 2 & -1 \\ -3 & 2 \end{vmatrix} = 4 - 3 = 1$$

and so $A_{23} = (-1)^5 M_{23} = -1$.

Example 4.   Determine $|A|$ if $A = \begin{bmatrix} 2 & 2 & 1 \\ -1 & 1 & 2 \\ 1 & -2 & 3 \end{bmatrix}$.

SOLUTION.   We shall evaluate the determinant in terms of the first row of the matrix. Hence, we must first determine A_{11}, A_{12}, and A_{13}.

$$A_{11} = (-1)^2 \begin{vmatrix} 1 & 2 \\ -2 & 3 \end{vmatrix} = 3 - (-4) = 3 + 4 = 7$$

$$A_{12} = (-1)^3 \begin{vmatrix} -1 & 2 \\ 1 & 3 \end{vmatrix} = (-1)(-3 - 2) = 5$$

$$A_{13} = (-1)^4 \begin{vmatrix} -1 & 1 \\ 1 & -2 \end{vmatrix} = 2 - 1 = 1$$

It now follows from the definition that $|A| = 2(7) + 2(5) + 1(1) = 25$.

We conclude this section with the statements of several theorems on determinants. The proofs of these theorems may be found in books that contain a more detailed treatment of determinants, but we shall not include any of these proofs. However, it is easy to check the validity of the theorems for matrices of low orders, and some of the problems of this section suggest checks of this type.

■ **THEOREM 3.1.**   *If each element of a row (or column) of a square matrix is multiplied by a number c, the determinant of the matrix is multiplied by c.*

■ **THEOREM 3.2.**   *If two rows (or columns) of a square matrix are interchanged, the determinant of the matrix is changed only in algebraic sign.*

■ **COROLLARY.**   *If two rows (or columns) of a square matrix are identical, the determinant of the matrix is 0.*

> PROOF. For it follows from Theorem 3.2 that an interchange of the two identical rows (or columns) would change the sign of the determinant. But because these rows (or columns) are identical, no change could result in the determinant, and so this number must be 0.

■ **THEOREM 3.3.**   *If any multiple of a row (or column) of a matrix is added element by element to another row (or column), the determinant of the matrix is unchanged.*

Problems 2.3

1. If $A = [a_{ij}] = \begin{bmatrix} 1 & 3 & -1 & 1 \\ 2 & 0 & 1 & -1 \\ -1 & 2 & 1 & 2 \end{bmatrix}$ is designated as an $m \times n$ matrix, identify (a) m and n; (n) $a_{21}, a_{11}, a_{32}, a_{34}$.

2. List the entries in the second column and those in the third row of the matrix in Problem 1.

3. If $A = \begin{bmatrix} -1 & 2 & 1 \\ 1 & 2 & 5 \\ 0 & -1 & 4 \end{bmatrix}$, determine the minor (a) M_{12}; (b) M_{13}; (c) M_{22}.

4. Use the results in Problem 3 to determine the cofactor (a) A_{12}; (b) A_{13}; (c) A_{22}.

5. With A given in Problem 3, evaluate det A in terms of the (a) second row; (b) first column; (c) third column.

6. If $A = \begin{bmatrix} 2 & 1 & 0 \\ -1 & 3 & 1 \\ 0 & 2 & 3 \end{bmatrix}$, determine the minor (a) M_{13}; (b) M_{22}; (c) M_{23}.

7. Use the results in Problem 6 to determine the cofactor (a) A_{13}; (b) A_{22}; (c) A_{23}.

8. With A given in Problem 6, evaluate det A in terms of the (a) first row; (b) third row; (c) second column; (d) third column.

9. If $B = \begin{bmatrix} 2 & -1 & 1 & 2 \\ 3 & 8 & 4 & 0 \\ 0 & 7 & -2 & 4 \\ 1 & 1 & 8 & 1 \end{bmatrix}$, determine the cofactor (a) B_{21}; (b) B_{13}.

10. Find det B, for the matrix B in Problem 9, and check your answer by using a different row or column as the basis for the expansion.

11. If $B = \begin{bmatrix} 1 & 0 & -1 & 3 \\ 2 & 1 & 2 & -1 \\ 0 & 3 & 0 & 1 \\ 1 & 1 & -1 & 1 \end{bmatrix}$, determine the cofactor (a) B_{12}; (b) B_{23}.

12. Find det B, for the matrix B in Problem 11, and check your answer by using a different row or column as the basis for the expansion.

13. Verify the corollary to Theorem 3.2 for the case of a third-order matrix with two identical columns.

14. Verify that (a) $\begin{vmatrix} 4 & 1 & -1 \\ 2 & 1 & 3 \\ 1 & 2 & 1 \end{vmatrix} = \begin{vmatrix} 4 & 2 & 1 \\ 1 & 1 & 2 \\ -1 & 3 & 1 \end{vmatrix}$; (b) $\begin{vmatrix} 1 & 2 & 3 \\ 2 & 4 & 4 \\ 1 & 2 & 5 \end{vmatrix} = 0$.

15. Check that det $A = 5$, where $A = \begin{bmatrix} 4 & 1 \\ 3 & 2 \end{bmatrix}$. Find two different matrices of order 2 whose determinants are also equal to 5. What conclusion can be drawn from this result?

16. If $A = \begin{bmatrix} 4 & 4 & 2 \\ 2 & 7 & 5 \\ 0 & 0 & 1 \end{bmatrix}$ and $B = \begin{bmatrix} 3 & 1 \\ 1 & 2 \end{bmatrix}$, determine (a) $|A| + |B|$; (b) $|A|/|B|$.

17. Compute $\begin{vmatrix} \begin{vmatrix} 1 & 1 \\ 2 & 1 \end{vmatrix} & \begin{vmatrix} 2 & 1 \\ -1 & 1 \end{vmatrix} \\ \begin{vmatrix} 3 & 2 \\ 1 & -1 \end{vmatrix} & \begin{vmatrix} 2 & 1 \\ 3 & 1 \end{vmatrix} \end{vmatrix}$.

18. Verify that $\begin{vmatrix} a & b & 0 \\ c & d & 0 \\ e & f & g \end{vmatrix} = g \begin{vmatrix} a & b \\ c & d \end{vmatrix}$.

19. Verify that $\begin{vmatrix} 1 & 1 & 1 \\ x & y & z \\ x^2 & y^2 & z^2 \end{vmatrix} = (z - x)(y - x)(z - y)$.

20. Establish the truth of each of the following indicated equalities:

(a) $\begin{vmatrix} a + x & b \\ c + y & d \end{vmatrix} = \begin{vmatrix} a & b \\ c & d \end{vmatrix} + \begin{vmatrix} x & b \\ y & d \end{vmatrix}$

(b) $\begin{vmatrix} a + x & b + y \\ c & d \end{vmatrix} = \begin{vmatrix} a & b \\ c & d \end{vmatrix} + \begin{vmatrix} x & y \\ c & d \end{vmatrix}$

21. Find a simple expression for $\begin{vmatrix} 2x & y \\ -x & -y \end{vmatrix} + \begin{vmatrix} x & -y \\ 2x & y \end{vmatrix}$.

22. Express as a polynomial in x:

(a) $\begin{vmatrix} x & 1 - x \\ 2 & 5 \end{vmatrix}$; (b) $\begin{vmatrix} 1 - x & -2x \\ 1 & 1 + x \end{vmatrix}$; (c) $\begin{vmatrix} -1 & 2x \\ x & -1 \end{vmatrix}$.

23. Expand each of the following: (a) $\begin{vmatrix} 1 & x & 1 \\ 2 & -x & x \\ 3 & y & y \end{vmatrix}$; (b) $\begin{vmatrix} 1 & x & x^2 \\ 1 & y & y^2 \\ 1 & z & z^2 \end{vmatrix}$.

24. Express the following determinant as a polynomial in x:

$$\begin{vmatrix} x & 0 & 0 & 1 \\ 0 & x & 0 & 0 \\ 0 & 0 & x & 0 \\ 1 & 0 & 0 & x \end{vmatrix}$$

25. Without expansion of the determinant, show that (x_1, y_1) and (x_2, y_2) lie in the
set of solutions for (x, y) of the equation $\begin{vmatrix} x & y & 1 \\ x_1 & y_1 & 1 \\ x_2 & y_2 & 1 \end{vmatrix} = 0.$

26. Check that our definition of the determinant of a square matrix is reasonable by verifying that all six expansions of a general third-order matrix are the same.

27. Prove Theorem 3.1 for a general square matrix of order 3.

28. Prove Theorem 3.2 for a general square matrix of order 3.

29. Prove Theorem 3.3 for a general square matrix of order 3.

30. If $A = [a_{ij}]$ is a square matrix of odd order such that $a_{ij} = -a_{ji}$ for every i, j, prove that $\det A = 0$.

2.4 Linear Systems and Cramer's Rule

It is possible to use some of the results in §2.3 on matrices to generalize the method of solution given in §2.2. Instead of a pair of equations, we could consider a general system of n linear equations in n real unknowns. However, the method becomes awkward if $n > 3$, and so we shall confine our discussion to the case of three equations in three unknowns.

The general system under consideration may be expressed in the following form:

$$a_{11}x + a_{12}y + a_{13}z = k_1$$
$$a_{21}x + a_{22}y + a_{23}z = k_2$$
$$a_{31}x + a_{32}y + a_{33}z = k_3$$

The *coefficient matrix A* of the system is the matrix $\begin{bmatrix} a_{11} & a_{12} & a_{13} \\ a_{21} & a_{22} & a_{23} \\ a_{31} & a_{32} & a_{33} \end{bmatrix}$. In the above system x, y, z are considered to be real unknowns, whereas the coefficients $a_{11}, a_{12}, a_{13}, a_{21}, a_{22}, a_{23}, a_{31}, a_{32}, a_{33}$ and k_1, k_2, k_3 are arbitrary real numbers—which are assumed to be known. We shall have found a solution to the system when we have determined $x = c_1$, $y = c_2$, $z = c_3$ to satisfy simultaneously all three equations of the system. The set of all solutions (c_1, c_2, c_3) is, of course, the solution set of the system.

The following is the key theorem of this section, which leads to the method known as Cramer's Rule.

■**THEOREM 4.1.** *If the elements of any row (or column) of a matrix are multiplied by the cofactors of the corresponding elements of another row (or column), the sum of the products is 0.*

PROOF. Let us consider the products of the elements of the ith row by the corresponding cofactors of those of the jth row ($i \neq j$) of the matrix. If we were to replace the elements of the jth row by the elements of the ith row, it is apparent that the cofactors of the elements of the new jth row would be the same as those for the original jth row. However, two rows of the new matrix would be identical, and so its determinant is 0 by the corollary to Theorem 3.2. The expansion of this determinant in terms of the elements of the (new) jth row is precisely the same as the sum of the products of the elements of the ith row by the cofactors of the elements of the jth row of the original matrix. Hence, this latter sum is 0, and the proof is complete.

In order to use this theorem for the desired purpose, we introduce the following notation:

$$D = \begin{vmatrix} a_{11} & a_{12} & a_{13} \\ a_{21} & a_{22} & a_{23} \\ a_{31} & a_{32} & a_{33} \end{vmatrix} \qquad K_1 = \begin{vmatrix} k_1 & a_{12} & a_{13} \\ k_2 & a_{22} & a_{23} \\ k_3 & a_{32} & a_{33} \end{vmatrix}$$

$$K_2 = \begin{vmatrix} a_{11} & k_1 & a_{13} \\ a_{21} & k_2 & a_{23} \\ a_{31} & k_3 & a_{33} \end{vmatrix} \qquad K_3 = \begin{vmatrix} a_{11} & a_{12} & k_1 \\ a_{21} & a_{22} & k_2 \\ a_{31} & a_{32} & k_3 \end{vmatrix}$$

As usual, we let A_{ij} designate the cofactor of the element a_{ij} in the coefficient matrix A. If we multiply both members of the first equation of the system by A_{11}, both members of the second equation by A_{21}, and both members of the third equation by A_{31}, and add the corresponding members of each transformed equation, the result is

$$(a_{11}A_{11} + a_{21}A_{21} + a_{31}A_{31})x + (a_{12}A_{11} + a_{22}A_{21} + a_{32}A_{31})y$$
$$+ (a_{13}A_{11} + a_{23}A_{21} + a_{33}A_{31})z = k_1 A_{11} + k_2 A_{21} + k_3 A_{31}$$

It follows from the above theorem that the coefficients of y and z are 0, whereas the coefficient of x is the determinant D of the coefficient matrix. Moreover, the right member of this equation may be seen to be an evaluation of the determinant K_1 in terms of the elements of the first column of the associated matrix. The equation we have obtained may then be written in the simple form $Dx = K_1$, from which we get

$$x = \frac{K_1}{D}$$

A similar analysis yields $y = K_2/D$ and $z = K_3/D$. This result, known as *Cramer's Rule*, may be used if $D \neq 0$. It may be noted that the method developed in §2.2 is the simplest case of Cramer's Rule, adapted to two equations in two unknowns. For purposes of emphasis, we repeat the statement of this result.

Cramer's Rule. *If $D \neq 0$, the system of equations $a_{11}x + a_{12}y + a_{13}z = k_1$, $a_{21}x + a_{22}y + a_{23}z = k_2$, $a_{31}x + a_{32}y + a_{33}z = k_3$ has a unique solution, and $x = K_1/D$, $y = K_2/D$, $z = K_3/D$.*

Example. Use Cramer's Rule to solve the following system of equations:

$$3x + y + 3z = 8$$
$$x - 2y - z = 1$$
$$2x + 5y + 2z = 1$$

SOLUTION. We must first determine D, K_1, K_2, and K_3 for this system of equations:

$$D = \begin{vmatrix} 3 & 1 & 3 \\ 1 & -2 & -1 \\ 2 & 5 & 2 \end{vmatrix} = 26 \qquad K_1 = \begin{vmatrix} 8 & 1 & 3 \\ 1 & -2 & -1 \\ 1 & 5 & 2 \end{vmatrix} = 26$$

$$K_2 = \begin{vmatrix} 3 & 8 & 3 \\ 1 & 1 & -1 \\ 2 & 1 & 2 \end{vmatrix} = -26 \qquad K_3 = \begin{vmatrix} 3 & 1 & 8 \\ 1 & -2 & 1 \\ 2 & 5 & 1 \end{vmatrix} = 52$$

With these results, it follows from Cramer's Rule that $x = K_1/D = 1$, $y = K_2/D = -1$, and $z = K_3/D = 2$. It is a simple matter to check that $(x, y, z) = (1, -1, 2)$ is the solution of the given system.

In applications of Cramer's Rule, it is often easier to solve for the final unknown by substitution in one of the equations. For instance, in the preceding example we could determine $x = 1$ and $y = -1$ by Cramer's Rule, and then substitute these solutions in, say, the first equation. The result is $3 - 1 + 3z = 8$, from which we obtain $3z = 6$ and $z = 2$. The remaining equations may then be used for purposes of checking.

The method of Cramer's Rule is very useful in solving systems of linear equations, and we have noted that the method can be generalized to more than three equations. However, the method has certain limitations, which we list:

1. The method may be used only if $D \neq 0$.
2. The computation of the determinants can be very laborious if there are more than three equations.
3. The method is applicable only if there are the same number of equations as there are unknowns.

In §2.5 we shall outline a method of solving linear systems of equations by means of matrices, which is free of these undesirable features.

Problems 2.4

1. Write down a general system of linear equations whose coefficient matrix is

$$\begin{bmatrix} 2 & 1 & -1 \\ 1 & 2 & 3 \\ 3 & -1 & 0 \end{bmatrix}$$

2. Write down a general system of linear equations whose coefficient matrix is

$$\begin{bmatrix} 2 & 0 & 1 \\ 0 & 3 & -2 \\ 0 & 2 & 5 \end{bmatrix}$$

3. Assuming the notation in this section, find D, K_1, K_2, K_3 for the linear system written down in Problem 1.

4. Assuming the notation in this section, find D, K_1, K_2, K_3 for the linear system written down in Problem 2.

Use Cramer's Rule to solve each of the systems of equations given in Problems 5–17.

5. $3x + 4y = 6$
$2x - 5y = -19$

7. $2.5V - 6H = 5$
$V - H = 2.5$

9. $3x - 2y + z = 5$
$x + y - 2z = -2$
$2x - 2y + 4z = 8$

11. $2x - y = 0$
$4x - y + z = \frac{1}{2}$
$x + 4z = -\frac{3}{2}$

13. $2x - y = 0$
$4x + 16z = 1$
$64y - 16z = 65$

15. $4x - 5z = 6$
$y + 6z = 2$
$3x - 4z = 3$

17. $2/x + 3/y + 1/z = 4$
$4/x - 6/y + 3/z = -7$
$3/x - 5/y + 2/z = -5$

6. $3x + 2y = 2$
$2x - 3y = 36$

8. $0.6X + 0.8Y = 100$
$0.8X - 0.6Y = 0$

10. $x - 4y + 3z = -10$
$2x - y + z = -4$
$4x - 3y + z = -12$

12. $5x - 7y + z = 4$
$x + 3y - 5z = -14$
$2x + y - z = -5$

14. $x - 2y + z = 7$
$y + 2z = 1$
$2x + 3z = 4$

16. $4/x - 2/y + 1/z = 11$
$3/x - 1/y - 1/z = 9$
$1/x + 2/y - 1/z = -1$

18. Explain why any solution found by Cramer's Rule, for a system of equations, must be unique.

19. Write down an arbitrary matrix of order three with integral entries. Then check the truth of Theorem 4.1 by applying it to (a) the elements of the first column and the cofactors of the elements of the third column; (b) the elements of the second row and the cofactors of the elements of the first row.

20. A linear system is said to be *homogeneous* if all right members of the equations are zero. What conclusion can be drawn from Cramer's Rule for any homogeneous system of n equations in n unknowns?

21. Verify that the determinant of the coefficient matrix of the following homogeneous (see Problem 20) system is zero:

$$2x - 4y = 0$$
$$-x + 2y = 0$$

Use "trial and error" to find three solutions of the system, and make a conjecture concerning the solutions of systems of this type.

22. Find a value for $k \in \mathbf{R}$ such that the following linear system has a solution other than $x = y = z = 0$ (see Problems 20 and 21):

$$
\begin{aligned}
(k - 2)x + 3y \quad\quad &= 0 \\
kx + 2y - 2z &= 0 \\
x - 3y + 4z &= 0
\end{aligned}
$$

23. Find the condition on $a, b, c \in \mathbf{R}$ if the following system of equations is to have a unique solution:

$$
\begin{aligned}
ax \quad\quad + 3z &= 2 \\
by - 2z &= 1 \\
x \quad\quad + cz &= 2
\end{aligned}
$$

24. Derive the portion of Cramer's Rule pertaining to y and z.

25. The perimeter of a rectangle is 160 centimeters. Find the length and width of the rectangle if its length exceeds its width by 20 centimeters.

26. The sum of the numbers represented by the digits of a three-digit numeral is 13, whereas the number represented by the middle digit is 5 less than the sum of the numbers represented by the other two. If the last two digits are reversed in order, the number represented is 27 larger than the original number. Find the original numeral.

27. The sum of the numbers represented by the digits of a three-digit numeral is 9, whereas a reversal of order of the digits decreases the number represented by 99. If the number represented by the ten's digit is 1 less than the number represented by the unit's digit, find the original numeral.

28. Is it possible to trim one edge of a rectangular sheet of paper to obtain one whose area and perimeter are both decreased by one half? Can it be done by trimming two edges?

29. The weight of an object on the surface of the moon is approximately one sixth its weight on earth. If an object weighs 40 pounds less on the moon than on earth, determine the weight of the object (a) on the moon; (b) on earth.

30. Two cars leave a garage at the same time and travel in opposite directions, the speed of one being 8 miles per hour greater than the speed of the other. Determine the speed of both cars if they are observed to be 280 miles apart in 5 hours.

2.5   Matrices in Echelon Form

In this section we describe a method of reducing a matrix that will be very useful in determining the set of solutions of any system of linear equations. There are three *elementary row* operations that we shall use in this reduction procedure. It may be noted that they are quite similar to the first three of the row operations for equations as discussed in §2.2.

1. The interchange of any two rows of the matrix
2. The multiplication of all entries of any row of the matrix by a nonzero real number

3. The addition of a nonzero multiple of the entries of any row of the matrix to the corresponding entries of another row

If we perform any finite sequence of such operations on a given matrix A, the final matrix—as well as any intermediate matrix—is said to be *row-equivalent* to A.

For example, suppose $A = \begin{bmatrix} 1 & -1 & 2 & 3 \\ 2 & 3 & 8 & -1 \\ 0 & 1 & 5 & -1 \end{bmatrix}$. If we interchange the

second and third rows of A, we obtain $A_1 = \begin{bmatrix} 1 & -1 & 2 & 3 \\ 0 & 1 & 5 & -1 \\ 2 & 3 & 8 & -1 \end{bmatrix}$. If we now

add three times the entries of the first row of A_1 to the entries of its second row,

the result is $A_2 = \begin{bmatrix} 1 & -1 & 2 & 3 \\ 3 & -2 & 11 & 8 \\ 2 & 3 & 8 & -1 \end{bmatrix}$. Finally, we can multiply each entry

of the first row of A_2 by two and obtain $A_3 = \begin{bmatrix} 2 & -2 & 4 & 6 \\ 3 & -2 & 11 & 8 \\ 2 & 3 & 8 & -1 \end{bmatrix}$. It is a

consequence of our definition above that the matrix A_3—as well as A_2 and A_1—is row-equivalent to A.

The above illustration shows that row-equivalent matrices may be very different in their outward appearances. However, it can be shown that, if we use a suitable sequence of elementary row operations, any matrix can be transformed into a row-equivalent matrix which is the most useful for our present purposes. If all entries of a row of a matrix are zero, the row is called a *zero row*, whereas one with at least one nonzero entry is referred to as a nonzero row. The first nonzero entry in a nonzero row—as the elements are read from left to right—is the *leading entry* of the row. We are now ready to state the conditions that characterize a matrix in the useful and simple form desired.

Definition.   *A matrix with integral elements is said to be in* modified row-echelon *form if it satisfies the following conditions:*

1. *All zero rows (if any) lie below the nonzero rows.*
2. *The greatest common divisor of the entries of any nonzero row is* 1, *and the leading entry of each such row is positive.*
3. *The column that contains the leading entry of any row has all of its other entries zero.*
4. *If there are r nonzero rows and the leading entry of row i appears in column t_i ($i = 1, 2, \ldots, r$), then*

$$t_1 < t_2 < \cdots < t_r$$

The fourth condition above can be interpreted less formally as asserting that the ordered set of leading entries of the nonzero rows forms a progression which is "downward and to the right." The following are examples of matrices in modified row-echelon form:

$$\begin{bmatrix} 1 & 0 & 0 \\ 0 & 1 & 0 \\ 0 & 0 & 1 \end{bmatrix} \qquad \begin{bmatrix} 2 & 0 & 1 & 0 \\ 0 & 7 & 0 & -2 \\ 0 & 0 & 0 & 0 \end{bmatrix}$$

$$\begin{bmatrix} 3 & 8 & 0 & 0 & 0 & 0 \\ 0 & 0 & 2 & 0 & 0 & -1 \\ 0 & 0 & 0 & 1 & 0 & 2 \\ 0 & 0 & 0 & 0 & 2 & 1 \end{bmatrix} \qquad \begin{bmatrix} 3 & 0 & 5 & 7 \\ 0 & 1 & 0 & 0 \\ 0 & 0 & 0 & 0 \\ 0 & 0 & 0 & 0 \\ 0 & 0 & 0 & 0 \end{bmatrix}.$$

It may have been correctly implied that our modified row-echelon form is a special case of a more general form for a matrix. In this general *row-echelon* form, the entries may be arbitrary real numbers, but the leading entry of any nonzero row must be 1. A matrix in this form would be of theoretical use in solving a system of equations with arbitrary real coefficients. However, from a practical point of view, there is nothing lost by assuming that the coefficients are rational numbers—and, in fact, integers. It will then be seen in §2.6 that the modified row-echelon form is quite satisfactory for our present use.

We now state the important theorem of this section.

■ **THEOREM 5.1.**   *Any matrix with integral entries is row-equivalent to a matrix in modified row-echelon form.*

We shall not give a formal proof of this theorem, but prefer to include two illustrations of how a reduction to the desired form can be carried out. In order to describe the steps in the reduction process, it will be convenient to designate the first row by (1), the second row by (2), twice the first row by 2(1), etc.

Example 1.   Reduce the following matrix to modified row-echelon form:

$$\begin{bmatrix} 3 & 1 & -1 & 2 \\ 2 & 0 & 3 & 4 \\ 1 & 1 & 5 & 7 \end{bmatrix}$$

SOLUTION

$$\begin{bmatrix} 3 & 1 & -1 & 2 \\ 2 & 0 & 3 & 4 \\ 1 & 1 & 5 & 7 \end{bmatrix} \xrightarrow{\text{interchange (1) and (3)}} \begin{bmatrix} 1 & 1 & 5 & 7 \\ 2 & 0 & 3 & 4 \\ 3 & 1 & -1 & 2 \end{bmatrix}$$

$$\xrightarrow{\text{subtract 2(1) from (2)}} \begin{bmatrix} 1 & 1 & 5 & 7 \\ 0 & -2 & -7 & -10 \\ 3 & 1 & -1 & 2 \end{bmatrix} \xrightarrow{\text{subtract 3(1) from (3)}} \begin{bmatrix} 1 & 1 & 5 & 7 \\ 0 & -2 & -7 & -10 \\ 0 & -2 & -16 & -19 \end{bmatrix}$$

$$\xrightarrow{\text{multiply (2) and (3) by } -1} \begin{bmatrix} 1 & 1 & 5 & 7 \\ 0 & 2 & 7 & 10 \\ 0 & 2 & 16 & 19 \end{bmatrix} \xrightarrow{\text{subtract (2) from (3)}} \begin{bmatrix} 1 & 1 & 5 & 7 \\ 0 & 2 & 7 & 10 \\ 0 & 0 & 9 & 9 \end{bmatrix}$$

multiply (1) by 2 $\longrightarrow$
$\begin{bmatrix} 2 & 2 & 10 & 14 \\ 0 & 2 & 7 & 10 \\ 0 & 0 & 9 & 9 \end{bmatrix}$
subtract(2) from (1) $\longrightarrow$
$\begin{bmatrix} 2 & 0 & 3 & 4 \\ 0 & 2 & 7 & 10 \\ 0 & 0 & 9 & 9 \end{bmatrix}$

divide (3) by 9 $\longrightarrow$
$\begin{bmatrix} 2 & 0 & 3 & 4 \\ 0 & 2 & 7 & 10 \\ 0 & 0 & 1 & 1 \end{bmatrix}$
subtract 3(3) from (1) $\longrightarrow$
$\begin{bmatrix} 2 & 0 & 0 & 1 \\ 0 & 2 & 7 & 10 \\ 0 & 0 & 1 & 1 \end{bmatrix}$

subtract 7(3) from (2) $\longrightarrow$
$\begin{bmatrix} 2 & 0 & 0 & 1 \\ 0 & 2 & 0 & 3 \\ 0 & 0 & 1 & 1 \end{bmatrix}$

The final matrix is in the form desired.

Example 2. Reduce the following matrix to modified row-echelon form:

$$\begin{bmatrix} -2 & 3 & -6 \\ 1 & -2 & 3 \\ 2 & -4 & 7 \end{bmatrix}$$

SOLUTION

$\begin{bmatrix} -2 & 3 & -6 \\ 1 & -2 & 3 \\ 2 & -4 & 7 \end{bmatrix}$
interchange (1) and (2) $\longrightarrow$
$\begin{bmatrix} 1 & -2 & 3 \\ -2 & 3 & -6 \\ 2 & -4 & 7 \end{bmatrix}$

add 2(1) to (2) $\longrightarrow$
$\begin{bmatrix} 1 & -2 & 3 \\ 0 & -1 & 0 \\ 2 & -4 & 7 \end{bmatrix}$
subtract 2(1) from (3) $\longrightarrow$
$\begin{bmatrix} 1 & -2 & 3 \\ 0 & -1 & 0 \\ 0 & 0 & 1 \end{bmatrix}$

multiply (2) by -1 $\longrightarrow$
$\begin{bmatrix} 1 & -2 & 3 \\ 0 & 1 & 0 \\ 0 & 0 & 1 \end{bmatrix}$
add 2(2) to (1) $\longrightarrow$
$\begin{bmatrix} 1 & 0 & 3 \\ 0 & 1 & 0 \\ 0 & 0 & 1 \end{bmatrix}$

subtract 3(3) from (1) $\longrightarrow$
$\begin{bmatrix} 1 & 0 & 0 \\ 0 & 1 & 0 \\ 0 & 0 & 1 \end{bmatrix}$

This final matrix is in the desired form.

There is no fixed sequence of operations necessary for the reduction of a matrix with integral entries to modified row-echelon form. However, the following list of suggestions may be of use as a general guide in this process:

1. If the first column contains an entry 1, interchange the necessary rows to put this element in the upper left-hand corner of the matrix.
2. After the position of the leading entry of any row has been established, use elementary row operations to reduce to 0 all other entries of the column in which this leading entry occurs.

3. Proceed in a systematic way with the reduction from the left to the right side of the matrix.
4. If, at any stage of the reduction, all entries of any row have a common factor different from 1 and it is apparent that this factor is not needed for subsequent reductions, divide each entry of the row by this factor.

Problems 2.5

Reduce each of the matrices, given in Problems 1–9, to modified row-echelon form.

1. $\begin{bmatrix} 3 & -1 & 2 \\ 1 & 4 & -2 \\ 4 & -2 & 0 \end{bmatrix}$
    2. $\begin{bmatrix} 4 & -1 & 5 & 0 \\ 1 & -1 & 5 & 2 \\ 4 & -2 & 15 & 4 \\ 5 & -2 & 25 & 10 \end{bmatrix}$

3. $\begin{bmatrix} 0 & 1 & 0 & -2 \\ 2 & 2 & 3 & 0 \\ 5 & 3 & -1 & 7 \end{bmatrix}$
    4. $\begin{bmatrix} 0 & -1 & -4 & 12 & 19 \\ 6 & 3 & 0 & 3 & 12 \\ 2 & 1 & 4 & 0 & 4 \\ -6 & -3 & 0 & 9 & 12 \end{bmatrix}$

5. $\begin{bmatrix} 4 & 2 & -1 & 2 \\ 4 & 3 & 0 & 1 \\ 2 & 5 & 3 & 2 \\ 1 & 1 & 1 & 2 \end{bmatrix}$
    6. $\begin{bmatrix} 4 & 5 & -6 \\ 2 & -4 & 3 \\ 7 & -1 & 0 \end{bmatrix}$

7. $\begin{bmatrix} 3 & 5 & 7 & 1 & 1 \\ 2 & 5 & -1 & 0 & 0 \\ 0 & 0 & 1 & -2 & 5 \end{bmatrix}$
    8. $\begin{bmatrix} -1 & 1 & 4 & 2 \\ 2 & 5 & -2 & 5 \\ 1 & 4 & 2 & 6 \\ 0 & -2 & 1 & 5 \end{bmatrix}$

9. $\begin{bmatrix} 0 & 0 & 1 & -4 \\ 2 & 5 & -2 & 6 \\ 1 & 1 & -1 & 5 \\ 0 & 0 & 1 & 0 \end{bmatrix}$

10. Try to decide whether two different matrices in modified row-echelon form can be row-equivalent to the same matrix—and thus row-equivalent to each other. In other words, is there a *unique* matrix in modified row-echelon form that is row-equivalent to a given matrix?

2.6 Use of Matrices in Solving Linear Systems

We now return to the problem of obtaining simultaneous solutions of a system of linear equations. Although the method of this section does not eliminate the usefulness of the determinant method, it does not have any of the defects of this latter method as listed in §2.4.

The *coefficient matrix* of a linear system of equations has already been defined. If we include the right-hand members of the equations as an extra column to the coefficient matrix, we have what is called the *augmented* matrix of the system. Every system of linear equations has a uniquely associated augmented matrix, and every matrix can be considered the unique augmented matrix of a linear system. *Let us first suppose that the augmented matrix of a system of linear equations is in modified row-echelon form.* The solution possibilities for the system then fall into three categories, each of which we shall discuss in some detail.

1. *The augmented matrix and its coefficient submatrix have the same number of nonzero rows, and this is equal to the number of unknowns in the system.*

    For example, let us suppose that we have a linear system with three unknowns x, y, z and that the augmented matrix is

$$\begin{bmatrix} 4 & 0 & 0 & 3 \\ 0 & 1 & 0 & -3 \\ 0 & 0 & 5 & 2 \end{bmatrix}$$

The equations associated with this matrix are

$$\begin{aligned} 4x &= 3 \\ y &= -3 \\ 5z &= 2 \end{aligned}$$

It is apparent that the only solution of the system is $(x, y, z) = (\frac{3}{4}, -3, \frac{2}{5})$, and we remark that uniqueness of solution is a characteristic of any system whose augmented matrix (in modified row-echelon form) is in this first category.

2. *The augmented matrix and its coefficient submatrix have the same number of nonzero rows, but this is less than the number of unknowns in the system.*

    For example, let us suppose that we have a linear system with four unknowns x, y, z, w and that the augmented matrix of the system is

$$\begin{bmatrix} 3 & 0 & 0 & 1 & -6 \\ 0 & 2 & -4 & 1 & 5 \\ 0 & 0 & 0 & 0 & 0 \\ 0 & 0 & 0 & 0 & 0 \end{bmatrix}$$

The two bottom rows of the matrix have no significance for equations, but if we "translate" the other two rows into equations we obtain

$$\begin{aligned} 3x + w &= -6 \\ 2y - 4z + w &= 5 \end{aligned}$$

From these two equations it is easy to obtain solutions for, say, x and y in terms of z and w. For example, if we let $z = c$ and $w = d$, for arbitrary

$c, d \in \mathbf{R}$, we find immediately that $3x = -6 - d$ and $2y = 5 - d + 4c$, so that

$$x = -2 - \frac{d}{3}$$

$$y = \frac{5}{2} - \frac{d}{2} + 2c$$

The general solution of the system can then be expressed in the form

$$(x, y, z, w) = \left(-2 - \frac{d}{3}, \frac{5}{2} - \frac{d}{2} + 2c, c, d \right) \qquad \text{for arbitrary } c, d \in \mathbf{R}$$

We can find particular solutions of the system by assigning special values to c and d. For example, if $c = d = 0$, we obtain $(x, y, z, w) = (-2, \frac{5}{2}, 0, 0)$ as one particular solution. An infinitude of solutions will always result from a system in this second category.

3. *The number of nonzero rows of the augmented matrix is unequal to—and so greater than—the number of nonzero rows of its coefficient submatrix.*

   To illustrate this situation, let us suppose the unknowns are x, y, z and the augmented matrix of the system is

$$\begin{bmatrix} 1 & 0 & 0 & 0 \\ 0 & 1 & 0 & 0 \\ 0 & 0 & 1 & 0 \\ 0 & 0 & 0 & 1 \\ 0 & 0 & 0 & 0 \end{bmatrix}$$

If we interpret the rows of this matrix as equations, the result is

$$x = 0$$
$$y = 0$$
$$z = 0$$
$$0 = 1$$
$$0 = 0$$

Since the assertion $0 = 1$ is not true for any choice of x, y, z, the given system of equations has no solution. The absence of any solution is characteristic of this type of system.

It must be recalled, of course, that in the above discussions *the augmented matrices were all assumed to be in modified row-echelon form.* Our analysis then shows that, if the augmented matrix of a system is in this form, we are able to tell by inspection whether there is a unique solution, no solution, or an infinitude of solutions to the system. Moreover, one can determine all solutions directly from the augmented matrix. The problem of solving a system of linear equations is then one of reducing its augmented matrix to modified row-echelon form— but without altering the solutions of the system. A little reflection will reveal that the following operations on a system of equations will not alter its set of solutions:

1. The interchange of any two equations of the system
2. The multiplication of both members of any equation of the system by a nonzero real number
3. The addition of any nonzero real multiple of both members of any equa- tion of the system to the corresponding members of another equation

A quick check of these allowable operations with the elementary row operations for matrices in §2.5 shows us that the two are essentially the same, with the notions of "row of a matrix" and "equation" playing parallel roles. The following theorem is then an immediate consequence of Theorem 5.1.

■ **THEOREM 6.1.** *If the augmented matrix of a system of linear equations is reduced to modified row-echelon form by elementary row operations, the solutions of the system of equations associated with the reduced matrix are the same as those of the original system.*

We have already seen how easy it is to solve a linear system whose augmented matrix is in modified row-echelon form, and so this theorem gives us the following procedure for solving any system of linear equations with integral coefficients:

By means of elementary row operations, reduce the augmented matrix of the given system to modified row-echelon form, and solve the system associated with the reduced matrix.

Example. Obtain simultaneous solutions for the following system of equations:

$$3x + y - z = 2$$
$$2x + 3z = 4$$
$$x + y + 5z = 7$$

SOLUTION. The augmented matrix of the system is

$$\begin{bmatrix} 3 & 1 & -1 & 2 \\ 2 & 0 & 3 & 4 \\ 1 & 1 & 5 & 7 \end{bmatrix}$$

and we saw in Example 1 of §2.5 that the associated modified row-echelon matrix is

$$\begin{bmatrix} 2 & 0 & 0 & 1 \\ 0 & 2 & 0 & 3 \\ 0 & 0 & 1 & 1 \end{bmatrix}$$

But then $2x = 1$, $2y = 3$, and $z = 1$, so that $x = \frac{1}{2}$, $y = \frac{3}{2}$, and $z = 1$, and the unique solution of the system is seen to be $(x, y, z) = (\frac{1}{2}, \frac{3}{2}, 1)$.

The examples given for systems whose augmented matrices are in modified row-echelon form will serve to illustrate the other possibilities that may arise: The procedure is merely to reduce the matrix to this simple form and solve the associated system of equations. For a different matrix approach to the solution of a system of linear equations, the student is invited to read the brief discussion of *matrix inversion* contained in Appendix B.

Problems 2.6

1. Write down the augmented matrix of the system of equations given in §2.4 in (a) Problem 5; (b) Problem 6.
2. Write down the augmented matrix of the system of equations given in §2.4 in (a) Problem 11; (b) Problem 12.
3. Write down the augmented matrix of the system of equations given in §2.4 in (a) Problem 13; (b) Problem 14.
4. If the general solution of a system of linear equations is given as $(x, y, z) = (2, 3c - 1, 2c + 1)$, for arbitrary $c \in \mathbf{R}$, find the particular solution when (a) $c = 0$; (b) $c = 1$; (c) $c = -1$.
5. If the general solution of a system of linear equations is given as $(x, y, z, w) = (2c - d, 3d, c + d, 2d)$, for arbitrary $c, d \in \mathbf{R}$, find the particular solution when (a) $c = d = 0$; (b) $c = d = 1$; (c) $c = -1, d = 1$.
6. Explain why there is no loss in generality in assuming that all coefficients of an equation with rational coefficients are integers.
7. Explain why there is no loss in *practical* generality in assuming that all coefficients of an equation with real coefficients are integers (see Problem 6).
8. The following are the augmented matrices of systems of linear equations in x, y, z; determine all solutions of each system:

(a) $\begin{bmatrix} 2 & 0 & 0 & 5 \\ 0 & 5 & 0 & -6 \\ 0 & 0 & 4 & 1 \end{bmatrix}$ (b) $\begin{bmatrix} 4 & 0 & 0 & -3 \\ 0 & 2 & 0 & 5 \\ 0 & 0 & 1 & -1 \end{bmatrix}$

9. The following are the augmented matrices of systems of linear equations in x, y, z; determine all solutions of each system:

(a) $\begin{bmatrix} 1 & 0 & 0 & 2 \\ 0 & 3 & 0 & 4 \\ 0 & 0 & 1 & 5 \\ 0 & 0 & 0 & 2 \\ 0 & 0 & 0 & 0 \end{bmatrix}$ (b) $\begin{bmatrix} 2 & 0 & 0 & 7 \\ 0 & 1 & 0 & -6 \\ 0 & 0 & 0 & 0 \\ 0 & 0 & 0 & 0 \\ 0 & 0 & 0 & 0 \end{bmatrix}$

10. Each of the following matrices is the augmented matrix of a system of linear equations in x, y, z [and w in the case of (c)]; solve each system completely:

(a) $\begin{bmatrix} 1 & 2 & 1 & 4 \\ 3 & -1 & 2 & -1 \\ 4 & 2 & 3 & 3 \end{bmatrix}$ (b) $\begin{bmatrix} 2 & -1 & 3 & 2 \\ 1 & 0 & 2 & -1 \\ 5 & -2 & 8 & 3 \end{bmatrix}$

(c) $\begin{bmatrix} 2 & 0 & 0 & 0 & -5 \\ 0 & 5 & -1 & 0 & 8 \\ 0 & 0 & 0 & 4 & 7 \end{bmatrix}$

11. Write down the modified row-echelon matrix which results from the reduction of the augmented matrix of a linear system in x, y, z that has the unique solution $(x, y, z) = (1, 2, 3)$.

In Problems 12–21, use the method described in this section to determine the complete solution set of each system of equations displayed.

12. $2x + 3y + 4z = 0$
$3x + 4y + 5z = 0$
$5x + 7y + 9z = 0$

13. $4x - 3y + 5z = 1$
$2x + 5y + 2z = -5$
$3x - 7y + 4z = 2$

14. $\quad x + 2y - \quad z = 1$
$-x + 2y + 2z = 2$
$2x - 3y - 3z = -3$

15. $\quad x - 2y + 3z = -3$
$3x - \quad y - 2z = -4$
$x + \quad y - 2z = 0$

16. $2x + 3y - \quad z - \quad t = 0$
$x - \quad y - 2z - 4t = 0$
$3x + 3y \quad\quad - 7t = 0$

17. $2x - \quad y + 4z = -4$
$x + 3y - \quad z = 8$
$2x + 3y - 4z = 12$

18. $2x - \quad y + 3z + 4w = -2$
$x - \quad y - \quad z - 3w = 2$
$3x - 2y - 2z + \quad w = 4$

19. $2x + 3y + 11z + 13w = -2$
$3x - 2y + \quad 4z - \quad w = -5$
$5x + 5y + \quad 3z + \quad w = 10$
$7x - 7y - \quad 2z + \quad w = 12$

20. Problem 17 of §2.4

21. $2x_1 \quad\quad\quad\quad - 2x_5 = 0$
$x_1 + \quad x_2 \quad\quad\quad - 3x_5 = 0$
$\quad\quad 2x_2 + \quad x_3 + x_4 \quad = 1$
$\quad\quad\quad\quad 2x_3 + x_4 + 5x_5 = 1$
$3x_1 - \quad x_2 + \quad x_3 \quad\quad = 0$

22. Determine k if the following system of equations is to have a nonempty solution set:

$$x + y = 1$$
$$ky + z = 1$$
$$z + x = 1$$

23. Use an example to verify that it is possible for a *nonhomogeneous* (see Problem 20 of §2.4) system of linear equations to be inconsistent, even though there are more unknowns than equations (cf. the second category of system in this section).

24. Prove that, if two linear equations—not identically zero—have the same solution set, one equation is a nonzero multiple of the other.

25. There are 50 coins in a bag, made up of nickels, dimes, and quarters, the total value being $5. Should you believe an assertion that the bag contains four times as many nickels as dimes?

Note: For purposes of machine calculation—which capitalizes on a routine process at the expense of efficiency—it is desirable to reduce augmented matrices to *row-echelon* rather than the "modified" form under discussion in this section. In the row-echelon form (mentioned in §2.5) any rational numbers are allowed as entries, except that the leading entry of any nonzero row is required to be 1. The other conditions remain the same as those for the modified form. In the reduction of a matrix to row-echelon form, each leading entry is "normalized" to 1 as soon as it is identified, and the column containing each normalized 1 is "swept" free of other nonzero entries by successive subtraction of the proper multiples of the row that contains the normalized 1. The whole reduction proceeds in order from left to right and culminates with a matrix in row-echelon form. Use this method of reduction for the solution of the following problems, each of which appeared earlier in this problems set:

26. Problem 12   **27.** Problem 13   **28.** Problem 14
29. Problem 16   **30.** Problem 18

2.7 Systems Involving Quadratic Equations

There are times when it is necessary to solve systems of equations in which one or more of the equations is not linear. A general method satisfactory for all such systems would be very complicated to describe, and we shall not attempt to do this here. Instead, we shall consider a few examples of isolated types that occur quite frequently. Only equations in two unknowns will be discussed.

Example 1. Solve the following system of equations for $(x, y) \in \mathbf{R} \times \mathbf{R}$:

$$3x^2 + y^2 = 4$$
$$2x - y = 1$$

SOLUTION. We first solve the linear equation to express y in terms of x, and obtain $y = 2x - 1$. On substitution of $2x - 1$ for y in the first equation, the result is

$$3x^2 + (2x - 1)^2 = 4$$

or

$$7x^2 - 4x - 3 = 0$$

Hence,

$$(7x + 3)(x - 1) = 0$$

and

$$x = -\tfrac{3}{7} \text{ or } x = 1$$

If $x = -\tfrac{3}{7}$, $y = 2(-\tfrac{3}{7}) - 1 = -\tfrac{13}{7}$; if $x = 1$, $y = 2(1) - 1 = 2 - 1 = 1$. The solution set of the equation is then

$$\{(1, 1), (-\tfrac{3}{7}, -\tfrac{13}{7})\}$$

The method of substitution, as used in Example 1, may also be used successfully on occasion when neither equation is linear.

Example 2. Solve the following system for $(x, y) \in \mathbf{R} \times \mathbf{R}$:

$$x^2 + 2y^2 = 33$$
$$xy = 10$$

SOLUTION. From the second equation we obtain $y = 10/x$, and on substituting $10/x$ for y in the first equation, the result is

$$x^2 + 2\left(\frac{100}{x^2}\right) = 33$$

Then

$$x^4 - 33x^2 + 200 = 0$$

or

$$(x^2 - 25)(x^2 - 8) = 0$$

and so

$$x = \pm 5$$

or

$$x = \pm 2\sqrt{2}$$

The corresponding solutions for y are ± 2 and $\pm 5\sqrt{2}/2$, and so the solution set of the system is

$$\left\{(5, 2), (-5, -2), \left(2\sqrt{2}, \frac{5\sqrt{2}}{2}\right), \left(-2\sqrt{2}, \frac{-5\sqrt{2}}{2}\right)\right\}$$

It sometimes happens that two quadratic equations are "linear" in the *squares* of the unknowns, and then the methods of linear systems are applicable.

Example 3. Solve the following system for $(x, y) \in \mathbf{R} \times \mathbf{R}$:

$$2x^2 + 3y^2 = 7$$
$$x^2 - y^2 = 1$$

SOLUTION. If we let $x^2 = u$ and $y^2 = v$, the equations become

$$2u + 3v = 7$$
$$u - v = 1$$

The unique solution for u and v in this linear system is easily found to be $u = 2$, $v = 1$. Hence, the complete solution of the original system is $\{(\sqrt{2}, 1), (\sqrt{2}, -1), (-\sqrt{2}, 1), (-\sqrt{2}, -1)\}$. It would be quite easy to solve this particular system without introducing the new unknowns u and v. However, in some nonlinear systems of this sort, the method used does simplify the solution process.

Note: We should caution at this point that before a "solution" can be accepted, it must be checked by substitution in *each* equation of the system. There are, in general, many solutions of one equation of a system that may not be solutions of another.

It is sometimes possible to solve a quadratic system by some special device peculiar to the given system.

Example 4.   Solve the following system for $(x, y) \in \mathbf{R} \times \mathbf{R}$:

$$9x^2 + 4y^2 = 10$$
$$3xy - 2y^2 = -2$$

SOLUTION.   If we multiply the members of the second equation by 5 and add them to the corresponding members of the first equation, the result is: $9x^2 + 15xy - 6y^2 = 0$ or $3x^2 + 5xy - 2y^2 = 0$. It then follows that $(3x - y)(x + 2y) = 0$, so that $y = 3x$ or $x = -2y$.

  (a) If $y = 3x$, the first equation becomes $9x^2 + 36x^2 = 10$ and so $x^2 = \frac{2}{9}$. Hence, $x = \pm\sqrt{2}/3$, and solutions are $(\sqrt{2}/3, \sqrt{2})$ and $(-\sqrt{2}/3, -\sqrt{2})$.
  (b) If $x = -2y$, the first equation becomes $36y^2 + 4y^2 = 10$ or $y^2 = \frac{1}{4}$. Hence, $y = \pm\frac{1}{2}$, and solutions are $(1, -\frac{1}{2})$ and $(-1, \frac{1}{2})$.

The complete solution set of the given system is then

$$\left\{ \left(\frac{\sqrt{2}}{3}, \sqrt{2}\right), \left(\frac{-\sqrt{2}}{3}, -\sqrt{2}\right), (1, -\tfrac{1}{2}), (-1, \tfrac{1}{2}) \right\}$$

That these are all solutions of the system may be verified by substitution in both equations.

Our final example illustrates why certain "solutions" that arise in the process of solving a system of equations must be rejected from the solution set because of our present requirement that all numbers be real.

Example 5.   Solve the following system for $(x, y) \in \mathbf{R} \times \mathbf{R}$:

$$2x^2 + xy - y^2 = 2$$
$$6x^2 - xy - 4y^2 = 4$$

SOLUTION.   We first subtract twice the members of the first equation from the corresponding members of the second and obtain the equivalent system:

$$2x^2 + xy - y^2 = 2$$
$$2x^2 - 3xy - 2y^2 = 0$$

On factoring each member of the second equation, this system becomes

$$2x^2 + xy - y^2 = 2$$
$$(2x + y)(x - 2y) = 0$$

This one system is now seen to be equivalent to the two simpler systems below, much like the case in Example 4:

$$2x^2 + xy - y^2 = 2 \qquad\qquad 2x^2 + xy - y^2 = 2$$
$$2x + y = 0 \qquad\qquad\qquad x - 2y = 0$$

If y is replaced by $-2x$ in the quadratic equation of the left system, the resulting equation has no *real* solutions for x, and so no real solutions of the original system are obtained from this simpler system. On the other hand, if x is replaced by $2y$ in the quadratic equation of the right system, we find that the solution set of this simpler system is $\{(2\sqrt{2}/3, \sqrt{2}/3),$ $(-2\sqrt{2}/3, -\sqrt{2}/3)\}$. This is then also the real solution set of the original system as desired.

The methods that we have discussed here are by no means exhaustive for nonlinear systems, but we prefer not to pursue the matter further.

Problems 2.7

In Problems 1–16, solve each of the given systems for $(x, y) \in \mathbf{R} \times \mathbf{R}$.

1. $x = y^2$
   $y = x^2$

2. $x - y = 0$
   $x^2 - y^2 = 0$

3. $xy + 6 = 0$
   $x + y + 1 = 0$

4. $6x^2 - 7y^2 = 5$
   $2x^2 + 9y^2 = 13$

5. $x^2 + 4y^2 = 61$
   $3x^2 + 2y^2 = 93$

6. $4x^2 - 3y^2 = 9$
   $5x^2 - 8y^2 = -27$

7. $x^2 + y^2 = 25$
   $x - 7y + 25 = 0$

8. $3x + 2y - 6 = 0$
   $xy + 12 = 0$

9. $xy + 1 = a^2$
   $x - y = 2$

10. $x^2 + xy = 3$
    $xy + 2y^2 = 2$

11. $4x^2 + 9y^2 = 36$
    $3x^2 - 5y^2 = 27$

12. $xy + 4y^2 = 0$
    $2xy + x^2 - 4y^2 = 0$

13. $2x^2 - 3xy = 5$
    $2xy - 3y^2 = 2$

14. $x^2 - xy + y^2 = 7$
    $x^2 + xy - y^2 = 1$

15. $2x^2 - 3xy + 4y^2 = 3$
    $3x^2 - 4xy + 3y^2 = 2$

16. $x^2 + 2xy - y^2 = 4$
    $x^2 - 3xy + y^2 + 4 = 0$

17. Do not attempt to solve, but explain why there can be no real solution to either of the following systems of equations:
    (a) $2x - y = 5$
        $3x^2 + 2y^2 + 5 = 0$
    (b) $x + \sqrt{y} = 2$
        $\sqrt{xy} + 1 = 0$

18. The sum of the squares of two positive integers is 290, whereas the square of one exceeds the square of the other by 48. Find the numbers.

19. The product of two positive integers is 12, whereas the sum of their reciprocals is $\frac{7}{12}$. Find the numbers.

20. The area of a right triangle is 225 square inches. Find the two sides if the hypotenuse is 30 inches in length.

21. The area of a right triangle is 240 square inches. Find the two sides if the hypotenuse is 34 inches in length.

22. Three rational numbers a, b, c are so related that $b - a = c - b$. If their sum is 25 and the difference between the smallest and largest is 2 less than twice the intermediate number, determine the numbers.

23. Two cars are racing in the same direction around a circular 1-mile track. If one car makes the circuit in 6 seconds less time than the other and also passes the other car every 3 minutes, find the speeds of the cars.

24. Each page of a book is to have a 1-inch margin on all four sides. The pages are to have individual areas of 54 square inches, with 28 square inches of each page devoted to printing. What must be the dimensions of each page?

25. An open box is to be constructed by cutting 1-inch squares from each corner of a rectangular sheet of cardboard and then folding it up in the appropriate way. If the volume of the box is to be 32 cubic inches and the perimeter of the base is to be 24 inches, determine the dimensions of the original sheet of cardboard.

3

Order and Inequalities

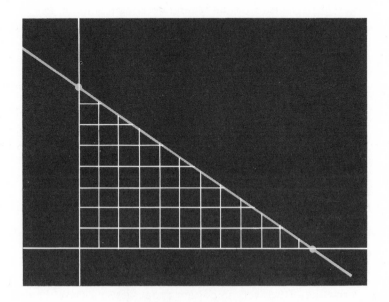

3.1 Order Properties of Real Numbers

Up to this point in the text, we have made only passing references to the "less than" or natural ordering relation ($<$) in the system **R** of real numbers. However, it is well known that this relation is defined so that, for any two distinct real numbers a and b, either $a < b$ or $b < a$. In the present chapter, we shall take a closer look at this relation, which is so important in any discussion of real numbers.

Our intuitive approach to the relation is motivated by the algebraic scale, the points of which are associated in a one-to-one correspondence with the real numbers. The number a is *less than* the number b (that is,

$a < b$) if the point associated with a on the scale is to the left of the point associated with b. The zero point of the scale then separates the real numbers into two important types: the number x is *positive* if $0 < x$, and x is *negative* if $x < 0$. (It should be recalled from §1.2 that the inequalities $a < b$ and $b > a$ are considered to be identical, the symbol $>$ being read "greater than.") If a and b are real numbers such that $a < b$, there exists a positive real number h such that $b = a + h$; and, conversely, the latter equality implies the truth of the former inequality. It then follows that the notions of "positive" and "negative" are closely associated with the natural ordering relation in **R**.

We now proceed, somewhat as we did in Chapter 1, with the field properties of real numbers and list without proof the basic (or "axiomatic") properties of the "less than" order relation. It could be shown in a more thorough development that all order properties of the real numbers follow from these axioms. We remind the student again that we are continuing the axiomatic approach to algebra, which we began in Chapter 1. In the following statements a, b, c are assumed to be real numbers, arbitrary except as indicated:

O_1: Exactly one of the following holds: $a < b, a = b, a > b$. This is known as the *Trichotomy law*.
O_2: If $a < b$ and $b < c$, then $a < c$.
O_3: If $a < b$, then $a + c < b + c$.
O_4: If $a < b$ and $c > 0$, then $ac < bc$.

In view of the presence of this order relation in **R**, the real numbers may be said to form an *ordered* field.

It is now possible to use the above axiomatic properties to derive other—equally familiar—order properties of real numbers. We illustrate this method with the derivation of two very important properties, but leave the derivation of many others to the student in the problem set for this section. It is convenient to use the reference designations of the field axioms of **R**, as introduced in Chapter 1.

■ **THEOREM 1.1.**   *If $a < 0$ and $b < 0$, then $ab > 0$, for $a, b \in$ **R**.*

PROOF
$$a + (-a) < 0 + (-a) \qquad\qquad [O_3]$$
$$b + (-b) < 0 + (-b) \qquad\qquad [O_3]$$

Hence,

$$0 < -a \quad\text{and}\quad 0 < -b \quad\text{or, equivalently, } -b > 0 \qquad [A_4]$$

Then,

$$0 = 0(-b) < (-a)(-b), \quad\text{and so } (-a)(-b) > 0 \qquad [O_4]$$

It then follows from Theorem 5.9 (Chap. 1) that $ab > 0$, as asserted. We note that this result implies, in particular, that $-a < 0$ if $a > 0$ and $-a > 0$ if $a < 0$.

■ **THEOREM 1.2.** *If $a < b$ and $c < 0$, for $a, b, c \in \mathbf{R}$, then $ac > bc$.*

PROOF

$$a + (-a) < b + (-a) \qquad [O_3]$$
$$0 < b - a \qquad [A_4]$$
$$c(b - a) < 0(b - a) \qquad [O_4]$$
$$cb - ca < 0 \qquad [D]$$
$$cb - ca + ca < 0 + ca \qquad [O_3]$$
$$cb < ca \qquad [A_3, A_4]$$
$$ac > bc \qquad [M_5]$$

In the sequel, we shall often find it convenient to replace a pair of inequalities of the type $a < b$, $b < c$ by the compact form $a < b < c$. Other analogous compact forms will be used when other symbols of inequality or equality occur, and their meanings will be clear. The important notion of "absolute" value of a real number is closely associated with order. Intuitively, we often think of this absolute value as the magnitude of the number, without any regard to its sign. [In this connection, it may be well to emphasize that a number $-a$ is not necessarily negative! It could be, for example, that $a = -2$, so that $-a = -(-a) = 2$.] The following definition makes the concept precise.

Definition. *The* absolute value *of a real number a is the nonnegative number, denoted by $|a|$, defined so that*

$$|a| = \begin{cases} a & \text{if } a \geq 0 \\ -a & \text{if } a < 0 \end{cases}$$

It follows immediately from the definition that $|a| \geq 0$ for any $a \in \mathbf{R}$. For example, $|-3| = 3$ and $|5| = 5$. It is sometimes useful to observe that $\sqrt{x^2} = |x|$, for any $x \in \mathbf{R}$, recalling that the left member is defined as the *nonnegative* square root of x^2. Two of the most important consequences of the definition of absolute value are stated in Theorems 1.3 and 1.4 below, and other useful results may be found in the problems of this section.

■ **THEOREM 1.3.** $|a| \leq b$ *if and only if* $-b \leq a \leq b$, *for real numbers a, b.*

PROOF. The truth of this theorem is intuitively evident, but it is possible to give a formal proof. *We first assume that $|a| \leq b$*, which implies incidentally that $b \geq 0$ and $-b \leq 0$. Then, if $a \geq 0$, we see that $a = |a| \leq b$, and so $-b \leq a \leq b$. On the other hand, if $a < 0$, our definition of absolute value asserts that $-a = |a|$, so that $-a \leq b$. Hence, in either case, $-b \leq a \leq b$. Conversely, *let us now assume that $-b \leq a \leq b$*. If $a \geq 0$, then $a = |a|$, and so $-b \leq |a| \leq b$; in particular, $|a| \leq b$. If $a < 0$, $|a| = -a$, so that $-b \leq -|a| \leq b$ and so we have $-b \leq |a| \leq b$. It follows, in both cases, that $|a| \leq b$. We have shown that each of the two inequalities implies the other, and so the proof is complete.

■**THEOREM 1.4.** $-|a| \le a \le |a|$, *for any $a \in \mathbf{R}$.*

PROOF. This result—like that of the preceding theorem—is intuitively evident, but we include a proof. If $a \ge 0$, the definition of absolute value asserts that $a = |a|$; if $a < 0$, then $0 < -a$ and $|a| = -a$, and so $a < |a|$. Hence, for any $a \in \mathbf{R}$, we have shown that $a \le |a|$. A similar argument shows that $-|a| \le a$, so that $-|a| \le a \le |a|$ is true for every real number a.

Problems 3.1

1. Order the numbers in the following set to form a sequence of inequalities: $\{2, 0, -1, \pi, \sqrt{2}, -\pi, |-3|\}$.
2. What is $|x|$ if (a) $x = -2$; (b) $x = 3$; (c) $x = -4$; (d) $x = 0$; (e) $x = -\sqrt{2}$?
3. Find a simple form for x if (a) $x = |\frac{1}{3} - \frac{3}{4}|$; (b) $x = |\frac{1}{2} - \frac{2}{3}|$.
4. Express each of the following conditions on x in terms of an absolute value: (a) $-2 \le x \le 2$; (b) $-10 \le x \le 10$; (c) $x \le -2$ or $x \ge 2$; (d) $x \le -10$ or $x \ge 10$.
5. Express each of the following conditions in a form without an absolute-value sign: (a) $|a| \le 1$; (b) $|x| \ge 5$; (c) $|x| = 2$.
6. Replace each of the following systems of inequalities (considered to hold simultaneously) by a single inequality: (a) $x < -3, x < 0, x < 2$; (b) $x > -2, x > -1, x > 5$.
7. Designate each of the following sets of real numbers on an algebraic scale: (a) $\{x|-2 \le x \le 2\}$; (b) $\{x|-2 \le x \le 0 \text{ or } 1 \le x \le 2\}$; (c) $\{x||x| < 2\} \cup \{x|0 \le x \le 4\}$; (d) $\{x|-5 \le x \le 1\} \cap \{x|-2 \le x \le 4\}$; (e) $\{x||x| < 5 \text{ or } |x| > 2\}$.
8. Replace each of the following systems of inequalities (considered to hold simultaneously) by an inequality of the form $a \le x \le b$, for real numbers a, b: (a) $x \le -2, x \ge -5, x \le 10$; (b) $x \ge 0, x \le 5, x \le 1$; (c) $x < 5, |x| < 2, x > -3$.
9. Express the inequality in Theorem 1.4 for the case (a) $a = 6$; (b) $a = -6$.
10. Explain why there is no smallest positive number and no largest negative number.
11. Assuming that $1 \ne 0$, use the axioms or other results in this section to prove that $1 > 0$.
12. Give the details of the proof that $\sqrt{x^2} = |x|$, for any $x \in \mathbf{R}$.
13. Use the result in Problem 12 to prove that $|-x| = |x|$.
14. Explain why the results in this section imply that $|x| \ge 0$, for any $x \in \mathbf{R}$, as asserted following the definition of absolute value.

   Establish the inequalities in Problems 15–30, basing each proof on the theorems or other problems in this section. The symbols used denote real numbers, which are arbitrary except as indicated.

15. If $a < b$ and $c < d$, then $a + c < b + d$.
16. If $a < b$, then $b - a > 0$.
17. If $a < 0$, then $-a > 0$. (See remark following proof of Theorem 1.1.)
18. If $a > 0$ and $b > 0$, then $a + b > 0$.

19. If $a < b$, then $-a > -b$.
20. If $a > 0$ and $b > 0$, then $ab > 0$.
21. $a^2 > 0$, for any $a \neq 0$. (*Hint:* Use Trichotomy Law.)
22. $1/a > 0$ if and only if $a > 0$. (*Hint:* Use Trichotomy Law.)
23. If $a > b$ and $ab > 0$, then $1/a < 1/b$.
24. If $a > 0$, then $a + 1/a \geq 2$.
25. $a^2 + b^2 \geq 2ab$.
26. $a^2 + b^2 + c^2 \geq ab + ac + bc$. (*Hint:* Use result in Problem 25.)
27. $|ab| = |a|\,|b|$.
28. $|a/b| = |a|/|b|$, if $b \neq 0$.
29. $|a + b| < |a| + |b|$. (*Hint:* Consider first when $a + b \geq 0$ and then when $a + b < 0$.)
30. (a) $|a - b| \geq |a| - |b|$; (b) $|a + b| \geq |a| - |b|$.

3.2 The Solution of Simple Inequalities

A statement of inequality is very similar in external appearance to an equality, the only essential difference being the presence in an inequality of at least one of the following symbols: $<, >, \leq, \geq, \neq$. The symbolic statements $2 < 3 + 5$, $1 \neq 0$, and $5 + 2 > 1$ are simple examples of inequalities in which some of these symbols occur. It may be, of course, that an inequality involves one or more unknowns, and it is then an illustration of an open sentence—a concept introduced in §2.1. It would be quite consistent with the language of equations to refer to an open sentence of this kind as an "inequation," but we prefer to be slightly ambiguous and not make any verbal distinction between the two types of inequalities. We are then quite willing to refer to both $1 + 3 < 7$ and $2x + 1 < 3$ as inequalities, but the latter type will sometimes be called *open*. As with equations, we solve (open) inequalities by finding replacements for the unknowns from their respective universes, so that the resulting real-number inequalities are true. The *solutions*, or *solution sets*, of inequalities are then constructed from the collections of the suitable replacements. *In the absence of any statement to the contrary or if the context does not dictate otherwise, we shall always assume that the universe of every variable in an inequality is* **R**.

It will be useful for purposes of expressing the solution sets of inequalities to have available the symbolism of *intervals*. If a and b are real numbers with $a < b$, we have already introduced a compact notation that replaces the simultaneous inequalities $x > a$, $x < b$ by $a < x < b$, allowing for obvious variations when the symbols $\leq, >$, or $\geq$ occur. The set $\{x \in \mathbf{R} \mid a < x < b\}$ then consists of all real numbers between a and b and is an example of an *open interval*, often denoted by (a, b). The set $\{x \in \mathbf{R} \mid a \leq x \leq b\}$ is called a *closed* interval and is denoted by $[a, b]$, whereas the meaning of the *half-open* (or *half-closed*) intervals $(a, b]$ and $[a, b)$ should be clear. In any of these cases, the numbers a and b are called the *end points* of the interval. For example, $(2, 3)$ and $[2, 3]$ denote, respectively, open and closed intervals, each of which has 2 and 3 as end points. Sets of the types $\{x \in \mathbf{R} \mid x < a\}$ and $\{x \in \mathbf{R} \mid x > b\}$, for $a, b \in \mathbf{R}$, occur quite often in the solution of inequalities, and it is convenient to extend the notion of a (finite) interval to include them as *intervals of infinite extent*. The first of the two types just mentioned would then be denoted by $(-\infty, a)$, and the second by (b, ∞), with the symbols $(-\infty, a]$ and $[b, \infty)$ being used if the finite end points are included in the intervals. It must be emphasized that the symbols $-\infty$ and ∞ used here are *not* numbers but merely indicators of the infinite extent—in either a positive or negative direction—of the intervals involved.

We extend the idea of equivalence from equations to inequalities and say that two inequalities are *equivalent* if they have the same solution set. The procedure for solving an inequality is much like that used for solving an equation: We apply various operations to reduce the inequality to a simple but equivalent one—from which we can easily obtain the solution set. The permissible operations for inequalities are the same as those for equations, but with one notable exception (see Theorem 1.2): *If each member of an inequality is multiplied or divided by the same negative number, the sense of the inequality is reversed.* Thus, any multiplication or division of an inequality by a negative number requires that $<$ (or $>$) be replaced by $>$ (or $<$).

Example 1.   Solve $3x - 2 < 5x + 3$ for $x \in \mathbf{R}$.

SOLUTION

$$3x - 5x < 2 + 3 \qquad \text{[adding } 2 - 5x \text{ to both members]}$$
$$-2x < 5 \qquad \text{[combining terms]}$$
$$2x > -5 \qquad \text{[multiplying both members by } -1]$$
$$x > -\tfrac{5}{2} \qquad \text{[dividing both members by 2]}$$

Any real number greater than $-\tfrac{5}{2}$ is then a solution of the given inequality, so the desired solution set is the infinite interval $(-\tfrac{5}{2}, \infty)$.

Example 2.   Solve $|2x + 1| \leq 3$ if the universe of x is (a) $\mathbf{Z}$; (b) $\mathbf{R}$.

SOLUTION.   The given inequality is equivalent (see Theorem 1.3) to $-3 \leq 2x + 1 \leq 3$. On adding -1 to each member of this inequality, the result is $-4 \leq 2x \leq 2$ or, more simply, $-2 \leq x \leq 1$.
    (a) If the universe of x is $\mathbf{Z}$, the solution set is then $\{-2, -1, 0, 1\}$.
    (b) If the universe of x is $\mathbf{R}$, the solution set is the interval $[-2, 1]$.

Example 3.   Solve $x^2 - 2x < 3$ for $x \in \mathbf{R}$.

SOLUTION.   The given inequality is equivalent to $x^2 - 2x - 3 < 0$, and this may be written as

$$(x + 1)(x - 3) < 0.$$

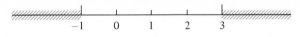

Figure 8

The equation $(x + 1)(x - 3) = 0$ has -1 and 3 for its real solutions, and these two points partition the real line into three intervals, as shown in Figure 8. Two of these intervals are observed to be of the infinite variety. It is a characteristic—though *admittedly intuitive*—property of the real numbers that the algebraic sign of $(x + 1)(x - 3)$ is invariant (i.e., *always the same*) for all points in any one of the associated intervals. (This is a property of "continuity," a topic that we shall not discuss here.) It is now a simple matter to check the sign of the left member of the simplified inequality at some arbitrary point in each of the intervals. For example, we might proceed as follows:

$$\text{If } x = -2, \quad (x + 1)(x - 3) = (-1)(-5) = \quad 5 > 0$$
$$\text{If } x = \quad 0, \quad (x + 1)(x - 3) = \quad (1)(-3) = -3 < 0$$
$$\text{If } x = \quad 4, \quad (x + 1)(x - 3) = \quad (5)(1) \quad = \quad 5 > 0$$

Hence the solution set of the given inequality is the open interval $(-1, 3)$.

By these examples we have illustrated methods of solving some of the simpler types of linear and quadratic inequalities.

Problems 3.2

1. Check that $\{-1, 0, 1\}$ is a subset of the solution set of each of the following inequalities:
   (a) $2x + 1 < 7$
   (b) $3x - 2 < 5$
   (c) $|x| \leq 3$
   (d) $x^2 - 5 \neq 2$
2. If possible, express each of the following pairs of inequalities in the form $a \leq x \leq b$ (or with either $\leq$ replaced by $<$), for appropriate real numbers a, b:
   (a) $x \leq 3, x \geq -1$
   (b) $x \leq 2, x > -1$
   (c) $x \leq 5, x > 0$
   (d) $x \leq 5, x \geq 2$
   (e) $x < 5, x \geq -2$
   (f) $x \geq 0, x \leq -1$
   (g) $x > -3, x < 2$
   (h) $x > 0, x \leq 3$
3. Use interval notation to express the set of real numbers x that satisfy the following condition:
   (a) $-1 \leq x \leq 2$
   (b) $2 < x \leq 5$
   (c) $0 < x < 10$
   (d) $0 \leq x \leq 10$
   (e) $x < -2$
   (f) $x > -2$
4. Give a simpler designation for each of the following sets of real numbers:
   (a) $(2, 3) \cap [2, 3]$
   (b) $\{1\} \cup (1, 2) \cup \{2\}$
   (c) $[-1, 3] \cap [0, 5]$
   (d) $(1, 3) \cap (2, 4)$
5. Designate each of the following intervals on an algebraic scale:
   (a) $\{x \in \mathbf{R} \mid x > 2\}$
   (b) $\{x \in \mathbf{R} \mid -2 < x \leq 5\}$
   (c) $\{x \in \mathbf{R} \mid x < -1\}$
   (d) $\{x \in \mathbf{R} \mid |x| < 1\}$

6. Solve the following equations for $x \in \mathbf{R}$:
   (a) $|x - 5| = |2x - 3|$ (b) $|x + 1| = |1 - x|$
7. Solve the following equations for $x \in \mathbf{R}$:
   (a) $|x - 3| = |3x - 3|$ (b) $|5x + 3| = |2x - 4|$

   Find the solution sets of the inequalities listed in Problems 8–28 for $x \in \mathbf{R}$, except as indicated otherwise.

8. $3x - 2 < x + 5$ 9. $x - 5 \leq 3x + 4$
10. $5x - 2 \geq 5 + x$ 11. $|2x - 1| \leq 4$
12. $|x + 4| \leq 4$, where (a) $x \in \mathbf{Z}$; (b) $x \in \mathbf{R}$.
13. $|2x - 4| \geq 4$, where (a) $x \in \mathbf{Z}$; (b) $x \in \mathbf{R}$.
14. $|3x| < -1$ 15. $|3x| > 1$
16. $-1 \leq 2x + 1 < 87$ 17. $x^2 - 2x + 1 > 0$
18. $2x^2 - 4x + 1 \leq 0$, where (a) $x \in \mathbf{Z}$; (b) $x \in \mathbf{R}$.
19. $x^2 - 3x + 2 \geq 0$, where (a) $x \in \mathbf{Z}$; (b) $x \in \mathbf{R}$.
20. $3x^2 - 2x + 1 \leq 0$ 21. $-3x^2 + 4x < 1$
22. $|x - 1| \leq |x| + 1$ 23. $-4 \leq 1 - 2x \leq 8$
24. $-2 < 3x - 1 < \frac{2}{3}$ 25. $|x - 3| \leq 3x - 1 < \frac{2}{3}$
26. $1/3x < 2$ 27. $1/x - 1 < k$, where $0 < k < 1$.
28. $x^2 - 16 < k$, where $k > 0$.

29. Use interval notation to describe the following set, and designate it on an algebraic scale: $\{x \in \mathbf{R} \mid |x - 2| + |7 - x| = 5\}$.
30. Find the solution set of the following inequality for $x \in \mathbf{R}$:

$$|2x - 1| + |x + 3| \geq |3x + 2|$$

3.3 More on Inequalities

It is necessary to exercise extreme caution in solving an inequality, at any point where each member is multiplied by an expression involving an unknown. If the universe of such an unknown contains both positive and negative numbers, any multiplication by the expression becomes subject to the exception concerning signs noted in §3.2. In such an instance, there is no way of knowing in advance whether the sense of the inequality should then be reversed or remain the same. This difficulty is illustrated in Example 1, and we have given two slightly different methods of attack—each being the better suited for a particular type of situation. But first it is helpful to establish an elementary result.

■ **THEOREM 3.1.** *If $a < b$, for $a, b \in \mathbf{R}$, then*

(a) $1/a > 1/b$, *provided* $ab > 0$
(b) $1/a < 1/b$, *provided* $ab < 0$

PROOF

(a) If $ab > 0$ and we multiply both members of the given inequality by $1/ab$, the result is $1/b < 1/a$ by property O_4 in §3.1.
(b) If $ab < 0$ and we multiply both members of the given inequality by $1/ab$, the result $1/a < 1/b$ follows from Theorem 1.2.

As a consequence, it should be noted that $a < b < c$ does *not* necessarily imply that $1/c < 1/b < 1/a$. The truth or falsity of this latter assertion depends on the algebraic signs of a, b, c.

Example 1.   Solve the inequality $-1 < \dfrac{10}{10 + x} < 1$ for $x \in \mathbf{R}$.

SOLUTION 1.   We consider two cases: $10 + x > 0$ and $10 + x < 0$.
(a) If $10 + x > 0$, we may multiply all members of the inequality by $10 + x$ and obtain $-10 - x < 10 < 10 + x$. On adding 10 to each member, the result is $-x < 20 < 20 + x$, and this is seen to be true for any replacement of x which is *positive*.
(b) If $10 + x < 0$, we may multiply all members of the inequality by $10 + x$ and obtain $-10 - x > 10 > 10 + x$, which may also be written $10 + x < 10 < -10 - x$. On adding -10 to each member of this inequality, the result is $x < 0 < -20 - x$, which is seen to be true for any replacement of x such that $x < -20$.

The complete solution set of the given inequality is then

$$\{x \in \mathbf{R} \mid x < -20 \text{ or } x > 0\}$$

or, alternatively,

$$(-\infty, -20) \cup (0, \infty).$$

SOLUTION 2.   We again consider two cases: $10 + x > 0$ and $10 + x < 0$. However, in this variation of the solution, we break up the given inequality into two inequalities with two members each:

$$-1 < \frac{10}{10 + x} \qquad \frac{10}{10 + x} < 1$$

(a) If $10 + x > 0$, we may multiply through by $10 + x$ and obtain

$$-10 - x < 10 \qquad 10 < 10 + x$$

These may be seen to be equivalent to $x > -20$ and $x > 0$, and *both* conditions are satisfied if $x > 0$.
(b) If $10 + x < 0$, we may multiply through by $10 + x$ and obtain

$$-10 - x > 10 \qquad 10 > 10 + x$$

These may be seen to be equivalent to $x < -20$ and $x < 0$, and *both* conditions are satisfied if $x < -20$.

As before, the solution set of the given inequality may be expressed as either

$$\{x \in \mathbf{R} \mid x < -20 \text{ or } x > 0\}$$

or

$$(-\infty, -20) \cup (0, \infty).$$

If the unknown of an inequality occurs in the denominator of a member, it is possible to "clear fractions" without reversing the sense by multiplying through by the *square* of the least common denominator. However, this procedure usually increases the degree of the inequality. For example, if we multiply through by x^2, the inequality $-3/x < 1 < 5/x$ becomes the second-degree inequality $-3x < x^2 < 5x$.

The next example illustrates two useful techniques for solving more complicated types of inequalities.

Example 2.   Solve $\dfrac{(x-1)(x+2)}{x-3} < 0$ for $x \in \mathbf{R}$.

SOLUTION 1.   This method of solution is essentially the method used in Example 3 of §3.2. If we set each factor (occurring in either numerator or denominator) equal to 0, we obtain the three "critical points" $x = -2$, $x = 1$, and $x = 3$. These points partition the real line into four subintervals, two of infinite extent. Again we use the *intuitive fact* that the sign of the left member of the given inequality is the same for all points in any one of these subintervals. We then check the sign for an arbitrary point in each of the subintervals, as shown in Figure 9, and we have our solution.

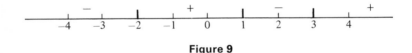

Figure 9

For example, if $x = -3$,

$$\frac{(x-1)(x+2)}{x-3} = \frac{(-4)(-1)}{-6} = -\tfrac{2}{3}$$

if $x = 0$,

$$\frac{(x-1)(x+2)}{x-3} = \frac{(-1)(2)}{-3} = \tfrac{2}{3}$$

if $x = 2$,

$$\frac{(x-1)(x+2)}{x-3} = \frac{(1)(4)}{-1} = -4$$

if $x = 4$,

$$\frac{(x-1)(x+2)}{x-3} = \frac{(3)(6)}{1} = 18$$

It follows that

$$\frac{(x-1)(x+2)}{x-3}$$

is negative in both the first and third subintervals, and so the solution set of the given inequality may be expressed as either

$$\{x \in \mathbf{R} \mid x < -2 \text{ or } 1 < x < 3\}$$

or

$$(-\infty, -2) \cup (1, 3)$$

SOLUTION 2. This method is slightly more geometric and requires that we draw an algebraic scale corresponding to each component of the left member of the inequality and place them horizontally so that their scale readings are in vertical alignment. For the factors $x - 1$, $x + 2$, and $x - 3$ in this problem, the scales are shown in Figure 10. On each scale, we designate the real numbers (if any) for which the associated factor is undefined by means of a wavy line and those for which the factor is positive by means of a heavy line, and we leave the rest of the scale (if any) un-changed. We now recall that the product or quotient of an even number of negative numbers is positive, whereas an odd number of negative numbers results in a negative number. It is then possible to tell at a glance those portions of the real line for which the given expression is negative. The desired solution set is easily found from Figure 10 to be $\{x \in \mathbf{R} \mid x < -2$ or $1 < x < 3\}$ or $(-\infty, -2) \cup (1, 3)$, as before.

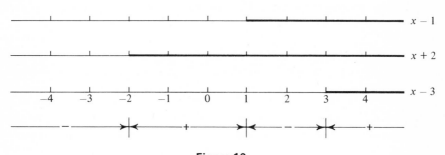

Figure 10

Example 2 did not illustrate the case in which one or more of the component factors is undefined for certain ranges of x. This situation gives no trouble, however, if we simply note that an expression is undefined for any replacement of x which results in *any one* of its component factors being undefined. For example, the factor $\sqrt{x - 1}$ is undefined for $x < 1$, and its associated algebraic scale would be shown as in Figure 11.

Figure 11

Problems 3.3

Find the solution set of each of the inequalities in Problems 1–28 for $x \in \mathbf{R}$.

1. $|2x + 1| < 2$ **2.** $|3x + 4| > 2$
3. $|x/(1 - x)| < 2$ **4.** $|2x/(x + 1)| > 1$
5. $(2x + 1)/(x - 3) > 0$ **6.** $(2x + 1)/(x + 1) \leq 0$
7. $(x - 1)/(x - 3) \leq 0$ **8.** $1/x + 1 > 0$
9. $|(x + 1)/x| < 1$ **10.** $(2x - 1)/(x^2 + 1) \geq 0$
11. $-1 \leq x/(x + 2) < 3$ **12.** $-3 \leq x/(x + 2) \leq 5$
13. $x^2 - 5x + 6 < 0$ **14.** $x^2 - x - 12 \geq 0$
15. $|x(x - 5)| \leq x$ **16.** $|x^2 - 7| < 2$
17. $x(x^2 + 1)(x^4 + 1) < 0$ **18.** $x(x + 1)/(x - 2) < 0$
19. $x^2(x + 1)(x - 1)/(x - 2) < 0$ **20.** $x^2(x + 1)\sqrt{1 - x} > 0$
21. $(x + 1)(x + 2)(x + 3) < 0$ **22.** $(x - 1)/\sqrt{1 + x} > 0$
23. $x\sqrt[3]{1 - x^2} > 0$ **24.** $(x + 1)/\sqrt{1 - x} > 0$
25. $(2x - 1)|x| \geq 0$ **26.** $(2x + 1)|x| \leq 0$
27. $\sqrt{x - 1}\,|x| < 0$ **28.** $\sqrt{x - 1}\,|x| > 0$

29. $a < b < c$, formulate a theorem that relates the reciprocals $1/a$, $1/b$, $1/c$.
30. If ϵ is an arbitrary positive number, show that $|(3x - 1) - 2| < \epsilon$ provided $|x - 1| < \epsilon/3$.

3.4 The Completeness Property

The order properties discussed in §3.1 are not distinctively characteristic of the *real* numbers, for these properties are also possessed by the rational numbers. However, the property of "completeness," which we are now about to describe, is possessed by the real but *not* by the rational numbers and so is an intrinsic property of **R**. Even though this property is not used in any of the discussions of algebra in this book, we include a brief commentary on it here in order that we may thereby bring to a proper conclusion the axiomatic development of **R** begun in Chapter 1. In a minimal course, however, this section may be omitted without any loss of continuity in the sequel.

Definition.   *A set S of real numbers is* bounded above *by b (or has b as an* upper bound), *if* $x \leq b$ *for every x in S. Similarly, S is* bounded below *by a (or has a as a* lower bound), *if* $a \leq x$ *for every x in S.*

If S is the set of all rational numbers x such that $x^2 < 2$, it is clear that $\sqrt{2}$ or any larger number is an upper bound of S, whereas $-\sqrt{2}$ or any numerically larger negative number is a lower bound. The set **N** of natural numbers has 1 for a lower bound, but no upper bound exists; and neither an upper nor a lower bound exists for the set of all integers. We have implied, of course, that if a bound exists, it is never a unique number. As a final example, if S is the set of numbers consisting of 1, -2, 3, two upper bounds of S are 4 and 5.5, while two lower bounds are -2 and -3.75.

If c is any real number such that $a < c < b$, the order properties of **R** require that $a < (a + c)/2 < c < (c + b)/2 < b$. Hence, no such c can be either a lower or upper bound of (a, b) or $[a, b]$, a fact that is geometrically evident. Hence b is the "least" upper bound and a is the "greatest" lower bound of either interval, two notions more carefully described by the following definition.

Definition. *Let S be a set of real numbers. A lower bound l of S is called a greatest lower bound if $a \leq l$, for every lower bound a of S. Similarly, an upper bound u of S is a least upper bound if $u \leq b$, for every upper bound b of S.*

The left and right end points of an interval are, respectively, the greatest lower bound and the least upper bound of the set of points in the interval (whether open or closed). Moreover, if a greatest lower bound or least upper bound of a set of real numbers exists, this number is unique. (Why?) The following is a description of the characteristic property of **R**, to which we referred above.

Completeness Property. *If a nonempty set of real numbers is bounded above, it has a least upper bound; if the set is bounded below, it has a greatest lower bound. In short, any bounded set of real numbers has a greatest lower bound and a least upper bound.*

We emphasize that this property cannot be proved as a theorem, but it is a very deep property which we should regard as axiomatic along with the additive, multiplicative, and order axioms. We have already remarked that the completeness property—which may be given in many other equivalent forms—is not possessed by the rational numbers. For example, the set $\{x \in \mathbf{Q} \mid x^2 < 3\}$ has no *rational* least upper bound, but $\sqrt{3}$ is the *real* least upper bound both of this set and of the larger set $\{x \in \mathbf{R} \mid x^2 < 3\}$. We have already implied that the property of completeness is not essential in an elementary study of algebra. However, it does play a key role in discussions of the calculus in questions related to the length of a curve and the area of a nonpolygonal figure—to mention but two points of interest in what is considered to be elementary mathematics. It is now proper to refer to the system **R** of real numbers as a *complete ordered field*.

Problems 3.4

1. Find the least upper bound and the greatest lower bound of each of the following sets of real numbers: (a) $\{1, 4, 5, -3\}$; (b) $\{0, -2, 5, 10\}$; (c) $\{-\frac{1}{2}, -\frac{2}{3}, \frac{1}{4}, 1, 0\}$.
2. Find the least upper bound and the greatest lower bound of each of the following sets of real numbers: (a) $\{-3, -2, 0, 3, 4\}$; (b) $\{1\}$; (c) $\{x \in \mathbf{R} \mid -2 < x < 5\}$; (d) $\{x \in \mathbf{Q} \mid -3 < x < 1\}$.

3. Find the least upper bound and greatest lower bound of each of the following intervals of real numbers: (a) [2, 5]; (b) (−2, 3); (c) [−1, 1]; (d) (0, 7).
4. Find the least upper bound and greatest lower bound (if they exist) of each of the following sets of real numbers: (a) $(-\infty, 1)$; (b) $(1, \infty)$; (c) $\{x \in \mathbf{R} | \ x < 3\}$; (d) $\{x \in \mathbf{R} | \ x^2 < 5\}$; (e) $\{x \in \mathbf{R} | \ x^2 \leq 5\}$.
5. Find the least upper bound and greatest lower bound (if they exist) of each of the following sets of real numbers: (a) $\{x \in \mathbf{R} | \ x < 4 \text{ and } x > -2\}$; (b) $\{x \in \mathbf{R} | \ x^2 < 5\} \cap \{x \in \mathbf{R} | \ x^2 > 1\}$;   (c) $\{x \in \mathbf{R} | \ -2 < x < 5\} \cup \{x \in \mathbf{R} | \ 0 \leq x \leq 8\}$; (d) $(-\infty, 5) \cap (-3, \infty)$; (e) $(-\infty, 0) \cup (0, \infty)$.
6. Explain why a least upper bound (or greatest lower bound) is unique, if it exists.
7. Give an example of a set that contains its greatest lower bound and an example of one that does not.
8. Use the directions in Problem 7, but with "least upper bound" replacing "greatest lower bound."
9. Prove that every finite set of real numbers contains both its least upper bound and greatest lower bound.
10. Explain the difference between a set of real numbers being "bounded" and being "finite." Illustrate with examples of sets that are bounded but not finite.
11. With $c > 0$, let S be the set of all positive integral multiples of c; that is, $S = \{c, 2c, 3c, \ldots\} = \{nc| \ n \ (> 0) \in \mathbf{Z}\}$. Prove that S has no upper bound, and so no least upper bound.
12. Use the result in Problem 11 to prove the "Archimedean Principle": If c and d are real numbers, $c > 0$, there exists a positive integer n such that $nc > d$.

Use Problem 12 to prove the assertions in Problems 13–15.

13. The least upper bound of the set $\{\frac{1}{2}, \frac{2}{3}, \frac{3}{4}, \ldots, n/(n+1), \ldots\}$, for arbitrary $n \ (> 0) \in \mathbf{Z}$, is 1.
14. The greatest lower bound of the set $\{\frac{1}{1}, \frac{1}{2}, \frac{1}{3}, \ldots, 1/n, \ldots\}$, for arbitrary $n \ (> 0) \in \mathbf{Z}$, is 0.
15. There exists a rational number between any two distinct real numbers.

3.5 Polygonal Convex Sets

A study of inequalities, in spite of certain serious complications, may be seen to parallel a study of equations. In the earlier sections of this chapter, our principal interest has been in linear and quadratic inequalities in one unknown, and their solutions. The next stage in a systematic study of inequalities would involve some kind of generalization of the manner in which they are constructed, and there is no limit to the diversity of such generalizations. However, in view of the complications that can develop, we shall restrict ourselves to what is probably the simplest extension of our earlier study: *linear inequalities in two variables x and y of the form* $ax + by + c < 0$ and simple variations thereof. Our point of view will be largely geometric.

We shall use the symbolism introduced earlier for equations in two unknowns and shall use ordered pairs of real numbers to denote solutions. A solution of an inequality in x and y would then be denoted by (c_1, c_2), where a replacement of x by c_1 and y by c_2 transforms the open inequality into a true inequality involving real numbers. The solution set of an inequality of this kind is again a subset of **R** × **R**, as in the case of equations. If a Cartesian coordinate system (as discussed in §2.1) is used, the solution set of either an equation or an open inequality in two unknowns is represented geometrically by a set of points in the plane. This representation is also known as the *locus* or *graph* of the equation or inequality, a terminology that is likely quite familiar to the student.

It is shown in a study of geometry that the graph of a linear *equation* $ax + by + c = 0$ is a straight line. For example, in Figure 12 we have shown a portion of the graph of $2x - 3y - 4 = 0$, with a few of the solution pairs of the equation included beside the associated points of the linear graph.

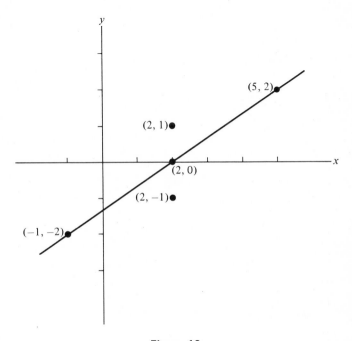

Figure 12

Any straight line in a plane partitions the plane into two *half planes*, which may or may not include the line itself. If the line is included, the half plane is said to be *closed*, whereas a half plane that does not include its boundary line is said to be *open*. Let us now consider the five algebraic open statements given below:

(a) $2x - 3y = 4$
(b) $2x - 3y < 4$
(c) $2x - 3y > 4$
(d) $2x - 3y \leq 4$
(e) $2x - 3y \geq 4$

If we let $x = 2$ and $y = 1$ in (b), we find that $2(2) - 3(1) = 4 - 3 = 1 < 4$ is a true statement. Hence, the graph of (b) includes the point $(2, 1)$. We note (see Figure 12) that this point is *above* the straight-line locus of (a), and it is a fact that the complete graph of (b) is the set of points above the line—and so may be described as the open half plane above the line. Similarly, if we let $x = 2$ and $y = -1$ in (c), we observe that $2(2) - 3(-1) = 4 + 3 = 7 > 4$ is a true statement. Hence the point $(2, -1)$ lies on the graph of (c), and the half plane of points *below* the straight line comprises this complete graph. The solution set of (d) is the union of the solution sets of (a) and (b), and so its graph is the closed half plane above the line. Similarly, the solution set of (e) is the union of the solution sets of (a) and (c), and the graph of this set is the closed half plane below the line.

In general, the locus of any linear equation $ax + by = c$, with a and b real numbers, is a straight line, whereas the graphs of $ax + by < c$ and $ax + by > c$ are the open half planes on either side of the line. *We have not given a proof of this latter remark*, but a proof is suggested in Problem 22. By checking any point not on the line, it is easy to decide which side of the line is the graph of either inequality. If $<$ or $>$ are replaced by $\leq$ or $\geq$, of course, the half planes become closed.

The problem of solving a *system* of inequalities now arises, and we consider the simultaneous solutions of such a system. For example, let us examine the system

$$2x + 3y \leq 6$$
$$x - y \leq 0$$
$$x \geq 0$$

The solution set of this system is the intersection of the solution sets of the individual inequalities. Because each of these solution sets is a closed half plane, the desired solution set is the intersection of these three half planes. The checking of a few points will show, in this case, that the solution set of the given system is the set of points within and on the finite triangle shown in Figure 13.

Definition. *A plane set is said to be* convex *if whenever two points belong to the set so do all points of the line segment joining the two points.*

It is intuitively evident that *the intersection of any finite number of closed half planes is a convex set*. The case of most common occurrence is that in which the convex set has finite extent with the shape of a polygon, and it is then called a *polygonal convex* set. It is possible to give a formal proof of the above italicized statement, but we shall merely indicate its proof in some of the problems of this section.

Because the solution set of any linear inequality in two unknowns, involving $\leq$ or $\geq$, is a closed half plane, it is apparent that the common solutions of any system of inequalities of this kind comprise either a polygonal convex set—as in Figure 13—or a set of infinite extent—as for the solutions of the system $x \geq 0$, $y \geq 0$.

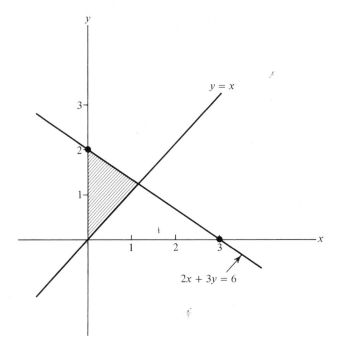

Figure 13

Example. A boy is allowed to spend up to $24 for records and paperbacks. If paperbacks cost $2 each and records cost $3 each, use a system of inequalities to investigate the possibilities.

SOLUTION.   Let us suppose that the boy buys x paperbacks and y records. The requirements of the purchase may then be represented by the following system of inequalities:

$$2x + 3y \le 24$$
$$x \qquad \ge 0$$
$$y \ge 0$$

The latter two inequalities hold, of course, because it is impossible to buy a negative number of records or paperbacks. We also observe that the context of the problem requires that the universe of both unknowns x and y is a subset of nonnegative integers. If we make a graph of the system, we obtain the convex set shown in Figure 14. We note in passing that, if we replace x and y by 0 in the first inequality of the system, we obtain $2(0) + 3(0) = 0 \le 24$, and we observe that this is a true statement. Thus the point $(0, 0)$—and with it every point below the line $2x + 3y - 24 = 0$

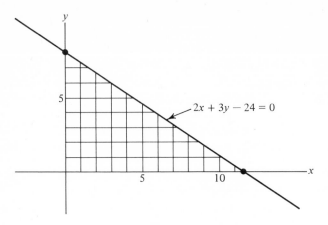

Figure 14

—satisfies the inequality. Any point (x, y) within or on the boundary of the triangle shown in the figure, and with x and y in the universe of nonnegative integers, provides us with a solution to the problem.

For example, one solution would be $(5, 4)$; that is, the boy could purchase five paperbacks and four records.

Problems 3.5

1. Verify that $(1, 2)$ is a solution of each of the following inequalities:
(a) $x + 2y > 4$; (b) $3x - y > 0$; (c) $2x + 3y - 4 \geq 0$; (d) $x - 5y \leq 10$.

2. Give a graphical representation of the solution set of each of the following inequalities: (a) $x - 2y + 1 \leq 0$; (b) $2x + y < 3$; (c) $x + y \leq 5$.

3. Use "trial and error" to find one solution of each of the following systems of inequalities:

(a) $x + 2y < 3$ (b) $x - 3y \leq 2$ (c) $x - 2y \leq 5$
    $x + y < 1$ $2x + y \leq 3$ $2x + y \geq 1$

4. Use "trial and error" to find a solution of $2x - 3y + 6 = 0$ that is also a solution of (a) $x + 2y + 1 < 0$; (b) $x + 2y + 1 > 0$; (c) $x - y \geq 0$; (d) $x - y \leq 0$.

In Problems 5–10, give graphical representations of the convex sets that are the solutions of the given systems of inequalities.

5. $x \geq 2$ **6.** $3x + 2y \geq 5$
    $y \leq 5$ $x + y \leq 2$
    $2x - 3y \leq 0$ $y \geq 0$

7. $x \leq 3$ **8.** $x - 2y \geq -2$
    $x \geq -3$ $x + 2y \leq 0$
    $y \leq 2$ $y \geq 0$
    $y \geq -2$

9. $x - y \geq 0$
    $2x + 3y \leq 6$
    $x + y \geq 1$
    $y \geq 0$

10. $x + y \leq 0$
    $-2x + y \geq 1$
    $y \leq 0$
    $x \geq -2$

11. Use the definition of a convex set to prove that the intersection of two or more convex sets is also a convex set.

12. Prove that any half plane—either open or closed—is a convex set.

13. Deduce from the results in Problems 11 and 12 that the intersection of any number of half planes is a convex set.

14. Modify appropriately the diagram of the example if there are only three available paperbacks of interest to the boy.

15. Modify appropriately the diagram of the example if there are only six records available and of any interest to the boy.

16. If the boy in the example is to buy at least twice as many paperbacks as records, make an appropriate modification of the diagram.

17. If the boy in the example is to spend $12 on records, make an appropriate modification of the diagram.

18. A farmer wishes to spend not over $300 for young pigs and lambs. If lambs cost $10 each and pigs cost $5 each, construct a polygonal set to display the different possibilities for the farmer.

19. Give the appropriate modification of the diagram in Problem 18 if the farmer must buy at least six pigs and ten lambs.

20. A manufacturer of fruit cocktail wishes to produce a fruit mixture that will cost not over 20 cents per pint. To the main body of the mixture, which costs 15 cents per pint, he will add some special kinds of red and green cherries. Each pint is to have at least five cherries of each color. If the red cherries cost 0.2 cents each and the green cherries cost 0.1 cents each, use a diagram to display the possible number of red and green cherries in each pint of the cocktail.

21. If each pint of the fruit cocktail in Problem 20 is to have twice as many red as green cherries, modify the diagram in that problem appropriately.

22. Prove that the half plane that represents the solutions of the inequality $ax + by < c$ is the portion below the line graph of $ax + by = c$ if and only if $b > 0$.

23. Use the result in Problem 22 to describe the solution set of each of the following inequalities: (a) $2x - 3y + 2 < 0$; (b) $3x - 2y > 7$; (c) $x + 3y < -3$; (d) $2x + 5y > 8$.

   Note: A problem in *linear programming* results if one attempts to maximize or minimize the numerical value of a linear polynomial in two variables, subject to certain conditions or "constraints," the common universe of the variables being the polygonal convex set that is determined by the constraints. It can be shown that *the polynomial takes on its maximal and minimum values at some corner of the polygon. Assume this result* for Problems 24–30.

24. A convex polygon is defined by the inequalities: $x - 2y \leq 0$, $x + 3y \leq 0$, $2x - 3y + 6 \geq 0$. Using the points within or on the polygon as the universe of the variables, determine the maximum and minimum values of each of the following polynomials: (a) $2x - 3y$; (b) $x + 2y$; (c) $3x - y$; (d) $x + 3y$.

25. Using the same universe as in Problem 24, find the maximum and minimum values of each of the following polynomials: (a) $x - 2y + 2$; (b) $2x - 5y + 5$; (c) $2x - 3y + 6$.

26. The profit per unit of time in producing x units of one product and y units of another is known to be $3x + 4y$ dollars. Let us suppose that the conditions of manufacture are such that the following constraints must be met: $x - y \geq 2$, $3x + y \leq 14$, $x + 6y \geq 10$. Determine the number of units of each product to be produced for maximum total profit.

27. Use the same constraints as in Problem 26 and determine the maximum profit, if profit is expressible in the form $2x + 6y - 12$.

28. Joe and Pete are in partnership in the manufacture of two novelty items A and B. Each item requires 2 hours of Joe's time, whereas Pete needs 2 hours on item A and 3 hours on item B. Joe can work 6 and Pete can work 8 hours per day at the job. If the profit on each A item is \$3 and each B item is \$4, determine the most profitable number of each type of item to produce in a day.

29. A small furniture manufacturer makes tables and chairs and uses machines A, B, C in their production. The manufacture of a table requires the use of A for 4 hours, B for 2 hours, and C for 1 hour; for a chair, 2 hours are needed on A, 1 hour on B, and 3 hours on C. Only one of each of the three machines is available, but 24-hour daily operation is permitted. If the profits on the sale of a table and chair are \$15 and \$10, respectively, determine how many of each article should be manufactured per 5-day week for maximum total profit.

30. With reference to Problem 29, if the profit per table drops to \$12, determine the new weekly output of tables and chairs for maximum total profit.

4

Functions

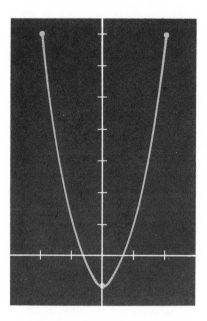

4.1 The Function Concept

The concept to be examined in this section takes its place, along with that of a set, as one of the most basic in all of modern mathematics. And because it is so basic, it is somewhat elusive! We are referring to a *function*, or *mapping*, that associates the elements of one nonempty set in some way with those of another—or subset of the same—set. In §4.2, a precise set-theoretic definition of the concept will be given, but for the purposes of this section, an intuitive approach will suffice. Let X and Y be two nonempty sets, which, for the convenience of a diagram, we designate as point sets in Figure 15.

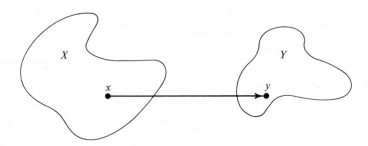

Figure 15

If, with each point $x \in X$, there is associated a unique $y \in Y$, we say that this association defines a function on *(or* mapping of) *X to (or* into) *Y. It is customary to say that the function* maps x onto y *and to refer to the set X of mapped points as the* domain *of the function and to the subset of Y of ("*image*") points onto which X is mapped as the* range *of the function.*

When we say that a function f is defined *on* a set X, we are emphasizing that the whole set X—and not possibly some proper subset—is the domain of f. On the other hand, the terminology "into Y" or "to Y" does not distinguish whether Y or a proper subset of Y is the range. It is convenient to abbreviate the information that "f is a function on X to Y" with the following symbolism:

$$f \colon X \to Y$$

We also use either $y = f(x)$ or $x \xrightarrow{f} y$ to indicate that the function f maps the element x of its domain onto the element y of its range. The element $f(x)$—which is read "f of x"—or y is called the *value of the function f at x*; the notation $y = f(x)$ is intended to emphasize that the element y is uniquely determined by the function f and the element x of its domain. In this symbolism, the range of a function f on X can be described as the set $\{f(x) \mid x \in X\}$.

There are many illustrations in everyday life of the function or mapping concept just introduced. In a retail store, each and every item for sale is associated in a unique way with its price. A "price" function is then defined on the set of store items, each item being mapped by the function onto its price. If P denotes this function, $P(x)$ would denote the price of the article x in the store. The local telephone directory provides us with the requirements for another simple function, provided we agree to associate a particular number—say the first—with any subscriber having more than one telephone number listed. This "telephone" function may then be said to be defined on the set of local subscribers, and maps any given subscriber onto his telephone number. If we denote this function by T, $T(x)$ will designate the telephone number of x, where x stands this time for an arbitrary telephone subscriber.

The basic ingredients of what we are loosely referring to as a "function" are then two sets—the domain and range of the function—along with an association between the elements of the sets that uniquely maps each element of the domain onto an element of the range. It should be clear that, if all the element associations of a function are known, the memberships of both the domain and range of the function are also apparent. On the other hand, it is possible for many different functions to have the same domain and the same range. If the domain of a function is finite, perhaps the simplest way to give a complete description of the function is to list the associated elements explicitly. For example, if $S = \{1, 2, 3, 4, 5\}$ and $T = \{0, 1, 2\}$, a function g on S to T can be defined unambiguously as follows:

$$1 \to 1, \quad 2 \to 0, \quad 3 \to 1, \quad 4 \to 0, \quad 5 \to 1$$

In the symbolism introduced earlier, this implies that $g(1) = 1$, $g(2) = 0$, $g(3) = 1$, $g(4) = 0$, and $g(5) = 1$. In the more typical case in which the domain is an infinite set, it is customary to use a *rule* to define the association (or correspondence) between the elements of the domain and range of the function. For example, the following rule could be used to define a function on any subset X of real numbers: $x \to y = x^2$, for $x \in X$. If f denotes this function, we may say that f has been defined on X to $\mathbf{R}$, where $f(x) = x^2$. It may be well to point out again that the definition of a function on S to T requires that each element of S be mapped onto an element of T, but not every element of T is necessarily an image point of the function. For the two functions just defined, we observe that the range of g is $\{0, 1\}$, a proper subset of T, and the range of f is a subset of nonnegative numbers—a proper subset of $\mathbf{R}$.

In the great majority of cases occurring in elementary mathematics, both the domains and ranges of the functions are subsets of real numbers, and a function is completely defined if we know its domain and rule of correspondence. If it happens that the domain consists of all real numbers for which the rule makes sense, it is common practice in most books of an elementary nature not to make any specific mention of the domain and to consider that the function has been adequately defined by its rule of correspondence. For example, by tradition x and y are corresponding elements of the domain and range, respectively, and it has become cutomary to speak of functions such as "the function $y = x^2$," without further comment on the domain or range. It is to be understood for this function that the domain is the set $\mathbf{R}$, with the range the set of nonnegative real numbers. In the discussions of this book, however, we shall try to be explicit and state what is to be considered the domain in most cases.

Example 1. If $S = \{1, 2, 3, 4, 5\}$, describe the function f on S defined by $f(x) = x^2$.

SOLUTION.   The domain is finite in this case, and the complete function is described by the indicated correspondences:

$$1 \to 1, \quad 2 \to 4, \quad 3 \to 9, \quad 4 \to 16, \quad 5 \to 25$$

Example 2.   A function f is defined on the set of real numbers x ($\neq 1$) by $y = 1/(x - 1)$, where $y = f(x)$. Determine $f(0)$, $f(2)$, and $f(-1)$.

SOLUTION.   Because $f(x) = y = 1/(x - 1)$, it is immediate on replacing x by the appropriate number that: $f(0) = 1/(0 - 1) = -1$; $f(2) = 1/(2 - 1) = 1$; $f(-1) = 1/(-1 - 1) = -\frac{1}{2}$.

Example 3.   A body falls 64 feet from a ledge to the ground below. If we assume the ideal conditions of a vacuum and that the body falls d feet in t seconds where $d = 16t^2$, describe the function defined here by this equation.

SOLUTION.   The equation defines a function whose domain is the (time) interval $[0, 2]$ and whose range is the (distance) interval $[0, 64]$. The rule $d = 16t^2$ allows us to calculate the distance d that the body falls in any time $t \in [0, 2]$. For instance, if $t = 1$, $d = 16$, and if $t = \frac{3}{2}$, $d = 36$.

Problems 4.1

1. A function F is defined by the following table:

x	1	2	3	4	5
$F(x)$	-1	0	1	2	3

   (a) What are $F(2)$ and $F(3)$?
   (b) List the elements in the domain and range of F.
2. If a function f is defined on $\{1, 2, 3, 4, 5, 6\}$ by $f(x) = x^2 + 1$, find (a) $f(2)$; (b) $f(3)$; (c) $f(2) - 2f(3)$; (d) $2f(1) + 3f(3)$.
3. If the function f is defined on $\{-2, 3, 5, 6\}$ by $f(x) = x^2 + 1$, list the elements of the range of f.
4. If $\{-1, 0, 1, 2\}$ is a subset of the domain of a function f whose rule of mapping is $f(x) = 2x^2 - 1$, determine $f(-1)$, $f(0)$, $f(1)$, and $f(2)$.
5. If g is the function defined on **R** by $g(x) = 1 - 2x + x^2$, determine the value of g at each of the following points: (a) 1; (b) -2; (c) $\frac{1}{2}$; (d) 0.
6. Is it possible for the range of a function to be (a) a set containing only one element; (b) the empty set?
7. If $S = \{1, 2, 3, 4, 5\}$, $T = \{1, 2, 3\}$, and f is a function on S to T, define two functions on S to T where the range of f is T.
8. Use the directions in Problem 7, except that the range of f is to be a proper subset of T.
9. Under what circumstances could the considerations leading to the price function P, as discussed in this section, be used to define a function on the set of prices?
10. If the same assumption is used as that for the illustration in the text, could the considerations leading to the definition of the telephone function T be used to define a function on the set of telephone numbers? Could the assumption be dropped in this case?

11. Give a complete description of the function that, in loose terms, can be described by (a) $y = x^2$; (b) $y = 1/x$; (c) $y = \sqrt{1 - x^2}$.

12. Use the rule $x \rightarrow x^2$ to define three distinct functions on subsets of real numbers.

13. Each of the following mapping rules defines a function; assign a letter name to each function, state its domain and range, and find a formula to replace the rule: (a) Each positive integer is mapped onto 0; (b) Each positive integer is mapped onto the next largest integer; (c) Each real number is mapped onto the sum of the number and its square; (d) Each nonnegative real number is mapped onto the sum of the number and its nonnegative square root; (e) Each nonzero number is mapped onto the sum of the number and its reciprocal.

14. If the rule of correspondence of a function f is given as $f(x) = x/|x|$, what is the maximal real domain that could be assigned to f? Describe the corresponding range of f.

15. If a function F is defined on **R** by $F(x) = 2x - 1$, find (a) $F(2)$; (b) $3F(-1)$; (c) $F(|a|)$; (d) $F(y^2)$; (e) $F(t + 1) - F(t)$.

16. If a function G is defined on **R** by $G(x) = 2x^2 - 1$, find (a) $G(\sqrt{2})$; (b) $G(y - z)$; (c) $G(y) - G(z)$; (d) $G(2 \cdot 3)$; (e) $[G(2)][G(3)]$; (f) $G[G(-1)]$.

17. A function F is defined by $F(x) = 2x/(x - 1)(x + 1)$ on the maximal subset of **R** for which this rule has meaning. Find the domain of F, and determine $F(0)$ and $F(-2)$.

18. Find the range of the function f on D, where (a) $D = $ **Z**, $f(x) = x^2 + 1$; (b) $D = \{x \in $ **Z** $\mid x \neq 0\}$, $f(x) = 2/x$; (c) $D = \{x \in $ **Z** $\mid x$ is odd$\}$, $f(x) = 2x$; (d) $D = $ **R**, $f(x) = 2x$.

19. Is there any difference between "the function g defined on the subset of nonzero real numbers by $g(h) = h/2 - 1/h$" and "the function h defined on the subset of nonzero real numbers by $h(g) = g/2 = 1/g$"?

20. If S and T are subsets of real numbers, would the correspondence $|s| \rightarrow t$, with $s \in S$ and $t \in T$, define a function on S? Explain your answer.

21. Find the maximal domain that can be associated with the function f if (a) $f(x) = 2/x$; (b) $f(x) = \sqrt{1/x}$; (c) $f(x) = \sqrt{x^2 - 2x - 6}$; (d) $f(x) = |x|/x$.

22. The symbol $[x]$ denotes the greatest integer not exceeding x, for $x \in $ **R**. If f is the *greatest-integer* function defined on the set of all real numbers by $f(x) = [x]$, describe the range of f.

23. Let g be the function defined on the set of positive integers such that $g(n)$ is the integer represented by the digit in the nth decimal place in the unending decimal representation of π. Using the symbol defined in Problem 22, find a formula for this rule of mapping.

24. If f is the *absolute-value* function defined on **R** by $f(x) = |x|$, decide which of the following statements are true for arbitrary $x, y \in $ **R**:
    (a) $f(x + y) = f(x) + f(y)$ (b) $f(3x) = 3f(x)$
    (c) $f(|x|) = |f(x)|$ (d) $f(x^2) = [f(x)]^2$
    (e) $f(xy) = [f(x)][f(y)]$

25. If f is the greatest-integer function (see Problem 22) defined on **R** by $f(x) = [x]$, which (if any) of the statements given in Problem 24 are true?

26. The "identity" function on a set maps each element of the set onto itself. Which of the statements in Problem 24 are true if f is the identity function on **R**?

27. If h is a function such that $h(n)$ is the number of primes less than, or equal to, the positive integer n, find $h(5)$, $h(71)$, and $h(83)$. What are the domain and range of h?

28. From each corner of a square sheet of cardboard, 25 inches on a side, a square of side x inches is removed. If the edges of the sheet are now turned up to form an open box of height x inches, express its volume V as a function of x.

29. A sphere of radius r is concentric with a sphere of radius $2r$. Express the volume V of the shell between the spheres as a function of r.

30. A Norman window (in the shape of a rectangle surmounted by a semicircle) has a perimeter of 100 inches. If the vertical dimension of the rectangle is x inches, express the area A of the window as a function of x.

4.2   Graphs of Functions

We are now about to supply the formal definition of a function, as promised in §4.1. If f is a function on a set X to a set Y, it is clear that the mapping information conveyed by either $y = f(x)$ or $x \rightarrow y$ may be abbreviated by the ordered pair (x, y). It should be understood in the use of such an abbreviation, of course, that $x \in X$, $y \in Y$ and that the first member x of the pair is mapped onto the second member y by the function. With this understanding, the function f is completely described by the set of all such ordered pairs, and for some purposes it is convenient actually to *identify* f with the set $\{(x, y)| \ y = f(x)\}$. This identification has the further advantage of providing a set-theoretic description of the function and thus leads us to the following definition.

Definition.   *Let X and Y be nonempty sets. Then a* function on X to Y *is a set of ordered pairs $\{(x, y)| \ x \in X, \ y \in Y\}$ such that each element of X occurs once and only once as a first component.*

The condition on the ordered pairs in the definition is equivalent to the statement that $(x, y_1) = (x, y_2)$ implies that $y_1 = y_2$. Moreover, it should be observed that the definition identifies a function on X to Y with a subset of the Cartesian product set $X \times Y$, but that not every subset of $X \times Y$ is a function. For example, consider the function f defined on $\{1, 2, 3\}$ by $f(x) = x + 2$. As a consequence of the definition, f is a subset of $X \times Y$, where $X = \{1, 2, 3\}$ and $Y = \{3, 4, 5\}$, and $f = \{(1, 3), (2, 4), (3, 5)\}$. On the other hand, the subset $\{(1, 2), (1, 3), (2, 5)\}$ does not define a function, because the condition on the ordered pairs that define a function is violated by the inclusion of two pairs, $(1, 2)$ and $(1, 3)$, with the same first component. It may be well to point out that a subset of ordered pairs (x, y) may be used to define many different structures, and *it is only when the mapping $x \rightarrow y$ is implied* that a function is defined. This should help to remove some of the strangeness that is inherently associated with the formal abstract definition of a function.

The matter of constructing a graph of a Cartesian product set or a subset thereof was considered in §2.1. It then follows that we can construct the graph of a function by graphing the subset of ordered pairs that we have identified with the function. For example, the graph of the function f described in the preceding paragraph is shown in Figure 16. We illustrate the graphical aspect of a function with further examples.

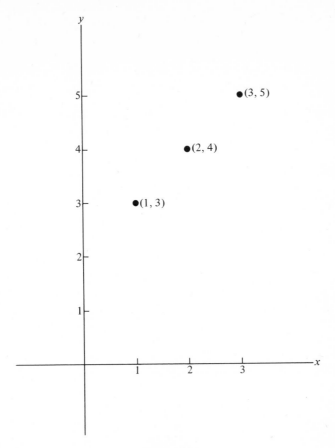

Figure 16

Example 1. Graph the function F defined on the set $\{-2, -1, 0, 1, 2\}$ by $F(x) = x^2$.

SOLUTION. From the definition, we may write the following equality:

$$F = \{(-2, 4), (-1, 1), (0, 0), (1, 1), (2, 4)\}$$

The graph of F is then the five distinguished points shown in Figure 17a.

In cases where the domain of a function contains an infinite number of elements, or when the domain is of infinite extent on an algebraic scale, it is possible to graph only a representative set of points of the function. If the domain happens to be an interval $[a, b]$, it is *very often* quite proper that these representative points be then joined with a smooth curve. However, we must emphasize that the graph is *not* a curve unless the domain is such an interval, and even with a domain of this kind common sense must decide whether a smooth curve should be drawn. The property of a function that guarantees a smooth graph is "continuity," a topic that is discussed in a first course in analysis—and to which we have previously referred.

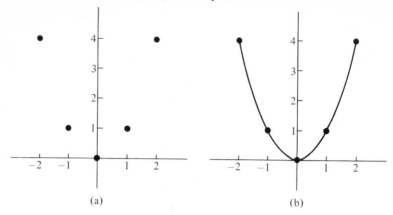

(a)   (b)

Figure 17

Example 2. Graph the function f defined on the interval $[-2, 2]$ by $f(x) = x^2$.

SOLUTION. In this case, we reproduce the graph of Example 1, and then join these points with a smooth curve, for it is intuitive that intermediate points of the domain will be associated with intermediate points of the range. The graph is shown as the solid curve in Figure 17*b*.

Inasmuch as most functions that occur in mathematics have subsets of real numbers for both domain and range, the graph of a mathematical function is usually the graph of a subset of $\mathbf{R} \times \mathbf{R}$.

It may be recalled that our earlier discussion of relations (such as those of equality and inequality) was conducted at a very intuitive level—somewhat like our discussion of functions in §4.1. Although the concept of a relation is important, it is not as important for our purposes here as that of a function, and so we shall not give a detailed examination of relations. However, it may be of passing interest to point out that it is also possible to give a set-theoretic definition that defines a relation from a set X to a set Y as a subset of $X \times Y$. From this point of view, a function then becomes a special case of a relation. These foundational ideas for the concept of a relation will be pursued further in the later problems of the problem set of this section.

The symbol $[x]$ and the *greatest-integer* function were defined in Problem 22 of §4.1, but because they will keep recurring throughout the text, we repeat the definitions in more formal terms.

Definition. *For any real number* x, *the symbol* $[x]$ *denotes the greatest integer that does not exceed* x.

For example, $[2.5] = 2$, $[2.9] = 2$, $[-3.45] = -4$, $[-3] = -3$, $[6] = 6$.

Definition.   *The function f defined on* **R** *so that* $f(x) = [x]$ *is called the* greatest-integer *function.*

Example 3.   Graph the portion of the greatest-integer function for $-4 \leq x \leq 4$.

SOLUTION.   The desired graph is shown in Figure 18.

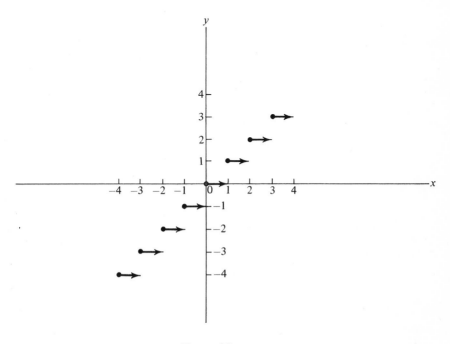

Figure 18

It will be noted that the graph of the greatest-integer function consists of a succession of horizontal line segments, each displaced one unit above and to the right of the preceding segment, and each with one point missing at its right extremity. An arrow in Figure 18 is intended to indicate that exactly one point is missing—at its tip.

Problems 4.2

1. Each of the following tables gives a complete definition of a function *f* for which $y = f(x)$. Make a graph of each function.

(a)

x	1	2	3
y	0	1	2

(b)

x	−1	0	2	−3
y	−2	1	3	4

(c)

x	1	2	3	4
y	2	2	2	2

2. If $A = \{-2, -1, 1, 2, 3\}$, make a graph of the function f defined on A by $f(x) = 2x^2 - 1$.

3. Make a graph of the function F defined on S by $F(x) = x^2 - 2$, where (a) $S = \{0, 1, 2, 3, 4\}$; (b) $S = \{-2, -1, 0, 1, 2, 3, 4\}$.

4. A function G consists of the following set of ordered pairs:

$$\{(-2, 6), (1, 3), (2, 3), (3, -2)\}.$$

   (a) Determine $G(2)$ and $G(1)$.
   (b) Determine $[G(-2) + 2G(3)]/G(1)$.
   (c) Make a graph of the function G.

5. If S is the interval $[-2, 2]$, graph the function f on S defined by (a) $f(x) = 2x + 1$; (b) $f(x) = 3x^2 - 1$; (c) $f(x) = x^3$.

6. Think of an example of a function for whose graph it would be incorrect to join any finite set of points of the graph by a smooth curve.

7. Let f be a function on S to T where $S = \{1, 2, 3\}$ and $T = \{0, 1\}$. If it is known that $(1, 1) \in f$ and $(2, 0) \in f$, complete the description of f in all possible ways.

8. Let f_1 and f_2 be functions defined as the following sets: $f_1 = \{(1, 2), (2, 3), (3, 4), (4, 5)\}$; $f_2 = \{(4, 5), (5, 6), (6, 7), (8, 9)\}$. Determine $f_1 \cup f_2$ and $f_1 \cap f_2$, and observe that both of these constructed sets are also functions.

9. Let $S = \{(1, 2), (1, 3), (2, 5), (3, 6), (7, 1)\}$ and $T = \{(1, 3), (3, 6), (3, 7), (4, 5)\}$. Determine $S \cup T$ and $S \cap T$, and decide whether any of the four sets (given or determined) define functions.

10. The *identity* function on a set of real numbers maps every element of the set onto itself (see Problem 26, §4.1), and the corresponding *zero* function maps every element onto zero. Describe the graphs of these functions.

11. If S and T are sets containing m and n elements, respectively, how many distinct functions can be defined on (a) S to T; (b) S to S? Describe explicitly all functions on S to S where $S = \{0, 1\}$.

12. Express the set $\{(x, y) \mid x^2 + y^2 = 1\}$ as the union of two functions on $[-1, 1]$, noting that the given set is not a function.

13. Let S be a subset of A. Then the *characteristic function* of the subset S is the function on A defined as follows: $f(x) = 1$, if $x \in S$; $f(x) = 0$, if $x \notin S$. Let $A = [0, 5]$, and construct a graph of f if (a) $S = \{0, 1, 2, 3, 4, 5\}$; (b) $S = [0, 3]$; (c) $S = [0, 2] \cup [3, 5]$.

14. Refer to Problem 13 for the definition, and describe the characteristic function of S on A, if $A = \mathbf{R}$ and S is the subset of rational numbers. Could you construct a graph of f in this case?

15. Graph the function F defined on $[-2, 2]$ by $F(x) = |x|$.

16. Graph the function f defined on $[-3, 2]$ by $f(x) = [x]$.

17. Construct a graph of the function f defined on $[-3, 3]$ by (a) $f(x) = |x| - x$; (b) $f(x) = |x| + x$; (c) $f(x) = |x| + x$ if $x > 0$, $f(x) = |x| - x$ if $x \le 0$.

18. Construct a graph of the function f defined on $[-2, 2]$ by $f(x) = [2x]$.

19. Construct a partial graph of the function described in Problem 23 of §4.1.

20. If I amperes of current flows in a long wire, a magnetic field of H gauss is established at a point r centimeters from the wire where $H = 2I/r$. Let $I = 10$, and graph the function defined for $2 \le r \le 10$.

21. The distance d that a body falls in time t under gravity is given approximately by the equation $d = 16t^2$, where d is in feet and t in seconds. Graph d as a function of t, assuming that the body falls from a height of 100 feet.

   Note: For Problems 22 to 30, use the following definition: If X and Y are arbitrary sets, a *relation* $\Re$ *from* X *to* Y is a subset of $X \times Y$, and any such subset defines a relation of this kind; a relation from X to X will be called a relation *in* X. The symbolism $a\Re b$, for a relation $\Re$, is now equivalent to the statement that $(a, b) \in \Re$.

22. If $X = \{1, 2, 3, 4, 5\}$ and $Y = \{0, 1, 2\}$, graph the following relations from X to Y:
   (a) $\{(1, 1), (1, 2), (2, 0), (3, 2), (4, 1), (4, 0)\}$
   (b) $\{(1, 2), (2, 2), (2, 0), (1, 1), (5, 1)\}$
   (c) $\{(3, 0), (4, 1), (4, 2), (5, 0), (5, 1)\}$
23. Construct graphs of the following relations in **R**:
   (a) $\{(1, 1), (2, -1), (2, 1), (3, 4)\}$
   (b) $\{(-1, 1), (-2, 2), (-2, 0), (0, 3)\}$
   (c) $\{(-2, 1), (-2, 2), (-1, 0), (-1, 1), (1, 0), (2, 1)\}$
24. Construct partial graphs of the following (*inequality*) relations in **R**:
   (a) $\{(x, y) \mid x < y\}$; (b) $\{(x, y) \mid x \leq y\}$; (c) $\{(x, y) \mid x > y\}$; (d) $\{(x, y) \mid x \geq y\}$.
25. Construct partial graphs of the following relations in **R**: (a) $\{(x, y) \mid x = y^2\}$;
   (b) $\{(x, y) \mid y = x^2\}$; (c) $\{(x, y) \mid x = y^2 \text{ or } y = x^2\}$.
26. If $X = [0, 3]$, construct the graph of the "universal" relation in X, defined as the Cartesian set $X \times X$. Would it be consistent with our definition of a relation to consider the empty subset of $X \times Y$ to be the "void" relation from a set X to a set Y?
27. Graph the following relations in $[-2, 2]$:
   (a) $\{(x, y) \mid x^2 + y^2 = 1\}$ (b) $\{(x, y) \mid x^2 + y^2 \leq 1\}$
28. Graph the following relations in $[-5, 5]$:
   (a) $\{(x, y) \mid |x| + 2|y| = 1\}$ (b) $\{(x, y) \mid |x| + 2y = 1\}$
29. In the language of §1.3, an *equivalence* relation in a set S is a relation $\Re$ such that (i) $a\Re a$; (ii) $b\Re a$ if $a\Re b$; (iii) $a\Re c$ if $a\Re b$ and $b\Re c$, for arbitrary $a, b, c \in S$. Think of some examples—say from geometry—of equivalence relations.
30. Describe the general features of the graph of any equivalence relation (see Problem 29).

4.3 Polynomial Functions

In this section, we introduce what is probably the most important single type of function. But first we give an important preliminary definition.

Definition. *A (real) polynomial in a symbol x is an expression of the form*
$$a_0 x^n + a_1 x^{n-1} + \cdots + a_{n-1} x + a_n \quad \text{for real number coefficients}$$
$a_0, a_1, \ldots, a_{n-1}, a_n$ *and a nonnegative integer n. If $a_0 \neq 0$, the polynomial is said to have* degree n *and to have a_0 as its* leading coefficient. *No degree is assigned to the zero polynomial (in which all coefficients are zero), but*

the definition implies that nonzero *constants may be considered as polynomials of degree zero.*

It is only natural to regard two polynomials in x as *equal* if coefficients of the same powers of x are equal, and this implies that there is no essential change in a polynomial if terms with zero coefficients are added to or deleted from it.

Our present interest is not with polynomials *per se* in which x is an abstract symbol, but rather with polynomial expressions in which x is regarded as a *variable* whose values range over some subset of real numbers. It is then appropriate to refer to this kind of symbol x as a *real* variable.

Definition. *A function f whose rule of correspondence is $y = f(x)$, where $f(x)$ is a polynomial of degree n in a real variable x, is called a polynomial function of degree n. The universe of x is, of course, the same as the domain of the function f.*

In elementary courses, it is customary to refer to polynomial functions of the first and second degrees as "linear" and "quadratic," respectively. However, although the graph of any first-degree polynomial function is a straight line—and thus suggests the word "linear"—we shall use this word only when the constant (i.e., independent of x) term of the defining polynomial is zero. This is in deference to the acceptable usage of the word in more advanced mathematics. The defining polynomial of a general *linear* function then has the form mx, with $m \in \mathbf{R}$, whereas a polynomial of the form $ax^2 + bx + c$, with $a\ (\neq 0)$, b, $c \in \mathbf{R}$, defines a *quadratic* function. Any polynomial of the form $ax + b$, with $a\ (\neq 0)$, $b \in \mathbf{R}$, will define a polynomial function of the first degree, but as we have just said, we shall not refer to the function as "linear" unless $b = 0$.

If f is a function defined by an equation $y = f(x)$, the "set" definition of a function given in §4.2 allows us to identify f with the solution set of the equation. We remind the student at this point that the universe of the variable x in the equation $y = f(x)$ must be the same as the domain of the function f. In particular, if $f(x) = ax + b$, with $a, b \in \mathbf{R}$, we consider f to be the solution set—with x in the domain of f—of the equation $y = ax + b$. It was recalled above—and noted also in §3.5—that the graph of the complete solution set of an equation of the first degree is a straight line. If the universes of the variables are restricted in some way, the graph is still a *subset* of the points of a straight line. A case of special interest occurs when the domain of a first-degree function f is an interval $[a, b]$, and in this important case the graph of f is a *line segment*. These graphical considerations may help explain both the use and misuse of the word "linear," as applied to a function!

The fact that the graph of a first-degree polynomial function is a portion of a straight line makes the construction of its graph quite easy, because a line is determined by any two of its points. If the domain is an interval, the complete graph is then the line segment joining the points determined by the end points of the interval.

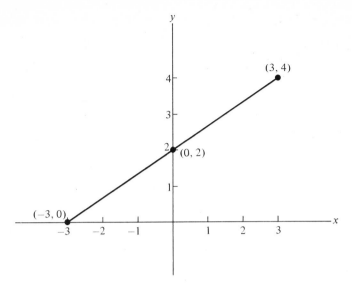

Figure 19

Example 1. Graph the function f defined on $[-3, 3]$ by $2x - 3y + 6 = 0$,
where $y = f(x)$.

SOLUTION.   Three ordered pairs of the function are easily found to be:
$(0, 2)$, $(-3, 0)$, $(3, 4)$. If we plot these points on a Cartesian plane, it is a
simple matter to complete the line-segment graph as shown in Figure 19.
(Although only two points are needed to determine a line, it is useful to
have at least one additional point as a check on the other two.)

We have already referred to a *quadratic* function f as one whose rule of
correspondence has the form $y = f(x) = ax^2 + bx + c$, for a $(\neq 0)$, $b, c \in \mathbf{R}$.
Any section of an infinite right circular cone, cut by a plane parallel to one of its
generating elements, is a geometric curve known as a *parabola*. It can be shown
that the Cartesian graph of any quadratic function consists of points that lie
on a parabola. We leave the verification of this statement to books on analytic
geometry, but the mere plotting of a few selected points will indicate the plau-
sibility of the assertion. When graphed in the usual way (with horizontal and
vertical coordinate axes), the underlying parabola opens "upward" if $a > 0$
and "downward" if $a < 0$. If the domain of a quadratic function is an interval
of the real line, the graph of the function is a portion of a parabola.

Example 2.   Graph the quadratic function f defined on $\{-2, -1, 0, 1, 2\}$
by $y = 2x^2 + x - 1$, where $y = f(x)$.

SOLUTION.   The elements of the function are as follows: $(-2, 5)$, $(-1, 0)$,
$(0, -1)$, $(1, 2)$, $(2, 9)$. The graph is shown in Figure 20, where it may be
observed that the points of the function appear to lie on what might be a
portion of a parabola.

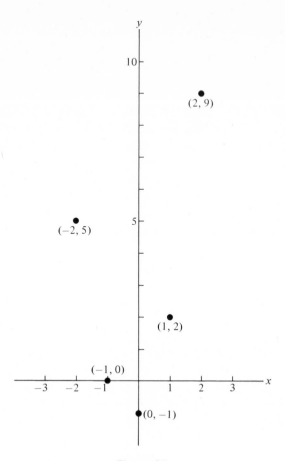

Figure 20

Example 3. Graph the function f defined on $[-3, 2]$ by $f(x) = -x^2 + x + 10$.

SOLUTION. A representative collection of points of the function may be seen to be: $(-3, -2)$, $(-2, 4)$, $(-1, 8)$, $(0, 10)$, $(1, 10)$, $(2, 8)$. The complete graph of the function is shown in Figure 21, the points being located on a portion of a parabola opening downward.

The graph of any polynomial function of degree greater than 2 can be obtained in a similar way, but there are very few geometric features common to all such graphs. It is a fact, however, that if the domain of any polynomial function is an interval, its graph is a smooth curve, and the number of times that the curve changes direction increases with the degree of the polynomial. We do not wish to dwell further on this topic of "curves of higher degree," but shall content ourselves with an example.

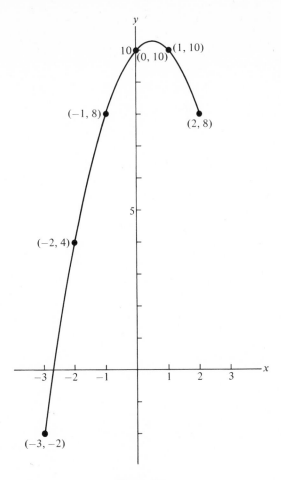

Figure 21

Example 4.   Graph the function f defined on $[-2, 2]$ by $f(x) = 2x^3 - 8x$.

SOLUTION.   A representative set of points of the graph may be obtained as follows: $(0, 0)$, $(-1, 6)$, $(-2, 0)$, $(1, -6)$, $(2, 0)$. The complete graph is then the smooth curve drawn through these points as shown in Figure 22.

Problems 4.3

Sketch the graph of each of the functions, whose rules of correspondence and domains are given in Problems 1–14.

1. $f(x) = 2x - 5, [-2, 2]$

2. $f(x) = x - 2, [-3, 3]$

3. $2x + 3y - 5 = 0, [-1, 3]$

4. $3x - 2y + 6 = 0, [-3, 2]$

5. $3x^2 - 2x = y, [-1, 1]$

6. $2x^2 + 3x - 4 = y, [-2, 2]$

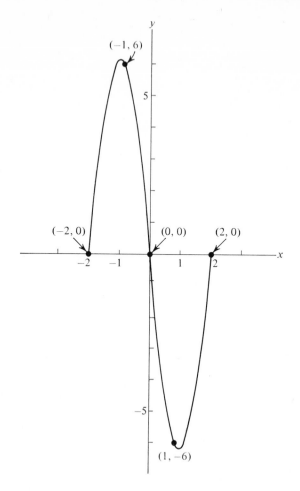

Figure 22

7. $2x - y + 1 = 0$, $\{-2, -1, 0, 1, 2, 3\}$
8. $x + y - 2 = 0$, $\{0, 1, 2, 3\}$ **9.** $f(x) = 3x^2$, $\{-3, -2, -1, 1, 2\}$
10. $f(x) = -2x^2 + x - 1$, $\{-1, 3, 5, 7\}$
11. $f(x) = 2x^2$, $\{-\frac{3}{2}, -1, -\frac{1}{2}, 0, 1, \frac{1}{2}, \frac{3}{2}\}$
12. $f(x) = -3x^2$, $\{-\frac{3}{2}, -1, -\frac{1}{2}, 0, 1, \frac{1}{2}, \frac{3}{2}\}$
13. $f(x) = x^3 + 2x$, $[-2, 2]$ **14.** $f(x) = x^4 - 2x^2 - 2$, $[-2, 2]$

15. Determine the formula for $f(x)$ if f is a first-degree polynomial fucntion on **R** such that:
    (a) $3f(x) = f(3x)$ (b) $f(x + 1) = f(x) + 1$ (c) $f(1) = f(2)$
16. Determine the formula for $f(x)$ if f is a first-degree polynomial function on **R** such that:
    (a) $f(1) = 2$ and $f(-1) = 1$ (b) $f(2) = 1$ and $f(3) = -1$
    (c) $|f(x)| = f(|x|)$ (d) $[f(x)] = f([x])$

17. Determine the formula for $f(x)$ if f is a first-degree polynomial function whose graph contains the points (a) $(1, 0)$ and $(0, -1)$; (b) $(1, 1)$ and $(2, 1)$; (c) $(0, 0)$ and $(-1, -2)$.

18. Prove that any first-degree polynomial function f on $\mathbf{R}$ such that $f(1) + f(2) = f(3)$ must be linear; that is, show that $f(x) = mx$, for some real number m.

19. Find the defining equation for a quadratic function if its graph contains the points $(1, 0)$, $(2, 1)$, and $(-1, 4)$.

20. The graph of a quadratic function is known to contain the origin and to intercept the x-axis at the point $(2, 0)$. Find its defining equation if the point $(1, -3)$ also lies on the graph.

21. If (a, b) is a point on the graph of the function defined on $\mathbf{R}$ by $y = 2/x$, determine which of the following points also lie on the graph: (b, a), $(-a, b)$, $(a, -b)$, $(-a, -b)$, $(-b, -a)$.

22. Sketch the graph of the function defined on $[0, 4]$ by $y = \sqrt{x}$, and use the graph to obtain a decimal approximation for each of the following numbers: (a) $\sqrt{2}$; (b) $\sqrt{\pi}$; (c) $\sqrt[3]{2}$.

4.4 An Algebra of Functions

If S is a set of functions, *each with the same domain D*, it is possible to define operations of addition and multiplication in S and obtain an "algebra" (or "arithmetic") of functions quite similar to the system of rational numbers. We proceed to these definitions.

Definition. *If $f \in S$ and $g \in S$, then $f + g$ is a function (called the* sum *of f and g) on D such that $(f + g)(x) = f(x) + g(x)$, for each $x \in D$.*

Definition. *$f \cdot g$ is a function (called the* product *of f and g) on D such that $(f \cdot g)(x) = f(x) \cdot g(x)$, for each $x \in D$.*

According to these definitions, the sum and product of two functions are obtained by merely adding and multiplying the corresponding functional values.

Example 1. If f and g are functions on $[0, 2]$ defined so that $f(x) = 2x^2$ and $g(x) = 3x - 1$, describe $f + g$ and $f \cdot g$. In particular, determine $(f + g)(1)$ and $(f \cdot g)(2)$.

SOLUTION. By the above definitions, $f + g$ and $f \cdot g$ are defined on $[0, 2]$ as follows:

$$(f + g)(x) = f(x) + g(x) = 2x^2 + 3x - 1$$
$$(f \cdot g)(x) = f(x) \cdot g(x) = 2x^2(3x - 1)$$

Hence,

$$(f + g)(1) = 2 + 3 - 1 = 4$$

and

$$(f \cdot g)(2) = 8(6 - 1) = 8(5) = 40$$

If we are to develop an algebra of functions similar to the rational numbers, we must define a *zero* function and *additive inverse* (or *negative*) functions. This is done according to the following definitions (see Problem 10 of §4.2).

Definition.   *The* zero *function on a set D is a function, designated* 0, *such that* $0(x) = 0$, *for each* $x \in D$.

Definition.   *If f is a function on a set D, $-f$ is the function on D such that* $(-f)(x) = -f(x)$, *for each* $x \in D$.

The zero function on any domain is then so defined that its value at any point of the domain is 0. The same symbol 0 will be used to designate any zero function, regardless of its domain, for the context will remove any ambiguity. The context will also distinguish between the number 0 and a zero function. It is possible, of course, that the function 0 is not contained in a set of functions. It follows from the pertinent definition that $[f + (-f)](x) = f(x) + (-f)(x) = f(x) + [-f(x)] = f(x) - f(x) = 0$, for any $x \in D$, and so $f + (-f)$ is the 0 function on D. We define $f - g$ to be the same as $f + (-g)$, and so the *subtraction* of two functions is accomplished by subtracting their functional values. In particular, $f - f = 0$.

Example 2.   Describe the zero function on $[0, 2]$ and the function $-f$, where f is the function given in Example 1.

   SOLUTION.   The zero function on $[0, 2]$ is the function 0, such that $0(x) = 0$, for every $x \in [0, 2]$. By definition, $-f$ is the function such that $(-f)(x) = -2x^2$, for each $x \in [0, 2]$.

The zero function on any domain D is a special case of a whole class of *constant* functions, whose values are the same for all points of D. For each $c \in \mathbf{R}$, it is then possible to define a constant function—also denoted by c— such that $c(x) = c$, for every $x \in D$. As in the case of 0, the context will distinguish numbers from functions with the same symbolism. In particular, the function 1, which maps each element of D onto $1 \in \mathbf{R}$, will be useful.

   Finally, we wish to introduce the idea of division for two suitable functions. We do this by means of *reciprocal* functions, and use the function 1 in their definition.

Definition.   *Let f be a function defined on D such that $f(x) \neq 0$, for $x \in D$. Then the* reciprocal *function $1/f$ is the function on D such that $(1/f)(x) = 1/f(x)$, for each $x \in D$.*

It follows from this definition that $f(x)[1/f(x)] = 1$, for any $x \in D$, and so $f \cdot (1/f)$ is the function 1. Moreover, if we define f/g to be identical with $f \cdot (1/g)$, *we are identifying division by g with multiplication by the reciprocal of g.* This rule of division and the earlier rule of subtraction are in harmony with the corresponding rules for rational numbers, and it may be seen that the requirement for the existence of $1/f$ that $f(x) \neq 0$, for $x \in D$, corresponds to the arithmetic rule which forbids division by 0.

Example 3. Describe f/g, where f and g are functions defined on $[0, 2]$ by $f(x) = 3x^2$ and $g(x) = 2x + 1$. Determine $(f/g)(1)$.

SOLUTION. By our definition of division, $(f/g)(x) = f(x)/g(x) = 3x^2/(2x + 1)$, for each $x \in [0, 2]$. In particular, $(f/g)(1) = \frac{3}{3} = 1$.

It is easy to see that the associative, commutative, and distributive properties of the real numbers are inherited by real-valued functions. That is, $f + (g + h) = (f + g) + h$, $f \cdot (g \cdot h) = (f \cdot g) \cdot h$, $f + g = g + f$, $f \cdot g = g \cdot f$, and $f \cdot (g + h) = f \cdot g + f \cdot h$, for any real-valued functions f, g, h with common domain D. We shall prove the associative law of addition and leave the verification of the rest to the student.

■ **THEOREM 4.1.** $f + (g + h) = (f + g) + h$, *for any real-valued functions* f, g, h *on* a common domain D *of real numbers.*

PROOF. Let $x \in D$. Then,

$$[f + (g + h)](x) = f(x) + [g + h](x) = f(x) + [g(x) + h(x)]$$
$$= [f(x) + g(x)] + h(x) = [f + g](x) + h(x)$$
$$= [(f + g) + h](x).$$

Hence, $f + (g + h) = (f + g) + h$, as desired.

A slight variation is sometimes made in the definitions of $f + f, f - g, f \cdot g$, and f/g in an algebra of functions. If D_f and D_g are the respective domains of f and g, we are simply to *understand* in these definitions that the domain of $f + g, f - g$, and $f \cdot g$ is D where $D = D_f \cap D_g$, and that the domain of f/g is $\{x \in D| \ g(x) \neq 0\}$. However, we shall use in the sequel the definitions given earlier. If a set S of functions has the operations of addition and multiplication properly defined on it and if it contains the constant functions 0 and 1, the negative $-f$ of every function $f \in S$, and the reciprocal $1/f$ of every nonzero $f \in S$, then the set S is an algebraic system with the usual formal properties of the system of rational numbers. It is then appropriate to refer to S as a *field* of functions.

It is possible, of course, that $g = f$ in the definitions of the sum and product of two functions, in which case the functions $f + f$ and $f \cdot f$ arise. It is quite natural to write $f + f$ as $2f$, and this notational convention is generalized in the following definition.

Definition. *If f is a function with domain D, and $c \in \mathbf{R}$, then cf is the function on D defined so that $(cf)(x) = cf(x)$, for each $x \in D$.*

It may be observed that cf is then the same as the product $c \cdot f$ of the constant function c and the function f. It might be expected that the symbol $f \cdot f$ would be condensed to f^2, but this latter compact symbol is being reserved for another, more important use in §4.5. Inasmuch as the type of product discussed in the present section is not used extensively, we shall not introduce any additional symbolism pertaining to it.

Example 4. If f and g are functions defined on the common domain D by $f(x) = 2x^2$ and $g(x) = 3x - 1$, respectively, describe the functions (a) $2f + g$; (b) $3f + 2$.

SOLUTION. The results follow from an immediate application of the preceding definitions and with the stated understanding concerning constant functions.

(a) $(2f + g)(x) = (2f)(x) + g(x) = 2f(x) + g(x) = 2(2x^2) + 3x - 1 = 4x^2 + 3x - 1$.

(b) $(3f + 2)(x) = (3f)(x) + 2(x) = 3f(x) + 2(x) = 3(2x^2) + 2 = 6x^2 + 2$.

Problems 4.4

1. Is it correct to state that all zero functions are identical? Explain your answer.
2. Is it correct to assume that the constant function c is the same on every occurrence? If not, why not?

   Note: For the purposes of Problems 3 to 9, assume the functions f and g are defined on an interval of positive real numbers by $f(x) = 3x^2 + 1$ and $g(x) = 2x + 7$, respectively, and give the rule of mapping for each of the indicated functions.

3. $f + g$ 4. $f \cdot g$ 5. f/g 6. $1/f$
7. $1/g$ 8. $f + 1/f$ 9. $g/f + g \cdot f$

10. If $f(x) = 1/x + 2/(x - 2)$ and $g(x) = 3x$ for functions f and g, what is the maximal common domain that can be attached to these functions such that the sum $f + g$ is defined? What is the rule of mapping of $f + g$?
11. If $f(x) = 1/(x - 1)$ and $g(x) = 1/(x - 2)^2$ for functions f and g, what is the maximal common domain that can be attached to these functions, such that the product $f \cdot g$ is defined? What is the rule of mapping of $f \cdot g$?
12. Answer the questions raised in Problem 10, but relative to the functions $f - g$ and f/g.
13. Answer the questions raised in Problem 11, but relative to the functions $f - g$ and f/g.
14. Describe $f + g$ and $f \cdot g$, with f and g defined below:

$$f(x) = \begin{cases} 2/x & \text{for } x \neq -1, 0, 1 \\ 15 & \text{for } x = 1 \end{cases}$$

$$g(x) = \begin{cases} 2/(x^2 - 1) & \text{for } x \neq -1, 0, 1 \\ 10 & \text{for } x = 1 \end{cases}$$

15. Prove the commutative laws of addition and multiplication for real-valued functions on a common domain.
16. Prove the distributive law for real-valued functions on a common domain.
17. According to our definition of the reciprocal $1/f$ of a function f, should the symbol 1 in the numerator be regarded as a real number or the constant function 1? What about 1 in the right member of the equality $f \cdot (1/f) = 1$?
18. If functions f and g are defined on a common domain by $f(x) = 2x^2 - x$ and $g(x) = 3x + 1$, respectively, assume the same domain for any constant functions and describe
    (a) $f - 2g + 1$ (b) $2f + g - 2$ (c) $f \cdot g + 3$
19. Describe the graph of a constant function. Is a vertical line segment a portion of the graph of any function, assuming the usual disposition and interpretation of coordinate axes?
20. If we regard a function as a set of ordered pairs—as in the definition in §4.2— what rules of addition and multiplication of the pairs will be consistent with our definitions of sums and products given in this section?
21. Take any real number x, and perform in order the following sequence of operations on x: add 3; double the result; subtract 4; divide the result by 6; multiply by 3; subtract the original number. If $f(x)$ is the final number, describe the function f by means of a formula.
22. In the construction of the function f in Problem 21, reverse the order of the first three operations given and compare your result with that obtained before.
23. The functions f and g are completely defined on $\{-1, 0, 1\}$ by the following table:

x	$f(x)$	$g(x)$
-1	2	3
0	-1	-3
1	5	6

Construct a similar table for the function (a) $f + g$; (b) $f - g$; (c) $f \cdot g$; (d) f/g.

24. With f and g in Problem 23 regarded as sets of ordered pairs, express $f + g$, $f \cdot g$, and $2f$ in this symbolism of sets, and construct the graphs of all five functions.
25. With f and g defined in Problem 23, construct a similar table for the function
    (a) $3f$; (b) $3f + 2g$; (c) $4(f \cdot f)$; (d) $2f + 3g - 1$; (e) $4(g \cdot g) + 3f - 2$.
26. Let $f(x) = 2$ and $g(x) = [x]$, for each $x \in [0, 5]$, and construct the graph of $f + g$.
27. With f and g as in Problem 26, describe $f \cdot g$ and $f - g$.
28. Let $f(x) = |x|$ and $g(x) = x$, for each $x \in [-3, 3]$, and construct graphs of the functions $f + g$, $g - f$, and $f \cdot g$.
29. Explain how the definitions of f and g, as given in Problem 28, would need to be adjusted so that the function f/g is defined.
30. Let f be the characteristic function (see Problem 13 of §4.2) of a subset A of a set B, and let $g(x) = 1$ for every $x \in B$. Prove that $g - f$ is the characteristic function of A', where $A' = \{x \notin B \mid x \notin A\}$.

4.5 Composite and Inverse Functions

It is possible to define the product of two functions in an entirely different way from that given in §4.4 and thereby obtain a different algebra of functions. For suitable functions f and g, the new product—which we shall call the *composite* of f by g—will be designated fg.

Definition.   *Let f and g be two functions so related that the range of g is a subset of the domain of f. Then the* composite fg *of f and g is the function defined on the domain D of g such that $(fg)(x) = f[g(x)]$, for every $x \in D$. If $g = f$ and the composite ff is defined, we denote it by f^2, and f^n is given the obvious extended meaning for any positive integer n.*

It is convenient to use $g(D)$ to refer to the range of g even though the notation is inexact. If we think of a function as an intuitive mapping of the elements of its domain onto its range, the composite fg is a sequence of two such mappings, first by g and then by f. Thus, if g maps D onto $g(D)$, and f maps $g(D)$ onto $f[g(D)]$, the function fg maps D directly onto $f[g(D)]$. These mappings are shown pictorially in Figure 23. In particular, an arbitrary element $x \in D$ is mapped by g onto $g(x)$, and this element is then mapped by f onto $f[g(x)]$. By definition of fg, the element x is mapped by fg onto $f[g(x)]$.

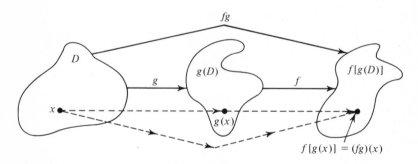

Figure 23

Example 1.   If f is defined on $\mathbf{R}$ by $f(x) = 2x - 1$ and if g is defined on $[-2, 2]$ by $g(x) = x^2$, describe and graph the function fg.

SOLUTION.   The domain of fg is $[-2, 2]$, and for each x in this domain $(fg)(x) = f[g(x)] = f(x^2) = 2x^2 - 1$. The graph of fg, shown in Figure 24, may be seen to be a portion of a parabola.

It should have been observed in §4.4 that our definitions of the constant functions 0 and 1 cause them to play roles in function theory quite similar to those played by their real number counterparts in ordinary arithmetic. In ordinary arithmetic, for a real number a: $a + 0 = 0 + a = a$; $a - a = 0$;

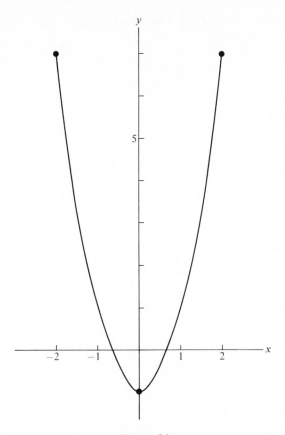

Figure 24

$a(1) = (1)a = a$; and $a(1/a) = (1/a)a = 1$, if $a \neq 0$. In function theory, for a function f and constant functions 0 and 1 with the same domains as f: $f + 0 = 0 + f = f; f - f = 0; f \cdot 1 = 1 \cdot f = f$; and $f \cdot (1/f) = (1/f) \cdot f = 1$, provided $1/f$ exists. We now define an "identity" function I, and with certain functions f, we associate "inverse" functions f^{-1}. In this new arithmetic of functions, I plays the role formerly played by the constant function 1, and f^{-1} replaces the reciprocal function $1/f$ (cf. Problem 26 of §4.1).

Definition.   *The* identity *function I on a domain D is defined so that $I(x) = x$, for any $x \in D$.*

In other words, the identity function I maps every element of its domain onto itself. As for the constant functions, we shall use the same symbol I to denote *any* identity function, regardless of its domain. It follows, *with this under-standing*, that $If = If = f$, for any function f. In view of the somewhat-similar symbolisms, it may be well to emphasize the distinction between the constant function 1 and the identity function I. The function 1 maps every element of its domain onto 1, whereas I maps every element x of its domain onto the same x. Possibly their graphs make the differences between the two functions more apparent: the graph of 1 is a subset of a line parallel to and 1 unit above the x-axis, whereas the graph of I is a subset of the diagonal line whose equation is $y = x$. The student is cautioned at this point that he may find some variation in the literature with respect to the meaning of some of the symbolism used here: The number symbol c is used by some writers to denote the function cI, with no special symbolism attached to constant functions—except for 0—and, occasionally, the meanings of the two indicated products of functions ($f \cdot g$ and fg) are the reverse of what we are using. We feel, however, that our usage is the most widely accepted.

If we think of a function f as a mapping of its domain onto its range, the function which is *inverse* to f reverses the mapping due to f. Hence the following definition is appropriate.

Definition. *Let f be a function with domain D and range $f(D)$. Then the function f^{-1} (if it exists) is defined on $f(D)$ so that $f^{-1}(y) = x$ where $f(x) = y$. If f^{-1} exists, the function f is said to be* invertible.

That is, if f maps the element x onto the element y, the function f^{-1} maps y onto x. Inasmuch as each of these functions reverses the mapping of the other, it follows that $ff^{-1} = f^{-1}f = I$, provided we attach a flexible meaning to the function I—as discussed previously.

We have implied that it is possible that f^{-1} does not exist for a given function f. In fact, f^{-1} cannot exist if $f(x_1) = f(x_2) = y$, with $x_1 \neq x_2$, because any attempted definition of $f^{-1}(y)$ would be ambiguous. A function f is *one-to-one* provided the function mappings define a one-to-one correspondence between the elements of the domain and the elements of the range of f: that is, provided $f(x_1) = f(x_2)$ if and only if that $x_1 = x_2$. This means that a *necessary* condition for the existence of f^{-1} is that f be one-to-one. On the other hand, because a reverse mapping of a one-to-one function can always be defined unambiguously, this condition is also *sufficient*. We repeat this result for the sake of emphasis:

A necessary and sufficient condition for the existence of the inverse function f^{-1} is that f be one-to-one.

It should be understood that although the domains of a function and its reciprocal (if it exists) are the same, the domains of a function and its inverse (if it exists) are generally different.

Example 2. If f is the function defined on $[-2, 2]$ by $f(x) = 2x - 3$, describe f^{-1} and graph both f and f^{-1}.

SOLUTION. Let $y = 2x - 3$, so that $f(x) = y$. If $2a - 3 = 2b - 3$, it follows that $a = b$, and so the function f is one-to-one. Hence f^{-1} exists and is defined so that $f^{-1}(y) = x$. But $x = (y + 3)/2$, and so $f^{-1}(y) = (y + 3)/2$, for each y in $f([-2, 2])$, i.e., in $[-7, 1]$. If we now replace y

by the usual "domain variable" x, the definition of f^{-1} is as follows: $f^{-1}(x) = (x + 3)/2$, for each $x \in [-7, 1]$. On checking ff^{-1} and $f^{-1}f$, we find that $(f^{-1}f)(x) = f^{-1}[f(x)] = f^{-1}(2x - 3) = (2x - 3 + 3)/2 = x$, for each $x \in [-2, 2]$; and also $(ff^{-1})(x) = f[f^{-1}(x)] = f[(x + 3)/2] = 2(x + 3)/2 - 3 = x$, for each $x \in [-7, 1]$. Hence, $f^{-1}f = ff^{-1} = I$, which is the characterizing equation for inverses. The graphs of f and f^{-1} are shown in Figure 25.

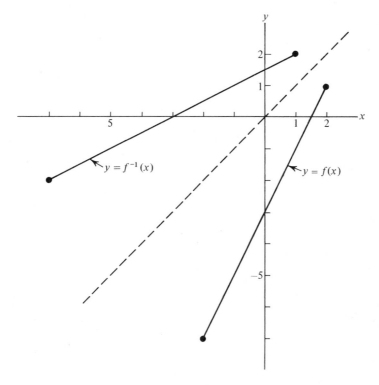

Figure 25

If we think of a function as a set of ordered pairs, our definition of f^{-1} implies that $(a, b) \in f$ if and only if $(b, a) \in f^{-1}$. The geometric effect of this is that the graph of a function and its inverse are the reflections of each other in the diagonal line $y = x$ drawn through the first and third quadrants. We may observe that the line segments in Figure 25 have this property.

Example 3. If f is completely defined by the following table, construct a similar table for f^{-1} and graph both functions.

x	0	1	2	3	4
$f(x)$	2	-2	3	0	-5

SOLUTION.   We first note that each functional value occurs only once, and so f^{-1} exists. The function table for f^{-1} then follows from the reverse mapping.

x	-5	-2	0	2	3
$f^{-1}(x)$	4	1	3	0	2

Both graphs are shown in Figure 26.

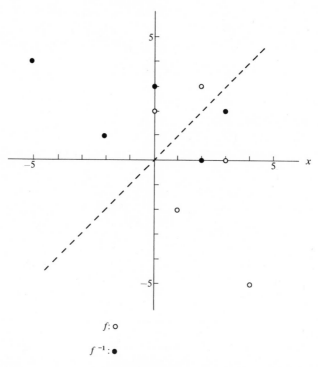

f: ○

f^{-1}: ●

Figure 26

A function f is said to be *strictly increasing* if $f(x) < f(y)$ if and only if $x < y$, for elements x, y in the domain of f. If $f(x) > f(y)$ if and only if $x < y$, the function is said to be *strictly decreasing*. It is a geometrically intuitive fact that the inverse f^{-1} of a function f defined on an interval $[a, b]$ exists whenever f is either strictly increasing or strictly decreasing. For the increasing case, the domain of f^{-1} is then the interval $[f(a), f(b)]$; for the decreasing case, the domain of f^{-1} is $[f(b), f(a)]$. We used this intuitive fact in Example 2 without comment. It is not difficult to see, however, that the inverse of a function can exist without the function being either strictly increasing or strictly decreasing. Some examples of this are given in the problems that follow.

Problems 4.5

1. If f is an invertible function, explain what assumption must be made if the equality $ff^{-1} = f^{-1}f = I$ is to be correct.
2. If f and g are functions defined on **R** by $f(x) = 2x^2 - 1$ and $g(x) = 3x - 2$, describe the functions fg, gf, and f^2.
3. If f and g are functions defined on **R** by $f(x) = 3x - 2$ and $g(x) = 3x^3$, describe the functions fg, gf, and g^2.
4. If functions f and g are defined so that $f(x) = 2x^2 + 1$, for each $x \in$ **R**, and $g(x) = 2x - 3$, for each $x \in [0, 2]$, describe and graph the function fg. Does gf exist as a function on **R**?
5. If functions f and g are defined so that $f(x) = 2/x$, for each $x \in [2, 4]$, and $g(x) = 3x - 1$, for each $x \in$ **R**, describe and graph the function gf. Does fg exist as a function on **R**?
6. Each of the following rules defines a function f whose domain is understood to be the maximal subset of real numbers for which the rule makes sense. Decide which of the functions are invertible.
   (a) $f(x) = 2x^2$; (b) $f(x) = 3x + 2$; (c) $f(x) = 2/x$; (d) $f(x) = x^3$.
7. Use the directions given in Problem 6 for the functions defined below: (a) $f(x) = \sqrt{1 - x}$; (b) $f(x) = 2x^2 + 1$; (c) $f(x) = 2/(x^2 + 1)$; (d) $f(x) = 1 - 1/x$.
8. The table below defines a function f. Construct a similar table for f^{-1}, and graph both functions.

x	-2	-1	0	1	2	3
$f(x)$	3	1	-2	2	-1	4

9. What is the inverse of an identity function I? Is any constant function invertible? Explain.
10. Let the function f be defined on $[0, 3]$ so that

$$f(x) = \begin{cases} x & 0 \le x \le 1 \\ 1 - x & 1 < x \le 3 \end{cases}$$

Then show that f^{-1} exists, noting that f is neither strictly increasing nor strictly decreasing.
11. Give an example—different from that in Problem 10—of an invertible function that is neither strictly increasing or strictly decreasing.
12. Describe a function with domain D and range R for which D and R are defined as follows, and indicate whether the function is invertible:
    (a) $D = \{1, 2, 3\}$, $R = \{2, 4, 5\}$; (b) $D =$ set of integers, $R =$ set of even integers; (c) $D = R =$ **R**.
13. Let the function f be defined on **R** by $f(x) = x^2$. Restrict the domain of f in some manner to obtain a new function defined by the same rule, but such that the new function is invertible.
14. Prove that the composition of functions is an associative operation, whenever the products are defined; that is, prove that $f(gh) = (fg)h$, for functions with suitable domains.

15. Assume the domains of the functions 1, I, and f are such that the indicated products are defined, and compare (a) $f \cdot 1$ with fI; (b) If with $1 \cdot f$.

16. If f is an invertible function, determine (a) $f^{-1}[f(t)]$, for t in the domain of f; (b) $f[f^{-1}(t)]$, for t in the range of f.

17. Use the functions f and g defined on **R** by $f(x) = x^2 + 1$ and $g(x) = 2x - 1$, respectively, to illustrate the difference between $f \cdot g$ and fg.

18. Use the function f defined in Problem 17 to illustrate the difference between $f \cdot f$ and f^2.

19. If the functions f and g are defined on **R** so that $f(x) = x^2$ and $g(x) = 1 - x$, show that $fg, f \cdot g, f^2$, and g^2 are defined, and give the rules of mapping.

20. Give an example of functions f and g such that (a) fg is defined, but $f \cdot g$ is not; (b) $f \cdot g$ is defined but fg is not.

21. Justify the validity of the following rule: A function f is invertible if and only if every horizontal straight line intersects the graph of f in not more than one point. Would it be appropriate to replace "not more than" by "precisely"? Explain.

22. If the function f is defined on $[-2, 3]$ by $f(x) = 3x - 2$, give the rule of mapping of the function (a) f^{-1}; (b) f^2; (c) f^3.

23. If the function g is defined on the set of nonnegative real numbers by $g(x) = (2 + x)/(3 + x)$, give the rule of mapping of the function (a) g^{-1}; (b) g^2.

24. If functions f and g are defined on **R** by $f(x) = |x|$ and $g(x) = |x| + 1$, respectively, describe both fg and gf.

25. If $f(x) = |x|$ and $g(x) = [x]$, for any $x \in \mathbf{R}$, describe the functions fg and gf. Is there any difference between f and f^2 or between g and g^2?

26. Explain why neither of the functions f or g in Problem 25 has an inverse.

27. If f is an invertible function, is it proper to refer to f as the inverse of f^{-1}? Is it true that $(f^{-1})^{-1} = f$?

28. If f and g are functions, is it possible that (a) fg is invertible, but not both f and g are invertible; (b) fg is defined but not invertible, even if both f and g are invertible?

29. If f, g, and fg are invertible functions, show that $(fg)^{-1} = g^{-1}f^{-1}$.

30. If f and g are constant functions on a set D, prove that the solution set of $f(x) = g(x)$ is either D or $\varnothing$.

5

Exponential and Logarithmic Functions

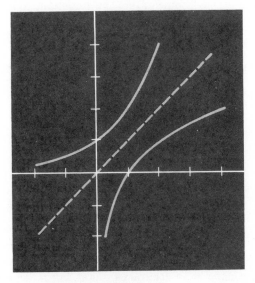

5.1 The Meaning of Exponents

If n real numbers, each equal to a, are multiplied together, an easy extension of the associative law of multiplication shows that this product is independent of the order in which the numbers are grouped. The product that is common to all the groupings is denoted by a^n and is called the nth *power of* a where the natural number n is called an *exponent*. Thus $a^n = (a)(a)\cdots(a)$, where the factor a occurs n times, and the exponent n in a^n tells how many times the *base* number a occurs as a factor. Clearly, this notion of an exponent has meaning only if n is a positive integer. For example, 3^4 is a short symbolism for $(3)(3)(3)(3)$, the exponent 4 indicating that the base 3 has been used 4 times as a factor. On many occasions we have already used this type of positive integral exponent without comment, and its properties are reviewed in Appendix A.

The *laws of exponents*, which we now state, follow immediately from the primitive concept just reviewed, and we shall omit any proof for them. In the statement of these laws, a and b may designate arbitrary real numbers (*except that no denominator may be zero*), but for the present the exponents m and n are assumed to be positive integers. We shall see later that, as this condition on the exponents is relaxed, some of these laws continue to hold *only if a* and b are *positive* real numbers.

LAWS OF EXPONENTS

1. $a^m a^n = a^{m+n}$
2. $(a^m)^n = a^{mn}$
3. $(ab)^n = a^n b^n$
4. $a^m / a^n = \begin{cases} a^{m-n} & \text{if } m > n \\ 1/a^{n-m} & \text{if } m < n \\ 1 & \text{if } m = n \end{cases}$
5. $(a/b)^n = a^n / b^n$

Although it is possible to *prove* the above laws from the primitive concept of an exponent and the properties of real numbers, the extension of the exponent concept beyond the positive integers is a matter of *definition*. However, these definitions are not made in an arbitrary fashion, but rather with the following guiding principle in mind: *We wish the laws of exponents to continue to hold, insofar as possible, for any extension of the exponent concept.*

As a first application of this principle, let us see what possible real number may be denoted by the symbol a^0, for any nonzero $a \in \mathbf{R}$. If the first of the laws of exponents is to continue to hold when $m = 0$ and $n = 1$, we must have $a^0 a^1 = a^{0+1}$, and this is equivalent to $a^0 a = a$. Since $a \neq 0$, on dividing both members of this equality by a, we obtain $a^0 = 1$. The following definition is then forced upon us.

Definition. $a^0 = 1$, *for any real number $a \neq 0$.*

It is any easy matter to verify that all five of the laws of exponents remain valid if either (both) of the exponents m or (and) n is (are) equal to 0.

The operation that is "inverse" to raising a number to the nth power is a determination of an "nth root." For example, 2 and -2 are 4th roots of 16, because $2^4 = (-2)^4 = 16$; -3 is a "3rd" or cube root of -27, because $(-3)^3 = -27$; and both 5 and -5 are "2nd" or square roots of 25, because $5^2 = (-5)^2 = 25$. If a is a positive real number, it is a fact that there is *exactly one* nth root of a that is positive; and if a is negative, there is a real nth root of a only if n is odd, and this negative real root is unique. In either of these cases, we refer to the unique real nth root as the *principal nth* root of a, and denote it by $\sqrt[n]{a}$, with n omitted from the symbol if $n = 2$. As a special application of this definition, it is instructive to point out that $\sqrt{x^2} = |x|$ and so, for example, $\sqrt{(-2)^2} = 2$. On the other hand, $\sqrt[3]{x^3} = x$, regardless of the algebraic sign of x. We call attention to the fact that $\sqrt[n]{a}$ has not been defined when $a < 0$ and n is an even integer. For example, $\sqrt{4} = 2$, and $\sqrt[3]{-8} = -2$, but $\sqrt{-9}$ does not designate any real number. For the sake of emphasis, we repeat the essential part of the above remarks in the form of a definition.

Definition. *The symbol $\sqrt[n]{a}$, for a positive integer n and real number a, denotes (if it is defined) the* principal *nth root of a. If $a > 0$, this is the unique positive nth root; if $a < 0$ and n is odd, this is the unique real nth root; and is negative; if $a = 0$, $\sqrt[n]{a} = 0$ for any n; if $a < 0$ and n is even, $\sqrt[n]{a}$ is without meaning as a real number.*

In a later section of this chapter, we shall discover how to compute approximations for any existing principal nth roots, but for the present, we are concerned only with the *meanings* of the symbols.

Example 1. Give a simpler representation for each of the numbers denoted by the following symbols (provided such a real number exists): (a) $\sqrt{16}$; (b) $\sqrt[3]{8}$; (c) $\sqrt[3]{-8}$; (d) $\sqrt[4]{16}$; (e) $\sqrt[4]{-16}$.

SOLUTION.   If we use the definition just given, we find that the answers are as follows: (a) 4; (b) 2; (c) -2; (d) 2; (e) no real number.

We are now in a position to extend the concept of exponents to include both positive and negative rational numbers, but first we consider those which are positive. If m and n are positive integers, and $a^{m/n}$ is to denote a number that obeys the laws of exponents—in particular, the second—we must have $(a^{m/n})^n = a^m$. Hence, the symbol $a^{m/n}$ must denote an nth root of a^m, and so one is lead to the following definition.

Definition. $a^{m/n} = \sqrt[n]{a^m}$, *provided m/n is a rational fraction reduced to lowest terms, both m and n are nonnegative integers, and $\sqrt[n]{a^m}$ is defined. If $r/s = m/n$ for other nonnegative integers r, s, then $a^{r/s} = a^{m/n}$, whenever $a^{m/n}$ has meaning.*

If $\sqrt[n]{a}$ is defined, we must have $(\sqrt[n]{a})^m = (\sqrt[n]{a^1})^m = (a^{1/n})^m = a^{m/n}$, in accordance with the second law of exponents, and so $a^{m/n} = \sqrt[n]{a^m} = (\sqrt[n]{a})^m$. Hence $\sqrt[n]{a^m} = (\sqrt[n]{a})^m$, whenever these real numbers exist, and it may be that one of these forms is easier to compute than the other. For example, $\sqrt[5]{32^3} = (\sqrt[5]{32})^3$, and it is easily seen from the *second* form of the symbol that $\sqrt[5]{32^3} = 2^3 = 8$. Although we prefer not to go through the details, it can be shown without great difficulty that all of the laws of exponents continue to hold for nonnegative rational exponents, provided the component symbols have meaning and zero denominators are excluded.

Example 2. Simplify each of the following expressions, assuming that x and y are appropriate real numbers:

$$\text{(a) } \left(\frac{x^{3/2}y^0}{x}\right)^4 ; \quad \text{(b) } \frac{6x^{5/2}y^{5/3}x^{3/4}}{2x^{3/2}y} ; \quad \text{(c) } \left(\frac{2x^{1/2}}{y}\right)^0 .$$

SOLUTION.

(a) $\left(\dfrac{x^{3/2}y^0}{x}\right)^4 = (x^{3/2-1}y^0)^4 = (x^{1/2})^4 = x^2.$

(b) $\dfrac{6x^{5/2}y^{5/3}x^{3/4}}{2x^{3/2}y} = 3x^{5/2+3/4-3/2}y^{5/3-1} = 3x^{7/4}y^{2/3}.$

(c) $\left(\dfrac{2x^{1/2}}{y}\right)^0 = 1.$

Finally, if the laws of exponents—and, in particular, the first—are to hold for a "number" a^{-r}, where r is a positive rational number and $a \neq 0$, we must have $(a^r)(a^{-r}) = a^0 = 1$. This motivates our extension of the exponent concept to include negative rational numbers.

Definition. $a^{-r} = 1/a^r$, *for any nonzero real number a and an arbitrary rational number r, provided a^r has been defined.*

For example, this definition implies that $3^{-2} = 1/3^2 = 1/9$, and $2^{-2/3} = 1/2^{2/3} = 1/\sqrt[3]{4}$. Again it may be checked that not only does the "motivating" first law of exponents hold in this extension, but all five laws remain valid in this general context. It may be noted that the fourth law can now be expressed in a simpler form, independent of the magnitude of the rational numbers m and n.

4'. $a^{m/n} = a^{m-n} = 1/a^{n-m}$, for a real number a and arbitrary rational numbers m and n, provided only that the members of the equality have meaning.

To summarize: If a is a positive real number, a^r has been defined for any rational number r; if a is negative, a^r has been defined for any rational number r whose reduced fractional form has an odd integer for its denominator. It is beyond the scope of this book to consider the further extension of the exponent concept to include irrational numbers. For example, we have not given—nor shall we give—any meaning to such a number symbol as $2^{\sqrt{3}}$, although it would be possible to do this. In Chapter 8, however, with the introduction of complex numbers, we shall give meaning to certain symbols that until then will remain undefined.

Example 3. Express each of the following as a single radical, assuming x is a suitable real number:

$$\text{(a) } \frac{\sqrt[3]{x}\,\sqrt[4]{x^3}}{\sqrt{x}} ; \quad \text{(b) } \sqrt{\sqrt[3]{x^2}}.$$

SOLUTION.

(a) $\dfrac{\sqrt[3]{x}\;\sqrt[4]{x^3}}{\sqrt{x}} = \dfrac{(x^{1/3})(x^{3/4})}{x^{1/2}} = x^{1/3+3/4-1/2} = x^{7/12} = \sqrt[12]{x^7}.$

(b) $\sqrt{\sqrt[3]{x^2}} = (x^{2/3})^{1/2} = x^{1/3} = \sqrt[3]{x}.$

Example 4.   Write each of the following expressions in a form that does not involve any negative exponents:

$$\text{(a) } \dfrac{x^{-1}+y^{-1}}{(x+y)^{-2}}\,; \text{ (b) } (3^{-2}+4^{-2})^{1/2}.$$

SOLUTION.

(a) $\dfrac{x^{-1}+y^{-1}}{(x+y)^{-2}} = \dfrac{1/x+1/y}{1/(x+y)^2} = \dfrac{x+y}{xy}\dfrac{(x+y)^2}{1} = \dfrac{(x+y)^3}{xy}.$

(b) $(3^{-2}+4^{-2})^{1/2} = (\tfrac{1}{9}+\tfrac{1}{16})^{1/2} = (\tfrac{25}{144})^{1/2} = \tfrac{5}{12}.$

We close this section with a word of caution: It can happen that completely erroneous results are obtained if the laws of exponents are formally applied to undefined symbols. For example, an application of the first law to the formal product $(-2)^{1/2}(-2)^{1/2}$ produces $(-2)^1$ or -2. On the other hand, if we apply the third law to the same product, the result is $[(-2)(-2)]^{1/2} = 4^{1/2} = 2$. Since $2 \neq -2$, something is wrong: We have improperly applied the laws of exponents to the meaningless symbol $(-2)^{1/2}$.

Problems 5.1

1. Give the simplest representation for each of the indicated numbers:
   (a) $64^{2/3}$; (b) $-4^{2/3}$; (c) $3/3^0$; (d) $16^{2/3}$; (e) $1/2^{-2}$.
2. Give the simplest representation for each of the indicated numbers:
   (a) -2^{-3}; (b) $(-2)^{-3}$; (c) $(-2)^{-4}$; (d) -2^{-4}; (e) $-3/2^{-1}$.
3. Express each of the indicated numbers in the form of a radical:
   (a) $4^{2/3}$; (b) $6^{3/4}$; (c) $(-4)^{2/3}$; (d) $(-5)^{-3/5}$.
4. Express each of the indicated numbers in the form of a radical:
   (a) $2^{3.2}$; (b) $3^{1.52}$; (c) $5^{2.14}$; (d) $10^{0.0012}$.
5. Express each of the indicated numbers in a form that does not involve exponents:
   (a) $(3^{-2})^{-4}$; (b) $(\tfrac{2}{3})^3(\tfrac{1}{2})^0$; (c) $4^{-1/4}$; (d) $(2^{1/2}3^{-2/3})^4$; (e) $[(2^{-3})^2]^{-1}$.
6. On the basis of our definitions, does $4^{1/2}$ equal (a) -2; (b) 2; (c) ±2?
7. Give the correct natural ordering of the following real numbers, with x denoting any nonzero real number: $2x^0$, $(2x)^0$, $1/2x^0$.
8. Express each of the indicated numbers in a form that does not involve radicals, assuming x to be an unidentified real number:
   (a) $\sqrt{\tfrac{1}{9}}$; (b) $\sqrt{4x^2}$; (c) $\sqrt[3]{3x^3}$; (d) $\sqrt[5]{(-\tfrac{3}{2})^2}$.
9. Give the simplest form for the numbers represented in (b) and (c) of Problem 8, assuming that (a) $x > 0$; (b) $x < 0$.

10. Indicate which of the following real numbers are negative: (a) $(-2)^0$; (b) -2^0; (c) $5^{2/3}$; (d) $5^{-2/3}$; (e) $(-2)^{3/5}$; (f) $(-2)^{-3}$; (g) $4^{-1/2}$.

11. Simplify each of the following expressions, with $a, b, x, y \in \mathbf{R}$: (a) $a^2b^3a^3b^5$; (b) $(a^2)^3/a^3$; (c) $[(2)(3)]^3 2^2 3^4$; (d) $(xy)^4/x^3$; (e) $1/(x^{-1} + y^{-1})$.

12. Write a simpler form for $\sqrt{(x-1)^2}$, where (a) $x > 1$; (b) $x < 1$.

13. Write a simpler form, not involving negative exponents, for each of the following expressions, assuming $a, b, c, x, y \in \mathbf{R}$: (a) $(3x^{-1})^3/x^3$; (b) $(x^{-1}y^{-2})(x^2y^4)$; (c) $(ab^{-2}c)^2(abc)^{-3}$; (d) $(x^{-1}y^2/x^{-3}y^{-1})^{-2}$.

14. Assuming $x, y \in \mathbf{R}$, write each of the following in an equivalent form not involving negative or zero exponents: (a) $3^{-2} - 2^{-3}$; (b) $x^{-1} + y^{-1}$; (c) $(xy^0 + x)^{-1}$; (d) $(x + x^{-1})^2$; (e) $x^3y^3(x^{-1} + y^{-1})$; (f) $(x^{-1} - y^{-1})/xy$; (g) $x/(x^{-1} + x^{-2})$.

15. Review how we have defined $a^{m/n}$, for a real number a, where (a) both m and n are negative integers; (b) exactly one of m and n ($\neq 0$) is a negative integer?

16. Write each of the following in a fractional form with denominator 1, assuming a, b, c, x, y are nonzero real numbers: (a) $ab^3c/a^2b^2c^2$; (b) $3x^{-2}y^3/2xy^3$; (c) $1/x + 2/y$.

17. Assuming that x, y, z are suitable real numbers, simplify each of the following expressions: (a) $x^{-3}y^2/x^{-1}y^{-4}$; (b) $xy^{-2}z^{-3}/3x^3yz^5$; (c) $(2x^{-1}y^3/x^2y^3)^{1/2}$.

18. Write each of the following expressions in an equivalent form with denominator 1: (a) $(\sqrt{2} - 1)/(\sqrt{2} + 1)$; (b) $(2 - \sqrt{3})/(2 + \sqrt{3})$; (c) $(1 - \sqrt{3})/(\sqrt{2} + 1)$; (d) $(\sqrt{2} - \sqrt{3})/(\sqrt{3} - \sqrt{5})$.

19. Assuming that a, b, x, y are positive real numbers, express each of the following in the form of a single radical: (a) $\sqrt[3]{x}\sqrt{x^4}/\sqrt{x^5}$; (b) $\sqrt{a}\sqrt[3]{2ab^2}\sqrt{3a^2b}$; (c) $\sqrt[4]{24x^5/y^2}\sqrt[3]{y^3/3x}$; (d) $\sqrt{3\sqrt{3\sqrt{3}}}$.

20. Write in an equivalent but simpler form without any negative exponents:

(a) $\dfrac{x^{-1} + y^{-2}}{x^{-2} + y^{-2}}$ (b) $\dfrac{a^{-3}b^{-3}}{a^{-3} + b^{-3}}$ (c) $\dfrac{(x^2 - y^2)^{-1}}{(x - y)^{-3}}$

21. Determine all real solutions for x in the equation $\sqrt{(x-1)^2} = 5$.

22. Determine all real solutions for x in the inequality (a) $|x - 1| < 2^{-1}$; (b) $|x|^{-1} > 2^{-3}$; (c) $(x + 1)^0 \leq x + 2$.

23. Decide which the the laws of exponents, as given in this section, would be valid for nonnegative exponents if we had defined $a^0 = 0$, for arbitrary nonzero $a \in \mathbf{R}$.

24. Decide the conditions on both the real number a and the exponent $n \in \mathbf{Z}$ if the following equalities hold:

(a) $|a^n| = |a|^n$ (b) $(-a)^n = -a^n$

25. Assuming that the symbol x^{m^n} denotes a properly defined real number, is this number equal to (a) $(x^m)^n$; (b) x^r, where $r = m^n$? In particular, express 2^{3^2} in the usual symbolism for an integer.

26. If x and y are real numbers, show that $0 \leq x \leq y$ if and only if $\sqrt{x} \leq \sqrt{y}$.

27. If x and y are real numbers, is it true that $\sqrt[3]{x} < \sqrt[3]{y}$ if and only if $x < y$ (cf. Problem 26)?

28. Give intuitive proofs of the laws of exponents for positive integral exponents, to cover the cases for which the exponential quantities have been defined in this section.

29. Assuming the result in Problem 28, prove that the laws of exponents hold for positive rational exponents for the analogous cases as in Problem 28.

30. Assuming the result in Problem 29, prove that the laws of exponents hold for arbitrary rational exponents, for the cases as in Problem 29.

5.2 Exponential Functions

We noted in Chapter 4 that a real-valued function is completely defined if we know its *domain* and the *rule* of correspondence between the elements of its domain and range. Now that the exponent concept has meaning (although in a somewhat restricted sense), it is possible to introduce a whole new class of very important functions.

Definition.   *A function f, defined on a subset of real numbers by $f(x) = y = a^x$, for some real number $a > 0$, is called an* exponental *function (with* base *a). If its domain is* **R**, *the function f is called* the basic exponential function with base *a*.

We emphasize again—as for functions in general—that, although an exponential function derives its name from its rule of mapping $x \to a^x$, the function is not completely defined unless we know or assume its domain.

Example 1.   Describe and graph the exponential function *f* which is defined on $\{-2, -1, 0, 1, 2\}$ by $f(x) = 2^x$.

SOLUTION.   The function *f* consists of the following ordered pairs: $(-2, \frac{1}{4})$, $(-1, \frac{1}{2})$, $(0, 1)$, $(1, 2)$, $(2, 4)$. In Figure 27 we have shown the complete graph of the function.

In most instances where exponential functions occur, the domain is an *interval* of real numbers. This raises a difficulty, because every interval of real numbers contains irrational numbers, and we have not given a meaning to a^x if x is irrational (*even if $a > 0$*—as we are assuming here). However, we can overcome the difficulty with a bit of intuition! Any irrational number can be expressed as an unending (nonrepeating) decimal, whereas any terminating decimal is a representation of a rational number. Hence, if we are willing to accept the intuitively evident (and true) assertion that any unending decimal can be approximated to any desired degree of accuracy by a terminating decimal, it is possible to approximate a^x, where x is irrational, by replacing x by one of its rational approximations. We shall accept this fact here without attempt at proof. For example, although we have not defined $3^{\sqrt{2}}$, it is possible to do so, and this "number" can be approximated by $3^{1.4}$, $3^{1.41}$, $3^{1.414}$, etc., the radical form of these approximations being $\sqrt[5]{3^7}$, $\sqrt[100]{3^{141}}$, $\sqrt[500]{3^{707}}$, and so on. Even though numbers such as these may seem to be extremely difficult to express in decimal form at this time, we have at least given *meaning* to the symbols, and the matter of approximate decimal representation can be accomplished later. Hence, at least theoretically, we can approximate a^x, for any $a > 0$ and any $x \in \mathbf{R}$, and so use the equation $y = a^x$ to define a function on an interval of real numbers.

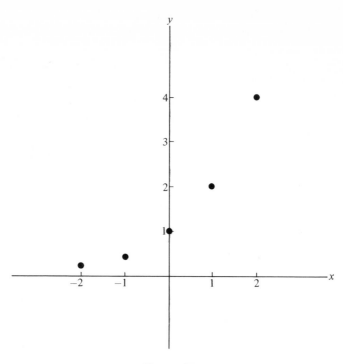

Figure 27

The graph of an exponential function, as of any other function, is merely the graph of all ordered pairs that belong to the function. In practice, we construct such a graph by plotting a sufficient number of points that can be easily determined, and joining them with a smooth curve if the domain of the function is an interval. The validity of the "smooth curve" feature of the graph is a consequence ("continuity" again!) of our assumption that a^{x_1} and a^{x_2} will differ by an arbitrary small amount if $|x_1 - x_2|$ is sufficiently close to 0. We illustrate this graphing procedure with two examples.

Example 2. Graph the function f defined on $[-2, 2]$ by $f(x) = 2^x$.

SOLUTION. We use the points shown in Figure 27 and join them with a smooth curve. The result, on a reduced scale, is shown in Figure 28*a*.

Example 3. Graph the function g defined on $[-2, 2]$ by $g(x) = (\frac{1}{2})^x$.

SOLUTION. A distribution of elements of the function are: $(-2, 4)$, $(-1, 2)$, $(0, 1)$, $(1, \frac{1}{2})$, $(2, \frac{1}{4})$. The graph of g is shown in Figure 28*b*.

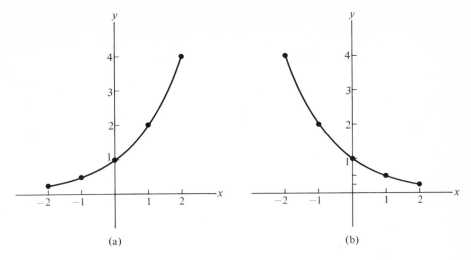

(a)   (b)

Figure 28

The graphs shown in Figures 28a and 28b are illustrative of all exponential functions on an interval (except the constant function defined by $y = 1^x$). Figure 28a is typical of a function defined by $y = a^x$, if $a > 1$; Figure 28b is typical when $0 < a < 1$. We also draw attention to the fact that the point $(0, 1)$ is common to the graphs of all exponential functions defined by $y = a^x$, provided only that 0 is in the domain of the function. The graph of any of these exponential functions lies entirely above the x-axis (i.e., the "domain" axis), even if its domain is the set **R** of all real numbers.

It is an interesting feature of exponential functions that, if x_1, x_2 and $x_1 + x_2$ are in the domain of such a function f, then $f(x_1 + x_2) = f(x_1) \cdot f(x_2)$. This is an immediate consequence of the first law of exponents (§5.1), because if $f(x) = a^x$, it follows that $f(x_1 + x_2) = a^{x_1 + x_2} = a^{x_1} \cdot a^{x_2} = f(x_1) \cdot f(x_2)$.

Although the rule of mapping of an exponential function has the form $y = a^x$, for some $a > 0$, an equation $y = ca^{kx}$ (with $c, k \in \mathbf{R}$) may be used to define a *modified exponential* function—also often referred to loosely as *exponential* (see Problem 22). If we accept the graphically intuitive fact that any real number $a > 0$ can be expressed in the form $a = b^k$, for some real k and any $b (\neq 1) > 0$, the base of an exponential function can be varied at will. For then $a^x = (b^k)^x = b^{kx}$, and so the defining rule $y = a^x$ of an exponential function can be replaced by $y = b^{kx}$, both rules defining the same exponential function.

Modified exponential functions occur often in descriptions of natural phenomena and, in particular, whenever the rate of change of the amount of a substance at a given time is proportional to the amount present at that time. An example of this occurs in radioactivity, where the rate of decomposition of a radioactive substance is proportional to the amount of the substance present. The law of growth of a bacteria culture under ideal conditions is another example of the occurrence of an exponential function. By way of illustration, it is known that under favorable conditions, a single cell of a certain bacterium will divide into two about once every 20 minutes. In other words, if a plate contains 1000 of these organisms at a certain time, we would expect to discover approximately $2(1000)$ of them 20 minutes later, $2[2(1000)]$ or $(1000)2^2$ of them 40 minutes later, $2[(1000)2^2]$ or $(1000)2^3$ of them 60 minutes later, and so on. In t hours (that is, in $3t$ periods of 20 minutes each), we would then expect to find $(1000)2^{3t}$ bacteria present on the plate. If N denotes the number of bacteria produced in t hours from an initial batch of 1000, the equation $N = (1000)2^{3t}$ shows that N is an exponential function of t. Other examples of exponential functions, such as charge on an electrical condensor and the growth of money invested at compound interest, will appear in the problem set that follows.

Example 4.   The half-life of radium is approximately 1600 years (i.e., any given amount of radium will be reduced to one half in 1600 years). If we assume an exponential-type relationship between the amount of radium and time elapsed, determine how much of 200 milligrams of radium will remain after 6400 years.

SOLUTION.   If f designates the function, our assumption is that $f(t) = (200) 2^{kt}$, for $t \geq 0$, where k is a real number to be determined and we have selected the base 2 for convenience. When $t = 1600$, $f(t) = 100$ and so $\frac{1}{2} = 2^{k(1600)} = 2^{-1}$. Hence $1600k = -1$ and $k = -1/1600$, so that $f(t) = (200) 2^{-t/1600}$. When $t = 6400$, $f(t) = (200) 2^{-4} = \frac{200}{16} = 12.5$, and so 12.5 milligrams of radium will be left in 6400 years.

Problems 5.2

1. Explain why it is graphically evident that, if $a > 0$ and $b > 0$, there exists a real number k such that $a = b^k$. Is this true if $a \leq 0$?
2. Explain why it is necessary for us to require that the base of an exponential function be positive.
3. Give an approximation for the irrational number $\sqrt{3}$ by a rational number with (a) two decimal places; (b) three decimal places; (c) four decimal places. Repeat the directions for the irrational number π.
4. Construct a careful graph of the function f on $[0, 4]$, where $f(x) = 2^x$, and use the graph to obtain an approximation for (a) $2^{\sqrt{2}}$; (b) $2^{\sqrt{3}}$; (c) $2^{3/5}$; (d) $\sqrt[5]{4}$; (e) 2^π.
5. Use a careful graph of an appropriate function to obtain an approximation for (a) $3^{\sqrt{2}}$; (b) 3^π; (c) $\sqrt[7]{9}$.
6. Use a single pair of coordinate axes to graph the functions f, g, h defined on $[-2, 2]$ by $f(x) = 2^x$, $g(x) = 3^x$, $h(x) = 4^x$, respectively.

7. Use a single pair of coordinate axes to graph the functions f, g, h defined on $[-2, 2]$ by $f(x) = (\frac{1}{2})^x$, $g(x) = (\frac{1}{3})^x$, $h(x) = (\frac{1}{4})^x$, respectively.

8. What is the base number a if the graph of an exponential function defined by $y = a^x$ is known to contain the point (a) $(2, 16)$; (b) $(3, 27)$?

9. What is the base number a if the graph of an exponential function defined by $y = a^x$ is known to contain the point (a) $(3, 8)$; (b) $(-2, \frac{1}{4})$; (c) $(1, \pi)$?

10. Determine the rule of mapping $y = ca^x$ of a modified exponential function if its graph is known to contain the points $(1, 6)$ and $(2, 18)$.

11. Determine the rule of mapping $y = c(3^{kx})$ of a modified exponential function if its graph is known to contain the points $(0, 3)$ and $(3, 27)$.

12. Construct a graph of the function f defined on $\{-2, -\frac{3}{2}, -1, -\frac{1}{2}, 0, \frac{1}{2}, 1, \frac{3}{2}, 2\}$ by $f(x) = 2^x$. Graph the inverse function f^{-1} relative to the same coordinate axes.

13. Is there any exponential function that is not invertible? The domain of an exponential function can be the set of all real numbers, but what is the domain of the inverse of an invertible exponential function on $\mathbf{R}$?

14. Sketch the graph of the function f defined on $[-3, 3]$ by (a) $f(x) = (2^x + 2^{-x})/2$; (b) $f(x) = (2^x - 2^{-x})/2$.

15. Sketch the graph of the function f defined on $[-2, 2]$ by (a) $y = -2^x$; (b) $y = 2^{-x}$.

16. Sketch the graph of the function f defined on $[-2, 2]$ by (a) $y = 2(3^x)$; (b) $y = (\sqrt{2})^x$.

17. Sketch the graph of the function f defined on $[-1, 4]$ by (a) $y = 2^{|x|}$; (b) $y = [2^x]$.

18. Use the graph of an appropriate exponential function to verify that (a) $3^{\sqrt{2}} < 3^{\sqrt{3}}$; (b) $2^5 > 4^{\sqrt{5}}$.

19. Consider the graph of an appropriate exponential function as an aid and find the number of real solutions of each of the following equations: (a) $2^x = 5$; (b) $3^{-x} = 2$; (c) $2^{-x} = -4$.

20. Use a sketch of an appropriate exponential function as an aid and find the number of real solutions of each of the following equations: (a) $2^{x^2} = 4$; (b) $2^{x^2} = -4$; (c) $2^{x^2} = 1$.

21. Assume the intuitive fact that an exponential function defined by $y = a^x$ is either strictly increasing or strictly decreasing, according as $a > 1$ or $a < 1$. Now prove that, if $0 < a < b$, then (a) $a^x < b^x$, for $x > 0$; (b) $a^x > b^x$, for $x < 0$.

22. If the rule of mapping of a function is $y = ca^{kx}$, for real numbers c, k, a (> 0), show that the function is the composite of one or more linear functions and a function whose rule of mapping has the form $y = b^x$, for b (> 0) $\in \mathbf{R}$.

23. If a function f is defined so that $f(x) = ca^x$ for some real number $c \neq 1$, is it true that $f(x_1 + x_2) = [f(x_1)][f(x_2)]$ for $x_1, x_2, x_1 + x_2$ in the domain of f? Explain.

24. If f is the basic exponential function defined by $f(x) = a^x$, show that $f(cx) = [f(x)]^c$, for any $c \in \mathbf{R}$.

25. The half-life of a radioactive material is 1200 years. Refer to Example 4 and determine how much of 500 milligrams of the material will remain after 6000 years.

26. The population of a bacteria culture is known to increase exponentially so that the population p in t hours is given by $p = c(5^t)$. How many hours would it take for a culture of 2000 of these bacteria to increase to 250,000?

27. Let us assume that the population of a town is increasing exponentially so that the population p in t years is given by $p = c(\frac{3}{2})^t$, for some real number c. How many years would be needed for the population to increase from 8000 to 27000?

28. The gas in a balloon is escaping at such a rate that three fifths of what remains at any instant has escaped after an additional minute. If the balloon contains 2000 cubic feet of gas at some initial time, find a formula for the amount remaining in the balloon after a lapse of t minutes.

29. When a certain capacitor is discharged through a resistance, the current I, in amperes, that is flowing in t seconds from the time of initial discharge, is given by $I = 0.8(3.2)^{-t/120}$. Sketch a graph of this discharge function, and determine the amount of current flowing in 60 seconds.

30. A star loses heat at such a rate that its temperature T in degrees in t million years is given by the formula $T = 15000(10^{-0.075t})$. Determine the approximate temperature of the star in 40 million years.

5.3 Logarithmic Functions

If one considers the graph of any (nonconstant) exponential function defined by $y = a^x$, it is clear that a horizontal line through a point on the positive y-axis intersects the graph in *not more* than one point. In particular, if the domain of the function is **R** (so that we are considering a *basic* exponential function), we note that there is *one and only one* intersection point of this kind. This means that $a^{x_1} = a^{x_2}$, for any $a(\neq 1) > 0$, if and only if $x_1 = x_2$, and so the equation $y = a^x$ has a unique solution for x, for any $y > 0$.

Definition. *The unique solution for x of $y = a^x$, with $a (\neq 1) > 0$ and any $y > 0$, is called the* logarithm *of y to base a, and we write $x = \log_a y$.*

It must be emphasized that, although $\log_a y$ is a unique real number for any $y > 0$, the symbol here is without meaning for $y \leq 0$. If N is any positive real number and $N = a^x$, our definition implies that $x = \log_a N$. On the other hand, if $x = \log_a N$ for real numbers N and x, it is also an immediate consequence of the definition that $N = a^x$. Hence, the two equations

$$N = a^x \qquad x = \log_a N$$

may be considered equivalent: $N = a^x$ is the "exponential" form of $x = \log_a N$, and $x = \log_a N$ is the "logarithmic" form of $N = a^x$. If we combine these two equations—or merely make a direct application of the above definition—we obtain the following very important and fundamental formulas:

$$a^{\log_a N} = N \qquad \log_a a^x = x$$

Because $a^1 = a$, and $a^0 = 1$ for any $a \neq 0$, it follows for any real $a (\neq 1) > 0$ that

$$\log_a a = 1 \qquad \log_a 1 = 0$$

Example 1. Write the equality (a) $2^3 = 8$ in equivalent logarithmic form; (b) $\log_3 9 = 2$ in equivalent exponential form.

SOLUTION.

(a) The equality $2^3 = 8$ implies that 3 is the logarithm of 8 to base 2; in symbols, $\log_2 8 = 3$.
(b) The equality $\log_3 9 = 2$ implies that $3^2 = 9$, which is the desired exponential form.

Example 2. Determine $\log_2 16$ and $\log_{10} 0.001$.

SOLUTION. Our definition requires that $\log_2 16$ be the solution of the equation $2^x = 16$. It then follows by inspection that $x = 4 = \log_2 16$. Similarly, $\log_{10} 0.001$ is the solution of $10^x = 0.001$; and, because $0.001 = 10^{-3}$, we see that $x = -3 = \log_{10} 0.001$.

Example 3. If $\log_4 N = \frac{1}{2}$, determine N.

SOLUTION. The equality $\log_4 N = \frac{1}{2}$ is equivalent to $4^{1/2} = N$, from which it follows immediately that $N = 2$.

Example 4. Determine $\log_4 \frac{1}{32}$.

SOLUTION. We know from the definition of a logarithm that $\log_4 \frac{1}{32}$ is the solution of $4^x = \frac{1}{32}$, and this latter equation can be expressed in the form $(2^2)^x = 2^{2x} = 2^{-5}$. Hence $2x = -5$ and $x = -\frac{5}{2}$.

Example 5. Express 3^x as a power of 10.

SOLUTION. Because $3 = 10^{\log_{10} 3}$, it follows that $3^x = (10^{\log_{10} 3})^x = 10^{x \log_{10} 3}$, as desired. It may be noted that, although $\log_{10} 3$ is known to exist as a real number, we have only graphical methods for its approximate determination at this time.

Now that $\log_a x$ has been defined, for positive real numbers x and a ($\neq 1$), we are able to give the following definition.

Definition. *A function f defined on a set of positive real numbers by $f(x) = \log_a x$, for some a ($\neq 1$) > 0, is called a* logarithmic *function (with* base *a). If its domain is the subset of all positive real numbers, the function f is called* the basic logarithmic function with base a.

Although the domain of a logarithmic function may be any subset of positive real numbers, the case of most frequent occurrence is that in which all positive real numbers belong to the domain. This *basic logarithmic* function is the logarithmic analogue of the *basic exponential* function whose domain is the set **R** of all real numbers. We shall see presently that these two functions have another very important relationship. If the defining rule of a function f is

$f(x) = c \log_a kx$, for real numbers c and k ($\neq 0$), it is sometimes convenient to refer to f as a *modified logarithmic* function or—loosely and simply—as a *logarithmic* function. This practice is consistent with that adopted for exponential functions.

In §4.5 we observed that the characteristic feature of an inverse function is that it reverses the mappings induced by some original invertible function. In symbols, if f^{-1} is the inverse of the invertible function f, this implies that $ff^{-1} = f^{-1}f = I$ (a slightly inexact but useful equality that we have seen before). But now, if the domains are selected appropriately, the identities $a^{\log_a x} = x$ and $\log_a a^x = x$ may be used to pair off exponential and logarithmic functions so that one member of each pair is the inverse of the other. In particular, let us assume that the domain of the logarithmic function g defined by $g(x) = \log_a x$, is identical with the range of the exponential function f defined by $f(x) = a^x$. But then $(fg)(x) = f[g(x)] = f(\log_a x) = a^{\log_a x} = x$, for any x in the domain of g; and $(gf)(x) = g[f(x)] = \log_a a^x = x$, for any x in the domain of f. Thus $fg = gf = I$, and the uniqueness of an inverse function implies that f and g are respective inverses of each other. The most important special case of these inverse functions arises when the domain of the exponential function is $\mathbf{R}$ and the domain of the logarithmic function is the set of all positive real numbers. Either of these basic functions sets up a one-to-one correspondence between the set $\mathbf{R}$ of all real numbers and the subset of all positive real numbers: The basic exponential function (with base a) maps each real number x onto the positive number a^x, and the basic logarithmic function (with base a) maps each positive real number x onto the (positive, negative, or zero) real number $\log_a x$. *Each of the associated basic exponential and logarithmic functions* (not of modified type) *is then the inverse of the other.*

In view of the inverse relationship between exponential and logarithmic functions, it is instructive to remember the relationship between the graphs of a function and its inverse. We recall that a point $(b, a) \in f^{-1}$ if and only if $(a, b) \in f$ and that the graphs of f and f^{-1} are then geometric reflections of each other in the diagonal line through quadrants I and III. In Figure 29 we have drawn graphs of functions f and g $(= f^{-1})$, where f is defined on $[-2, 2]$ by $f(x) = 2^x$ and g is defined on $[\frac{1}{4}, 4]$ by $g(x) = \log_2 x$.

These two graphs are typical of inverse exponential and logarithmic functions, but it must be understood, of course, the domain of f might be a finite set or even the complete set $\mathbf{R}$ of real numbers. *In our discussion of logarithmic functions, we shall always assume that the base $a > 1$, so that our logarithmic graphs always have a "concave downwards" appearance.*

There are several useful conclusions that we can deduce (under the assumption just stated) from a graphical comparison like Figure 29:

1. Whereas $a^x > 0$, for any x, $\log_a x > 0$ if $x > 1$, and $\log_a x < 0$ if $x < 1$.
2. $\log_a x_1 < \log_a x_2$ if and only if $0 < x_1 < x_2$.
3. The graph of f, where $f(x) = a^x$, is "steeper" as a increases; hence, the graph of g, where $g(x) = \log_a x$, is "flatter" as a increases.

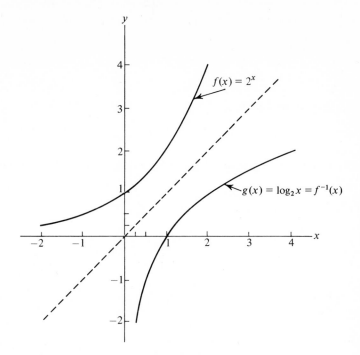

Figure 29

Problems 5.3

1. Write each of the following equalities in equivalent logarithmic form:
   (a) $2^4 = 16$; (b) $10^3 = 1000$; (c) $10^0 = 1$; (d) $3^3 = 27$; (e) $25^{1/2} = 5$.
2. Write each of the following equalities in equivalent exponential form:
   (a) $2 = \log_3 9$; (b) $-2 = \log_{10} 0.01$; (c) $4 = \log_4 256$; (d) $\frac{3}{2} = \log_4 8$.
3. Express each of the following exponential equations in an equivalent logarithmic form: (a) $x^5 = 12$; (b) $5^x = 7$; (c) $6^7 = x$; (d) $10^x = 55$.
4. Express each of the following logarithmic equations in an equivalent exponential form: (a) $5 = \log_3 x$; (b) $x = \log_2 15$; (c) $13 = \log_x 5$; (d) $\frac{8}{3} = \log_x 2$.
5. Explain why 1 would not be a suitable base for a logarithmic function.
6. Find by inspection the real solution for x in each of the following equations:
   (a) $\log_3 x = 2$; (b) $\log_4 x = \frac{3}{2}$; (c) $\log_x 16 = 4$; (d) $\log_4 8 = x$; (e) $\log_9 3 = x$.
7. Explain why it is true, for any real $a\,(\neq 1) > 0$, that (a) $\log_a 1 = 0$;
   (b) $a^{\log_a 8} = 8$; (c) $\log_a a = 1$.
8. Use the graph in Figure 29 to determine a rough approximation for (a) $\log_2 2.5$;
   (b) $\log_2 3$; (c) $\log_2 3.5$.
9. Construct a graph of the function f, where f is defined on $\{-2, -1, 0, 1, 2\}$
   by $f(x) = 3^x$.
10. Use a piece of transparent paper and the graph constructed in Problem 9 to
    construct a graph of the function g defined on $[\frac{1}{9}, 9]$ by $g(x) = \log_3 x$. From
    the graph of g, determine approximations for (a) $\log_3 2$; (b) $\log_3 4$; (c) $\log_3 7$.
11. Use one pair of coordinate axes to sketch graphs of the logarithmic functions
    f and g defined on $[\frac{1}{2}, 10]$ by $f(x) = \log_3 x$ and $g(x) = \log_{10} x$.

12. Use graphical methods to approximate the solution of the equation $\log_2 x = \log_3 \frac{2}{3}$.

13. If $f(x) = \log_6 x$, for each x $(> 0) \in \mathbf{R}$, determine (a) $f(36)$; (b) $f(\frac{1}{6})$; (c) $f(\sqrt{6})$.

14. If $f(x) = \log_8 x$, for each x $(> 0) \in \mathbf{R}$, find (a) $-1/[2f(\frac{1}{2})]$; (b) $|f(\frac{1}{8})|$; (c) $[f(70)]$.

15. Use the definition of a logarithm to obtain a rough approximation for x if (a) $\log_{10} x = 0.3$; (b) $\log_{10} x = 0.4$; (c) $\log_{10} x = 0.5$.

16. Solve each of the following equations for x, with a $(\neq 1) > 0$: (a) $\log_a x = 0$; (b) $\log_a x = 1$; (c) $\log_x x = 1$.

17. Solve each of the following equations for x: (a) $\log_3 |x| = -2$; (b) $\log_{25} |x| = \frac{1}{2}$; (c) $\log_2 |x| = 0$.

18. Solve each of the following equations for x: (a) $4^{\log_2 x} = 16$; (b) $5^{\log_5 x} = 5$; (c) $x^{\log_x 3} = 3$.

19. Determine $x \in \mathbf{R}$ from each of the following equations: (a) $3^{\log_3 x} = 7$; (b) $x^{\log_3 8} = 8$; (c) $\log_{10} 10^x = -2$; (d) $\log_x 1 = 0$.

20. Let f be a logarithmic function defined on its domain by $f(x) = \log_a x$. Determine the base a if (a) $f(3) = 1$; (b) the graph of f contains the point $(32, 5)$.

21. If the graph of a basic logarithmic function contains the point $(64, 3)$, what base is being used?

22. Find (a) a^y, where $y = \log_a a^x$; (b) $\log_a y$, where $y = \log_a a^x$.

23. If $\log_a x = 3$, for a $(\neq 1)$ and x positive real numbers, find (a) $\log_{1/a} x$; (b) $\log_{a^2} x$; (c) $\log_a (1/x)$.

24. Prove that $\log_{1/a} x = \log_a (1/x)$, for positive real numbers a $(\neq 1)$ and x.

25. If a (> 1) and N (> 0) are real numbers, show that $a^{[\log_a N]} \leq N$.

26. Write x in the form $c(a^{ky})$, for real numbers c, a, k, where (a) $y = 2\log_2 3x$; (b) $y = 3\log_5 2x$; (c) $5y = -3\log_7 5x$.

27. What is the logarithmic equivalent of the statement for a basic exponential function f that $f(x_1 + x_2) = [f(x_1)][f(x_2)]$?

28. Write x in the form $c \log_a ky$, for real numbers c, a, k, where (a) $y = 2(3^{2x})$; (b) $y = 5(10^{-x})$; (c) $2y = 3(5^{2x+1})$.

29. If you were to make a careful graph of the logarithmic function f, defined by $f(x) = \log_{10} x$ with range $[0, 10]$, determine the approximate dimensions of a suitable (!) sheet of paper, using a 1-inch scale.

30. At a point h miles above sea level, a measure p of atmospheric pressure is given by the formula $p = p_0 e^{-0.193h}$, where e is a positive irrational number to be introduced later. Express the formula in an equivalent logarithmic form. What is necessarily represented by p_0?

5.4   The Laws of Logarithms

In view of the inverse relationship existing between basic exponential and logarithmic functions, it might seem that a study of both kinds of functions would involve a great amount of duplication. Although this is true, there are, nonetheless, good reasons for studying both kinds, because some relationships occur naturally in logarithmic form whereas others are more natural in terms of exponential functions. In addition, logarithms are useful in computation work, and although this role is much less important than before the advent of electronic computers, we shall devote the later sections of the chapter to this topic. By a logarithmic *base* we shall always mean a positive number different from 1.

We have already noted the important fact (which is intuitive graphically) that for any base a there is a one-to-one correspondence $x \leftrightarrow \log_a x$ established between the set of positive real numbers x and the set of all real numbers $\log_a x$. This means that every positive real number has a unique real number as its logarithm to the given base, and every real number (positive, negative, or zero) is the unique logarithm to this base of some positive real number. The theorems given in this section, known collectively as the *laws of logarithms*, are essentially the logarithmic equivalents of the laws of exponents. For the statements of the theorems [in addition to our assumption that $a \, (\neq 1) > 0$] we shall assume that M and N are *positive* real numbers.

■ **THEOREM 4.1.** $\log_a MN = \log_a M + \log_a N$. *In words: A logarithm of the product of two positive numbers is equal to the sum of the logarithms of the numbers.*

    PROOF.   Because every positive real number can be expressed in exponential form with base a, $M = a^m$ and $N = a^n$, for real numbers m and n. The definition of a logarithm then implies that $m = \log_a M$ and $n = \log_a N$. By the laws of exponents, $MN = (a^m)(a^n) = a^{m+n}$, and so $m + n = \log_a MN$. But this means that $\log_a MN = \log_a M + \log_a N$, as desired.

■ **THEOREM 4.2.** $\log_a (M/N) = \log_a M - \log_a N$. *In words: A logarithm of the quotient of two positive numbers is equal to the difference of the logarithms of the numbers.*

    PROOF.   With the same notation as in the proof of Theorem 4.1, $M/N = a^m/a^n = a^{m-n}$, and so $\log_a (M/N) = m - n$. Hence $\log_a (M/N) = \log_a M - \log_a N$, as desired.

■ **COROLLARY.** $\log_a (1/N) = -\log_a N$.

This result follows directly from the theorem if we note that $\log_a 1 = 0$.

■ **THEOREM 4.3.** $\log_a M^p = p \log_a M$, *for any real number p. In words: A logarithm of the pth power of a positive number is equal to the p-multiple of the logarithm of the number.*

    PROOF.   With the notation of the proof of Theorem 4.1, $M^p = (a^m)^p = a^{mp}$, and so $mp = \log_a M^p$. Hence $\log_a M^p = p \log_a M$, establishing the theorem.

Example 1.   Given that $\log_{10} 3 \approx 0.4771$ and $\log_{10} 2 \approx 0.3010$, find $\log_{10} 6$ and $\log_{10} 27$.

    SOLUTION.   By Theorem 4.1, $\log_{10} 6 = \log_{10} 3 + \log_{10} 2 \approx 0.4771 + 0.3010 = 0.7781$. Since $27 = 3^3$, an application of Theorem 4.3 gives $\log_{10} 27 = 3 \log_{10} 3 \approx 3(0.4771) = 1.4313$.

Example 2.   Use the data given in Example 1 to determine $\log_{10} \sqrt{3}$ and $\log_{10} \sqrt[5]{6}$.

SOLUTION.   By Theorem 4.3, $\log_{10} \sqrt{3} = \log_{10} 3^{1/2} = \frac{1}{2} \log_{10} 3 \approx \frac{1}{2}(0.4771) \approx 0.2386$. By Theorems 4.1 and 4.3, $\log_{10} \sqrt[5]{6} = \log_{10} 6^{1/5} = \frac{1}{5} \log_{10} 6 \approx \frac{1}{5}(0.7781) \approx 0.1556$.

It happens quite often that it is necessary to change from one logarithmic base to another, and in such instances the following theorem is important.

■ **THEOREM 4.4.**   *For any two logarithmic bases a and b, $\log_b N = (\log_a N)/(\log_a b)$. In words: To change a logarithm from base a to base b, divide the original logarithm by $\log_a b$.*

PROOF.   The proof of this theorem follows directly from the following identity noted in §5.3:
$$N = b^{\log_b N}$$

For then, by Theorem 4.3,

$$\log_a N = \log_b N \cdot \log_a b$$

and so

$$\log_b N = \frac{\log_a N}{\log_a b}$$

■ **COROLLARY.** $\log_b a = 1/(\log_a b)$.

Thus, if we let $N = a$ in the theorem and note that $\log_a a = 1$, the result follows immediately.

Example 3.   If $\log_{10} 2 \approx 0.3010$, determine $\log_5 2$.

SOLUTION.   By Theorem 4.4, $\log_5 2 = (\log_{10} 2)/(\log_{10} 5)$. But $5 = \frac{10}{2}$, and so

$$\log_{10} 5 = \log_{10} 10 - \log_{10} 2 = 1 - \log_{10} 2 \approx 1 - 0.3010 = 0.6990.$$

Hence,
$$\log_5 2 \approx 0.3010/0.6990 \approx 0.4306.$$

The laws of logarithms allow one to break up a compact expression involving products and powers into a sum of simpler components. For example, $\log_a (x^3 y^2/\sqrt{z}) = 3 \log_a x + 2 \log_a y - \frac{1}{2} \log_a z$, with x, y, z positive real numbers; and for some mathematical purposes this expanded sum is more useful. On the other hand, it is often desirable to express a sum of logarithmic terms in a final compact form, as in Example 4.

Example 4. Express $\frac{5}{2}\log_2 x + 3\log_2 y - 2\log_2 xy = 4$ in an equivalent compact form, assuming x and y are positive real numbers.

SOLUTION. The laws of logarithms allow us to write the given equation in the form $\log_2 [x^{5/2}y^3/(xy)^2] = 4$ or, more simply, $\log_2 x^{1/2}y = 4$. This equation may now be written in equivalent exponential form as

$$x^{1/2}y = 2^4 \quad \text{or} \quad x^{1/2}y = 16$$

Problems 5.4

1. Given that $\log_a 2 \approx 0.693$, $\log_a 3 \approx 1.099$, and $\log_a 5 \approx 1.609$, find an approximation of the logarithm to base a of each of the following numbers: (a) 6; (b) 20; (c) 36; (d) 150; (e) $\sqrt{30}$; (f) $36^{2/3}$; (g) $225^{3/5}$.

2. Using the data given in Problem 1 and $\log_a 7 \approx 1.946$, find an approximation of the logarithm to base a of each of the following numbers: (a) 350; (b) 28; (c) 140; (d) $\sqrt{35}$; (e) $28^{3/4}$; (f) $30^{-1/2}$; (g) $7^{-2/5}$.

3. Apply the directions given in Problem 2 to the following numbers: (a) $\sqrt{\frac{2}{3}}$; (b) $\sqrt[3]{\frac{2}{7}}$; (c) $35/a^2$; (d) $\sqrt[3]{\frac{3}{35}}$; (e) $\sqrt[5]{\frac{1}{30}}$.

4. Use the data given in Problems 1 and 2 to compute approximately (a) $(\log_a 7)/(\log_a 35)$; (b) $(\log_a 35)(\log_a 20)$; (c) $(\log_a 14)^2$.

5. Use the data given in Problems 1 and 2 to determine approximations for the logarithms to base a of the following numbers: (a) $\frac{1}{12}$; (b) $\frac{1}{15}$; (c) $1/\sqrt{30}$; (d) $(\frac{1}{18})^{5/6}$; (e) $(\frac{4}{9})^{2/3}$; (f) $(\frac{3}{25})^{1/4}$.

6. Use the data given in Problems 1 and 2, if necessary, to determine each of the following: (a) $\log_a a^3$; (b) $\log_a \frac{1}{2}a$; (c) $\log_a \sqrt{a}$; (d) $a^{\log_a \sqrt{a}}$.

7. Given that $\log_{10} 2 \approx 0.3010$ and $\log_{10} 3 \approx 0.4771$, determine an approximation for (a) $\log_{10} 5$; (b) $\log_{10} 20$; (c) $\log_{10} 45$; (d) $\log_{10} \sqrt{90}$; (e) $\log_{10} (\frac{1}{20})^{2/3}$.

8. Solve each of the following equations for a real number x: (a) $\log_6 1 = x$; (b) $\log_{10} x = -2$; (c) $\log_x 7 = -1$; (d) $\log_{16} x = -\frac{1}{2}$.

9. Solve each of the following equations for $x \in \mathbf{R}$: (a) $|\log_3 x| = 2$; (b) $2\log_a \frac{12}{5} + 3\log_a 15 - \log_a 18 = \log_a x$.

10. Solve each of the following equations for $x \in \mathbf{R}$: (a) $|\log_3 x| + 2\log_3 x = 5$; (b) $\log_2 x = \log_2 \frac{7}{12} + \log_2 \frac{4}{3} - \log_2 \frac{3}{4}$.

11. Express each of the following in the form of a single logarithm:
    (a) $2\log_a x + \frac{1}{2}\log_a xy^2 - 3\log_a x^3$;
    (b) $\log_a (2 - x^2) - 3\log_a (2 + x) + \log_a 2$;
    (c) $\log_a (3/\sqrt{x}) - \frac{2}{3}\log_a x^{1/2} + \log_a \sqrt{x}$.

12. Simplify each of the following, assuming x, y and a are real numbers that are appropriate in order for the indicated logarithms to exist: (a) $\log_a x^2 - 2\log_a \sqrt{x}$; (b) $\log_a (x^2 - 4) - \log_a (x - 2)$; (c) $\log_a (a/\sqrt{x}) - \log_a \sqrt{ax}$.

13. Simplify each of the following, assuming x, y, and a are real numbers that are appropriate in order for the indicated logarithms to exist: (a) $\log_a |x^3 - y^3| - \log_a |x - y|$; (b) $\log_a (x^2 + y^2) - \log_a |x + y|$.

14. Assuming x and y to be positive real numbers, simplify
    (a) $3^{2\log_3 5}$; (b) $2^{2\log_2 x + 3\log_2 y}$.

15. Assuming x and y to be real numbers, simplify (a) $\log_3 [2^x(3)2^y]$; (b) $\log_2 (2^x 2^y)^4$; (c) $[\log_2 (2^x 2^y)]^4$.

16. Write the equation $\log_b y - \log_b c + kt = 0$ in an equivalent exponential form, assuming b, c, k, t to be appropriate real numbers.

17. The formula $N = 10 \log_{10} (P_2/P_1)$ expresses the decibel gain for a telephone element having input and output power of P_1 and P_2, respectively. Give an equivalent formula that does not involve logarithms.

18. The formula $I = I_0 e^{-(R/L)t}$ expresses the current I at time t in a coil whose characteristics are R and L, the initial current being I_0. Give the equivalent logarithmic formula for I. (See Problem 30 of §5.3.)

19. If $\log_b c = 0.234$, determine $\log_c b$. Is it ever the case that these two logarithms are equal?

20. If $\log_b a = 2.3026$ and $\log_b 4 = 1.3863$, determine $\log_a b$ and $\log_a 4$.

21. Make explicit use of the theorems in this section to prove that $\log_a MNP = \log_a M + \log_a N + \log_a P$, for arbitrary positive real numbers M, N, P and any logarithmic base a.

22. With the symbolism and directions given in Problem 21, prove that $\log_a (M/NP) = \log_a M - \log_a N - \log_a P$.

23. Solve the following system of equations for real x and y (a) with the use of logarithms to base 2; (b) without the use of logarithms:

$$x^2 y = 2^4$$
$$x^5 y^3 = 2^{11}$$

24. Apply the directions given in Problem 23 [but using base 3 in part (a)] to the following system:

$$x^3 y^2 = 3^5$$
$$x^2 y^4 = 3^2$$

25. If $y/x^p = k$, for positive real numbers x, y, p, find the relationship between $\log_a y$ and $\log_a x$, for any logarithmic base a. What type of equation is obtained to describe this relationship?

26. If a and b are positive real numbers such that $ab \neq 1$, prove that $\log_{ab} a + \log_{ab} b = 1$.

27. If $f(x) = \log_a x^2$ and $g(x) = 2 \log_a x$ are the rules of mapping of two functions f and g, and their domains are maximal, are the functions identical?

28. If $y = (\log_a N)/(\log_a b)$, for positive real numbers $N (\neq 1)$, $b (\neq 1)$ and any logarithmic base a, show that $b^y = N$.

29. If $x = (\log_b N)(\log_b a)$ and $y = (\log_b a)^2$, for positive real numbers $a, b (\neq 1)$, N, show that $a^x = N^y$.

30. Prove each of the following assertions:
(a) If f is a function such that $f(xy) = f(x) + f(y)$, for $x, y \in \mathbf{R}$, then $f(1) = 0$;
(b) If g is a nonzero function such that $g(x + y) = g(x)g(y)$, for $x, y \in \mathbf{R}$, then $g(0) = 1$.

5.5 Natural Logarithms and the Basis for Logarithmic Computation

We implied earlier that any positive number $a (\neq 1)$ can be used as an exponential or logarithmic base. However, although a number such as 2 occurs quite frequently in exponential functions (as in Example 4 of §5.2), there are two other special numbers that predominate as bases in logarithmic work. For computational work, base 10 is almost always used, and logarithms to this base are called *common* logarithms. For theoretical work, on the other hand, it is more customary to use as logarithmic base a certain irrational number e, an approximation to this number being $e = 2.71828 \cdots$. Logarithms to base e are called *Naperian*, or *natural*, logarithms; the first name is in honor of John Napier (1550–1617) who invented logarithms, whereas the name "natural" refers to the many occurrences of this number in mathematical descriptions of natural phenomena. We shall use $\log x$ in the sequel to refer to the common logarithm of a number x, and $\ln x$ will be used if natural logarithms are to be understood. When some other base b is used, we shall continue to designate such a logarithm as $\log_b x$.

The approximation to e shows that $2 < e < 3$, and it can be shown that the graph of the basic exponential function defined on **R** by $y = e^x$ crosses the y-axis at a point where the tangent line to the graph makes an angle of 45° with the x-axis. In view of the intrinsic importance of this function in theoretical work, we shall sometimes refer to it as *the basic exponential function*, the natural base e being understood. A portion of the graph of this function is shown in Figure 30.

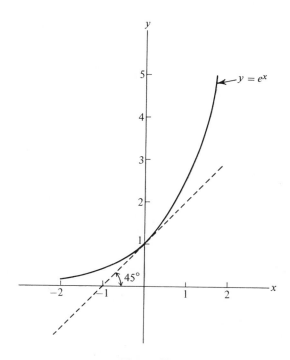

Figure 30

We shall introduce the manner in which logarithms are used for computation by means of an illustration. Let us suppose that we wish to simplify the expression $(27 \cdot 81 \cdot 9)/(243 \cdot 3)$. We notice that each number in the expression is an integral power of 3, and if we write these numbers as powers of 3 and then use the laws of exponents, the computation is quite simple. Thus, $(27 \cdot 81 \cdot 9)/(243 \cdot 3) = (3^3 \cdot 3^4 \cdot 3^2)/(3^5 \cdot 3^1) = 3^{3+4+2}/3^{5+1} = 3^9/3^6 = 3^{9-6} = 3^3 = 27$. It should be observed in this illustration that, although the original problem was one of multiplication and division, the computation was accomplished with addition and subtraction—except for the first and last steps. This is the basic idea involved in the use of logarithms for computation, and if the student has appreciated what has been accomplished by this very simple example, he is well on his way to understanding logarithmic computation.

It will have been noted by the alert student, of course, that the success of the method used in the above illustration depended on the fact that every number involved was a power of 3. However, it is clear that the number 3 played no essential role in the computation, except that all of the numbers were expressible *on inspection* as powers of 3. However, the identity $x = a^{\log_a x}$ shows that *any positive* number x can be written—at least theoretically—as a power of *any number* $a\ (\neq 1) > 0$, and so the method of the illustration can be applied to similar computations in which a plays the role of 3. We know, in particular, that $x = 10^{\log x}$, so that *any positive real number can be expressed as a power of* 10, and this is the important computational device associated with common logarithms. The various laws of logarithms, as given in §5.4 with $a = 10$, are then convenient expressions of some of the most common procedures used in a problem similar to the illustration above.

In order to carry out a computation by means of logarithms, two things are necessary: One must be able to find the logarithm of any positive real number, and one must be able to determine a real number from its logarithm. We shall consider both of these matters after the introduction of "scientific notation."

It is possible to write any positive real number as the product of a number between 1 and 10 and some integral power of 10. For example, we can write 245 as $2.45(10^2)$ and 0.00359 as $3.59(10^{-3})$. More generally, if $N = c(10^x)$, where x is an integer and $1 \le c < 10$, the number N is said to be expressed in *scientific notation*. This notation is specially adapted for a determination of logarithms. Since $c = 10^{\log c}$, for $c > 0$, $N = c(10^x) = 10^{\log c} \cdot 10^x = 10^{\log c + x}$, and so $\log N = \log c + x$. Inasmuch as x can be read from an inspection of the scientific notation for the number, the common logarithm of any number can be determined with a knowledge of the logarithms of all numbers between 1 and 10. The integer x is called the *characteristic* and the nonnegative number $\log c$—which is less than 1—is called the *mantissa* of $\log N$.

Example 1.   (a) $\log 245 = \log 2.45(10^2) = \log 2.45 + 2$.
(b) $\log 0.00134 = \log 1.34(10^{-3}) = \log 1.34 - 3$.

The common logarithm of any "two-decimal" number between 1.00 and 9.99 can be read directly as a "four-decimal" number from Table 1 in the back of the book. We shall accept these logarithms as given without any discussion of how they have been obtained, but it should be pointed out that the logarithms listed are rational *approximations* of the exact logarithms. In most instances we shall continue the practice of using $\approx$ to designate an *approximate* equality. In Table 1 all decimal points have been omitted, but we should understand that they are located immediately *after* the first digit of any number whose logarithm is given, and immediately *before* the first digit of its logarithm. Because $10^0 = 1$ and $10^1 = 10$, it is clear that the common logarithm of any number between 1 and 10 is a number between 0 and 1, and so this understanding about the location of decimal points in Table 1 is reasonable. For example, after inserting the decimal points as required, we find from Table 1 that

$$\log 2.45 \approx 0.3892$$

and

$$\log 1.34 \approx 0.1271$$

It is now possible to complete Example 1:

$$\log 245 \approx 0.3892 + 2 = 2.3892$$
$$\log 0.00134 \approx 0.1271 - 3 = -2.8729$$

The determination of the logarithms in Example 1 suggests two very important facts about common logarithms: The common logarithm of any positive number less than 1 is negative; the common logarithms of two positive numbers that differ only in the location of their decimal points differ only by an integer. For example, $\log 0.245 = \log 2.45(10^{-1}) = 0.3892 - 1$, and $\log 24500 = \log 2.45(10^4) = 0.3892 + 4$. It should be realized that the second simplification property would not be available if a base different from 10 were used, and this important fact explains the choice of base 10 for common logarithms.

The procedure for finding a number from its logarithm is simply to use Table 1 in reverse. The number is then sometimes called the "antilog" of the given logarithm, but we shall not use this word. We illustrate with an example.

Example 2. If $\log N = 0.5465 - 2$, find N.

SOLUTION. From Table 1 we note that

$$\log 3.52 \approx 0.5465$$

Hence, because $\log c + x = \log c(10^x)$,

$$N \approx 3.52(10^{-2}) = 0.0352$$

It must be emphasized that a correct determination of a number from its common logarithm requires that the logarithm be written in a form that exposes its mantissa as a *nonnegative number less than* 1. If a logarithm is not written this way initially, its form must be altered to satisfy this requirement. The following examples are illustrative of this procedure.

Example 3. Determine N if $\log N = -0.1267$.

SOLUTION. $\log N = -0.1267 = (1 - 0.1267) - 1 = 0.8733 - 1$. We now refer to Table 1 and note that

$$\log 7.47 \approx 0.8733$$

Hence,

$$N \approx 7.47(10^{-1}) = 0.747$$

Example 4. Determine N if $\log N = -2.6180$.

SOLUTION. $\log N = -2.6180 = (3 - 2.6180) - 3 = 0.3820 - 3$. Because $\log 2.41 \approx 0.3820$, it follows that $N \approx 2.41(10^{-3}) = 0.00241$.

Problems 5.5

1. Write the characteristic of the common logarithm of each of the following numbers: (a) 356.2; (b) 0.00043; (c) 24000; (d) 0.0012.
2. Give a convenient rule for determining the characteristic of the common logarithm of any positive real number.
3. Use Table 1 to obtain an approximation to the common logarithm of (a) 2.56; (b) 1.07; (c) 8.21; (d) 5.37; (e) 4.55.
4. Determine an approximate common logarithm of (a) 352; (b) 0.0352; (c) 3.5200; (d) 352000; (e) 0.000352.
5. Determine an approximate common logarithm of (a) 23.5; (b) 0.764; (c) 12.8; (d) 0.0043; (e) 34500.
6. Express each of the following numbers as a *symbolic* power of 2, but without using any tables: (a) 5; (b) 27; (c) 34; (d) 45.
7. Express each of the following expressions as a *symbolic* power of 2, but without using any tables:

   (a) $\dfrac{(5)(3)(12)(48)}{(4)(15)(9)}$ (b) $\dfrac{(15)(5^3)(27)(64)}{(17^2)(51)}$

8. Express each of the following as a *symbolic* power of 10, but without using any tables:

   (a) $\sqrt[3]{\dfrac{(45)(86)}{\sqrt{341}}}$ (b) $\sqrt{\dfrac{(2.4)(87.6)}{(0.023)^3}}$

9. Write each of the following numbers as the sum of an integer and a positive real number less than 1: (a) 3.1010; (b) -3.146; (c) -1.4392; (d) -5.201.
10. Express each of the following numbers in scientific notation: (a) 286; (b) 47.21; (c) 0.00121; (d) 120010; (e) 249.67; (f) 50000.
11. It is possible to find $\log (a/b)$ by using the identity $\log (a/b) = \log a - \log b$ or by first finding the quotient a/b. Use both of these procedures to determine (with the help of Table 1) the common logarithm of the following fractions, and explain any slight discrepancy discovered in the two answers for any one case: (a) $\frac{3}{5}$; (b) $\frac{2}{3}$, (c) $\frac{4}{7}$.
12. If base 10 were not used for logarithms, explain why the logarithms of numbers whose numerals have the same sequence of digits would generally differ by a number that is not an integer.

13. Find log N if (a) $N = 10^4$; (b) $N = 10^{2.5}$; (c) $N = 10^{-1.76}$; (d) $N = 10^{-0.01}$.
14. Express N as a power of 10 if log N is (a) 2.54; (b) -1.26; (c) 3.71; (d) -0.027.
15. Determine N if log N is (a) 5; (b) -2; (c) -3; (d) 4.
16. Find an approximation for N if log N is given as (a) $0.6031 + 2$; (b) $0.6580 - 2$; (c) 0.7168; (d) $0.8457 - 3$; (e) $0.7716 + 2$.
17. Find an approximation for N if log N is given as (a) 2.8488; (b) 3.8169; (c) 1.9294; (d) 3.7404.
18. Find an approximation for N if log N is given as (a) -2.2277; (b) -3.1355; (c) -1.1574; (d) -4.4522; (e) -0.4584.
19. Use Table 1 to find an approximation for (a) $10^{2.5259}$; (b) $10^{1.3696}$; (c) $10^{-3.3261}$; (d) $10^{-2.2899}$.
20. Use Table 1 to find an approximation for (a) $10^{1.6513}$; (b) $10^{-2.6038}$; (c) $10^{2.8102}$; (d) $10^{-1.2565}$.
21. If $N = \dfrac{(24.5)(15.7)(0.0025)}{(1.54)(0.113)}$, express each component number as a power of 10, and then give a similar representation for N.
22. Apply the directions in Problem 21 to $N = \dfrac{(0.1120)(4.65)(3450)}{(3.65)(76.8)}$.
23. Find an approximate solution for $x \in \mathbf{R}$: (a) $10^x = \sqrt[3]{15.7}$; (b) $10^x = \sqrt[3]{0.0147}$; (c) $10^{-x} = 2.74/5.36$; (d) $10^{x-2} = (0.0124)^3$.
24. Find an approximate solution for $x \in \mathbf{R}$: (a) $10^x = 3.87$; (b) $10^x = 0.542$; (c) $10^x = 34.5$; (d) $10^x = 0.002$.
25. Find approximate solutions for $x \in \mathbf{R}$: (a) log $x = 2.5465$; (b) log $x = 1.4713$; (c) log $x = -2.2628$; (d) log $x = -3.6819$.
26. Use Theorem 4.4 and Table 1 to express 25.3 as an approximate power of (a) 3; (b) 7; (c) 12.
27. Use Theorem 4.4 and Table 1 to compute an approximation for (a) $\log_3 12$; (b) $\log_7 35$; (c) $\log_9 56.7$; (d) $\log_2 17.5$.
28. Use Theorem 4.4 and Table 1 to compute an approximation for (a) $\log_5 10$; (b) $\log_3 7$; (c) $\log_3 2$; (d) $\log_5 8$.
29. Use Theorem 4.4 and Table 1 to compute an approximation for (a) $\log_8 47.1$; (b) $\log_3 0.0237$; (c) $\log_5 0.128$
30. Establish the fact that the characteristic of log N, for any $N > 0$, is $[\log N]$ and that log $N - [\log N]$ is its mantissa.

5.6 Computation with Logarithms

Before giving any detailed illustrations of logarithmic computation, it is important to see how Table 1 can be extended by means of *linear interpolation*. This method of interpolation can be used for finding either the logarithm of a number or a number from its logarithm—but we shall see later that the general process has a much wider area of applicability. In our present context, however, the underlying assumption is that, if two positive real numbers a and b are sufficiently near to each other, the graph of the basic (common) logarithmic function approximates a *line segment* on the interval $[a, b]$, and so we are able to use simple proportions. In interpolating from Table 1, we assume that "sufficiently near" means that a and b are adjacent entries in the table. We illustrate the procedure with an example.

Example 1. Use Table 1 to determine an approximation for log 2.456.

SOLUTION. We are not able to read log 2.456 directly from Table 1, but we can obtain the adjacent entries log 2.450 and 2.460. Thus,

$$\log 2.450 = \log 2.45 \approx 0.3892$$
$$\log 2.460 = \log 2.46 \approx 0.3909$$

and we assume that numbers and their logarithms between these entries are proportional. Since 2.456 is located $\frac{6}{10}$ of the way between 2.450 and 2.460, the approximate location of log 2.456 must be $\frac{6}{10}$ of the way between 0.3892 and 0.3909. Hence,

$$\log 2.456 \approx 0.3892 + (0.6)(0.0017) \approx 0.3892 + 0.0010 = 0.3902.$$

The following example illustrates how interpolation can be used in the determination of a number from its logarithm.

Example 2. If $\log N = 0.4658 - 2$, find an approximation for N.

SOLUTION. We observe that 0.4658 does not occur in the body of Table 1, but 0.4654 and 0.4669 are present and 0.4658 lies between them.

$$\log 2.920 = \log 2.92 \approx 0.4654$$
$$\log 2.930 = \log 2.93 \approx 0.4669$$

The logarithm 0.4658 is located $\frac{4}{15}$ of the way between 0.4654 and 0.4669, and so the number whose logarithm is 0.4658 must be located approximately $\frac{4}{15}$ of the way between 2.920 and 2.930. An approximation for this number N is then

$$2.920 + \tfrac{4}{15}(0.010) \approx 2.920 + 0.003 = 2.923$$

whence,

$$N \approx 2.923(10)^{-2} = 0.02923$$

The laws of logarithms were listed as theorems in §5.4, and we now use several examples to illustrate the use of these laws for computational purposes.

Example 3. Use the laws of logarithms to compute an approximation for the product $N = (12.3)(0.0651)$.

SOLUTION

$$\log 12.3 = \log 1.23(10)^{1} = 0.0899 + 1$$
$$\log 0.0651 = \log 6.51(10)^{-2} = 0.8136 - 2$$
$$\log N = \overline{0.9035 - 1}, \text{ by Theorem 4.1}$$

Because $\log 8.008 \approx 0.9035$, $N \approx 8.008(10)^{-1} = 0.8008$, or (to three decimals) $N \approx 0.801$.

Example 4.   Use the laws of logarithms to compute an approximation for
$N = 15.6/0.0212$.

SOLUTION

$$\log 15.6 = \log 1.56(10)^1 \approx 0.1931 + 1 = 1.1931 + 0$$
$$\log 0.0212 = \log 2.12(10)^{-2} \approx 0.3263 - 2 = \underline{0.3263 - 2}$$
$$\log N \approx 0.8668 + 2, \text{ by Theorem 4.2}$$

Because $\log 7.358 \approx 0.8668$, $N \approx 7.358(10)^2 = 735.8 \approx 736$.

Example 5.   Use the laws of logarithms to compute an approximation for
$N = (0.128)^{2/3}$.

SOLUTION.   By Theorem 4.3,

$$\log N = \tfrac{2}{3} \log 0.128 \approx \tfrac{2}{3}(0.1072 - 1) = \tfrac{2}{3}(2.1072 - 3)$$
$$= 1.4048 - 2 = 0.4048 - 1$$

Because $\log 2.54 \approx 0.4048$, $N \approx 2.54(10)^{-1} = 0.254$.

It may be seen, especially from Example 5, that one must take great care in manipulating negative logarithms. However, if a student realizes that a logarithm —whether positive or negative—is *merely a real number*, an application of a little common sense in these manipulations is likely to be more fruitful than an exhaustive set of rules. We wish to emphasize that the form in which we leave a logarithm is entirely dependent on what we are going to do with it. *Whenever a number is to be found from its logarithm, however, it is necessary to keep the logarithm in such a form that the decimal part is nonnegative.* It is to emphasize this fact that we usually separate the integral part (or characteristic) from the decimal part (or mantissa), and write the characteristic *after* the mantissa.

We complete this section with the solution of several somewhat more complicated computational problems. The student is urged to pay particular attention to the arrangement of the work in the displayed solutions.

Example 6.   Compute $N = \dfrac{(23.4)\,(18.61)}{(0.0042)(396)}$, using logarithms.

SOLUTION

$$\log 23.4 \approx 0.3692 + 1 \qquad \log 0.0042 \approx 0.6232 - 3$$
$$\log 18.61 \approx \underline{0.2697 + 1} \qquad \log 396 \approx \underline{0.5977 + 2}$$
$$0.6389 + 2 \qquad\qquad 1.2209 - 1 = 0.2209 + 0$$
$$\underline{0.2209 + 0}$$
$$\log N \approx 0.4180 + 2$$

Hence, $N \approx 2.618(10)^2 = 261.8 \approx 262$.

Example 7.   Determine an approximation for x if $0.214^x = 84.2$.

SOLUTION.   From the given equation, and Theorem 4.3, $x \log 0.214 = \log 84.2$, so that $x = \log 84.2 / \log 0.214$.

$$\log 84.2 \approx 0.9253 + 1 = 1.9253$$
$$\log 0.214 \approx 0.3304 - 1 = -0.6696$$

Hence,

$$x \approx -\frac{1.9253}{0.6696}$$

This quotient can be computed by long division, or it can be done by logarithms as indicated below.

$$\log 1.9253 \approx \log 1.925 \approx 0.2845 + 0 = 1.2845 - 1$$
$$\log 0.6696 \approx \log 0.670 \approx 0.8261 - 1 = \underline{0.8261 - 1}$$
$$\log |x| \approx \overline{0.4584 + 0}$$

It follows that $|x| \approx 2.873$, and so $x \approx -2.873$.

Note: In Example 7 we have illustrated a case in which a negative logarithm is *not* left in the mantissa-characteristic form, but is reduced to a form more suitable for division. Example 7 also illustrates that, although a negative number does not have a logarithm, the presence of negative numbers in a computation does not prevent the use of logarithms in the computation—because the algebraic sign of the answer can always be determined by inspection.

Example 8.   Compute $N = \sqrt[5]{\dfrac{(2.4)\sqrt{0.16}}{(3.46)^4}}$, using logarithms.

SOLUTION

$$\log 2.4 \approx 0.3802 = 0.3802 + 0$$
$$\tfrac{1}{2}\log 0.16 \approx \tfrac{1}{2}(0.2041 - 1) = \tfrac{1}{2}(1.2041 - 2) \approx \underline{0.6021 - 1}$$
$$0.9823 - 1$$
$$4\log 3.46 \approx 4(0.5391) = 2.1564 = \underline{0.1564 + 2}$$
$$0.8259 - 3$$

$$\log N \approx \tfrac{1}{5}(0.8259 - 3) = \tfrac{1}{5}(2.8259 - 5) \approx 0.5652 - 1$$

Hence,

$$N \approx 3.675(10)^{-1} = 0.3675 \approx 0.37$$

In working with negative logarithms, some people prefer a form in which
-10 always appears or is understood. For example, in this system, the logarithm $0.234 - 1$ would be written as $9.234 - 10$, $0.458 - 3$ would be written
as $7.458 - 10$, and $0.2967 - 6$ would be written as $4.2967 - 10$. Logarithms
in this form (with the -10 omitted but understood) are found most frequently
as entries in tables of logarithms of trigonometric functions (to be discussed in
Chapter 6). Although there may be some computational advantages associated
with this formulation of negative logarithms, we have decided not to use it
here for two reasons: with the advent of electronic computers, the actual use
of logarithms in computing is beoming less important; we feel that this form
tends to disguise the meaning of a logarithm to a greater extent than is the
case with the form we have been using. The choice of form, however, is a matter
of personal taste.

Problems 5.6

1. The "meaning" of the statement that $\log 100 = 2$ is that 100 can be expressed as the square of 10; similarly, $\log 4 \approx 0.6$ "means" that 4 may be
   expressed approximately as the positive fifth root of 1000. In like manner, give
   meaning to each of the following approximate equalities: (a) $\log 3.54 \approx 0.5490$;
   (b) $\log 5.18 \approx 0.7143$; (c) $\log 8.42 \approx 0.9253$.
2. Apply the directions in Problem 1 to each of the following:
   (a) $\log 707 \approx 0.85 + 2$; (b) $\log 3860 \approx 0.587 + 3$;
   (c) $\log 0.00123 \approx 0.09 - 3$; (d) $\log 0.0582 \approx 0.765 - 2$.
3. Write each of the following negative logarithms in the form $r - 10$, with $r > 0$:
   (a) $0.3548 - 3$; (b) $0.2984 - 6$; (c) $0.0105 - 4$; (d) $0.7722 - 1$.
4. Noting that $\log_3 9 = 2$ and $\log_3 27 = 3$, use the method of linear interpolation
   to approximate (a) $\log_3 12$; (b) $\log_3 18$. Now use Theorem 4.4 to approximate
   these logarithms, and explain any discrepancies with the results obtained by
   interpolation.
5. Use the values of $\log 8.6$ and $\log 8.7$, as tabulated in Table 1, to obtain $\log 8.62$
   by interpolation. Also find $\log 1.32$ by interpolating between $\log 1.3$ and $\log$
   1.4. Compare these two results with those given in the table.
6. If f and g are functions defined on **R** by $f(x) = 3x - 2$ and $g(x) = 2x^3 + 4$,
   respectively, the following values may be obtained immediately: $f(1) = 1$,
   $f(2) = 4$; $g(1) = 6$, $g(2) = 20$. Use linear interpolation to obtain $f(1.5)$ and
   $g(1.5)$; compare the results with those found directly from the formulas, and
   explain any discrepancies.
7. Determine which number in each of the following pairs is the larger: (a) $16^{4/5}$,
   $18^{3/4}$; (b) $27^{3/5}$, $36^{2/7}$, (c) $2^{\sqrt{3}}$, $3^{\sqrt{2}}$.
8. Use logarithms to compute approximations for each of the following products:
   (a) $(234.6)(0.00429)$; (b) $(142.6)(34.9)$; (c) $(0.00542)(0.059)$.
9. Use logarithms to compute approximations for each of the following quotients:
   (a) $435.8/0.543$; (b) $436000/12.4$; (c) $0.00542/0.954$.
10. Use logarithms to compute approximations for each of the following:
    (a) $(34.7)^{1/2}$; (b) $(0.00543)^{2/3}$; (c) $(0.765)^{3/4}$.

11. Use logarithms to compute approximations for each of the following:
(a) $(123600)^{1/2}$; (b) $(12.5)^{-1/2}$; (c) $(0.0054)^{-0.3}$.

12. Determine rational approximations in decimal form for $10^{0.0001}$ and $e^{0.0001}$, where $e \approx 2.718$.

13. Use logarithms to compute an approximation for (a) $10^{\pi} + \pi^{10}$; (b) $\sqrt{3.14} + 1/\sqrt{3.14}$; (c) $1.57(x^{2.7} - 1)^{1.53}$, where $x = 3.47$.

14. If $f(x) = (1 + 1/x)^x$, for any $x(\neq 0) \in \mathbf{R}$, find (a) $f(1)$; (b) $f(10)$; (c) $f(100)$.

15. Use logarithms to find an approximation for $\sqrt{\sqrt{\sqrt{0.213}}}$.

Use logarithms to find an approximation for each of the expressions given in Problems 16–20.

16. $\dfrac{(54.7)(0.00528)(54.73)}{(765.8)(0.00215)}$

17. $\dfrac{(54.32)^5(0.0183)}{\sqrt[5]{5.657}}$

18. $\sqrt[4]{\dfrac{(19.5)(437.9)}{(54.58)^3}}$

19. $\dfrac{\sqrt{43.6}(-0.463)^2}{(-62.6)(1.038)}$

20. $\dfrac{(43.7)(\log 12.6)}{\log 0.0142}$

21. An approximation to the period T in seconds of a simple pendulum of length L feet is given by $T = 2\pi\sqrt{L/32.2}$. Use logarithms to determine the period of a pendulum 4.12 feet in length.

22. The formula $H = d^3N/50$ gives the number H of units of horsepower transmissible by cold-rolled shafting, where N is the number of revolutions of the shaft per minute and d is the diameter of the shaft in inches. Determine the approximate diameter of a shaft that will deliver 27 units of horsepower with the shaft rotating at 240 revolutions per minute.

23. If $250 is invested for 20 years at 5 per cent interest compounded semiannually, use Table 1 to compute the amount of the accrued investment.

24. The volume V of a sphere of radius r is given by the formula $V = \frac{4}{3}\pi r^3$. Determine the approximate radius of a sphere of volume 100 cubic feet.

25. Assuming the earth is a sphere of radius 3960 miles, use the formula in Problem 24 to determine its approximate volume.

26. The wave length of a certain gamma ray is given as 0.613 angstrom, where 1 angstrom is 10^{-8} centimeter. Find the approximate wave length in inches, where 1 centimeter ≈ 0.3937 inch.

27. Make a sheet of "logarithmic" graph paper by marking logarithmic scales on both of two perpendicular axes, using the range from 1 to 10, and with 1 as the common intersection point or "origin." Then draw a graph of the function defined on [1, 10] by (a) $y = x^2$; (b) $y = 3x^3$.

28. Make a sheet of logarithmic graph paper, as described in Problem 27, and draw a graph of the function defined on [1, 10] by (a) $y = 1/x$; (b) $y = 2/x$.

29. Make a sheet of "semilogarithmic" graph paper by marking a logarithmic scale for the range 1 to 10 on the vertical axis and an ordinary uniform scale on the horizontal axis for an appropriate range beginning with 0. Then graph the function defined on [0, 10] by (a) $y = 10^x$; (b) $y = 3(10^{-2x})$.

30. Give an explanation of the graphical results obtained in Problems 27 to 29. (cf. Problem 25 to §5.4.)

5.7 Exponential and Logarithmic Equations

In this final section of the chapter we introduce nothing really new, but rather review and assimilate earlier material that will be useful for solving equations involving exponential or logarithmic expressions. As always, the solution of such an equation is a determination of the substitutions for the unknowns, from some given universe, that will change the "conditional" equation into a true equality. There are essentially three types of exponential equations. If a and b are suitably restricted real numbers, these three types have the forms: (a) $a^b = x$; (b) $a^x = b$; (c) $x^a = b$. We shall illustrate the method of solving an equation of each type with an example. In these and subsequent examples the universe of the variable is assumed to be **R**.

Example 1. Solve $(1.5)^{3.2} = x$ for x.

SOLUTION. By Theorem 4.3,

$$\log x = 3.2 \log 1.5 \approx 3.2(0.1761) \approx 0.5635$$

Hence,

$$x \approx 3.66$$

or, to two-figure accuracy,

$$x \approx 3.7$$

Example 2. Solve $(3.5)^x = 0.214$ for x.

SOLUTION. By Theorem 4.3,

$$x \log 3.5 = \log 0.214$$

and so

$$x = \frac{\log 0.214}{\log 3.5} \approx \frac{0.3304 - 1}{0.5441} = -\frac{0.6696}{0.5441} \approx -1.23$$

(The final step of the solution could be accomplished by either long division or logarithms.)

Example 3. Solve $x^{2.05} = 1.46$ for x.

SOLUTION. By Theorem 4.3,

$$2.05 \log x = \log 1.46$$

and so,

$$\log x = \frac{\log 1.46}{2.05} \approx \frac{0.1644}{2.05} \approx 0.0802$$

Hence,

$$x \approx 1.203$$

or, to three-figure accuracy,

$$x \approx 1.20$$

As a general rule for solving any exponential equation, the following is useful: *Use Theorem 4.3 to reduce the given equation to an equivalent logarithmic equation, by equating the common logarithms of both members.* The following example is a slight variant of the method used in the preceding examples, but this same general rule is used.

Example 4.   Find an approximate solution of $3^{x+1} = 2^x$ for $x \in \mathbf{R}$.

SOLUTION.   An application of the preceding rule gives

$$(x + 1) \log 3 = x \log 2$$

Hence

$$x \log 3 - x \log 2 = -\log 3$$
$$x(\log 3 - \log 2) = -\log 3$$
$$(0.4771 - 0.3010)x \approx -0.4771$$
$$0.1761x \approx -0.4771$$
$$x \approx -\frac{0.4771}{0.1761} \approx -2.71$$

If an exponential equation involves the number e, it is often convenient to know—without reference to tables—that $\log e \approx 0.4343$ and $\ln 10 \approx 2.3026$.

Example 5.   Find an approximate solution of $e^x = 1.47$ for $x \in \mathbf{R}$.

SOLUTION.   By Theorem 4.3,

$$x \log e = \log 1.47$$

and so

$$x = \frac{\log 1.47}{\log e} \approx \frac{0.1673}{0.4343} \approx 0.385$$

The following example illustrates how the same methods can be used to solve an inequality. In solving an inequality, it is important that we use the graphically intuitive fact that $\log a < \log b$ if and only if $0 < a < b$.

Example 6.   Find the approximate solution interval of the inequality $(0.56)^x < \frac{5}{6}$ for $x \in \mathbf{R}$.

SOLUTION.   It follows from Theorem 4.3 and Theorem 4.2 (along with the intuitive fact just recalled) that

$$x \log 0.56 < \log 5 - \log 6$$

Hence,

$$(0.7482 - 1)x < 0.6990 - 0.7782$$
$$-0.2518x < -0.0792$$
$$0.2518x > 0.0792$$
$$x > \frac{0.0792}{0.2518} \approx 0.3145$$

or $x > 0.315$, approximately. The desired *approximate* solution interval is then $(0.3145, \infty)$.

It may happen that the original equation contains logarithms, and in such a case we proceed more directly to the solution.

Example 7. Solve $\log (2x + 4) - \log (x - 2) = \log 6$ for $x \in \mathbf{R}$.

SOLUTION.   By Theorem 4.3,

$$\log \frac{2x + 4}{x - 2} = \log 6$$

and so

$$\frac{2x + 4}{x - 2} = 6$$

Hence,

$$2x + 4 = 6x - 12$$
$$4x = 16$$
$$x = 4$$

This solution may be checked in the original equation by noting that $\log 12 - \log 2 = \log \frac{12}{2} = \log 6$.

Example 8. Find an approximate solution of $\log (5x + 7) - \log 3x = 1.3424$ for $x \in \mathbf{R}$.

SOLUTION.   By Theorem 4.3,

$$\log \frac{5x + 7}{3x} = 0.3424 + 1$$

Hence (because $\log 2.20 \approx 0.3424$),

$$\frac{5x + 7}{3x} \approx 2.20(10)^1 = 22$$

and so

$$5x + 7 \approx 66x$$
$$61x \approx 7$$
$$x \approx \tfrac{7}{61} \approx 0.115$$

We have noted earlier that the two logarithmic bases most widely used are 10 and e. It is then of importance to be able to change the logarithm of a number from one of these bases to the other. The pertinent theorem, of course, is Theorem 4.4 and its corollary. Because $\log e \approx 0.4343$ and $\ln 10 \approx 2.3026$, it is worthwhile to remember that

$$\log a = \frac{\ln a}{\ln 10} \approx \frac{\ln a}{2.3026} \approx 0.4343 \ln a$$

$$\ln a = \frac{\log a}{\log e} \approx \frac{\log a}{0.4343} \approx 2.3026 \log a$$

for any real number $a > 0$.

In this connection, it should be observed that solving the equation $e^x = a$ for x is equivalent to determining $\ln a$ (because $e^{\ln a} = a$). Hence $x = \ln a \approx 2.3026 \log a$, a result that we could also obtain by the more general method of Example 5.

Problems 5.7

1. Find an approximate solution for $x \in \mathbf{R}$:
   (a) $5^x = 3$ (b) $0.02^x = 3$ (c) $4^x = \tfrac{2}{3}$ (d) $2.5^x = 0.53$
2. Find an approximate solution for $x \in \mathbf{R}$:
   (a) $x^5 = 12$ (b) $x^{2/3} = 0.56$ (c) $x^{2/3} = 4.63$ (d) $x^{10} = 640$
3. Find an approximate solution for $x \in \mathbf{R}$:
   (a) $3^{x+1} = 2$ (b) $5^{2x+1} = 4$ (c) $4^{1-x} = 7^{2x+3}$ (d) $5^{x^2} = 65.3$
4. Find an approximation for $\ln x$ if (a) $x = 3.45$; (b) $x = 0.43$; (c) $x = 13.4$; (d) $x = 0.00156$.
5. Approximate each x of Problem 4 in the form e^a, for some $a \in \mathbf{R}$.
6. Use $\log e = 0.4343$ to approximate each of the following in the form 10^b, for some $b \in \mathbf{R}$: (a) $e^{2.5}$; (b) $e^{0.45}$; (c) $e^{-2.56}$; (d) $e^{-1.52}$.
7. Take rational approximations for e and π and use logarithms to determine which is the larger, e^π or π^e.
8. If e^{50} is rounded off to the nearest integer, how many digits would the number have?
9. Find an approximate solution for $x \in \mathbf{R}$ of the equation $\log (2x - 5) - \log (3x - 2) = \tfrac{4}{5}$.
10. Solve the following equation for $x \in \mathbf{R}$: $\log (x^2 - 4) - \log (x + 2) = 4$.

11. Solve the following equation for real x and check:

$$\log \left| \frac{3x + 1}{2x + 3} \right| = \log 2$$

12. Show that the following equation has no real solution:

$$\log (5x - 1) - \log (2x - 1) = \log 2$$

13. Approximate two real solutions for x of $27^{x^2} = 382$.

14. Solve the following equations for $x \in \mathbf{R}$:
   (a) $\log \sqrt{x(2x - 1)} = 1$; (b) $\log (x^2 - 10x) = 2$.

15. Solve for $x \in \mathbf{R}$: (a) $\log [\log (\log x)] = 0$; (b) $\ln [\ln (\ln x)] = 0$;
   (c) $\ln [\ln (\ln x)] = 1$.

16. Solve the following equations for $x \in \mathbf{R}$: (a) $|\log x| = \log |x|$; (b) $\log |\log x| = 1$.

17. Determine an approximate real solution for x of $\ln (\log x) = \log (\ln x)$.

18. Solve the following inequalities for integral $x < 5$:
   (a) $0.53^x < 4.57$; (b) $3.74^x > 157$; (c) $x^{-2.54} < 12$.

19. Determine upper and lower bounds for real x if $2 \le \log x^2 \le 4$.

20. Solve the following inequalities for $x \in \mathbf{R}$:
   (a) $2^{x-1} < 32^{2x}$; (b) $0 < \log (2x - 1) < \log (x + 5)$.

21. Convert the formula $p = p_0 e^{-0.193h}$ into an equivalent exponential form involving 10 instead of e.

22. Find the symbolic solution for n in each of the following equations:

   (a) $S = \dfrac{a(1 - r^n)}{1 - r}$;   (b) $y^{2/n} = x^n, n > 0$.

23. Approximate by the next largest integer the real solution for n in the following equation: $(1.06^n - 1)/0.06 = 18$.

24. Approximate by the next largest integer the real solution for n in the following equation: $(1.08^n - 1)/0.08 = 12$.

25. Does there exist a real number a such that $(\log a)^{-1} = \log a^{-1}$?

26. The area A of a triangle with sides a, b, c is given by the formula

$$A = \sqrt{s(s - a)(s - b)(s - c)},$$

   where $s = (a + b + c)/2$. Determine the approximate area of a triangle in which $a = 36.5$, $b = 27.3$, and $c = 50.2$.

27. If you have just inherited the accumulated amount of $100 that has been invested for 150 years at 4 per cent interest compounded annually, use logarithms to find the approximate value of your inheritance.

28. Without using interest tables, determine how long $100 would need to be invested at 5 per cent interest compounded annually to accumulate to an amount in excess of $10,000.

29. If an inductance of L henrys and a resistance of R ohms are in series with an electromotive force of E volts, the current I (in amperes) that is flowing in the circuit in t seconds is given by the formula $I = (E/R)(1 - e^{-\frac{R}{L}t})$. Determine the approximate current flow in $\frac{1}{100}$ of a second if $L = 0.1$, $R = 5$, and $E = 100$.

30. Use the formula given in Problem 29 to obtain, in terms of the circuit characteristics, an expression for t that involves (a) common logarithms; (b) natural logarithms. Which of the two results has the simpler form?

Historical Interlude (A Prelude to Trigonometry)

The primitive origins of trigonometry have been discovered in some of the early civilizations of the Middle and Far East, as well as in those of Eastern Europe. It is only natural that the early developments of mathematics in these regions were motivated by very practical considerations related in large measure to pursuits of agriculture and engineering. These civilizations thrived along the great rivers of Africa and Asia, and so we find much of the early history of mathematics associated with the Nile in Africa, the Tigris and Euphrates in the western part of Asia, and the Indus, Ganges, and Yangtze farther to the east. A great many of the primitive engineering projects were connected with problems of drainage, irrigation, and flood control; for these and related administrative and financial problems, there was need for a very considerable knowledge of technical matters—and, in particular, of mathematics. These basic needs included a usable calendar, a suitable system of weights and measures, satisfactory methods of surveying, along with concomitant matters of finance and taxation for purposes of trade with other countries.

Since before the middle of the nineteenth century, many hundreds of thousands of clay tablets have been unearthed in Mesopotamia; the inscriptions on the tablets relate to all phases of life over many periods in the history of what is loosely referred to as Babylonia. The key to the deciphering of these important messages was perfected in 1847, and much historical information has been gleaned from them of a period ranging from around 2100 B.C. to A.D. 300. However, most of our knowledge of the contents of the tablets has come since 1935, and the job of interpreting the inscriptions is still proceeding.

One of the most remarkable of the Babylonian tablets that have been analyzed to date is the one known as Plimpton 322, the name referring to its catalogue number in the collection of G. A. Plimpton at Columbia University. This particular tablet was written sometime in the period 1900–1600 B.C. and its contents were first described to the modern world in 1945. In one of the columns on the tablet is a list of numbers that today is recognized as being a partial table of squares of the values of one of the trigonometric functions—the *secant*—for angles within a certain range.

The mathematics of ancient Egypt did not reach the heights attained by the Babylonians, owing in part to the relative isolation of Egypt from the major trade routes of the day; but some elementary mathematics did nonetheless make its appearance. Our primary sources of information on early Egyptian mathematics are the Rhind (or Ahmes) and Moscow papyri, dating from approximately 1650 B.C. The Rhind papyrus now rests in the British Museum, and the Moscow papyrus is in a museum in Moscow, both of them containing lists of problems of a practical nature. In so far as trigonometry is concerned, the Rhind papyrus contains several problems that appear to involve a trigonometric function—the *cotangent*—of the dihedral angles at the base of a square pyramid.

After the civilizations of Babylon and Egypt waned during the second millenium B.C., other peoples such as the Greeks, Hebrews, and Assyrians came to the forefront. Their philosophy was such that the rather static outlook of the Orient was changed into one of rationalization in which the question *Why* as well as *How* was being asked more often. It was in this period that the basic ideas of deductive geometry came into being, for which much credit is given to Thales of Miletus—who lived during the first half of the sixth century B.C. Geometry was developed further by Pythagoras and others, and culminated with the production around 300 B.C. by Euclid of his *Elements*. This monumental work contains many references to trigonometric relations in the guise of geometry, including what we now refer to as the *law of cosines*. The most important development of Greek trigonometry, however, came later at the hands of Greek astronomers. In particular, we mention Hipparchus, who flourished around 140 B.C. and who has been credited with having made a *table of chords* for a circle in terms of the subtended central angles. The interesting thing about this, from the point of view of trigonometry, is that such a table is equivalent to one involving the trigonometric function that we now know as the *sine*. In view of their special interest in astronomy, it is only natural that the Greeks of this period did considerable work on certain aspects of spherical trigonometry. The definitive Greek work on astronomy was written by Claudius Ptolemy about A.D. 150 and was titled—in translation—*Mathematical Collections*. The Arabic translators considered it to be so elegant that it became known as the *Almagest* or "The Greatest."

The Hindu civilization also played a role in the development of mathematics, but there are few authentic records to detail their work. This is due in part to the series of invasions—including that by Alexander the Great—to which India was subjected. The Hindus—like the Greeks—regarded trigonometry as a tool for astronomy and used our familiar measures of angles (degrees, minutes, and seconds) in their investigations. They too developed a table of chords—which we noted before is equivalent to a table of values of the sine function. Although much of Hindu mathematics had merit, it was of uneven quality and was often phrased in obscure poetic language. It was thus much different from Greek mathematics, which was geometric and of a logically rigorous and demonstrative nature. One must presume, of course, that Greek mathematics of poor quality also appeared from time to time; but the Greeks had the fortunate instinct to preserve the good and get rid of the bad!

The Arabian empire became closely associated with India in the years following the flight of Mohammed from Mecca to Medina in A.D. 622. Within the span of one century, the influence of the Arabs and Moslem rule was felt all the way from the Arabian peninsula to Spain. The presence of Arabs in Europe persisted until the year A.D. 1400, when the last of Moorish rule in that continent came to an end. The importance of the Arabs, in so far as mathematics is concerned, is that they were responsible for the preservation of much of the learning of the Greeks and Hindus during this Moslem period of rise and fall. Many scientific works were translated into Arabic, and had it not been for these translations, a great deal of Greek and Hindu science would have been lost during these years—known as the Dark Ages. A celebrated Moslem mathematician of the tenth century is credited with the introduction of the *tangent* function into trigonometry, but the Arabs—like the Hindus—were primarily astronomers and their interest in trigonometry was corollary to this. However, they were probably the first to use all six of the functions usually associated with trigonometry.

Not long after the end of the Dark Ages, trigonometry made its reappearance in Western Europe along with various other practical aspects of mathematics. In this period, we recall especially Leonardo Fibonacci, who lived in the latter part of the twelfth century and who was responsible for the introduction of the Hindu-Arabic numerals into Europe. However, it was in the fifteenth century that the Renaissance really began—with the fall of Constantinople to the Turks in 1453. The ablest mathematician of that century was Johann Müller, who completed an earlier beginning of a translation of the *Almagest* and who gave the first European exposition of plane and spherical trigonometry that was not slanted toward astronomy. In the sixteenth century, we find the name of Viète, a man who made a number of important contributions to trigonometry—as well as to algebra and geometry. We have observed before that astronomers have been responsible for many contributions to mathematics, and Nicolas Copernicus (1473–1543) was one of those who provided a great stimulus to mathematicians of this Renaissance period. One of the leading Teutonic mathematical astronomers of the sixteenth century was Georg Joachim Rhaeticus (1514–1576), a disciple of Copernicus, who compiled still-useful tables of values of the trigonometric functions. One of the very interesting things about this man in our present context is that he was the first to define these functions in terms of the sides of a right triangle. There were many other people who made notable contributions to the subject of trigonometry in the sixteenth to eighteenth centuries; among them we mention John Napier (1550–1617), Abraham DeMoivre (1667–1754), and Joseph Fourier (1768–1830). It was in his book entitled *The Analytic Theory of Heat* that Fourier first introduced the germ of the present concept of a function. From that time on, the development of trigonometry has been increasingly independent of geometric figures. With the appearance of the works of Isaac Newton (1642–1727) and Leonhard Euler (1707–1783), the subject was noticeably less involved with arcs and angles and was well on its way to becoming a part of what we now refer to as analysis. With the invention of the calculus, analysis came to the forefront and traditional trigonometry was absorbed—at least theoretically—within the framework of functions. The birth of modern trigonometry—although lacking much of its present sophistication—had taken place.

There are two reasons for the insertion of this historical prelude before beginning the study of trigonometry. The first is the obvious one that any sort of historical survey has considerable innate interest to most people. The other—and possibly more important—reason is that we are using this historical background for the prime purpose of motivating our presentation of analytic trigonometry before that of the basic trigonometry of triangles. One observation to be made from the historical survey is that *the definitive viewpoint of the trigonometric functions has varied from time to time according to the main use to which they were put.* When trigonometry was a tool of astronomy, the emphasis was on chords and arcs of circles along with their subtended angles, and the pertinent definitions reflected this use. When trigonometry became more useful for surveying and navigation, we find triangles in the key position, and as only natural, the definitions were phrased in terms of them. However, in recent years the solution of triangles has become of less importance in mathematics, but it is nonetheless true that the definitions initiated by Rhaeticus in the sixteenth century have prevailed to some extent in elementary developments of trigonometry even to this day. There is no doubt about a certain pedagogical advantage in the simplicity of the appeal to the geometry of a right triangle, but this approach to trigonometry is becoming more of an anachronism in view of the role presently being played by the trigonometric functions. The modern trend in mathematics—as in other things—is toward unification; it is in harmony with this philosophy and in accord with the lesson learned from history to define the trigonometric functions—usually called *circular* in this setting—on sets of real numbers rather than on sets of angles. When this is done, the circular functions take their place alongside the polynomial, exponential and logarithmic functions to comprise the foundations of modern analysis. This will be our point of view in Chapter 6. However, in Chapter 7, it will be shown how the elementary trigonometry of triangles can be derived as a special case of analytic trigonometry; in that chapter, we shall include most of traditional trigonometry in an abbreviated form.

6

Circular Functions and Analytic Trigonometry

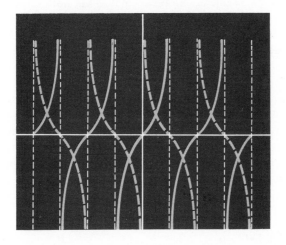

6.1 The Circular Functions

Whatever the exact definition that we adopt for a function, its essential feature is that it determines and is determined by a mapping of the elements of one set onto those of another. In the proper language, a function maps one nonempty set—its domain—onto another (or the same) set—its range. For example, the function f defined on $\mathbf{R}$ by $f(x) = x^2$ maps every real number onto its square; and the function g defined on the set of all positive real numbers by $g(x) = \ln x$ maps every such number onto its natural logarithm. Although pure mathematics deals, for the most part, with complete abstractions, much of elementary mathematics is concerned with the properties of certain subsets of real numbers and their mappings. It is our objective in this section to define the so-called *circular* functions—the modern formulation of the traditional functions of trigonometry—in such a way that real numbers comprise their domains. Before we are able to do this, however, it is necessary to make clear what is meant by a *length of arc* on a circle. Even though the notion may be quite intelligible from an intuitive point of view, there is nonetheless an underlying complication that has not arisen before in any of our discussions. Whenever a question of *length* has arisen in the past, we have understood the existence of some linear unit with which we made the measurement. However, there are serious difficulties *even with the concept* of using a linear unit to measure the length of a nonlinear arc on a curve, because a line segment—however small—will not fit any part of such an arc with exactness. The general problem of length of arc is a difficult one and one for which calculus is needed; but the special case of a circular arc—the one of interest to us here—can be handled with the help of the property of completeness of the real number system (see §3.4). We now proceed to a disposition of this problem.

In Figure 31, we have depicted the arc $\overparen{BC}$ on a circle of radius r, and our problem is to assign to $\overparen{BC}$ a real number as its length. Points $P_1, P_2, \ldots, P_n$ are chosen at random in this order on the arc between B and C, the figure showing the case when $n = 3$. These points are then joined by line segments to form an "inscripture" S of $\overparen{BC}$. Any inscripture S, being made up of line segments, has a length $|S|$, where

$$|S| = |BP_1| + |P_1P_2| + \cdots + |P_nC|$$

For the case of Figure 31,

$$|S| = |BP_1| + |P_1P_2| + |P_2P_3| + |P_3C|$$

If tangent lines are drawn to the circle at points B and C, with D as their point of intersection, it follows from elementary geometry that

$$|S| < |BD| + |CD|$$

All that is needed for this verification (which we omit) is a consideration of parallelograms, whose opposite sides are known to be equal. The general case may be deduced from the special case of three inscripture points as shown in the figure. Because $|S| < |BD| + |CD|$ is true for *any* inscripture of $\overparen{BC}$, we see that $|BD| + |CD|$ is an upper bound of the set of lengths of all these inscriptures. In case it exceeds a quarter of the circumference of the circle, the arc to be measured can be subdivided into four or fewer arcs of the type in the figure, and the above argument is applicable to each of these. Thus, for an arbitrary arc of a circle, *the set of lengths of its inscriptures is bounded above*, and the existence of a least upper bound to this set is guaranteed by the completeness property of **R**. It is then appropriate to make the following definition.

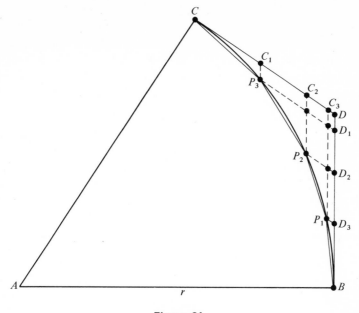

Figure 31

Definition.   *The* length *of an arc of a circle is the least upper bound of the set of lengths of all inscriptures of the arc.*

The preceding discussion gives us a theoretical solution to the length-of-arc problem for a circle, but the practical problem of determining the actual length of a circular arc remains. The method of inscriptures can be used in practice to approximate the length of such an arc to any desired degree of accuracy, and this method was in essence the one used by Archimedes and others of his time to discover a formula for the circumference of a circle. However, there are other more advanced techniques for doing this, and we shall merely state the well-known formula: *If c is the length of the circumference of a circle with diameter d, then $c = \pi d$, where $\pi = 3.14159 \cdots$ is an irrational number.* It may be worthwhile to emphasize at this point that the reason for including the discussion of inscriptures was simply to *give meaning* to the *idea of length* of a circular arc but not to use any results of the discussion for computational purposes. In particular, we are to be interested in a circle with unit radius—a so-called *unit circle*—and the length of the circumference of this circle is 2π. Because the number π appears in the length of the circumference, it is often convenient to express the lengths of other circular arcs also in terms of π. For example, the lengths of a semicircle, quarter-circle, and twelfth-circle may be expressed as π, $\frac{1}{2}\pi$, and $\frac{1}{6}\pi$, respectively.

Now that the notion of arc length on a circle has meaning, we are able to proceed to the definition of the circular functions without much difficulty. In Figure 32, we have shown a unit circle with center at the origin of a Cartesian

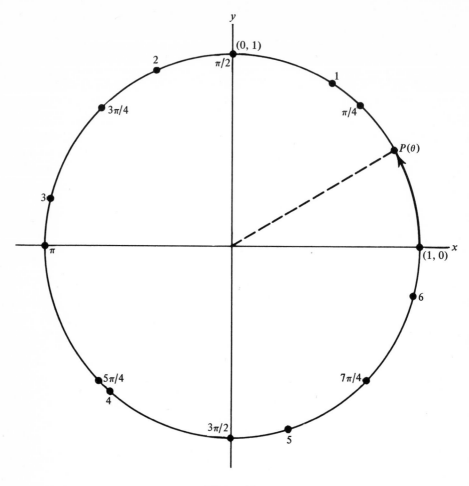

Figure 32

coordinate system for the plane. This system divides the plane into four *quadrants* and, in the sequel, it will sometimes be convenient to refer to them in counterclockwise order from the positive *x*-axis as I, II, III, IV. Let us now imagine an endless flexible tape wrapped around the circle in a *counterclockwise* direction, with the zero of the tape at the "unit" point (1, 0). At the same time, we may imagine a similar tape wrapped around the circle in a *clockwise* direction, the zeros of the two tapes in coincidence. If we consider the nonzero numbers on the first tape to be positive and those on the second to be negative, the two tapes together may be considered to comprise a flexible real "line" on which every real number is located. Moreover, in view of our preceding discussion, these numbers may be seen to measure the lengths of circular arcs (called *standard*, for convenience) starting from (1, 0), the measures being positive or negative according as the arcs are considered to have counterclockwise or clockwise generation. Because each real number is then associated (as a measure of directed arc length) with a unique point that terminates a standard circular arc, the following definition is quite natural.

Definition. *The point that terminates a standard circular arc of (directed) length θ on the unit circle is called the* trigonometric point $P(\theta)$.

An immediate observation is that, although each real number θ determines a unique point $P(\theta)$ on the unit circle, the same trigonometric point may be associated with many different real numbers. In other words, the mapping $\theta \rightarrow P(\theta)$ is a well-defined function (sometimes called the "winding" function on **R**), but the correspondence $\theta \leftrightarrow P(\theta)$ is not one-to-one. The reason for this is, of course, that a circular arc of given length may include more than one complete circumference of the circle, and in fact infinitely many arcs will start at $(1, 0)$ and terminate at the same point on the unit circle. For example, $(1, 0)$ is the trigonometric point associated with $0, \pm 2\pi, \pm 4\pi, \dots$; and $(0, 1)$ is the trigonometric point associated with $\frac{1}{2}\pi, \frac{5}{2}\pi, -\frac{3}{2}\pi, \dots$. In symbols, $P(0) = P(\pm 2\pi) = P(\pm 4\pi) = \cdots = (1, 0)$, and $P(\frac{1}{2}\pi) = P(\frac{5}{2}\pi) = P(-\frac{3}{2}\pi) = \cdots = (0, 1)$. We reemphasize that each real number associated with its trigonometric point by the winding function is the measure of the length of the arc that starts at $(1, 0)$ and terminates at the point. In Figure 32, we have labeled some of these trigonometric points $P(\theta)$, where $0 \leq \theta \leq 2\pi$. It is now possible to define the mappings that underlie the circular functions to which we have referred before. We shall include both the abbreviated and unabbreviated names for these mappings.

Definition. *If (x, y) is the trigonometric point $P(\theta)$ associated with the real number θ, then*

$$\text{sine } \theta = \sin \theta = y \qquad\qquad \text{cosecant } \theta = \csc \theta = \frac{1}{y} \ (y \neq 0)$$

$$\text{cosine } \theta = \cos \theta = x \qquad\qquad \text{secant } \theta = \sec \theta = \frac{1}{x} \ (x \neq 0)$$

$$\text{tangent } \theta = \tan \theta = \frac{y}{x} \ (x \neq 0) \qquad \text{cotangent } \theta = \cot \theta = \frac{x}{y} \ (y \neq 0)$$

Two of these mappings, for a typical real number θ, are illustrated in Figure 33. It is an immediate observation that these mappings are not independent of each other and that the following equalities hold whenever the denominators are nonzero:

$$\csc \theta = \frac{1}{\sin \theta} \qquad \sec \theta = \frac{1}{\cos \theta} \qquad \cot \theta = \frac{1}{\tan \theta}$$

$$\tan \theta = \frac{\sin \theta}{\cos \theta} \qquad \cot \theta = \frac{\cos \theta}{\sin \theta}$$

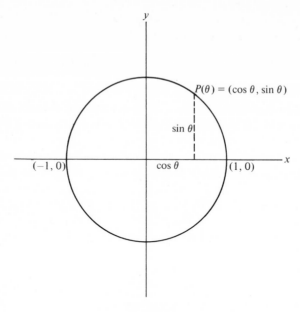

Figure 33

It is also clear from the definitions that

$$(\sin \theta)^2 + (\cos \theta)^2 = 1$$

There are many other so-called *trigonometric identities* to which we shall refer later, but the above are sufficient for our present needs. It is now merely a formalism to give the promised definitions of the circular functions.

Definition. *A function f is called a* sine *function if f(x) = sin x, for each x in its domain, with analogous definitions holding for* cosine, tangent, cosecant, secant, *and* cotangent *functions. They are collectively referred to as the* circular *functions of analytic trigonometry. If its domain is the maximal subset of real numbers for which the rule of mapping makes sense, a circular function is said to be* basic.

It should be noted that our use of the word "basic" is consistent with its usage in connection with exponential and logarithmic functions, *basic* functions being functions from which all others of similar nature (*i.e.*, exponential, logarithmic, sine, cosine, etc.) can be constructed. The domain of the basic sine and cosine functions is the set **R** of real numbers. However, the domain of the basic tangent and secant functions is the subset of all real numbers *except for odd multiples of $\frac{1}{2}\pi$*, and the domain of the basic cosecant and cotangent functions is the subset of all real numbers *except for all integral multiples of π*.

Example 1. Find the trigonometric point designated as (a) $P(\frac{3}{4}\pi)$; (b) $P(-\frac{9}{4}\pi)$.

SOLUTION. We recall first that the circumference of the unit circle is 2π units in length; our results then follow by simple algebra.

(a) The point $P(\frac{3}{4}\pi)$ will terminate a regular arc in the positive direction and three-fourths of a semicircle in length. Hence, the desired point must be (x, y) where $x = -y$, $x^2 + y^2 = 1$, and $x < 0$. It follows that $x = -1/\sqrt{2}$, $y = 1/\sqrt{2}$ and so $P(\frac{3}{4}\pi) = (-1/\sqrt{2}, 1/\sqrt{2})$.

(b) In this case, the desired point terminates a standard arc that is negatively oriented and includes one complete circumference plus an additional quarter of a semicircle. Thus $P(-\frac{9}{4}\pi) = (x, y)$, where $x = -y$, $x^2 + y^2 = 1$, and $y < 0$; and we find easily that $x = 1/\sqrt{2}$ and $y = -1/\sqrt{2}$. Hence $P(-\frac{9}{4}\pi) = (1/\sqrt{2}, -1/\sqrt{2})$, as desired.

Both parts of this example are illustrated in Figure 34.

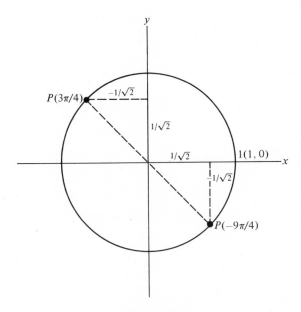

Figure 34

Example 2. Use the results found in Example 1 to determine (a) $\sin \frac{3}{4}\pi$; (b) $\cos(-\frac{9}{4}\pi)$; (c) $\tan \frac{3}{4}\pi$; (d) $\sec(-\frac{9}{4}\pi)$.

SOLUTION. Because the trigonometric points $P(\frac{3}{4}\pi)$ and $P(-\frac{9}{4}\pi)$ are now known, the desired values follow immediately from the earlier definitions: (a) $\sin \frac{3}{4}\pi = 1/\sqrt{2}$; (b) $\cos(-\frac{9}{4}\pi) = 1/\sqrt{2}$; (c) $\tan \frac{3}{4}\pi = (1/\sqrt{2})/(-1/\sqrt{2}) = -1$; (d) $\sec(-\frac{9}{4}\pi) = 1/(1/\sqrt{2}) = \sqrt{2}$.

The method used in the solution of Example 1 will be seen to be quite special, because we were able to capitalize on geometry in a way that would not be available to us in general. However, we shall leave any further discussion of the computation of circular functional values to later sections. Our central purpose here was to give the appropriate definitions.

Problems 6.1

1. Find the trigonometric point $P(\theta)$ where (a) $\theta = 2\pi$; (b) $\theta = -3\pi$; (c) $\theta = 8\pi$; (d) $\theta = -5\pi$.

2. Find the trigonometric point $P(\theta)$ where (a) $\theta = \frac{5}{2}\pi$; (b) $\theta = -\frac{3}{4}\pi$; (c) $\theta = \frac{7}{2}\pi$; (d) $\theta = -\frac{15}{2}\pi$.

3. Determine the length of the standard arc on a unit circle, which does not include a complete circumference, is generated counterclockwise, and terminates at the point (a) $(1, 0)$; (b) $(-1, 0)$; (c) $(-1/\sqrt{2}, -1/\sqrt{2})$; (d) $(1/\sqrt{2}, -1/\sqrt{2})$.

4. Determine the signed lengths of the standard arcs on a unit circle, which do not include a complete circumference, are generated clockwise, and terminate at the points listed in Problem 3.

5. Draw a unit circle with any convenient unit of length, and determine an approximation for π by finding the length of an inscripture of arc composed of three chords. Find an improved approximation by using five chords.

6. List the quadrant of the Cartesian plane in which each of the following points lies: (a) $P(30)$; (b) $P(-23)$; (c) $P(45)$; (d) $P(-50)$.

7. Find $P(\theta)$ and $P(-\theta)$ if (a) $\theta = \frac{1}{2}\pi$; (b) $\theta = \frac{5}{2}\pi$; (c) $\theta = -7\pi$; (d) $\theta = -\frac{7}{2}\pi$.

8. Find θ such that $|\theta|$ is minimal, where $P(\theta)$ is (a) $(0, -1)$; (b) $(0, 1)$; (c) $(-1/\sqrt{2}, -1/\sqrt{2})$; (d) $(1, 0)$.

9. Find θ if $2\pi \le \theta < 4\pi$ and $P(\theta)$ is (a) $(-1, 0)$; (b) $(1/\sqrt{2}, -1/\sqrt{2})$; (c) $(1, 0)$; (d) $(0, 1)$.

10. Repeat the directions given in Problem 9, but with the condition on θ replaced by $-2\pi < \theta \le 0$.

11. List five real numbers whose trigonometric points coincide with (a) $(0, 1)$; (b) $(0, -1)$.

12. Find the largest negative real number whose trigonometric point is (a) $(-1, 0)$; (b) $(0, -1)$; (c) $(-1/\sqrt{2}, -1/\sqrt{2})$.

13. If $P(\theta) = (-1, 0)$, find (a) $\sin\theta$; (b) $\tan\theta$; (c) $\sec\theta$.

14. If $P(\theta) = (\frac{1}{2}, \sqrt{3}/2)$, find (a) $\sin\theta$; (b) $\cos\theta$; (c) $\tan\theta$.

15. If $P(\theta) = (-\sqrt{3}/2, -\frac{1}{2})$, find (a) $\csc\theta$; (b) $\sec\theta$; (c) $\cot\theta$.

16. Noting that the radius of the "unit" circle in Figure 32 is 2 inches, use an ordinary ruler to determine a rough approximation to each of the following: (a) $\sin 2$; (b) $\cos 2$; (c) $\sin 3$; (d) $\cos 3$; (e) $\sin 5$; (f) $\cos 5$.

17. Use the results in Problem 16 to compute an approximation of (a) $\tan 2$; (b) $\tan 3$; (c) $\cot 5$.

18. Use Figure 32 (see Problem 16) to determine approximations for $\sin 1$, $\cos 1$, and $\tan 1$.

19. The domain of both the basic sine and cosine functions is $\mathbf{R}$. Use the set-builder symbolism to describe the domains of the other basic circular functions.

20. Find the smallest nonnegative real number θ such that (a) $\sin \theta = 0$;
(b) $\cos \theta = 1$; (c) $\sin \theta = -1$; (d) $\tan \theta = -1$; (e) $\sec \theta = 1$.

21. If $\sec \theta < 0$ and $P(\theta) = (x, \frac{1}{3})$, find x.

22. If $\sin \theta < 0$ and $P(\theta) = (-\frac{1}{5}, y)$, find y.

23. If $P(\theta) = (x, y)$, with $x < 0$ and $x = 2y$, use the geometric method of Example 1 to find $P(\theta)$. Then determine (a) $\sin \theta$; (b) $\tan \theta$; (c) $\cot \theta$.

24. If $P(\theta) = (x, y)$, with $x > 0$ and $x = y/\sqrt{2}$, use the geometric method of Example 1 to find $P(\theta)$. Then determine (a) $\cos \theta$; (b) $\csc \theta$; (c) $\sec \theta$.

25. Determine the exact value of each of the following:

(a) $\sin \frac{1}{2}\pi + 3 \cos \pi - 2 \csc \frac{3}{2}\pi + 5 \csc \frac{1}{2}\pi$ (b) $\dfrac{\sin \frac{3}{2}\pi + 2 \cos \pi - 3 \tan \frac{3}{4}\pi}{1 + 2 \sin \frac{1}{2}\pi + \cos \pi}$

26. Determine $\sin \theta$ if (a) $\tan \theta = \frac{2}{3}$ and $\pi < \theta < \frac{3}{2}\pi$; (b) $\cos \theta = \frac{1}{2}$ and $\frac{3}{2}\pi < \theta < 2\pi$; (c) $\cos \theta = \frac{3}{4}$ and $\tan \theta < 0$.

27. If W is the winding function defined so that $W(\theta) = P(\theta)$, for any $\theta \in \mathbf{R}$, show that (a) $W(\theta)$ and $W(-\theta)$ are symmetrically placed with respect to the x-axis; (b) $W(\theta)$ and $W(\pi - \theta)$ are symmetrically placed with respect to the y-axis; (c) $W(\theta)$ and $W(\pi + \theta)$ are symmetrically placed with respect to the origin.

28. With W as in Problem 27, explain why the "equality" $W(x + y) = W(x) + W(y)$ is nonsense!

29. If a is the length of a side of a regular polygon inscribed in a circle of radius r, show that each side of a regular inscribed polygon with twice as many sides has length $[2r^2 - r(4r^2 - a^2)^{1/2}]^{1/2}$. Explain how this formula can be used to compute an approximation of π.

30. Use the method of Example 1 to determine the values at $\frac{1}{3}\pi$ and $\frac{1}{6}\pi$ of the six basic circular functions.

6.2 Circular Functions of Special Numbers

The definitions of the basic circular functions that we have given are quite general in the sense that the domains of these functions are not bounded. However, although the domain of the basic sine and basic cosine functions is $\mathbf{R}$, the domain of each of the other basic circular functions is a proper subset of $\mathbf{R}$. This implies that, *even under the assumption of a maximal domain*, it is not true that $f(\theta)$ is a real number for every circular function f and every real number θ. It is clear that this happens because the abscissa or ordinate of a point on the unit circle may be 0, and a fraction with denominator 0 is meaningless. The real numbers whose associated trigonometric points have this characteristic may be said to be *quadrantal* because the points lie on the coordinate axes— which divide the Cartesian plane into four quadrants. Although there are infinitely many quadrantal numbers, there are only four trigonometric points associated with them; they are shown labeled in Figure 35. It should be observed that each of these points has either its abscissa or ordinate equal to 0. A direct application of the various definitions yields the table below, from which we can deduce the values of $\sin \theta$, $\cos \theta$, $\tan \theta$, $\csc \theta$, $\sec \theta$, and $\cot \theta$ for any quad-

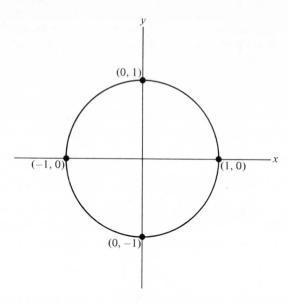

Figure 35

rantal number θ within the scope of the definitions. An entry $\cdot\,\cdot$ in the table indicates that the definition does not include this particular number θ.

θ	0	$\frac{1}{2}\pi$	π	$\frac{3}{2}\pi$
$\sin\theta$	0	1	0	-1
$\cos\theta$	1	0	-1	0
$\tan\theta$	0	$\cdot\,\cdot$	0	$\cdot\,\cdot$
$\csc\theta$	$\cdot\,\cdot$	1	$\cdot\,\cdot$	-1
$\sec\theta$	1	$\cdot\,\cdot$	-1	$\cdot\,\cdot$
$\cot\theta$	$\cdot\,\cdot$	0	$\cdot\,\cdot$	0

Example 1. Use the table to find (a) $\sin 7\pi$; (b) $\cos\frac{5}{2}\pi$; (c) $\csc\left(-\frac{7}{2}\pi\right)$.

SOLUTION. We observe immediately that $P(7\pi) = P(\pi)$, $P(\frac{5}{2}\pi) = P(\frac{1}{2}\pi)$, and $P(-\frac{7}{2}\pi) = P(\frac{1}{2}\pi)$, and we use the table to get the desired results. (a) $\sin 7\pi = \sin \pi = 0$; (b) $\cos\frac{5}{2}\pi = \cos\frac{1}{2}\pi = 0$; (c) $\csc\left(-\frac{7}{2}\pi\right) = \csc\frac{1}{2}\pi = 1$.

Example 2. If $\theta = -\frac{13}{2}\pi$, determine $\sin \theta$, $\cos \theta$, $\tan \theta$, $\csc \theta$, $\sec \theta$, and $\cot \theta$ (if it exists).

SOLUTION.   Because $-\frac{13}{2}\pi$ is the directed length of a standard circular arc that consists of three complete circumferences of the unit circle and one quarter of a third with negative orientation, we see that $P(-\frac{13}{2}\pi) = P(\frac{3}{2}\pi)$. Hence, a glance at the table shows us that $\sin (-\frac{13}{2}\pi) = -1$, $\cos (-\frac{13}{2}\pi) = 0$, $\csc (-\frac{13}{2}\pi) = -1$, $\cot (-\frac{13}{2}\pi) = 0$, whereas $\tan (-\frac{13}{2}\pi)$ and $\sec (-\frac{3}{2}\pi)$ are both undefined.

In addition to the integral multiples of $\frac{1}{2}\pi$ that we have just considered as quadrantal numbers, there are certain other numbers that have played important roles in the development of analytic trigonometry and that are convenient to use in illustrative examples. We are referring to the numbers $\frac{1}{6}\pi$, $\frac{1}{4}\pi$, $\frac{1}{3}\pi$, and to all other numbers whose trigonometric points coincide with $P(\frac{1}{6}\pi)$, $P(\frac{1}{4}\pi)$, or $P(\frac{1}{3}\pi)$. A bit of elementary Euclidean geometry—such as was used in Example 1 of §6.1—will determine the coordinates of each of these points, and from the coordinates we apply the definitions of $\sin \theta$, $\cos \theta$, $\tan \theta$, $\csc \theta$, $\sec \theta$, and $\cot \theta$ to obtain the desired values. In Figure 36, we have shown the location of $P(\frac{1}{4}\pi)$, $P(\frac{1}{3}\pi)$, and $P(\frac{1}{6}\pi)$, and our brief geometric arguments below assume the well-known fact that *equal arcs subtend equal chords and equal central angles.* The point U is the unit point in each of the cases.

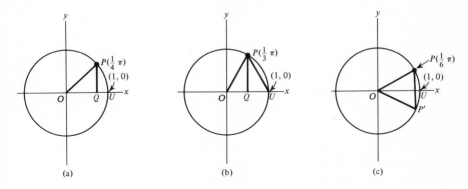

(a)   (b)   (c)

Figure 36

(a) In Figure 36a we have located $P(\frac{1}{4}\pi)$. We drop the perpendicular PQ to the x-axis, and note that POQ is an isosceles right triangle: the arc $\widehat{UP}$ is a quarter of a semicircle, so that $\angle POQ$ is 45°, and the right angle at Q requires that $\angle OPQ$ also be 45°. If we let $P(\frac{1}{4}\pi) = (x, y)$ with $y = x$, the equation $x^2 + y^2 = 1$ now leads to $2x^2 = 2y^2 = 1$, and so—noting that x and y are positive—we find that $x = y = 1/\sqrt{2}$. Hence $P(\frac{1}{4}\pi) = (1/\sqrt{2}, 1/\sqrt{2})$, so that $\sin \frac{1}{4}\pi = 1/\sqrt{2}$, $\cos \frac{1}{4}\pi = 1/\sqrt{2}$, $\tan \frac{1}{4}\pi = 1$, $\csc \frac{1}{4}\pi = \sqrt{2}$, $\sec \frac{1}{4}\pi = \sqrt{2}$, $\cot \frac{1}{4}\pi = 1$.

(b) Figure 36*b* shows the location of $P(\frac{1}{3}\pi)$. Inasmuch as arc $\overset{\frown}{UP}$ this time is one sixth of the circumference of the circle, $\angle UOP$ must be 60°; and so, noting that OP and OU are both radii, we see that the triangle OPU is equilateral. If we now drop the perpendicular PQ to the *x*-axis, $|OQ| = \frac{1}{2}$ and $|PQ| = \sqrt{3}/2$, whence $P(\frac{1}{3}\pi) = (\frac{1}{2}, \sqrt{3}/2)$. We now find immediately that $\sin\frac{1}{3}\pi = \sqrt{3}/2$, $\cos\frac{1}{3}\pi = \frac{1}{2}$, $\tan\frac{1}{3}\pi = \sqrt{3}$, $\csc\frac{1}{3}\pi = 2/\sqrt{3}$, $\sec\frac{1}{3}\pi = 2$, and $\cot\frac{1}{3}\pi = 1/\sqrt{3}$.

(c) The geometry of the situation for $P(\frac{1}{6}\pi)$ is much like that for $P(\frac{1}{3}\pi)$ and is illustrated in Figure 36*c*. If the point P' is taken on the circle so that $\overset{\frown}{UP}$ and $\overset{\frown}{UP'}$ are arcs of equal length, the triangle POP' is easily seen to be equilateral. A few geometrical considerations quite similar to those in (b) show us that $P(\frac{1}{6}\pi) = (\sqrt{3}/2, \frac{1}{2})$, and from this we deduce the following: $\sin\frac{1}{6}\pi = \frac{1}{2}$, $\cos\frac{1}{6}\pi = \sqrt{3}/2$, $\tan\frac{1}{6}\pi = 1/\sqrt{3}$, $\csc\frac{1}{6}\pi = 2$, $\sec\frac{1}{6}\pi = 2/\sqrt{3}$ and $\cot\frac{1}{6}\pi = \sqrt{3}$.

The results, which we have just obtained, have been collected into the following table for reference purposes:

θ	$\frac{1}{6}\pi$	$\frac{1}{4}\pi$	$\frac{1}{3}\pi$	θ	$\frac{1}{6}\pi$	$\frac{1}{4}\pi$	$\frac{1}{3}\pi$
$\sin\theta$	$\dfrac{1}{2}$	$\dfrac{1}{\sqrt{2}}$	$\dfrac{\sqrt{3}}{2}$	$\csc\theta$	2	$\sqrt{2}$	$\dfrac{2}{\sqrt{3}}$
$\cos\theta$	$\dfrac{\sqrt{3}}{2}$	$\dfrac{1}{\sqrt{2}}$	$\dfrac{1}{2}$	$\sec\theta$	$\dfrac{2}{\sqrt{3}}$	$\sqrt{2}$	2
$\tan\theta$	$\dfrac{1}{\sqrt{3}}$	1	$\sqrt{3}$	$\cot\theta$	$\sqrt{3}$	1	$\dfrac{1}{\sqrt{3}}$

The table refers explicitly to the numbers $\frac{1}{6}\pi$, $\frac{1}{4}\pi$, and $\frac{1}{3}\pi$, but it is easy to see that many more are implicitly included. All that is necessary to take care of the implied angles is to make the following geometrical observation:

Any two points, symmetrically placed with respect to either the x-axis, y-axis, or origin, have the same coordinates except for algebraic signs. Moreover, the algebraic signs can be determined by inspection.

A comparison of the coordinates of four such symmetrically placed points is shown in Figure 37*a*. It follows that, if θ is any real number such that $P(\theta)$ is placed symmetrical to $P(\frac{1}{6}\pi)$, $P(\frac{1}{4}\pi)$, or $P(\frac{1}{3}\pi)$, with respect to either axis or the origin, the values $\sin\theta$, $\cos\theta$, $\tan\theta$, $\csc\theta$, $\sec\theta$, and $\cot\theta$ may be found from the above table and the location of $P(\theta)$ on the unit circle.

Example 3. Determine (a) $\cos\frac{5}{6}\pi$; (b) $\tan(-\frac{5}{4}\pi)$.

SOLUTION. Both trigonometric points $P(\frac{5}{6}\pi)$ and $P(-\frac{5}{4}\pi)$ are shown in Figure 37*b*, from which it is clear that $P(\frac{5}{6}\pi)$, $P(\frac{1}{6}\pi)$ and $P(-\frac{5}{4}\pi)$, $P(\frac{1}{4}\pi)$ are pairs of points that are symmetrically placed with respect to the *y*-axis.

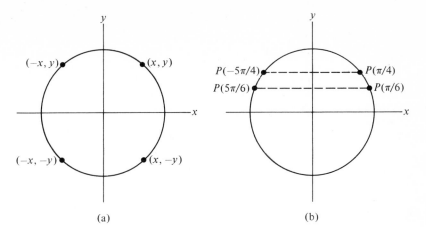

Figure 37

Because $\cos \frac{1}{6}\pi = \sqrt{3}/2$, a glance at the figure shows that $\cos \frac{5}{6}\pi = -\sqrt{3}/2$; and because $\tan \frac{1}{4}\pi = 1$, we conclude similarly that $\tan (-\frac{5}{4}\pi) = -1$.

Although only special numbers have been included in the actual discussion of this section, the geometric principle of symmetry enunciated and used above is applicable in general. Hence, a complete table of values of the circular functions *for all numbers* θ may be abbreviated *without any essential loss* to one for which $0 \le \theta \le \frac{1}{2}\pi$. Much more about this will be said in subsequent sections.

Problems 6.2

Find the indicated numbers in Problems 1–3.

1. (a) $\sin \frac{5}{2}\pi$; (b) $\cos (-6\pi)$; (c) $\tan 8\pi$; (d) $\sec 6\pi$; (e) $\cot (-\frac{5}{2}\pi)$;
   (f) $\csc (-\frac{7}{2}\pi)$; (g) $\sin \frac{4}{3}\pi$; (h) $\sec (-\frac{13}{6}\pi)$; (i) $\cos (-\frac{4}{3}\pi)$.
2. (a) $\sin \frac{3}{4}\pi$; (b) $\cos (-\frac{3}{4}\pi)$; (c) $\tan \frac{5}{4}\pi$; (d) $\csc (-\frac{7}{4}\pi)$; (e) $\tan \frac{5}{6}\pi$;
   (f) $\cos (-\frac{5}{6}\pi)$; (g) $\tan \frac{11}{6}\pi$; (h) $\cot \frac{7}{3}\pi$; (i) $\csc (-\frac{13}{3}\pi)$.
3. (a) $\sin \frac{28}{3}\pi$; (b) $\csc (-\frac{28}{3}\pi)$; (c) $\tan \frac{19}{4}\pi$; (d) $\cot (-\frac{19}{4}\pi)$; (e) $\sin 27\pi$;
   (f) $\sin (-27\pi)$; (g) $\sin \frac{15}{2}\pi$; (h) $\sin (-\frac{15}{2}\pi)$; (i) $\tan \frac{99}{4}\pi$.

4. List the other points on the unit circle that are symmetric to $(\frac{1}{3}, 2\sqrt{2}/3)$ relative to either axis or to the origin.
5. If $P(\theta) = (-\frac{1}{3}, 2\sqrt{2}/3)$, find $P(\theta_1)$ with $\theta_1 \in [0, \frac{1}{2}\pi]$ and such that $\cos \theta_1 = |\cos \theta|$.
6. If $P(\theta) = (-\frac{1}{3}, -2\sqrt{2}/3)$, find $P(\theta_1)$ with $\theta_1 \in [0, \frac{1}{2}\pi]$ and such that $\sin \theta_1 = |\sin \theta|$.
7. List the other points on the unit circle that are symmetric to $(\frac{1}{4}, -\sqrt{15}/4)$ relative to either axis or the origin.

8. If $P(\theta) = (\frac{1}{4}, -\sqrt{15}/4)$, use the result in Problem 7 to find $P(\theta_1)$ with $\theta_1 \in [0, \frac{1}{2}\pi]$ and such that $\sin \theta_1 = |\sin \theta|$, $\cos \theta_1 = \cos \theta$, and $\tan \theta_1 = |\tan \theta|$.

9. Find $\theta \in [\frac{1}{2}\pi, \frac{3}{2}\pi]$ such that (a) $\sin \theta = \sqrt{3}/2$; (b) $\sin \theta = -\sqrt{3}/2$; (c) $\tan \theta = -\sqrt{3}$.

10. Find $\theta \in [\frac{5}{2}\pi, \frac{7}{2}\pi]$ subject to the conditions in Problem 9.

11. Find $\theta \in [\pi, \frac{3}{2}\pi]$ such that (a) $\tan \theta = 1$; (b) $\sec \theta = -2$; (c) $\cot \theta = 1/\sqrt{3}$.

12. Find $\theta \in [3\pi, \frac{7}{2}\pi]$ subject to the conditions in Problem 11.

13. Find $\theta \in [-\frac{1}{2}\pi, \frac{1}{2}\pi]$ such that (a) $\sin \theta = -\frac{1}{2}$; (b) $\cos \theta = 1/\sqrt{2}$; (c) $\cot \theta = -1$; (d) $\csc \theta = -2/\sqrt{3}$; (e) $\tan \theta = \sqrt{3}$.

14. Find $\theta \in [-\frac{1}{2}\pi, \frac{1}{2}\pi]$ such that (a) $\sin \theta = \cos \theta$; (b) $\tan \theta = \cot \theta$; (c) $\cos \theta = -\sin \theta$.

15. If it is known that $\sin \theta_1 = 0.5736$ for some $\theta_1 \in [0, \frac{1}{2}\pi]$, find $\sin \theta$ for three other identified numbers $\theta \in [0, 2\pi]$ such that $|\sin \theta| = \sin \theta_1$.

16. If it is known that $\tan \theta_1 = 0.5317$, for some $\theta_1 \in [0, \frac{1}{2}\pi]$, find $\tan \theta$ for three other identified numbers $\theta \in [0, 2\pi]$, such that $|\tan \theta| = \tan \theta_1$.

17. Explain why $-1 \leq \sin \theta \leq 1$ and $-1 \leq \cos \theta \leq 1$ are true inequalities for any $\theta \in \mathbf{R}$. Is it possible to find real numbers a, b such that $a \leq \tan \theta \leq b$ for all $\theta \in \mathbf{R}$?

18. Explain why $|\csc \theta| \geq 1$ and $|\sec \theta| \geq 1$ for any $\theta \in \mathbf{R}$.

19. In what subinterval(s) of $[0, 2\pi]$ is it true for all θ that (a) $\sin \theta > 0$; (b) $\cos \theta > 0$; (c) $\tan \theta > 0$?

20. Apply the directions in Problem 19 for the interval $[0, 4\pi]$.

21. Explain why there is a unique $\theta \in [0, \pi]$ such that $\cos \theta > 0$, but not such that $\sin \theta > 0$.

22. For each of $\theta = \frac{1}{6}\pi$, $\theta = \frac{1}{4}\pi$, $\theta = \frac{1}{3}\pi$, find $(\sin \theta)^2$ and $(\cos \theta)^2$ and check these values in the related identity given in §6.1.

23. For each of the values of θ given in Problem 22, find (a) $(\tan \theta)^2$ and $(\sec \theta)^2$; (b) $(\cot \theta)^2$ and $(\csc \theta)^2$. Now use these values to *conjecture* an identity relating $\tan \theta$ with $\sec \theta$ and one relating $\cot \theta$ with $\csc \theta$ that might be true for all defined values of θ.

24. Verify each of the following equalities:
    (a) $\sin \frac{1}{3}\pi = 2 \sin \frac{1}{6}\pi \cos \frac{1}{6}\pi$
    (b) $\tan \frac{2}{3}\pi = 2 \tan \frac{1}{3}\pi/[1 - (\tan \frac{1}{3}\pi)^2]$
    (c) $\sin (\frac{2}{3}\pi - \frac{1}{6}\pi) = \sin \frac{2}{3}\pi \cos \frac{1}{6}\pi - \cos \frac{2}{3}\pi \sin \frac{1}{6}\pi$

25. Verify each of the following equalities:
    (a) $\cos (\frac{1}{6}\pi + \frac{1}{3}\pi) = \cos \frac{1}{6}\pi \cos \frac{1}{3}\pi - \sin \frac{1}{6}\pi \sin \frac{1}{3}\pi$
    (b) $\cos \frac{2}{3}\pi = (\cos \frac{1}{3}\pi)^2 - (\sin \frac{1}{3}\pi)^2$
    (c) $\sin (\frac{1}{6}\pi + \frac{1}{3}\pi) = \sin \frac{1}{6}\pi \cos \frac{1}{3}\pi + \cos \frac{1}{6}\pi \sin \frac{1}{3}\pi$

26. Use Table 1 to find approximations for (a) $\log \sin \frac{1}{4}\pi$; (b) $\log |\sec \frac{2}{3}\pi|$; (c) $\ln \cos \frac{1}{6}\pi$; (d) $\ln |\tan \frac{3}{4}\pi|$.

27. Find a solution for θ in $[0, 2\pi]$ of $\log |\sin \theta| = 0$ that is not a solution of $\log \sin \theta = 0$.

28. Evaluate each of the following expressions:
    (a) $2 \cos \frac{1}{3}\pi + \sin \frac{1}{6}\pi - 3 \tan \frac{2}{3}\pi$
    (b) $(\cos 0 - \tan \frac{1}{4}\pi + 2 \sin \frac{2}{3}\pi)/(1 + \sin \frac{1}{2}\pi + \cos 2\pi)$

29. Evaluate each of the following expressions:
    (a) $\csc \frac{2}{3}\pi + \tan (-\frac{2}{3}\pi) + 2 \cos \frac{3}{4}\pi$
    (b) $(\tan \frac{5}{4}\pi)/(2 \sin \frac{1}{3}\pi + \cos \frac{2}{3}\pi - \tan \frac{3}{4}\pi)$

30. Determine $P(\frac{1}{5}\pi)$ and then find exact values of $\sin \frac{1}{5}\pi$, $\cos \frac{1}{5}\pi$, and $\tan \frac{1}{5}\pi$. [*Hint:* Locate the point that divides into "golden section" the radius joining the origin to the point $(1, 0)$ of the unit circle; that is, find a real number t such that $1/t = t/(1 - t)$.]

6.3   Graphs of the Basic Circular Functions

It is possible to construct the graph of a circular function, as for other functions, by graphing its ordered-pair elements. If f is any circular function, the graph of f consists of the points $(\theta, f(\theta))$ in the Cartesian plane, for all θ in the domain of f. We shall consider each type of circular function, in some detail, from this graphical point of view. Moreover, there will be no loss in generality if we assume that *the domain of each function is maximal,* because every circular function is a subset of one of these six basic functions with its domain so characterized.

We first make the observation that each of the basic circular functions is "periodic" according to the following definition.

Definition.   *A function f is* periodic *if there exists a real number $c > 0$ such that $f(x + c) = f(x)$ for every x in the domain of f. The* period *of f is the smallest c that satisfies this condition.*

If we consider the manner in which the real numbers are associated with points on the unit circle, it is apparent that, as $|\theta|$ increases indefinitely (with $\theta > 0$ or with $\theta < 0$), the trigonometric point $P(\theta)$ recurs after each "cycle" of $|\theta| = 2\pi$. Because each circular function f is defined in terms of the coordinates of the point $P(\theta)$ associated with θ, it follows that $f(\theta + 2\pi) = f(\theta)$ for every θ in the domain of f. The *basic circular functions are then all periodic,* with periods *not exceeding 2π.*

Before attempting any detailed graphing of the basic circular functions, we must again realize that, up to this point in our discussions, we have become acquainted with the functional values of only very particular numbers in their domains. These values were found in §6.2, but we have given no practical way to determine $f(\theta)$ for an arbitrary θ in the domain of any basic circular function f. Of course, the definitions can be used to approximate $f(\theta)$ from the location of $P(\theta)$, but there are obvious practical limitations to the accuracy of this method. *We are not going to give an effective way to compute these functional values,* but we shall be content with asserting that more advanced techniques do exist for this computation, the results of which are embodied in Table 2 in the back of the book. As for Table 1 it should be emphasized that, although certain values found there are exact, the vast majority of them are mere approximations and should be treated as such. For example, we read from the table that $\sin 0.4625 \approx 0.4462$ and $\cos 0.4625 \approx 0.8949$, from which we could conclude that the approximate coordinate pair of $P(0.4625)$ is $(0.8949, 4462)$. It should be noted that the column headed θ in the table progresses *downward* with increasing θ in the interval $[0, \frac{1}{4}\pi]$, in association with the various other columns appropriately headed; but the entries for increasing θ in the interval $[\frac{1}{4}\pi, \frac{1}{2}\pi]$ progress *upward*, with the appropriate designations appearing at the bottom of the various columns. The reason for the validity of this double usage of the table—if it is not already apparent—will be clarified in the next section; for the present, the table should be accepted in its given form. In view of our discussions in the preceding section (in particular, the final paragraph) it should be clear that, with the use of Table 2, *we are now able to obtain an approximation for the value of any basic circular function at any point in its domain.*

It is appropriate at this time to include a comment and a caution concerning the use of Table 2. We shall make no use in this chapter of the first and last columns of this table, inasmuch as these entries are of significance only in connection with angles. The somewhat unfortunate result is that *our present* "lead" columns—the second and eighth—are not graduated in an exactly uniform fashion. However, the table does have the very desirable feature of compactness—playing the role, in fact, of four distinct tables. Although four such individual tables might have greater accuracy, our major aim here is to emphasize ideas rather than to achieve a high level of computational accuracy, and so Table 2 will be satisfactory for our purposes. If greater accuracy is desired, the student will have no trouble in obtaining more accurate tables from which to make his computations. As with most tables, it is possible to extend the coverage of Table 2 by means of linear interpolation (see §5.6 for Table 1). However, because all columns of this table take their lead from the first and last—which we are not using now—the process of interpolation between the other columns involves extra hazards of error. Hence, *if interpolations are used, it is suggested that not more than three-figure accuracy be claimed for any value obtained.* We review the process of interpolation and illustrate this point with an example.

Example 1.   Use Table 2 to approximate sin 0.2712.

SOLUTION.   The adjacent table entries in column two, on either side of 0.2712 are 0.2705 and 0.2723 and we read the following:

$$\sin 0.2705 \approx 0.2672$$
$$\sin 0.2723 \approx 0.2689$$

Hence, by linear interpolation—noting that 0.2712 is $\frac{7}{18}$ of the way from 0.2705 to 0.2723—we find that $\sin 0.2712 \approx 0.2672 + (\frac{7}{18})(0.0017) \approx 0.2672 + 0.0007 = 0.2679 \approx 0.268$.

Let us consider first the basic sine function in detail, recalling that $\sin \theta = y$, where $P(\theta) = (x, y)$ for any $\theta \in \mathbf{R}$. As θ varies from 0 to $\frac{1}{2}\pi$, $\sin \theta$ increases from 0 to 1; as θ varies from $\frac{1}{2}\pi$ to π, $\sin \theta$ decreases from 1 to 0; as θ varies from π to $\frac{3}{2}\pi$, sin θ decreases from 0 to -1; and as θ varies from $\frac{3}{2}\pi$ to 2π, sin θ increases from -1 to 0. It is clear from the definition of sin θ that, from this value of θ $(= 2\pi)$ on, *and not before*, the sequence of sine values begins to repeat, and so *this function has a period of 2π*. The graphical importance of the periodic nature of a function is that after one "cycle" (i.e., the set of values associated with one period-interval of its domain) has been graphed, the rest of the graph consists of duplications of this portion. The fact that $P(\theta)$ is on the unit circle requires that sin $\theta = y \leq 1$ and sin $\theta = y \geq -1$; that is, the basic sine function is bounded so that $-1 \leq$ sin $\theta \leq 1$, for every real number θ. The complete graph of this function is then contained between the horizontal lines one unit above and one unit below the θ axis. A portion of this graph is shown in Figure 38, in which the various geometric symmetries discussed in §6.2 are apparent.

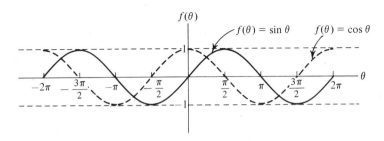

Figure 38

An analysis of the basic cosine function is very similar to that of the sine, with the abscissa x replacing the ordinate y of $P(\theta)$ in the preceding discussion. We then find that the cosine function is also bounded, with $-1 \leq$ cos $\theta \leq 1$ for any real number θ, and that *it is periodic of period 2π*. Let us consider that $P(\theta)$ $[= (x, y)]$ makes one circuit of the unit circle in a counterclockwise direction, starting at $P(0) = (1, 0)$. Then, because cos $\theta = x$, cos θ decreases from 1 to 0 as θ varies from 0 to $\frac{1}{2}\pi$, decreases from 0 to -1 as θ varies from $\frac{1}{2}\pi$ to π, increases from -1 to 0 as θ varies from π to $\frac{3}{2}\pi$, and increases from 0 to 1 as θ varies from $\frac{3}{2}\pi$ to 2π—and at this point the cycle of values begins to repeat. The graph of the basic cosine function is then very similar to that of the basic sine function, with various geometric symmetries again being present— as shown in Figure 38. We shall see in the following section—and it may already be apparent—that the graph of the basic cosine function is identical with that of the basic sine function, if the latter is considered translated $\frac{1}{2}\pi$ units to the left.

If we make use of the reciprocal relationships between sine and cosecant and between cosine and secant functions—as noted in §6.1—it is easy to obtain the graphs of the basic cosecant and secant functions from Figure 38. It is merely necessary to note that the reciprocal of a number of very small absolute value is of very large absolute value and becomes infinite ($+$ or $-$) as the number approaches 0. The graph of the basic cosecant (secant) function than has an "asymptote" at each point where the graph of the basic sine (cosine) function crosses the θ-axis, the function being undefined at such a point and unbounded in any interval containing it. The reciprocal relationship also requires that $|\csc\theta| \geq 1$ and $|\sec\theta| \geq 1$, and the graphs of the basic sine and cosecant (cosine and secant) functions touch only at the points where the values of both are 1 or -1. It is clear, of course, that *the periods of these functions are also* 2π, in view of their relationship with the basic sine and cosine functions. Portions of their graphs are shown in Figure 39.

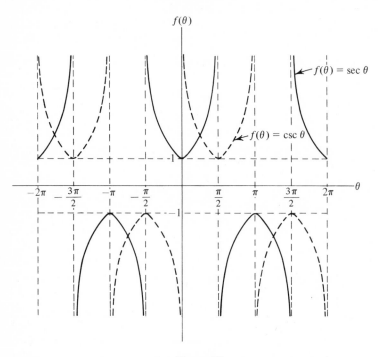

Figure 39

When we consider the basic tangent function, we must recall that $\tan\theta = y/x$, where $P(\theta) = (x, y)$. Furthermore, it is apparent that, as x and y are allowed to vary arbitrarily between -1 and 1, the value of y/x will assume any desired positive or negative value for suitable choices of x and y. The range of this circular function is then the whole set $\mathbf{R}$ of real numbers, and it has an asymptote at each point θ where the abscissa x of $P(\theta)$ is 0. If we consider that $P(\theta)$ traverses the unit circle in a counterclockwise direction from $(1, 0)$, the value of $\tan\theta$ increases without bound from 0 as θ varies from 0 to $\frac{1}{2}\pi$, increases from unbounded negative values to 0 as θ varies from $\frac{1}{2}\pi$ to π, and at this point the sequence of values begins to repeat. This means that *the period of the basic tangent function is* π. The basic cotangent function is reciprocal to the basic tangent function, and so either graph can easily be constructed from the other. The cotangent function, of course, becomes infinite—and so is undefined—at points where the tangent function has the value 0; and at points where the tangent function becomes infinite, the cotangent function assumes zero values. It should be clear that *the period of the basic cotangent function is* π, just as for the basic tangent function. Portions of the graph of both are shown in Figure 40.

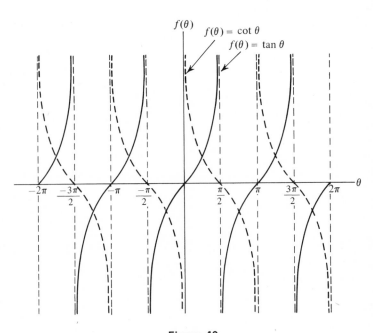

Figure 40

The graph of the basic sine function plays an important role in science and engineering, and in such a context it is often referred to as "the sine curve." It is a fact that the sine and cosine functions are of much more frequent occurrence than the other circular functions in scientific applications, because they are usually involved in the description of a periodic or repetitive motion. Although our emphasis in this section has been on the *basic* circular functions, other related functions can occur and will be discussed in the sequel. However, with a knowledge of the basic functions at hand, a discussion of these related functions is easy.

Example 2. Construct a graph of the function f, defined on the set

$$\{-\pi, -\tfrac{3}{4}\pi, [-\tfrac{1}{2}\pi, \pi]\} \text{ as follows:}$$

$$f(\theta) = \begin{cases} -1 & \theta = -\pi \\ 0 & \theta = -\tfrac{3}{4}\pi \\ 1 & -\tfrac{1}{2}\pi \leq \theta < 0 \\ \cos \theta & 0 \leq \theta \leq \tfrac{1}{2}\pi \\ \tan \theta & \tfrac{1}{2}\pi < \theta \leq \pi \end{cases}$$

SOLUTION.   The desired graph is shown in Figure 41.

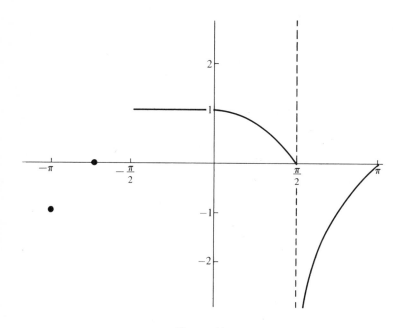

Figure 41

Problems 6.3

1. Use an appropriate graph to determine an approximation for each of the following: (a) sin 7; (b) cos (−2.5); (c) tan 1; (d) sin $\tfrac{6}{7}\pi$.
2. Use an appropriate graph to determine an approximation for each of the following: (a) sec 2; (b) csc 8; (c) tan (−1); (d) sec (−5); (e) cot 4.5.
3. Use an appropriate graph to deduce the truth of each of the following assertions: (a) sin (−θ) = −sin θ; (b) cos (−θ) = cos θ; (c) tan (−θ) = −tan θ.
4. Use an appropriate graph to deduce the truth of each of the following assertions: (a) sin ($\pi + \theta$) = −sin θ; (b) cos ($\tfrac{1}{2}\pi - \theta$) = sin θ; (c) tan ($\pi - \theta$) = −tan θ.

5. Use Table 2 to find a rough approximation for (a) $\sin 4$; (b) $\tan 2$; (c) $\cos (-4)$; (d) $\cot (-2)$.

6. Use Table 2 to find a rough approximation for (a) $\sec 6$; (b) $\sin 5$; (c) $\csc (-6)$; (d) $\cos (-5)$.

7. Use Table 2 to find approximate coordinates for the point (a) $P(0.34)$; (b) $P(0.56)$; (c) $P(0.67)$.

8. Use Table 2 to find approximate coordinates for the point (a) $P(-0.21)$; (b) $P(-0.34)$; (c) $P(-0.48)$.

9. Use Table 2 to find approximate coordinates for the point (a) $P(8.2)$; (b) $P(-8.2)$; (c) $P(5.4)$.

10. Use Figures 39 and 40 to determine approximate coordinates of the point of intersection of each pair of graphs, on the range $0 < \theta < \frac{1}{2}\pi$. Check each approximation with what you know to be the exact coordinates.

11. A function is said to be *increasing* or *decreasing* on an interval in its domain, according as the functional values increase or decrease with increasing elements from the interval. Decide whether the indicated basic circular function is increasing, decreasing, or neither on the given interval: (a) sine on $[0, \frac{1}{2}\pi]$; (b) cosine on $[\frac{1}{2}\pi, \frac{3}{2}\pi]$; (c) tangent on $[\frac{1}{4}\pi, \frac{3}{4}\pi]$; (d) secant on $[0, \frac{1}{4}\pi]$; (e) cotangent on $[\frac{1}{4}\pi, \frac{3}{4}\pi]$.

12. If $\theta_1 < \theta_2$, use a graph to illustrate that it is not necessarily the case that $\sin \theta_1 < \sin \theta_2$. Examine $\cos \theta$ and $\tan \theta$ in a similar manner.

13. Use Table 2 to find the largest interval of real numbers θ in which θ is indistinguishable as a two-digit approximation from (a) $\sin \theta$; (b) $\tan \theta$.

14. *According to our definitions*, a circular function is not necessarily periodic. What additional assumption is made so that the associated *basic* function is periodic?

15. If f is a periodic function of period c, prove that $f(x + kc) = f(x)$ for any integer k and any x in the domain of f.

In Problems 16–25, sketch the function f defined as indicated on the given domain, using Table 2 whenever necessary.

16. f on $[-2\pi, 2\pi]$, where $f(\theta) = \begin{cases} \sin \theta & -2\pi \le \theta \le 0 \\ \cos \theta & 0 < \theta \le 2\pi \end{cases}$

17. f on $[-2\pi, 2\pi]$, where $f(\theta) = \begin{cases} \cos \theta & -2\pi \le \theta \le \pi \\ \sin \theta & \pi < \theta \le 2\pi \end{cases}$

18. f on $(-\frac{1}{2}\pi, \frac{1}{2}\pi)$, where $f(\theta) = \begin{cases} \tan \theta & -\frac{1}{2}\pi < \theta \le 0 \\ \sec \theta & 0 < \theta < \frac{1}{2}\pi \end{cases}$

19. f on $[-2\pi, \frac{1}{2}\pi)$, where $f(\theta) = \begin{cases} \cos \theta & -2\pi \le \theta \le -\pi \\ \sin \theta & -\pi < \theta \le 0 \\ \tan \theta & 0 < \theta < \frac{1}{2}\pi \end{cases}$

20. f on $[-\pi, \pi)$, where $f(\theta) = \begin{cases} \sec \theta & -\pi \le \theta < -\frac{1}{2}\pi \\ \sin \theta & -\frac{1}{2}\pi \le \theta \le 0 \\ \sec \theta & 0 < \theta < \frac{1}{2}\pi \\ \csc \theta & \frac{1}{2}\pi \le \theta < \pi \end{cases}$

21. f on $[-2\pi, 2\pi]$, where $f(\theta) = \begin{cases} 1 & -2\pi \leq \theta \leq -\pi \\ \sin \theta & -\pi < \theta \leq 0 \\ e^{\theta} & 0 < \theta \leq \pi \\ 1 & \pi < \theta \leq 2\pi \end{cases}$

22. f on $[-\frac{3}{2}\pi, \frac{3}{2}\pi]$, where $f(\theta) = \begin{cases} \cos \theta & -\frac{3}{2}\pi \leq \theta \leq -\frac{1}{2}\pi \\ 0 & -\frac{1}{2}\pi < \theta < \frac{1}{2}\pi \\ \cos \theta & \frac{1}{2}\pi \leq \theta \leq \frac{3}{2}\pi \end{cases}$

23. f on $\{0, \pm\frac{1}{2}\pi, \pm\frac{1}{3}\pi, \pm\frac{1}{4}\pi, \pm\frac{1}{6}\pi\}$, where $f(\theta) = \begin{cases} \sin \theta & \theta \in \{0, \pm\frac{1}{2}\pi\} \\ \cos \theta & \theta \in \{\pm\frac{1}{3}\pi, \pm\frac{1}{4}\pi, \pm\frac{1}{6}\pi\} \end{cases}$

24. f on $\{0, \pm\frac{1}{3}\pi, \pm\frac{1}{4}\pi, \pm\frac{1}{6}\pi\}$, where $f(\theta) = \begin{cases} \tan \theta & \theta \in \{0, \pm\frac{1}{3}\pi, \pm\frac{1}{6}\pi\} \\ \cot \theta & \theta = \pm\frac{1}{4}\pi \end{cases}$

25. f on $\{0, \pm1, \pm2, \pm3\}$, where $f(\theta) = \begin{cases} \sin \theta & \theta = 0, \pm1 \\ \cos \theta & \theta = \pm2 \\ \tan \theta & \theta = \pm3 \end{cases}$

26. A graph is *symmetric with respect to the x-axis* if the point $(x, -y)$ is on the graph whenever (x, y) is present. Decide which, if any, of the basic circular functions have this kind of graphical symmetry.

27. A graph is *symmetric with respect to the y-axis* if the point $(-x, y)$ is on the graph whenever (x, y) is present. Decide which, if any, of the basic circular functions have this kind of graphical symmetry.

28. A graph is *symmetric with respect to the origin* if the point $(-x, -y)$ is on the graph whenever (x, y) is present. Decide which, if any, of the basic circular functions have this kind of graphical symmetry.

29. Construct a unit circle with center at the origin O of a Cartesian coordinate system, labeling the point $(1, 0)$ as U. With $P(\theta)$ trigonometric point, $(0 < \theta < \frac{1}{2}\pi)$ draw the radius OP and extend it to cut the vertical line through U at A. Then prove each of the following assertions: (a) $|AU| = |\tan \theta|$; (b) $\tan \theta \geq \sin \theta$, for $0 < \theta < \frac{1}{2}\pi$.

30. Use the diagram constructed in Problem 29 to infer intuitively that $\theta < \tan \theta$, for $0 < \theta < \frac{1}{2}\pi$.

6.4   Inverse Circular Functions

In §6.2 we made use of three real variables x, y, θ, for the sake of clarity in our definitions of the basic circular functions. However, we now propose to abandon the third variable θ, except when we have some specific need to use it. It is the *universe* of a variable, rather than its name, that is of importance, and so, unless there exists a possibility of ambiguity, one symbol for a real variable has no advantage over another. The symbol x has many years of historical usage to denote a real variable in the *domain* of a function, with y playing the corresponding role in the range, and we shall continue this practice. Thus, in the case of the circular functions, we shall use x instead of θ in describing the mappings of these functions. If we think in intuitive terms, we must now think of x as a real variable that measures arc length on the unit circle, whereas $\cos x$ and $\sin x$ are the coordinates of the trigonometric point $P(x)$. When we concentrate on the circular *functions*, however, the *point $P(x)$* begins to fade out of the picture, and the mappings $x \rightarrow y = \cos x$, $x \rightarrow y = \sin x$, $x \rightarrow y = \tan x$, and so forth, come to the forefront. In this way, we achieve a unification in symbolism for all of the elementary functions, with x and y denoting corresponding elements of the domain and range of each.

A glance at the graphs in the preceding sections shows immediately that the basic circular functions are not one-to-one, because each functional value is repeated periodically. For example, $\sin \frac{1}{2}\pi = \sin \frac{5}{2}\pi$, but $\frac{5}{2}\pi \neq \frac{1}{2}\pi$; $\cos 0 = \cos 2\pi$, but $2\pi \neq 0$; $\tan \frac{1}{4}\pi = \tan \frac{5}{4}\pi$, but $\frac{5}{4}\pi \neq \frac{1}{4}\pi$; and so forth. As we have noted earlier (in §4.5), a function must define a one-to-one mapping if its inverse is to exist, and so it follows that the basic circular functions do not have inverses. However, *it is possible to restrict the domains and thereby obtain restricted circular functions for which inverses do exist.* It is clear that there are infinitely many restricted circular functions with inverses. However, for each of the six basic circular functions, it is customary to select one restricted function of this kind *with maximal range* and use it to define the associated basic inverse function.

First, let us consider a portion of the graph of the basic sine function on **R**, as shown in Figure 38. The range of this function is the interval $[-1, 1]$, and we wish to select a subset of **R** such that every number in the interval occurs as $\sin x$ *for exactly one x in the subset.* It is clear from the figure that a suitable choice of subset would be the interval $[-\frac{1}{2}\pi, \frac{1}{2}\pi]$. Another choice would be $[-\pi, -\frac{1}{2}\pi] \cup [\frac{1}{2}\pi, \pi]$, but the interval $[0, \pi]$ would not be suitable. (Why?)

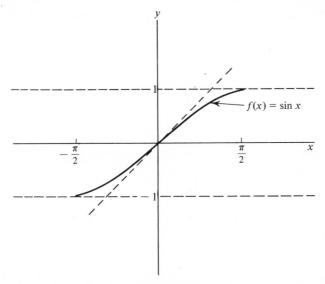

Figure 42

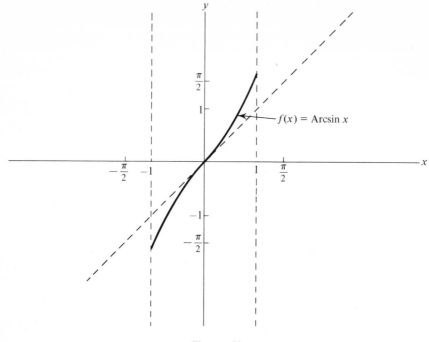

Figure 43

The subset mentioned first is the one usually chosen, and this leads us to the following preliminary definition.

Definition   *If* $y = \sin x$, *for* $x \in [-\frac{1}{2}\pi, \frac{1}{2}\pi]$, *we write* $x = \mathrm{Arcsin}\, y$, *the capital* A *intending to call attention to the fact that we have chosen a particular interval of real numbers in which the* x *(or "principal values" of* y *in the equation* $y = \sin x$) *are located.*

It is an immediate consequence of this definition that $\sin(\mathrm{Arcsin}\, y) = y$ for $y \in [-1, 1]$. We are now able to define our first basic inverse circular function, using x rather than y as our domain variable.

Definition   *Let f be the function defined on the interval* $[-\frac{1}{2}\pi, \frac{1}{2}\pi]$ *by* $f(x) = \sin x$. *The inverse function* f^{-1} *is now defined on the range* $[-1, 1]$ *of f so that* $f^{-1}(x) = \mathrm{Arcsin}\, x$. *The function* f^{-1} *is called the* basic inverse sine *or* basic Arcsine *function.*

It will now be consistent with our general practice in naming functions to refer to any function defined on a subset of $[-1, 1]$ and having $x \to \mathrm{Arcsin}\, x$ for its rule of mapping as *an inverse sine* or *Arcsine* function. In Figures 42 and 43, we have shown the graphs of the restricted sine function defined on $[-\frac{1}{2}\pi, \frac{1}{2}\pi]$, and its inverse—the basic Arcsine function—defined on $[-1, 1]$. The graph of *any* Arcsine function—with its domain some subset of $[-1, 1]$—is then a subset of points of the graph in Figure 43.

Example 1. Sketch a graph of the function f, defined on $[-\pi, 1]$ as follows:

$$f(x) = \begin{cases} \sin x & -\pi \leq x \leq 0 \\ \text{Arcsin } x & 0 < x \leq 1 \end{cases}$$

SOLUTION. The desired graph is shown in Figure 44.

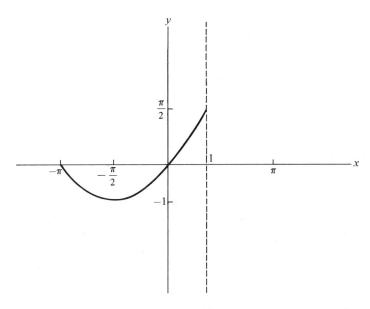

Figure 44

It is unnecessary to give a detailed discussion of the other basic inverse circular functions, because the idea that motivates their definition is the same as that for the sine: Choose a subdomain of the given basic circular function on which the function defines a one-to-one mapping onto its range, and the inverse of this mapping defines the desired basic inverse circular function. Although there is considerable latitude in the possible choices of domains to be associated with an invertible circular function—which is then the range of the inverse function—there is quite general agreement in these choices for sine, cosine, and tangent. We detail the definitions for cosine and tangent—as we have already done for sine—the motivation being provided by the appropriate diagram. The use of capital **A** continues to emphasize that a choice of values has been made for the range of a function.

Definition *If* $y = \cos x$ *for* $x \in [0, \pi]$, *we write* $x = \text{Arccos } y$.

Definition *If* $y = \tan x$ *for* $x \in (-\frac{1}{2}\pi, \frac{1}{2}\pi)$, *we write* $x = \text{Arctan } y$.

Our definitions imply that Arccos $x \in [0, \pi]$ and cos (Arccos x) $= x$, for any $x \in [-1, 1]$, but that Arctan $x \in (-\frac{1}{2}\pi, \frac{1}{2}\pi)$ and tan (Arctan x) $= x$, for any real number x.

Definition   *Let f be the function defined on the interval* $[0, \pi]$ *by* $f(x) =$ cos x. *The inverse function* f^{-1}, *called* the basic inverse cosine (*or* basic Arccosine) *function, is now defined on the range* $[-1, 1]$ *of f so that* $f^{-1}(x) =$ Arccos x.

Definition   *Let f be the function defined on the open interval* $(-\frac{1}{2}\pi, \frac{1}{2}\pi)$ *by* $f(x) =$ tan x. *The inverse function* f^{-1}, *called* the basic inverse tangent (*or* basic Arctangent) *function, is now defined on the range* **R** *of f so that* $f^{-1}(x) =$ Arctan x.

The graphs of these two *basic* inverse functions are shown in Figure 45 and Figure 46, and the graph of any inverse cosine or inverse tangent function is a subset of points of the appropriate one of the two graphs shown. We reemphasize that the ranges of the basic Arcsine and basic Arctangent function are the intervals $[-\frac{1}{2}\pi, \frac{1}{2}\pi]$ and $(-\frac{1}{2}\pi, \frac{1}{2}\pi)$, respectively, but the range of the basic Arccosine function is $[0, \pi]$. It may be of some passing interest to point out that the prefix "Arc" attached to the names of the inverse circular functions is derived from the fact that any value of such a function may be considered to measure a length of arc on the unit circle. For example, the number Arctan 5 is the length of such an arc, the tangent of whose measure of length is 5; and Arcsin 0.7 is the length of such an arc, the sine of whose measure of length is 0.7.

It is quite possible—as we have indicated—to define in a similar manner basic inverse cosecant, secant, and cotangent functions, but there is no general

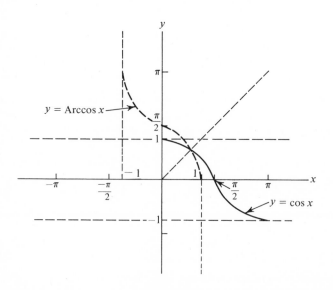

Figure 45

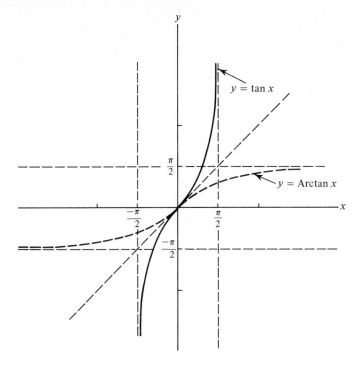

Figure 46

agreement on what ranges are most appropriate for these functions. There are some advantages possessed by certain of the possible choices, but not all are possessed by any one choice. We shall see later that an expression involving one of these inverse functions can usually be replaced by an equivalent expression involving one of the three inverse functions just discussed, and so we shall not include any further discussion of basic Arccosecant, Arcsecant, or Arccotangent functions. The reader is strongly advised, if he ever encounters one of these functions, to make sure of what range is being understood for it.

It may very well be the case that the reader finds these inverse circular functions quite artificial, and of no possible use. However, they do appear in some unexpected places! For example, in Figure 47, we have shown a portion of the graph of the function f, defined on $\mathbf{R}$ by $f(x) = 1/(1 + x^2)$. From a study of the calculus, it is found that the area of the shaded portion of the graph is Arctan b − Arctan a square units.

Example 2.   Determine (a) Arcsin $\frac{1}{2}\sqrt{2}$; (b) Arccos $(-\frac{1}{2})$;
         (c) Arctan (-0.4431).

SOLUTION

(a) We know from §6.3 that sin $\frac{1}{4}\pi = \frac{1}{2}\sqrt{2}$. Because $-\frac{1}{2}\pi < \frac{1}{4}\pi < \frac{1}{2}\pi$, it follows that Arcsin $\frac{1}{2}\sqrt{2} = \frac{1}{4}\pi$.

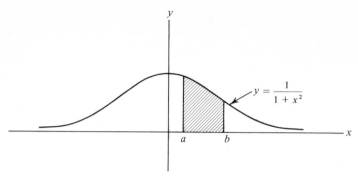

Figure 47

(b) We know that $\cos \frac{2}{3}\pi = -\frac{1}{2}$. Hence, because $0 < \frac{2}{3}\pi < \pi$, we see that Arccos $(-\frac{1}{2}) = \frac{2}{3}\pi$.

(c) We find from Table 2 that $\tan 0.4171 \approx 0.4431$, and so $\tan (-0.4171) \approx -0.4431$. Because $-\frac{1}{2}\pi < -0.4171 < \frac{1}{2}\pi$, it follows that Arctan $(-0.4431) \approx -0.4171$.

Example 3. Determine $\cos [\text{Arcsin} (-\frac{2}{3})]$.

SOLUTION.   We first note that Arcsin $(-\frac{2}{3})$ is a number x such that $\sin x = -\frac{2}{3}$, and $-\frac{1}{2}\pi \leq x \leq \frac{1}{2}\pi$. Because the trigonometric point $P(x)$ is in the fourth quadrant of the Cartesian plane, $\cos [\text{Arcsin} (-\frac{2}{3})] = \cos x = \sqrt{1 - \sin^2 x} = \sqrt{1 - \frac{4}{9}} = \sqrt{\frac{5}{9}} = \sqrt{5}/3$.

Problems 6.4

1. Find the number denoted by (a) Arcsin $\frac{1}{2}$; (b) Arccos $(-\frac{1}{2})$; (c) Arctan (-1); (d) Arctan 1.
2. Find the number denoted by (a) Arccos $\frac{1}{2}\sqrt{3}$; (b) Arcsin $(-\frac{1}{2}\sqrt{3})$; (c) Arctan $(-1/\sqrt{3})$; (d) Arctan $(1/\sqrt{3})$.
3. Find the number denoted by (a) Arcsin 0; (b) Arccos $(-\frac{1}{2}\sqrt{2})$; (c) Arccos (-1); (d) Arcsin (-1).
4. Use Table 2 to find an approximation for each of the following functional values: (a) Arcsin (-0.1236); (b) Arctan 1.6842; (c) Arccos (-0.4368); (d) Arcsin 0.4848.
5. Use Table 2 to find an approximation for each of the following functional values: (a) Arcsin (-0.4848); (b) Arccos 0.8018; (c) Arccos (-0.8018); (d) Arctan (-0.8541).
6. Which of the following numbers are not in the range of the basic Arcsine function: $1, -1.2, 3, \frac{6}{7}\pi, -\frac{1}{3}\pi, -1.5, 0.8, -\frac{1}{8}\pi$?
7. Which of the following numbers are not in the range of the basic Arccosine function: $2, 5, -1, 2.8, 4.2, -2, \frac{5}{8}\pi, -\frac{5}{8}\pi$?
8. Which of the following numbers are not in the range of the basic Arctangent function: $\pi, -\pi, 1.4, -1.3, \frac{6}{7}\pi, -\frac{3}{7}\pi, \frac{9}{20}\pi$?

9. Determine each of the following functional values: (a) $\sin (\text{Arctan } 1)$; (b) $\tan (\text{Arccos } \frac{1}{2})$; (c) $\tan (\text{Arctan } 1)$; (d) $\tan (\text{Arccos } 1)$; (e) $\tan (\text{Arcsin } \frac{1}{2})$.

10. Determine each of the following: (a) $\cos (\text{Arccos } \frac{2}{3})$; (b) $\sin [\text{Arccos } (-\frac{1}{2})]$; (c) $\sec (\text{Arcsin } \frac{1}{2})$; (d) $\cot (\text{Arcsin } \frac{1}{2}\sqrt{3})$.

11. Determine each of the following: (a) $\sin [\text{Arccos } (-1)]$; (b) $\cos [\text{Arctan } (-1)]$; (c) $\cot [\text{Arctan } (-\sqrt{3})]$; (d) $\csc [\text{Arccos } (-\frac{1}{2})]$.

12. Decide on a possible range of values for a basic (a) Arccosecant function; (b) Arcsecant function; (c) Arccotangent function.

13. Prove that $3 \text{ Arcsin } \frac{1}{2}\sqrt{3} = \text{Arccos } 0 + \frac{1}{2}\pi$.

14. Prove that $\text{Arcsin } \frac{1}{2} + \text{Arcsin } (-1) + \text{Arcsin } \frac{1}{2}\sqrt{3} = 0$.

15. Simplify the expression $\text{Arccos } (-\frac{1}{2}) + \tan \frac{1}{6}\pi - \tan \frac{1}{4}\pi$.

16. Use Table 2 to obtain an approximate solution for t in each of the following equations: (a) $\text{Arcsin } \frac{3}{5} + \text{Arccos } \frac{4}{5} = \text{Arcsin } t$; (b) $\text{Arctan } (-\frac{1}{3}) - \text{Arctan } \frac{2}{3} = \text{Arctan } t$.

17. Give an expression that is a solution for x in each of the following equations: (a) $y = \text{Arcsin } 2x$; (b) $y = \frac{1}{2}\pi - 2 \text{ Arccos } x$; (c) $4y = \frac{1}{6}\pi - 2 \text{ Arccos } (2x + 1)$.

18. Give an example to illustrate that $\text{Arcsin } (\sin x)$ is not necessarily equal to x. On the other hand, why is $\sin (\text{Arcsin } x) = x$, for any $x \in [-1, 1]$?

Construct a graph for each of the functions f defined in Problems 19–26, making use of Table 2 where necessary.

19. f on $[-\pi, \pi]$, where $f(x) = \begin{cases} \frac{1}{2}\pi & 1 < |x| \leq \pi \\ \text{Arcsin } x & -1 \leq x \leq 1 \end{cases}$

20. f on $[-\pi, \pi]$, where $f(x) = \begin{cases} \sin x & 1 < |x| \leq \pi \\ \text{Arcsin } x & -1 \leq x \leq 1 \end{cases}$

21. f on $[-\pi, \pi]$, where $f(x) = \begin{cases} \pi & -\pi \leq x < -1 \\ \text{Arccos } x & -1 \leq x \leq 1 \\ 0 & 1 < x \leq \pi \end{cases}$

22. f on $[-\frac{1}{2}\pi, \frac{1}{2}\pi)$, where $f(x) = \begin{cases} \text{Arctan } x & -\frac{1}{2}\pi \leq x \leq 0 \\ \tan x & 0 < x < \frac{1}{2}\pi \end{cases}$

23. f on $[-\pi, \pi]$, where $f(x) = \begin{cases} -\frac{1}{2}\pi & -\pi \leq x < -1 \\ \text{Arcsin } x & -1 \leq x \leq 1 \\ \ln x & 1 < x \leq \pi \end{cases}$

24. f on $[-1, 1]$, where $f(x) = \begin{cases} e^x & -1 \leq x < 0 \\ \text{Arcsin } x & 0 \leq x \leq 1 \end{cases}$

25. f on $\{-3, -2, -1, 0, 1, 2, 3\}$, where $f(x) = \begin{cases} \text{Arctan } x & x = \pm 3, \pm 2 \\ \text{Arcsin } x & x = \pm 1 \\ \text{Arccos } x & x = 0 \end{cases}$

26. f on $\{-3, -2, -1, 0, 1, 2, 3\}$, where $f(x) = \begin{cases} e^x & x = \pm 3, 0 \\ \ln |x| & x = \pm 2 \\ \text{Arcsin } x & x = \pm 1 \end{cases}$

27. If $-1 \le a < b \le 1$, decide which of the following numbers is the larger: (a) Arcsin a, Arcsin b; (b) Arccos a, Arccos b; (c) Arcsin $(a - b)$, Arcsin $(b - a)$; (d) Arccos $(a - b)$, Arccos $(b - a)$.

28. Find a real solution for x in the equation Arccos x + Arcsin $(1 - x) = 0$.

29. Prove for any $x \in [-1, 1]$ that (a) sin (Arccos x) = cos (Arcsin x); (b) Arcsin $(-x) = -$Arcsin x.

30. Determine an algebraic form for cos [Arctan x], for any $x \in \mathbf{R}$.

6.5 Special Graphing Techniques

The subject matters of algebra, trigonometry, and geometry overlap to such an extent that at times it is impossible to know with which of these disciplines we are most intimately involved. A treatment of trigonometry from the viewpoint of circular functions is, of course, a part of the general analysis of functions, and the graphical aspects of function analysis certainly overlaps much of analytic geometry—except in viewpoint. In analysis, the graph of a function is merely a pictorial representation of a *mapping* of its domain onto its range, whereas in geometry the same graph is considered a *set of points* that usually make up a geometric· *curve*. In analysis we emphasize $x \rightarrow y = f(x)$ for the function f, whereas in geometry the emphasis is on the points (x, y) that comprise its graph. The functions of most common occurrence have for their domains the maximal subsets of real numbers for which the defining rules of the functions have meaning. The domain is often the set $\mathbf{R}$ or a closed interval in $\mathbf{R}$. *In this section, we shall always assume that the domain of every function is "maximal" in the above sense.* If the defining rule of such a function is given by an equation—which in geometry is referred to as *the equation of a curve*—it is important to be able to graph the function or the curve. If unlimited time and space are available, it is possible to graph an arbitrarily large number of points, but more frequently it is of importance to be able to give a rough "sketch" of a graph, without the tedium of plotting more than a very few actual points. In this section, our aim is to give a few hints that will be useful for these sketches, although our discussion will be far from complete.

The descriptions of the circular and inverse circular functions concluded our definitions of what are known as the *basic elementary* functions of mathematics. However, even though these functions are basic, the functions usually encountered in practice are not these but rather slight variations from or combinations of these basic functions. For example, the basic sine function may occur very seldom, whereas functions of the type $y = A \sin (ax + b)$ occur frequently. The basic exponential function may be rarely seen, but many functions defined by an equation of the form $y = Ae^{bx}$ are found in the descriptions of physical phenomena. These *modified* circular, exponential, or logarithmic functions may be seen to be composites of circular, exponential, or logarithmic functions with one or more linear or polynomial functions, but we shall make no use of this fact here. (See Problem 22 of §5.2.) In addition, a function defined as the sum of two or more elementary functions (such as $y = 3 \sin 2x + 4x^2$) may occur in many applied problems. The hints that we give here for obtaining a quick sketch of these functions are classified into three categories: (1) effect of a multiplicative factor; (2) effect of an additive term; (3) sum of two functions. In the general discussion it will always be assumed that the graph of some basic elementary function f is familiar. For convenience in writing, we shall sometimes refer to "the function $y = f(x)$" as an abbreviation for "the function defined by $y = f(x)$," with domain understood to be maximal, as explained above.

1. *Effect of a Multiplicative Factor.* There are two cases to consider: $y = kf(x)$ and $y = f(kx)$, for a real number k. In the first case, it is apparent that the effect of k is to multiply every ordinate of the original graph by k. In the second case, if we note that kx plays the role in the transformed equation previously played by x, every "new" x must be $1/k$ times the original x. Hence, every abscissa of the new curve must be $1/k$ times as large as its correspondent in the original curve. These considerations give us the following rules:

(a) The graph of $y = kf(x)$ can be constructed from the graph of $y = f(x)$ by *multiplying all the ordinates* of the latter graph by k.
(b) The graph of $y = f(kx)$ can be constructed from the graph of $y = f(x)$ by *dividing all the abscissas* of the latter graph by $k (\neq 0)$.

Example 1. Sketch partial graphs of $y = 2 \sin x$ and $y = e^{2x}$.

SOLUTION. By rule 1(a), the graph of $y = 2 \sin x$ may be obtained from the graph of $y = \sin x$ by multiplying all the ordinates of the latter graph by 2. The result is shown in Figure 48. By rule 1(b), the graph of $y = e^{2x}$ may be obtained from the graph of $y = e^x$ by dividing all the abscissas of the latter graph by 2. This result is shown in Figure 49.

2. *Effect of an Additive Term.* There are two cases to consider: $y = f(x) + k$ and $y = f(x + k)$, for a real number k. In the first case, it is immediate that every ordinate y of the original graph has simply been increased by k. In the second case, we note that $x + k$ plays the role in the transformed equation

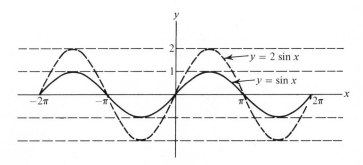

Figure 48

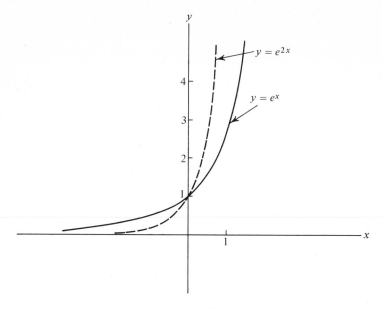

Figure 49

previously played by x, and so each "new" abscissa x is k less than its correspondent in the original curve. These considerations give rise to the following
rules:

(a) The graph of $y = f(x) + k$ can be constructed from the graph of $y =$
$f(x)$ by *increasing all ordinates* of the latter graph by k, that is, by translating the graph of $y = f(x)$ in a vertical direction k units.

(b) The graph of $y = f(x + k)$ can be constructed from the graph of $y =$
$f(x)$ by *decreasing all abscissas* of the latter graph by k, that is, by translating the graph of $y = f(x)$ a distance of $-k$ units in a horizontal
direction.

Example 2. Sketch partial graphs of $y = \ln x + 2$ and $y = \sin (x - \frac{1}{2}\pi)$.

SOLUTION.   By rule 2(a), the graph of $y = \ln x + 2$ may be obtained
from the graph of $y = \ln x$ by increasing each ordinate of the latter graph
by 2. The resulting graph is shown in Figure 50. By rule 2(b), the graph
of $y = \sin (x - \frac{1}{2}\pi)$ can be obtained from the graph of $y = \sin x$ by
translating the latter graph $\frac{1}{2}\pi$ units to the right. (*Note: Decreasing* by
$-\frac{1}{2}\pi$ is equivalent to *increasing* by $\frac{1}{2}\pi$.) The resulting graph is shown in
Figure 51.

3. *Sum of Two Functions.* If we wish to graph the function f defined by
$f = f_1 + f_2$, it is often convenient to do so by the method of "composition of

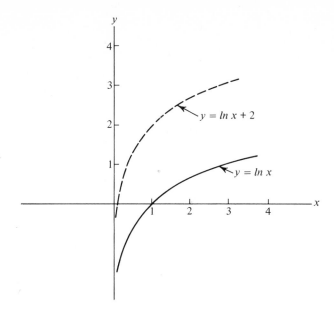

Figure 50

ordinates." By this method, we graph the two component functions f_1 and f_2 with the same coordinate axes and then add algebraically their respective ordinates. We illustrate this with an example.

Example 3. Sketch a partial graph of $y = \sin x + x$.

SOLUTION.   We first sketch partial graphs of the functions defined by $y = \sin x$ and $y = x$, respectively, these being the basic sine and linear functions. On adding the ordinates of the graphs of these basic functions, we obtain the desired graph as shown in Figure 52.

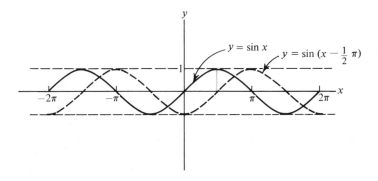

Figure 51

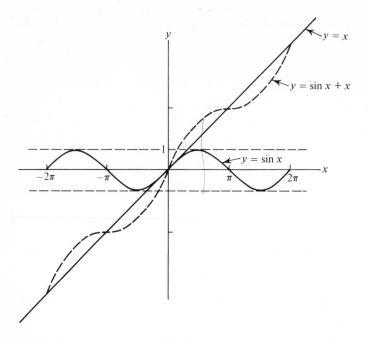

Figure 52

Of course, it may happen that a given defining function equation is more complicated than the result of applying any one of the above operations to the equations of a basic function. However, it will usually be possible to break the complex operation into a sequence of simple operations of the types discussed above. For example, the graph of $y = 2 \sin (3x + \frac{1}{4}\pi)$ is the result of three operations performed *in sequence* on the graph of $y = \sin x$: multiply ordinates by 2; decrease abscissas by $\frac{1}{4}\pi$; divide abscissas by 3.

If the underlying *basic* graph is not desired in the final display, it is usually easier to translate a coordinate axis than to translate a curve. For we observe that *a translation of a curve k units to the left*, say, is equivalent to *a translation of the y-axis k units to the right*. A similar remark applies to vertical translations.

As a final illustration of the graphical techniques of this section, let us consider the graph of the function $y = A \sin (ax + b)$, $a > 0$. We write this equation in the form $y = A \sin a(x + b/a)$ and note that the desired graph may be obtained from the graph of $y = \sin x$ by performing the following operations in sequence: (1) multiply ordinates by A; (2) divide abscissas by a; (3) translate the y-axis (curve) b/a units to the right (left). If we recall that the period of the basic sine curve is 2π, it is immediate that the *period* of $y = A \sin (ax + b)$ is $2\pi/a$, inasmuch as all abscissas have been divided by a. We call $-b/a$ the *phase shift* and note that it is negative if the graph of $y = \sin ax$ must be shifted to the left to coincide with the graph of $y = \sin (ax + b)$, and positive if this shift is to the right. (Some people prefer to reverse our usage of *positive* and *negative* in connection with phase shift.) If M and m are, respectively, the largest and smallest ordinates of a periodic function, the number $(M - m)/2$ is sometimes called the *amplitude* of the function. The numbers M and m are the "bounds" of the periodic function, as suggested in §6.3. The amplitude of the function $y = A \sin (ax + b)$ is then seen to be $|A|$, whereas the amplitude of the basic sine function is 1.

Problems 6.5

Note: For these problems, and in accordance with the understanding throughout this section, the domain of each function is to be considered maximal. For the graphs, of course, it will be appropriate to use a bounded subset of this maximal domain in each case.

In Problems 1–8, sketch the function defined by the given equation.

1. (a) $y = \sin 3x$; (b) $y = 2 \cos x$; (c) $y = \tan \frac{1}{2}x$; (d) $y = \tan 2x$; (e) $y = $ Arcsin $2x$; (f) $y = $ Arccos $2x$.
2. (a) $y = e^{3x}$; (b) $y = 3e^x$; (c) $y = \ln 2x$; (d) $y = 4 \ln x$.
3. (a) $y = 3x^2$; (b) $y = x^2/4$; (c) $y = x^2 + 5$; (d) $y = (2x)^2$; (e) $y = $ Arcsin $x - 3$; (f) $y = $ Arctan $x + 2$.
4. (a) $y = \cos x + 2x$; (b) $y = 2x + e^x$; (c) $y = 3x + \ln x$; (d) $y = 3x + $ Arcsin x; (e) $y = $ Arctan $x + 2x^2$.
5. (a) $y = \sin x - 2x$; (b) $y = e^x - \sin x$; (c) $y = 2x^2 - 3x$; (d) $y = \sin x - $ Arcsin x.
6. (a) $y = -\sin x$; (b) $y = -\cos x$; (c) $y = -x^2$; (d) $y = -\ln x$; (e) $y = -$ Arccos x.
7. (a) $y = 2 \sin 2x$; (b) $y = 3e^{x/2} + 3$; (c) $y = 2 \cos 4x$.
8. (a) $y = 2x^2 + 3x + 1$; (b) $y = e^{2x} + 4x + 1$; (c) $y = x + 2 + \cos 2x$.
9. Determine the amplitude, period, and phase shift for the function whose rule of mapping is the following: (a) $y = 3 \sin (2x - 3)$; (b) $y = \frac{1}{2} \cos (x + 2)$; (c) $y = 3 \sin (\frac{1}{2}x + \frac{3}{4})$; (d) $y = 2 \sin (\pi x + 2)$.
10. Determine the amplitude of the periodic function defined by the following: (a) $y = 2 \sin 3x + 4$; (b) $y = 8 + 5 \cos 2x$; (c) $y = |3 \sin (\pi x + 2)|$.
11. Decide which of the following functions defined below are periodic, and state the period for each such case: (a) $y = x \cos x$; (b) $y = 2 \sin x + \cos x$; (c) $y = x^2 - \sin x$; (d) $y = e^{\sin 2x}$.
12. If f and g are periodic functions on **R** with periods c_1 and c_2, respectively, decide which of the functions defined below are periodic, and describe the possible period for each such case: (a) $F(x) = f(x) \cdot g(x)$; (b) $F(x) = g(x^3)$; (c) $F(x) = [f(x)]^2$; (d) $F(x) = f[g(x)]$.
13. A periodic function is defined by the equation $y = e^{\cos x}$. Determine the amplitude and period of the function, and sketch two cycles of its graph.
14. Determine the amplitude and period of the periodic function defined by $y = 2 \sin^2 3\pi x$.
15. The graph of $y = \sin (3x + 5)$ may be obtained from the graph of $y = \sin x$ by (a) multiplying the abscissas of the latter curve by a, followed by a translation of the resulting curve b units in the positive horizontal direction; (b) translating the latter curve b' units in the positive horizontal direction, followed by a multiplication of the abscissas of the resulting curve by a'. Compare the numbers a and b in (a) with a' and b' in (b).

6.6 Elementary Identities

Now that we have completed our discussion of the circular functions and their graphs, we return to a more detailed study of the various mappings involved in their definitions. In §6.1, we gave definitions, that were quite independent of each other, of the mappings associated with the basic sine, cosine, tangent, cosecant, secant, and cotangent functions, although a few indications of existing relationships were included at that time. We now pursue this matter further, and we shall see very easily that, if the domains of the functions are suitably restricted, all of the mappings—except for special points—are determined by any one of them. The reason for these relationships is the key role played by the trigonometric point $P(x)$ associated with any real number x: If the coordinates of this point are known, so are $\sin x$, $\cos x$, $\tan x$, $\csc x$, $\sec x$, and $\cot x$ (provided they exist). Hence, if we are given conditions that determine $P(x)$ uniquely, all of the possible trigonometric mappings associated with x are determined. We illustrate with two examples.

Example 1. Determine $\cos x$ and $\tan x$ if $\sin x = \frac{1}{3}$ and $\frac{1}{2}\pi < x < \pi$.

SOLUTION. The point $P(x)$ must lie in the second quadrant of the Cartesian plane, and we are given its ordinate as $\frac{1}{3}$. Because $P(x)$ is on the unit circle, its abscissa must be $-2\sqrt{2}/3$, and so $P(x) = (-2\sqrt{2}/3, \frac{1}{3})$. It follows that $\cos x = -2\sqrt{2}/3$ and $\tan x = \sin x/\cos x = -\sqrt{2}/4$. The situation is illustrated in Figure 53.

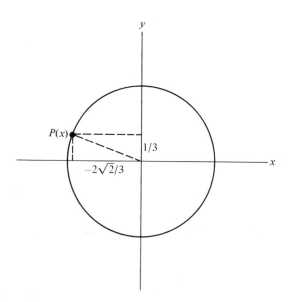

Figure 53

Example 2. If $\cos x = -1/\sqrt{2}$ and $0 < x < 2\pi$, find $\sin x$ and $\tan x$.

SOLUTION. In this case, the conditions allow two possibilities for the location of $P(x)$, one in the second and one in the third quadrants. Because the abscissa of either point is $-1/\sqrt{2}$, a simple application of the Pythagorean Theorem gives us the two ordinates, and the two points are shown in Figure 54. The desired mappings now follow easily:

If $\tfrac{1}{2}\pi < x < \pi$, then $\sin x = \dfrac{1}{\sqrt{2}}$ and $\tan x = \dfrac{1/\sqrt{2}}{-1/\sqrt{2}} = -1$

If $\pi < x < \tfrac{3}{2}\pi$, then $\sin x = \dfrac{-1}{\sqrt{2}}$ and $\tan x = \dfrac{-1/\sqrt{2}}{-1/\sqrt{2}} = 1$

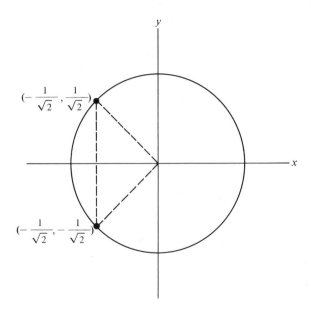

Figure 54

A number of so-called "identities" arise in the study of trigonometry, each of them expressing a relationship between certain of the mappings of the circular functions. The following definition describes the concept in a general setting.

Definition. *An equation in a variable x is an* identity *on a set E if a valid equality results when x is replaced by an arbitrary element of E.*

Many equations (such as $x + x = 2x$) are valid for every real number replacement of x, and so could properly be referred to as "identities on **R**." However, it is customary to refer to such an equation as simply an "identity." It is also common practice to extend the usage of this word to include any identity on a set E, provided E consists of all replacements of the variable *for which both members of the equation have meaning.* An identity of this sort is $1/(x - 1) + 1/(x + 1) = 2x/(x^2 - 1)$, this being more precisely an identity on the set $\{x \in \mathbf{R} \mid x \neq 1, -1\}$.

There is an abundance of identities that involve trigonometric mappings, and we have already taken note of several of the simplest ones in §6.1. For purposes of later reference, we make a new listing of them (with x replacing the variable θ that was used at that time).

$$\csc x = \frac{1}{\sin x} \tag{1}$$

$$\sec x = \frac{1}{\cos x} \tag{2}$$

$$\cot x = \frac{1}{\tan x} \tag{3}$$

$$\tan x = \frac{\sin x}{\cos x} \tag{4}$$

$$\cot x = \frac{\cos x}{\sin x} \tag{5}$$

$$\sin^2 x + \cos^2 x = 1 \tag{6}$$

In the case of (6), it may be well to remark that we are following the practice of writing powers, such as $(\sin x)^2$ and $(\cos x)^2$, as $\sin^2 x$ and $\cos^2 x$, respectively. In the sequel, we shall extend this notational practice without comment to include *arbitrary* exponents and *arbitrary* trigonometric mappings. For example, we shall write $(\sec x)^5$ as $\sec^5 x$ and $(\sin x)^{1/2}$ as $\sin^{1/2} x$, although, for fractional exponents, the basic notation may sometimes be preferred.

If we divide both members of (6) by $\sin^2 x$, and then both members of (6) by $\cos^2 x$, we obtain two further useful identities.

$$1 + \tan^2 x = \sec^2 x \tag{7}$$
$$1 + \cot^2 x = \csc^2 x \tag{8}$$

It is worthy of note that although Identity (6) is valid for *every* real x, the others are the more restricted kind of identities and are valid only when zero denominators are excluded. In other words, (6) is an identity on $\mathbf{R}$, whereas the others are identities on certain proper subsets of $\mathbf{R}$. However, with the understanding stated earlier, we shall refer to all eight as identities—the *basic elementary identities* of trigonometry. Every student should be entirely familiar with them, and with their aid it is possible to derive many more.

Example 3. Establish the validity of the following identity:

$$\frac{2 + 3 \cos x}{\sin x} = 2 \csc x + 3 \cot x$$

SOLUTION.

$$\frac{2 + 3 \cos x}{\sin x} = 2 \left(\frac{1}{\sin x}\right) + 3 \left(\frac{\cos x}{\sin x}\right) = 2 \csc x + 3 \cot x$$

It may be of interest to note that this identity is valid for every real number x except when x is a multiple of π.

Our method of proof in Example 3 was to show, with the help of some of the basic identities, that the left member of the stated identity is in fact equal to the right member. Sometimes, it is more convenient to show that both members are equal to the same third expression and so equal to each other.

Example 4.   Prove that $\dfrac{\tan^2 x}{\sin^2 x} = 1 + \tan^2 x$ is an identity.

PROOF.

$$\frac{\tan^2 x}{\sin^2 x} = \frac{\sin^2 x}{\cos^2 x} \frac{1}{\sin^2 x} = \frac{1}{\cos^2 x} = \sec^2 x$$

with the use of Identities (2) and (4). Moreover, $1 + \tan^2 x = \sec^2 x$ by Identity (7), and because both members are equal to $\sec^2 x$, the identity is established.

It is clear, of course, that it was not necessary to have altered the right member in Example 4, for the reverse use of Identity (7) would have completed the proof. However, this was a simple example, and for complicated identities it is usually desirable to simplify both of its members.

Problems 6.6

1. Determine $\sin x$ and $\sec x$ if $\tan x = 1/\sqrt{3}$ and $\pi < x < \frac{3}{2}\pi$.
2. Determine $\tan x$ and $\csc x$ if $\cos x = \frac{2}{3}$ and $\frac{3}{2}\pi < x < 2\pi$.
3. Determine $\cot x$ and $\sec x$ if $\sin x = -\frac{3}{4}$ and $-\pi < x < -\frac{1}{2}\pi$.
4. Determine $\cos x$ and $\cot x$ if $\sin x = \frac{2}{5}$ and $\frac{1}{2}\pi < x < \pi$.
5. Determine $\tan x$ and $\sec x$ if $\cos x = -\frac{1}{3}$ and $-\pi < x < -\frac{1}{2}\pi$.
6. Determine $\tan x$, $\sec x$, and $\csc x$ if we know that the point $(-1, 4)$ lies on the extension of the segment joining the origin to $P(x)$.
7. The point $(3, -7)$ is known to lie on the extension of the segment joining the origin to $P(x)$. Determine $\sin x$, $\cos x$, and $\cot x$.
8. Prove that $|\tan x| \geq |\sin x|$ and $|\tan x| < |\sec x|$, for any $x \in \mathbf{R}$ for which the indicated trigonometric mappings have meaning.
9. Examine each of the eight basic identities, and describe the precise subset of $\mathbf{R}$ on which each is an actual identity.
10. If $\sin x = \frac{3}{5}$, determine two possible values for $(\csc x + \tan x)/\cos x$.
11. Evaluate $(\tan x - 2 \sec x)/\cos x$ without altering the expression, if $\sin x = \frac{1}{3}$ and $\frac{1}{2}\pi < x < \pi$.

12. Evaluate $\sin x \cos y + \cos x \sin y$ if $\tan x = \frac{2}{3}$, $\csc y = \frac{3}{2}$, $\pi < x < \frac{3}{2}\pi$, and $\frac{1}{2}\pi < y < \pi$.

13. Assume that $0 < x < \frac{1}{2}\pi$, and express each of the following in terms of $\cos x$:
(a) $\sin x$; (b) $\tan x$; (c) $\sec x$; (d) $\csc x$; (e) $\cot x$.

Establish the validity of each of the identities listed in Problems 14–29.

14. $\dfrac{\cot x - \tan x}{\cot x + \tan x} = 1 - \sin^2 x$

15. $\dfrac{1}{1 - \sin x} = \sec^2 x + \sec x \tan x$

16. $\tan x \sin x + \cos x = \sec x$

17. $\dfrac{1 + \sin x}{\cos x} = \sec x + \tan x$

18. $\dfrac{2 + 5 \cos x}{\sin x} = 2 \csc x + 5 \cot x$

19. $\dfrac{\cot x + \csc x}{1 + \cos x} = \csc x$

20. $\dfrac{\sec x \csc x}{\tan x + \cot x} = 1$

21. $\dfrac{\cos x + \sin^2 x \sec x}{\sec x} = 1$

22. $\cos^2 (2 + x^2) + \sin^2 (2 + x^2) = 1$

23. $\dfrac{\tan x - \cot x}{\tan x + \cot x} = 2 \sin^2 x - 1$

24. $1 + \cot^2 x = \dfrac{\sec^2 x}{\sec^2 x - 1}$

25. $\dfrac{1}{1 - \sin x} + \dfrac{1}{1 + \sin x} = 2 \sec^2 x$

26. $\dfrac{\cos x}{\csc x} - \dfrac{\sin x}{\tan x} = (\sin x - 1) \cos x$

27. $\dfrac{\cot x - \sin x \cos x}{1 + 2 \csc x} = \dfrac{\cos^3 x}{2 + \sin x}$

28. $\dfrac{1 - \cos x}{\sin x} = \dfrac{\sin x}{1 + \cos x}$

29. $\dfrac{1 - \tan^2 x}{1 + \tan^2 x} = \cos^2 x - \sin^2 x$

30. Demonstrate that $(\sin x + \cos x)^2 = 1$ is *not* an identity by finding a real number x for which the equation is false. Find an x for which the equation is true. (Note, however, that both sides of the equation have meaning for every $x \in \mathbf{R}$.)

31. Express in simplest form:

$$\frac{\cos (\pi + x) \sin x}{1 - \sin^2 (\pi - x)}$$

32. Express in simplest form:

$$\frac{\sin^3 x - \cos^3 x}{\sin x - \cos x}$$

33. Express in simplest form:

$$\frac{\sin x}{\sec x + 1} + \frac{\sin x}{\sec x - 1}$$

6.7 The Addition Formulas

It is often of interest and importance to know, for a given function f, how $f(x + y)$ is related to $f(x)$ and $f(y)$, for arbitrary x, y in the domain of f. Any formula that connects these quantities in some way may be called an "addition formula." In the case of a *linear* function f, where $f(x) = mx$, for any real number m, there is a very simple answer: $f(x + y) = m(x + y) = mx + my = f(x) + f(y)$. If f is an *exponential* function, with $f(x) = a^x$ for any exponential base a, we know that $f(x + y) = a^{x+y} = a^x a^y = [f(x)][f(y)]$. Inasmuch as there does not exist a simple relationship between $\log_a (x + y)$ and $\log_a x$ and $\log_a y$, we do not have an addition formula for logarithmic functions. In this section, we shall examine the question of the existence of such formulas for the circular functions, and our results will give an affirmative answer to the question.

There are certain special cases of the addition formulas for the circular functions for which the results follow almost directly from the definitions. These various situations are depicted in Figure 55, *in which we assume—for convenience—that* $0 < x < \frac{1}{2}\pi$, but the formulas may be seen to be valid for arbitrary $x \in \mathbf{R}$. We consider each of the cases very briefly.

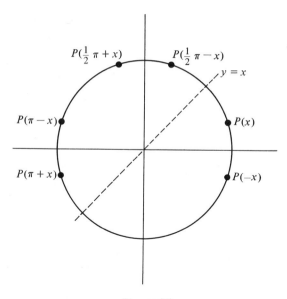

Figure 55

It is geometrically evident that the trigonometric points $P(x)$ and $P(-x)$ have coordinates that differ in only one algebraic sign. If one also takes note of the quadrants of the Cartesian plane in which the points are located, the following identities ensue:

$$\sin(-x) = -\sin x \qquad \csc(-x) = -\csc x$$
$$\cos(-x) = \cos x \qquad \sec(-x) = \sec x$$
$$\tan(-x) = -\tan x \qquad \cot(-x) = -\cot x$$

The points $P(x)$ and $P(\frac{1}{2}\pi - x)$ may be seen very easily to be geometric reflections of each other in the diagonal line through the first and third quadrants. It follows that $P(\frac{1}{2}\pi - x) = (\sin x, \cos x)$, and we have another set of useful identities:

$$\sin\left(\tfrac{1}{2}\pi - x\right) = \cos x \qquad \csc\left(\tfrac{1}{2}\pi - x\right) = \sec x$$
$$\cos\left(\tfrac{1}{2}\pi - x\right) = \sin x \qquad \sec\left(\tfrac{1}{2}\pi - x\right) = \csc x$$
$$\tan\left(\tfrac{1}{2}\pi - x\right) = \cot x \qquad \cot\left(\tfrac{1}{2}\pi - x\right) = \tan x$$

Any two numbers whose sum is $\frac{1}{2}\pi$ may be said to be *complementary to*, or *complements of*, each other. Moreover, if we agree further that each member of the pairs (sine, cosine), (secant, cosecant), (tangent, cotangent) is the *cofunction* of the other, it is possible to abbreviate the preceding listing by the following remark:

> *The value of any circular function of a number in its domain is equal to the value of the cofunction of the complement of the number.*

In other words, and even more briefly: *Any circular function of x is equal to the cofunction of the complement of x.* This particular relationship is a very useful one.

If we note that the coordinates of $P(\frac{1}{2}\pi + x)$ and $P(\frac{1}{2}\pi - x)$ are the same—except for one sign—the following are evident consequences of the preceding identities:

$$\sin\left(\tfrac{1}{2}\pi + x\right) = \quad\cos x \qquad \csc\left(\tfrac{1}{2}\pi + x\right) = \quad\sec x$$
$$\cos\left(\tfrac{1}{2}\pi + x\right) = -\sin x \qquad \sec\left(\tfrac{1}{2}\pi + x\right) = -\csc x$$
$$\tan\left(\tfrac{1}{2}\pi + x\right) = -\cot x \qquad \cot\left(\tfrac{1}{2}\pi + x\right) = -\tan x$$

The points $P(\pi - x)$ and $P(\pi + x)$ have coordinates that differ in only one sign from those of the point $P(x)$, and the following identities are an immediate consequence:

$$\sin\left(\pi - x\right) = \quad\sin x \qquad \csc\left(\pi - x\right) = \quad\csc x$$
$$\cos\left(\pi - x\right) = -\cos x \qquad \sec\left(\pi - x\right) = -\sec x$$
$$\tan\left(\pi - x\right) = -\tan x \qquad \cot\left(\pi - x\right) = -\cot x$$

$$\sin\left(\pi + x\right) = -\sin x \qquad \csc\left(\pi + x\right) = -\csc x$$
$$\cos\left(\pi + x\right) = -\cos x \qquad \sec\left(\pi + x\right) = -\sec x$$
$$\tan\left(\pi + x\right) = \quad\tan x \qquad \cot\left(\pi + x\right) = \quad\cot x$$

It is easy to develop the formulas for the circular functions of $\frac{3}{2}\pi - x$ and $\frac{3}{2}\pi + x$, but they are seldom used. The results are much like those for $\frac{1}{2}\pi - x$ and $\frac{1}{2}\pi + x$, respectively, but we leave the determination of them for the reader in the problems.

The reader is most likely familiar with the analytic formula for the distance between two points in the Cartesian plane. However, for the sake of complete-ness—and because we need the result in our general considerations—we include it here. In Figure 56, we have shown two arbitrary points $P(x_1, y_1)$, $Q(x_2, y_2)$ in the plane, and we wish to express the distance between them. The diagram shows that PQ is the hypotenuse of a right triangle, and the distance $|PQ|$ is found by a simple application of the Pythagorean Theorem. Thus $|PQ|^2 = (x_2 - x_1)^2 + (y_2 - y_1)^2$, and so

$$|PQ| = \sqrt{(x_2 - x_1)^2 + (y_2 - y_1)^2}$$

We note, as an immediate observation, that $|PQ| = |QP|$.

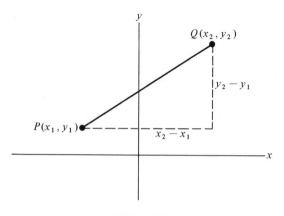

Figure 56

Example 1. Find the distance between the points $(-1, 2)$ and $(3, -3)$.

SOLUTION. If d is the desired distance, the preceding formula shows that $d^2 = (3 + 1)^2 + (-3 - 2)^2 = 16 + 25 = 41$. Hence $d = \sqrt{41}$.

We are now ready to proceed to the derivation of the three most important addition formulas: expressions for, or *expansions of*, sin $(x + y)$, cos $(x + y)$, tan $(x + y)$. In view of the possible confusion of x and y—which here are arbitrary and independent real numbers—with the abscissa and ordinate of some point, we shall return to a notation similar to that with which we first introduced the subject of circular functions. In this discussion, we shall then use θ_1 and θ_2 to denote arbitrary real numbers—regarded as the measures of length of arcs on the unit circle. Thus, let $P(\theta_1)$, $P(\theta_2)$, $P(\theta_1 - \theta_2)$ be the three trigonometric points associated on the unit circle in Figure 57 with the real numbers θ_1, θ_2, and $\theta_1 - \theta_2$, respectively. Irrespective of which real numbers θ_1 and θ_2 are selected, the distance along the circle from $P(\theta_2)$ to $P(\theta_1)$ is equal

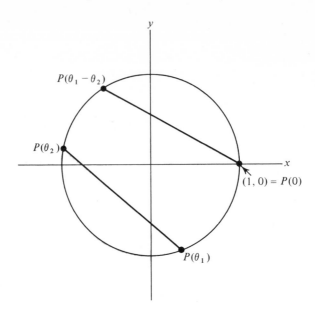

Figure 57

to the distance along the circle from $P(0)$ or $(1, 0)$ to $P(\theta_1 - \theta_2)$, where we assume distance is measured in a counterclockwise direction and $\theta_1 > \theta_2$. (If $\theta_1 < \theta_2$ we have merely to interchange the numbers to have our assumed inequality, so there is no loss in generality.) Moreover, as mentioned earlier, it is a familiar result of elementary geometry that the chords subtended by these arcs are also of equal lengths. It follows from the definitions of the sine and cosine functions that the coordinates of $P(\theta_1)$, $P(\theta_2)$, and $P(\theta_1 - \theta_2)$ are $(\cos \theta_1, \sin \theta_1)$, $(\cos \theta_2, \sin \theta_2)$, and $(\cos (\theta_1 - \theta_2), \sin (\theta_1 - \theta_2))$, respectively. Hence, by the distance formula that we developed in this section,

$$[\cos (\theta_1 - \theta_2) - 1]^2 + [\sin (\theta_1 - \theta_2) - 0]^2$$
$$= (\cos \theta_2 - \cos \theta_1)^2 + (\sin \theta_2 - \sin \theta_1)^2$$

and so

$$\cos^2 (\theta_1 - \theta_2) - 2 \cos (\theta_1 - \theta_2) + 1 + \sin^2 (\theta_1 - \theta_2)$$
$$= \cos^2 \theta_2 - 2 \cos \theta_1 \cos \theta_2 + \cos^2 \theta_1 + \sin^2 \theta_2 - 2 \sin \theta_1 \sin \theta_2 + \sin^2 \theta_1$$

An application of Identity (6) to this equality now gives us

$$2 - 2 \cos (\theta_1 - \theta_2) = 2 - 2 \cos \theta_1 \cos \theta_2 - 2 \sin \theta_1 \sin \theta_2$$

so that

$$\cos (\theta_1 - \theta_2) = \cos \theta_1 \cos \theta_2 + \sin \theta_1 \sin \theta_2$$

We rewrite this as our first *addition formula*, listing it serially with the identities in §6.6, but using a notation consistent with what was used there.

$$\cos (x_1 - x_2) = \cos x_1 \cos x_2 + \sin x_1 \sin x_2 \tag{9}$$

Example 2. Determine $\cos \frac{1}{12}\pi$ from known functional values.

SOLUTION.

$$\cos \tfrac{1}{12}\pi = \cos (\tfrac{1}{4}\pi - \tfrac{1}{6}\pi) = \cos \tfrac{1}{4}\pi \cos \tfrac{1}{6}\pi + \sin \tfrac{1}{4}\pi \sin \tfrac{1}{6}\pi$$

$$= \left(\frac{\sqrt{2}}{2}\right)\left(\frac{\sqrt{3}}{2}\right) + \left(\frac{\sqrt{2}}{2}\right)\left(\frac{1}{2}\right) = \frac{\sqrt{6} + \sqrt{2}}{4}$$

It is of importance to observe that the derivation of (9) did not depend in any way on either the magnitude or algebraic sign of the real numbers θ_1 or θ_2. In particular, the formula preceding (9) would remain valid if θ_2 is replaced by $-\theta_2$, and we obtain the following result—with the help of identities developed earlier in this section:

$$\cos (\theta_1 + \theta_2) = \cos [\theta_1 - (-\theta_2)] = \cos \theta_1 \cos (-\theta_2) + \sin \theta_2 \sin (-\theta_2)$$
$$= \cos \theta_1 \cos \theta_2 - \sin \theta_1 \sin \theta_2.$$

On replacing θ_1 and θ_2, respectively, by x_1 and x_2, the result takes the following form:

$$\cos (x_1 + x_2) = \cos x_1 \cos x_2 - \sin x_1 \sin x_2 \tag{10}$$

It is now easy to obtain the corresponding formulas for the sine function, making use of the rule noted earlier that a circular function of a number is equal to the cofunction of its complement. Thus,

$$\sin (x_1 + x_2) = \cos [\tfrac{1}{2}\pi - (x_1 + x_2)] = \cos [(\tfrac{1}{2}\pi - x_1) - x_2]$$
$$= \cos (\tfrac{1}{2}\pi - x_1) \cos x_2 + \sin (\tfrac{1}{2}\pi - x_1) \sin x_2$$
$$= \sin x_1 \cos x_2 + \cos x_1 \sin x_2$$

In like manner,

$$\sin (x_1 - x_2) = \sin [x_1 + (-x_2)] = \sin x_1 \cos (-x_2) + \cos x_1 \sin (-x_2)$$
$$= \sin x_1 \cos x_2 - \cos x_1 \sin x_2$$

We rewrite these as our next two identities.

$$\sin (x_1 + x_2) = \sin x_1 \cos x_2 + \cos x_1 \sin x_2 \tag{11}$$
$$\sin (x_1 - x_2) = \sin x_1 \cos x_2 - \cos x_1 \sin x_2 \tag{12}$$

There are two more addition formulas that can be obtained from the preceding, with the help of a little elementary algebra and trigonometry, and we merely list them without further comment.

$$\tan (x_1 + x_2) = \frac{\tan x_1 + \tan x_2}{1 - \tan x_1 \tan x_2} \tag{13}$$

$$\tan (x_1 - x_2) = \frac{\tan x_1 - \tan x_2}{1 + \tan x_1 \tan x_2} \tag{14}$$

There are many other formulas of this type that could be included in our list, but this will suffice. A working knowledge of analytic trigonometry requires complete familiarity with all fourteen of the listed identities, in addition to the special cases of the addition formulas discussed here—and which we regard as intuitively clear without any necessity of memorization.

Example 3. Determine an exact expression for $\sec \frac{5}{12}\pi$.

SOLUTION. We note that $\frac{5}{12}\pi = \frac{1}{4}\pi + \frac{1}{6}\pi$, and we are familiar with the circular functions of $\frac{1}{4}\pi$ and $\frac{1}{6}\pi$. Then

$$\cos \tfrac{5}{12}\pi = \cos (\tfrac{1}{4}\pi + \tfrac{1}{6}\pi) = \cos \tfrac{1}{4}\pi \cos \tfrac{1}{6}\pi - \sin \tfrac{1}{4}\pi \sin \tfrac{1}{6}\pi$$

$$= \left(\frac{\sqrt{2}}{2}\right)\left(\frac{\sqrt{3}}{2}\right) - \left(\frac{\sqrt{2}}{2}\right)\left(\frac{1}{2}\right) = \frac{\sqrt{6} - \sqrt{2}}{4}$$

It follows that

$$\sec \tfrac{5}{12}\pi = \frac{4}{\sqrt{6} - \sqrt{2}} = \frac{4(\sqrt{6} + \sqrt{2})}{6 - 2} = \sqrt{6} + \sqrt{2}$$

Example 4. Prove that $\text{Arccos } x + \text{Arcsin } x = \frac{1}{2}\pi$ for any real x such that $-1 \le x \le 1$.

PROOF. We know that $\text{Arcsin } x$ is a number y such that $\sin y = x$ and $-\frac{1}{2}\pi \le y \le \frac{1}{2}\pi$. If we let $z = \frac{1}{2}\pi - y$, it follows that $0 \le z \le \pi$, and $\cos z = \cos (\frac{1}{2}\pi - y) = \sin y = x$. Hence, $z = \text{Arccos } x$ and so $\text{Arccos } x + \text{Arcsin } x = z + y = \frac{1}{2}\pi$, as asserted.

Example 5. Find the numerical value of $\sin (\text{Arccos } \frac{1}{2} - \text{Arcsin } \frac{1}{4})$.

SOLUTION. Let $\text{Arccos } \frac{1}{2} = x$ and $\text{Arcsin } \frac{1}{4} = y$, so that we desire the value of $\sin (x - y) = \sin x \cos y - \cos x \sin y$. But, because $\cos x = \frac{1}{2}$, $\sin x = \sqrt{3}/2$; and because $\sin y = \frac{1}{4}$, $\cos y = \sqrt{15}/4$. Hence, the desired value is $(\sqrt{3}/2)(\sqrt{15}/4) - (\frac{1}{2})(\frac{1}{4}) = 3\sqrt{5}/8 - \frac{1}{8} = (3\sqrt{5} - 1)/8$.

Problems 6.7

1. Use (9) to obtain the analogous identity involving (a) $-x$; (b) $\pi - x$; (c) $\frac{1}{2}\pi - x$; (d) $\frac{3}{2}\pi - x$.

2. Use (10) to obtain the analogous identity involving (a) $\frac{1}{2}\pi + x$; (b) $\pi + x$; (c) $\frac{3}{2}\pi + x$.

3. Derive the formulas for $\tan(x_1 + x_2)$ and $\tan(x_1 - x_2)$ from the formulas involving the sine and cosine functions.

4. Use the appropriate addition formulas to obtain the circular functions of 0.

5. Establish the following identities:
   (a) $\sin(x_1 - x_2)\sin(x_1 + x_2) = \sin^2 x_1 - \sin^2 x_2$
   (b) $\cos(x_1 - x_2)\cos(x_1 + x_2) = \cos^2 x_1 - \sin^2 x_2$

6. Establish the following identities:
   (a) $\tan(x + \frac{1}{4}\pi) - \tan(x - \frac{3}{4}\pi) = 0$
   (b) $(1 + \tan x)/(1 - \tan x) = \tan(\frac{1}{4}\pi + x)$

7. Prove that
   (a) $\cos(x + \frac{1}{6}\pi) - \cos(x - \frac{1}{6}\pi) = -\sin x$
   (b) $\sin(x + \frac{1}{3}\pi) - \cos(x + \frac{1}{6}\pi) = \sin x$

8. Use (11) and (12) to prove that

$$\sin x_1 \cos x_2 = \frac{\sin(x_1 + x_2) + \sin(x_1 - x_2)}{2}$$

9. Use (9) and (10) to prove that
   (a) $\sin x_1 \sin x_2 = -\frac{1}{2}[\cos(x_1 + x_2) - \cos(x_1 - x_2)]$
   (b) $\cos x_1 \cos x_2 = \frac{1}{2}[\cos(x_1 + x_2) + \cos(x_1 - x_2)]$

10. Put $x_1 + x_2 = \alpha$ and $x_1 - x_2 = \beta$ in the identities of Problems 8 and 9 to establish the following new identities:
    (a) $\sin \alpha + \sin \beta = 2 \sin \frac{1}{2}(\alpha + \beta) \cos \frac{1}{2}(\alpha - \beta)$
    (b) $\sin \alpha - \sin \beta = 2 \cos \frac{1}{2}(\alpha + \beta) \sin \frac{1}{2}(\alpha - \beta)$

11. Use the directions given in Problem 10 to establish the following identities:
    (a) $\cos \alpha + \cos \beta = 2 \cos \frac{1}{2}(\alpha + \beta) \cos \frac{1}{2}(\alpha - \beta)$
    (b) $\cos \alpha - \cos \beta = -2 \sin \frac{1}{2}(\alpha + \beta) \sin \frac{1}{2}(\alpha - \beta)$

12. Express each of the following in terms of circular functions of x:
    (a) $\sin(\frac{1}{3}\pi + x)$; (b) $\cos(\frac{1}{6}\pi - x)$; (c) $\tan(x - \frac{1}{3}\pi)$; (d) $\sec(x - \frac{3}{4}\pi)$; (e) $\csc(\frac{2}{3}\pi + x)$.

13. Use an addition formula and known functional values of x, with $0 \le x \le \frac{1}{2}\pi$, to evaluate each of the following:
    (a) $\cos \frac{2}{3}\pi$ $\qquad$ (b) $\csc \frac{1}{12}\pi$ $\qquad$ (c) $\tan \frac{1}{12}\pi$
    (d) $\cot \frac{1}{12}\pi$ $\qquad$ (e) $\sec \frac{7}{12}\pi$ $\qquad$ (f) $\cos \frac{5}{12}\pi$

14. If $P(x_1)$ and $P(x_2)$ are trigonometric points in the first and third quadrants, respectively, determine $\sin(x_1 + x_2)$ and $\cos(x_1 + x_2)$ where (a) $\sin x_1 = \frac{1}{3}$ and $\cos x_2 = -\frac{2}{3}$; (b) $\cos x_1 = \frac{3}{5}$ and $\sin x_2 = -\frac{1}{2}$.

15. If $P(x_1)$ and $P(x_2)$ are trigonometric points in the second and third quadrants, respectively, determine $\sin(x_1 - x_2)$ and $\cos(x_1 - x_2)$ where (a) $\cos x_1 = -\frac{4}{5}$ and $\csc x_2 = -2$; (b) $\sec x_1 = -\frac{3}{2}$ and $\tan x_2 = 1$.

16. Use the identities established in Problems 10 and 11 to express each of the following sums or differences as a product: (a) $\sin \frac{1}{3}\pi + \sin \frac{2}{3}\pi$; (b) $\cos \frac{1}{6}\pi - \cos \frac{1}{3}\pi$; (c) $\sin \frac{3}{4}\pi - \sin \frac{1}{3}\pi$; (d) $\cos \frac{2}{3}\pi + \cos \frac{1}{3}\pi$.

17. Use the identities established in Problems 8 and 9 to express each of the following products as a sum or difference: (a) $2 \sin \frac{1}{3}\pi \cos \frac{1}{4}\pi$; (b) $2 \cos \frac{2}{3}\pi \cos \frac{1}{6}\pi$; (c) $\cos \frac{1}{6}\pi \sin \frac{1}{8}\pi$; (d) $\sin \frac{5}{6}\pi \sin \frac{2}{3}\pi$.

18. Prove that $\text{Arcsin } x + \text{Arcsin } y \ne \text{Arcsin } (x + y)$ if $xy \ne 0$.

Verify each of the equalities in Problems 19–23.

19. $2 \text{ Arctan } \frac{1}{3} + \text{Arctan } \frac{1}{7} = \frac{1}{4}\pi$
20. $\text{Arctan } \frac{1}{2} + \text{Arctan } \frac{1}{3} = \frac{1}{4}\pi$
21. $\text{Arctan } 2 + \text{Arctan } 3 = \frac{3}{4}\pi$
22. $\text{Arctan } 3 + \text{Arctan } \frac{1}{3} = \frac{1}{2}\pi$
23. $\tan (\text{Arctan } 2 - \text{Arctan } 1) = \frac{1}{3}$

24. Prove that $\tan (\text{Arctan } a - \text{Arctan } b) = (a - b)/(1 + ab)$
25. Derive an expression for $\tan (\text{Arctan } a + \text{Arctan } b)$ and compare it with the result in Problem 24.
26. Solve each of the following equations for x:
    (a) $\text{Arctan } \frac{1}{3} + \text{Arctan } \frac{1}{2} = \text{Arcsin } x$
    (b) $\text{Arccot } \frac{1}{3} + \text{Arccot } \frac{1}{2} = \text{Arccos } x$
    (c) $\cos (\text{Arcsin } \frac{1}{4} + \text{Arccos } \frac{1}{2}) = x$
27. Put each of the following equations in an equivalent form $y = A \sin (ax + b)$, with $A > 0$: (a) $y = -2 \sin (\pi + x)$; (b) $y = -3 \sin (2x - 3)$; (c) $y = 3 \cos (3x - \frac{1}{2}\pi)$; (d) $y = -4 \cos 2x$.
28. Put each of the following equations in an equivalent form $y = A \cos (ax + b)$, with $A > 0$: (a) $y = -2 \cos (2x + 3\pi)$; (b) $y = 5 \sin (x - \frac{1}{2}\pi)$; (c) $y = -2 \cos (x + 1)$; (d) $y = -\cos \pi x$.
29. Show that it is always possible to express $A \sin ax + B \cos ax$ in the form $C \sin (ax + b)$, with $C > 0$.
30. Show that it is always possible to express $A \sin ax + B \cos ax$ in the form $C \cos (ax + b)$, with $C > 0$.

6.8 Other Identities

It is possible to obtain a number of useful identities by specializing some of those in §6.7. If we let $x_1 = x_2 = x$ in the addition formulas for $\sin (x_1 + x_2)$, $\cos (x_1 + x_2)$, and $\tan (x_1 + x_2)$, we obtain the following results:

$$\sin 2x = 2 \sin x \cos x \tag{15}$$

$$\cos 2x = \cos^2 x - \sin^2 x \tag{16}$$

$$\tan 2x = \frac{2 \tan x}{1 - \tan^2 x} \tag{17}$$

These three identities, which we have listed serially with those of §6.7, are familiarly known as the "double-angle" formulas of trigonometry, in view of the early association of trigonometry with angles. In the modern context, they relate the basic circular functions of twice a real number with functions of the original number. For example, we have noted earlier that $\sin \frac{1}{3}\pi \neq 2 \sin \frac{1}{6}\pi$, but Identity (15) gives us the correct relationship that exists: $\sin \frac{1}{3}\pi = 2 \sin \frac{1}{6}\pi \cos \frac{1}{6}\pi$.

Example 1. Use the appropriate identity in this section to determine (a) $\sin \frac{2}{3}\pi$; (b) $\cos \frac{2}{3}\pi$.

SOLUTION

(a) $\sin \frac{2}{3}\pi = 2 \sin \frac{1}{3}\pi \cos \frac{1}{3}\pi = 2(\sqrt{3}/2)(\frac{1}{2}) = \sqrt{3}/2.$

(b) $\cos \frac{2}{3}\pi = \cos^2 \frac{1}{3}\pi - \sin^2 \frac{1}{3}\pi = (\frac{1}{2})^2 - (\sqrt{3}/2)^2 = \frac{1}{4} - \frac{3}{4} = -\frac{1}{2}.$

It is easy to transform (16) to obtain several other useful identities, known as the "half-angle" formulas. In this procedure, we make use of Identity (6). Thus,

$$\cos 2x = \cos^2 x - \sin^2 x = 1 - \sin^2 x - \sin^2 x = 1 - 2 \sin^2 x$$

so that

$$2 \sin^2 x = 1 - \cos 2x \text{ and } \sin^2 x = \frac{1 - \cos 2x}{2}$$

We may replace x by $\frac{1}{2}x$, with no loss in generality, and the result has the form

$$\sin^2 \frac{x}{2} = \frac{1 - \cos x}{2} \tag{18}$$

Similarly, $\cos 2x = \cos^2 x - (1 - \cos^2 x) = 2 \cos^2 x - 1$, whence $\cos^2 x = \frac{1}{2}(1 + \cos 2x)$. If we now replace x by $\frac{1}{2}x$ in this result, we obtain

$$\cos^2 \frac{x}{2} = \frac{1 + \cos x}{2} \tag{19}$$

We note that (18) and (19) do not give us the algebraic sign of $\sin \frac{1}{2}x$ or $\cos \frac{1}{2}x$, and in both cases the correct sign must be determined from observing the quadrant in which $P(\frac{1}{2}x)$ is located. It is immediately apparent that

$$\tan^2 \frac{x}{2} = \frac{\sin^2 \frac{1}{2}x}{\cos^2 \frac{1}{2}x} = \frac{1 - \cos x}{1 + \cos x}$$

but it is possible to obtain a more satisfactory formula for $\tan \frac{1}{2}x$ that includes the correct sign. Thus,

$$\tan \frac{x}{2} = \frac{\sin \frac{1}{2}x}{\cos \frac{1}{2}x} = \frac{2 \sin \frac{1}{2}x \cos \frac{1}{2}x}{2 \cos^2 \frac{1}{2}x} = \frac{\sin x}{1 + \cos x}$$

and we rewrite this and make a further elementary reduction to obtain our final result:

$$\tan\frac{x}{2} = \frac{\sin x}{1 + \cos x} = \frac{1 - \cos x}{\sin x} \tag{20}$$

The last three formulas express functions of half a real number in terms of functions of the real number.

Example 2. If we are given that $\cos\frac{8}{3}\pi = \cos\frac{2}{3}\pi = -\frac{1}{2}$, determine the exact value of (a) $\cos\frac{1}{8}\pi$; (b) $\tan\frac{1}{12}\pi$; (c) $\sin\frac{4}{3}\pi$.

SOLUTION

(a) We know from (19) that

$$\cos^2\frac{1}{8}\pi = \frac{1 + \cos\frac{1}{4}\pi}{2} = \frac{1 + \sqrt{2}/2}{2} = \frac{2 + \sqrt{2}}{4}$$

Because $P(\frac{1}{8}\pi)$ is in the first quadrant, $\cos\frac{1}{8}\pi > 0$, and so

$$\cos\frac{1}{8}\pi = \frac{\sqrt{2 + \sqrt{2}}}{2}$$

(b) A direct application of (20) gives us

$$\tan\frac{1}{12}\pi = \frac{\sin\frac{1}{6}\pi}{1 + \cos\frac{1}{6}\pi} = \frac{\frac{1}{2}}{1 + \sqrt{3}/2} = \frac{1}{2 + \sqrt{3}} = 2 - \sqrt{3}$$

(c) We know from (18) that

$$\sin^2\frac{4}{3}\pi = \frac{1 - \cos\frac{8}{3}\pi}{2} = \frac{1 + \frac{1}{2}}{2} = \frac{3}{4}$$

Because $P(\frac{4}{3}\pi)$ is in the third quadrant, it follows that $\sin\frac{4}{3}\pi = -\sqrt{3}/2$. (It is clear, of course, that this result could have been obtained much more easily by the direct methods of §6.3.)

Example 3. Simplify the expression $\dfrac{\sin 2x}{\sin x} - \dfrac{\cos 2x}{\cos x}$.

SOLUTION

$$\frac{\sin 2x}{\sin x} - \frac{\cos 2x}{\cos x} = \frac{2\sin x\cos x}{\sin x} - \frac{2\cos^2 x - 1}{\cos x}$$
$$= 2\cos x - 2\cos x + \sec x = \sec x$$

Example 4. Verify the following identity:

$$\left(\sin\frac{x}{2} + \cos\frac{x}{2}\right)^2 = \frac{\csc x + 1}{\csc x}$$

SOLUTION

$$\left(\sin\frac{x}{2} + \cos\frac{x}{2}\right)^2 = \sin^2\frac{x}{2} + 2\sin\frac{x}{2}\cos\frac{x}{2} + \cos^2\frac{x}{2}$$

$$= 1 + 2\sin\frac{x}{2}\cos\frac{x}{2} = 1 + \sin x$$

Also,

$$\frac{\csc x + 1}{\csc x} = \frac{1/\sin x + 1}{1/\sin x} = \frac{(1 + \sin x)/\sin x}{1/\sin x} = 1 + \sin x$$

Because both members of the asserted identity are equal to $1 + \sin x$, its truth has been verified.

We close this section with the reminder again that an identity in x is not necessarily a true equality for *every* real number x, but only for those that reduce both members of the equality to a real number. The numbers excluded from the universe of x will depend in part on the kinds of functions involved in the expressions that make up the identity.

Problems 6.8

1. Find the exact values of all basic circular functions of $\frac{1}{8}\pi$.
2. Use the appropriate formulas in this section to obtain the basic circular functions of $\frac{1}{3}\pi$ from those of $\frac{1}{6}\pi$.
3. Assume the basic circular functions of π to be given, and then use the formulas in this section to obtain the known functions of $\frac{1}{2}\pi$.
4. Use Table 2 and the appropriate formula in this section to obtain an approximation for (a) sin 2.6; (b) cos 3.0; (c) tan 1.96.
5. Derive an identity similar to (20) for $\cot\frac{1}{2}x$.
6. Simplify each of the following expressions:

   (a) $\cos 2x \cos x + \sin 2x \sin x$ (b) $\dfrac{\sec x - 1}{\sec x}$

   (c) $\dfrac{\tan x}{1 + \tan^2 x}$ (d) $\dfrac{\sin 2x + \sin x}{1 + \cos 2x + \cos x}$

   (e) $\dfrac{\sec^2 x}{2 - \sec^2 x}$ (f) $\dfrac{\sin^2 x}{1 - \cos x} - 1$

7. Express each of the following in terms of $\sin x$, where $0 < x < \frac{1}{2}\pi$: (a) $\tan x$; (b) $\sec x$; (c) $\cos 2x$; (d) $\csc\frac{1}{2}x$; (e) $\cot x$ (f) $\cos(\pi + \frac{1}{2}x)$.

8. Prove that $|\sin x + \cos x| = \sqrt{1 + \sin 2x}$.

9. Show that $\tan (a + b)$ can be expressed in the form $\dfrac{\sin 2a + \sin 2b}{\cos 2a + \cos 2b}$.

10. Find an expression for $\tan 2x + \sec 2x$ that involves only $\sin x$ and $\cos x$.

11. Derive an identity for $\sin 3x$ in terms of $\sin x$ and $\cos x$.

12. Determine the exact value of (a) $\sin \frac{1}{16}\pi$; (b) $\cos \frac{1}{16}\pi$.

13. Use Table 2 and the appropriate formula in this section to determine an approximate value for (a) $\sin \frac{1}{2} \cos \frac{1}{2}$; (b) $2 \cos^2 0.4$; (c) $(1 + \cos 2) \tan 2$; (d) $\cos^2 (\frac{1}{2}\pi - \frac{1}{5}) - \sin^2 \frac{1}{5}$.

14. If $0 < x < \frac{1}{4}\pi$ and $y = c \sin 2x$, write each of the following expressions in terms of y and c: (a) $\cos 4x$; (b) $\sin x$; (c) $\tan x$.

15. Verify that $[\sin x \cos x] \le [\sin x][\cos x]$, for each $x \in \mathbf{R}$.

16. What is the maximal domain of the function f whose rule of definition is $f(x) = \sin (\ln x)$? Also determine the range of f and show that $f(e^{\pi/2}x) = \cos (\ln x)$.

17. With f defined as in Problem 16, develop an expression for $f(xy)$, with both x and y in the domain of f (assumed to be maximal).

Note: In Problems 18–30, either prove that the given equation is an identity or exhibit a real number substitution for the variable to show that the equation is not an identity.

18. $\sin 2x = \dfrac{2 \tan x}{1 + \tan^2 x}$

19. $\tan 2\theta = \dfrac{1 + \cos 2\theta}{\sin 2\theta}$

20. $\sin^2 t \cos^2 t = \frac{1}{8}(1 - \cos 4t)$

21. $\cos 3x = 3 \sin x - 4 \sin^3 x$

22. $\cot \frac{1}{2}\theta = \csc \theta + \cot \theta$

23. $\sin^4 t = \frac{1}{8}(3 - 4 \cos 2t + \cos 4t)$

24. $\ln \tan x = \ln (\csc 2x - \cot 2x)$

25. $\ln (\tan^2 \theta + 2 \cot 2\theta \tan \theta) = 0$

26. $\dfrac{1 + \sin x - \cos x}{1 + \sin x + \cos x} = \tan \dfrac{x}{2}$

27. $\dfrac{\sin 3t}{\sin t} - \dfrac{\cos 3t}{\cos t} = 2$

28. $\sin \left(\dfrac{\pi}{4} - x\right) \sin \left(\dfrac{\pi}{4} + x\right) = \dfrac{\cos 2x}{2}$

29. $\csc 2t + \cot 2t = \cot t$

30. $\dfrac{\sin 2\theta + \sin 3\theta}{\cos 2\theta - \cos 3\theta} = \cot \dfrac{\theta}{2}$

31. Derive Identity (19) by using the addition formula for $\cos (x - \frac{1}{2}x)$.

32. Determine the subinterval of $[0, 2\pi]$ on which $\cos x + \sin 2x < 0$.

33. Prove that $A \sin x + B \cos x = \sqrt{A^2 + B^2} \sin (x + \alpha)$, for $A, B \in \mathbf{R}$, where $\sin \alpha = B/\sqrt{A^2 + B^2}$ and $\cos \alpha = A/\sqrt{A^2 + B^2}$.

Use the result in Problem 33 for Problems 34–36.

34. Reduce $3 \sin x + 4 \cos x$ to the form $C \sin (x + b)$, with $C > 0$.

35. Reduce $\sin 2t + 4 \cos 2t$ to the form $C \cos (2t + b)$, with $C > 0$.

36. Reduce $4 \cos 2\theta - 3 \sin 2\theta$ to the form $C \cos (2\theta + b)$, with $C > 0$.

6.9 Equations, Inequalities, and Approximations

An equation differs from an identity in that the solution set of an equation—which is *not* an identity—is much more restricted. We shall see in Chapter 9, for example, that there can be at most n distinct complex-number solutions of a polynomial equation of degree n. In this section, we shall consider a few elementary methods of solving certain types of equations that involve the mappings of circular or inverse circular functions. Equations of this kind belong to the general category of nonalgebraic or "transcendental" equations. The solving of such equations is, in general, extremely difficult, and we must usually be satisfied with approximate solutions. But even approximate solution methods, *with any pretense of generality*, are beyond the scope of this book!

Of course, the method that is adopted for solving an equation depends not only on the equation itself, but also on the universe of the variable that appears in the equation to be solved. For example, the equation $2x + 1 = 0$ has no integral solutions, but it does have $-\frac{1}{2}$ as a rational number solution. If we wish to solve an equation involving circular functions, it is important to know—in addition to the type of real number—whether there are any restrictions on the magnitude of any acceptable solution. For example, the equation $\tan x = 1$ has $\{\frac{1}{4}\pi, -\frac{3}{4}\pi, \frac{5}{4}\pi, -\frac{7}{4}\pi, \ldots\}$ or, otherwise expressed, $\{\frac{1}{4}\pi + n\pi, n \in \mathbf{z}\}$ as its complete solution set. However, if we are interested only in real solutions x such that $0 < x < \frac{1}{2}\pi$, the *unique* solution of the equation is $x = \frac{1}{4}\pi$. In practice, the conditions of a problem usually dictate the type —as well as any limitations on magnitude or algebraic sign—of the solutions of an equation.

The techniques that we present in the examples to follow are essentially the techniques of algebraic equations. They rest heavily on the field property of the real numbers [Theorem 5.10 (Chapter 1)] that *the product of two numbers is 0 if and only if at least one of them is 0*.

Example 1.   Solve the equation $(2 \cos x + 1) \sin x = 0$ for x such that $\frac{1}{2}\pi < x < \pi$.

SOLUTION.   The solution set of the given equation is the set-theoretic union of the solution sets of the two equations:

$$\sin x = 0$$
$$\cos x + \tfrac{1}{2} = 0$$

The first of these equations has no solution in the desired interval, but the second has the unique solution $\frac{2}{3}\pi$. This is then the only solution of the original equation, subject to the given condition.

Example 2.   Solve the equation $\sin^2 x - \sin x - 2 = 0$ for x such that $0 \leq x \leq 2\pi$.

SOLUTION.   The left member can be factored and the given equation can be written in the form $(\sin x - 2)(\sin x + 1) = 0$, from which it is seen that its solution set is the union of the solution sets of the equations:

$$\sin x - 2 = 0$$
$$\sin x + 1 = 0$$

The first of these equations requires that $\sin x = 2$, and this equation has no solution. The second equation may be written $\sin x = -1$, and the unique solution of this in the interval stipulated is $\frac{3}{2}\pi$. This then is the only solution of the original equation in the given interval.

It is often necessary to make use of certain trigonometric identities in order to put an equation in an appropriate form for solving.

Example 3. Solve $\sin 2x + \cos x = 0$ for x, where $0 \le x < 2\pi$.

SOLUTION. Because $\sin 2x = 2 \sin x \cos x$, the given equation becomes $2 \sin x \cos x + \cos x = 0$, and this may be expressed in the form $(2 \sin x + 1) \cos x = 0$. Hence $\cos x = 0$ or $\sin x = -\frac{1}{2}$. The solution set of the equation, with the given limitations on x, is then $\{\frac{1}{2}\pi, \frac{7}{6}\pi, \frac{3}{2}\pi, \frac{11}{6}\pi\}$.

Example 4. Solve $\sin^2 x - \cos x - 1 = 0$ for x such that $|x| \le \pi$.

SOLUTION. Because $\sin^2 x = 1 - \cos^2 x$, the given equation may be written

$$1 - \cos^2 x - \cos x - 1 = 0$$
$$\cos^2 x + \cos x = 0$$
$$(\cos x + 1) \cos x = 0$$

Hence $\cos x = -1$ or $\cos x = 0$. The solution set, within the given universe of x, is then $\{\frac{1}{2}\pi, \pi, -\frac{1}{2}\pi, -\pi\}$.

Example 5. Solve the equation $\text{Arctan}(1 + x) + \text{Arctan}(1 - x) = \frac{1}{4}\pi$ for all real x.

SOLUTION. An application of Identity (13) of §6.7 transforms the equation into

$$\frac{(1 + x) + (1 - x)}{1 - (1 + x)(1 - x)} = \tan\frac{\pi}{4} = 1$$

Hence $x^2 = 2$, and $x = \pm\sqrt{2}$.

We note, in passing, that the range of the basic Arctangent function requires that $-\frac{1}{2}\pi < \text{Arctan}(1 + x) < \frac{1}{2}\pi$ and $-\frac{1}{2}\pi < \text{Arctan}(1 - x) < \frac{1}{2}\pi$. This observation is of importance if the correct application of Identity (13) is to be made in this problem. (Why?)

For a sufficiently small positive real number x, the difference between x, $\sin x$, and $\tan x$ is very small. If $0 < x < \frac{1}{2}\pi$, it is evident intuitively that $\sin x < x < \tan x$; reference to this type of geometric observation was made in Problems 29 and 30 of §6.3. It is possible to make certain transformations of this inequality to obtain useful bounds on sin x, cos x, and tan x, and to these results we now proceed.

If we divide each number in the inequality sin $x < x <$ tan x by sin x, we obtain

$$1 < \frac{x}{\sin x} < \sec x$$

which is equivalent to

$$\cos x < \frac{\sin x}{x} < 1$$

But cos $x = \sqrt{1 - \sin^2 x} > \sqrt{1 - x^2}$, and this—when combined with the preceding inequality—gives us

$$\sqrt{1 - x^2} < \frac{\sin x}{x} < 1$$

We have now obtained the following bounds on sin x:

$$x\sqrt{1 - x^2} < \sin x < x \qquad (0 < x < \tfrac{1}{2}\pi) \qquad (1)$$

Because cos $x = 1 - 2 \sin^2 \frac{1}{2}x$, cos $x > 1 - 2(x^2/4) = 1 - x^2/2$. Hence,

$$1 - \frac{x^2}{2} < \cos x < 1 \qquad (0 < x < \tfrac{1}{2}\pi) \qquad (2)$$

Finally, we divide all members of the original inequality by tan x and obtain

$$\cos x < \frac{x}{\tan x} < 1$$

so that

$$\sqrt{1 - x^2} < \frac{x}{\tan x} < 1$$

It follows that

$$1 < \frac{\tan x}{x} < \frac{1}{\sqrt{1 - x^2}}$$

and so

$$x < \tan x < \frac{x}{\sqrt{1 - x^2}} \qquad (0 < x < \tfrac{1}{2}\pi) \qquad (3)$$

Inequalities (1), (2), and (3) can be used to estimate sin x, cos x, and tan x, for a small real number $x > 0$. In more advanced courses, it is discovered that infinite series can be used to express values of the basic circular functions. For example, it is well known that

$$\sin x = x - \frac{x^3}{3!} + \frac{x^5}{5!} - \frac{x^7}{7!} + \cdots$$

and

$$\cos x = 1 - \frac{x^2}{2!} + \frac{x^4}{4!} - \frac{x^6}{6!} + \cdots$$

for any real number x. These series "converge" and represent $\sin x$ or $\cos x$, as the case may be, in the sense that as more and more terms are included the closer is the approximation to the exact functional value. However, it may be the case that a great many terms of these series are needed to obtain a desired accuracy in our computed results, and then the preceding inequalities may be more useful.

Example 6.   Determine an approximation for (a) $\sin \frac{1}{100}\pi$; (b) $\cos \frac{1}{100}\pi$; (c) $\tan \frac{1}{100}\pi$.

SOLUTION

(a) We know from (1) that $(\frac{1}{100}\pi)/\sqrt{1 - \pi^2/10000} < \sin \frac{1}{100}\pi <$ 0.03142, so that $0.03140 < \sin \frac{1}{100}\pi < 0.03142$. Hence, correct to an accuracy of four decimal places, $\sin \frac{1}{100}\pi \approx 0.0314$ and is not to be distinguished from $\frac{1}{100}\pi$.

(b) From (2), we deduce that $1 - \pi^2/20000 < \cos \frac{1}{100}\pi < 1$, and so $1 - 0.00049 < \cos \frac{1}{100}\pi < 1$. Hence $0.99951 < \cos \frac{1}{100}\pi < 1 =$ $0.999 \cdots$. It follows that, with the maximum number of correct digits, $\cos \frac{1}{100}\pi \approx 0.999$, but with a (rounded) accuracy of four decimal places, $\cos \frac{1}{100}\pi \approx 1.0000$.

(c) It is a consequence of (3) that

$$\frac{1}{100}\pi < \tan \frac{1}{100}\pi < \frac{\pi/100}{\sqrt{1 - \pi^2/10000}}$$

and this is equivalent to

$$0.031416 < \tan \frac{1}{100}\pi < \frac{0.031416}{0.9995} \approx 0.03143$$

Thus, correct to an accuracy of four decimal places, $\tan \frac{1}{100}\pi \approx 0.0314$ and this, like $\sin \frac{1}{100}\pi$, is indistinguishable from $\frac{1}{100}\pi$.

Problems 6.9

For Problems 1–16, find all solutions (if any) of the given equations with x in the indicated universe.

1. $(1 + \cos x) \cot x = 0, 0 \le x \le 2\pi$ **2.** $\cos^2 x = 3, 0 \le x \le \pi$
3. $2 \tan x \cos x = \tan x, 0 \le x \le 2\pi$ **4.** $\cos 2x = \frac{1}{2}, \pi \le x \le 2\pi$

5. $3 \tan^2 x + 5 \sec x + 1 = 0, 0 < x < \pi$

6. $\sec^2 x = 4, -\pi < x < \pi$

7. $\sin 2x = \cos 2x, 0 < x < 2\pi$

8. $\sin x = \cos 2x, -\pi < x < \pi$

9. $3 \cos^2 x + \cos x - 2 = 0, |x| < \pi$

10. $\sin x + \cos x = 1, |x| < \pi$

11. $3 \sec^2 x + \cot^2 x - 7 = 0, 0 < x < \pi$

12. $\cos 2x = \sin 4x, |x| < \pi$

13. $\cos x - \sin x = \sqrt{2}, 0 < x < 2\pi$

14. $\cos 2x + \cos x + 1 = 0, |x| < \pi$

15. $\cos x = \dfrac{1}{2 \tan x}, 0 \le x \le 2\pi$

16. $\dfrac{1}{3 + \cos x} = \dfrac{1}{4 - \cos x}, 0 < x < 2\pi$

17. Find a solution in $(0, \pi)$ of the equation $\sin 2x = \sin x$ that is not a solution of $\sin x = 0$.

18. Show that the solution set of $\sin 2x \le 2 \sin x$ is the same as the solution set of $\sin x \ge 0$.

19. Determine simultaneous solutions of the equations $r = 1 - \cos \theta$ and $r = \cos \theta$, where $r > 0$ and $0 \le \theta < 2\pi$.

20. Use the directions in Problem 19 for the equations $r = 4 \cos \theta$ and $r = 3 \sec \theta$.

21. Determine the simultaneous solutions of the following equations, where $0 \le x \le 2\pi$ and $0 \le y \le 2\pi$:

(a) $\sin x + \cos y = 1$ (b) $\tan y = \cot x$

$\quad\;\; \sin 2x = 2 \sin y$ $\quad\;\; x = 3y + 2$

22. If $r = 1 - 2 \cos \theta$, determine θ such that $0 \le \theta < 2\pi$ and (a) $r = 0$; (b) r is maximal.

23. Use the directions in Problem 22 for the equation $r = 1 - \sqrt{2} \sin \theta$.

24. Use the inequalities listed in this section to compute the largest number of correct digits and also the best (rounded) approximation in the decimal representation of (a) $\sin \frac{1}{60}\pi$; (b) $\cos \frac{1}{60}\pi$.

25. Use the directions in Problem 24 for (a) $\sin \frac{1}{30}\pi$; (b) $\cos \frac{1}{30}\pi$; (c) $\tan \frac{1}{30}\pi$.

26. Approximate $\sin \frac{1}{60}\pi$ and $\cos \frac{1}{60}\pi$ by using the first three terms of the appropriate infinite series given near the end of this section, and compare these results with those obtained in Problem 24. (Use 3.14159 as an approximation for π.)

27. Use Inequalities (1) and (3), derived in this section, to verify that $\cos x < x/\tan x < 1$, for $0 < x < \frac{1}{2}\pi$.

28. Obtain an inequality similar to (1) that involves $\sin x$ but that does not involve any square roots.

29. Solve the following equations for real x:

(a) $\text{Arctan } (x - 1) = \frac{1}{3}\pi$ (b) $\text{Arcsin } (2x - x^2) = \text{Arcsin } \frac{1}{2}$

30. Solve the following equations for real t:

(a) $\text{Arcsin } \frac{3}{5} + \text{Arccos } \frac{4}{5} = \text{Arcsin } t$

(b) $\text{Arctan } (-\frac{1}{3}) - \text{Arctan } \frac{2}{3} = \text{Arctan } t$

31. Solve the following equations for real x: (a) $\text{Arcsin } (x^2 - 2x) = \text{Arcsin } (-\frac{1}{2})$; (b) $\text{Arctan } (x + 1) = \frac{1}{3}\pi$; (c) $2 \text{ Arcsin } \frac{1}{2}x = \text{Arctan } x$.

32. Find real numbers r, θ, ϕ, with $r > 0, 0 \le \theta \le \pi, 0 \le \phi \le 2\pi$, such that $r \sin \theta \cos \phi = 1 \qquad r \sin \theta \sin \phi = 1 \qquad r \cos \theta = 2$

7

Applications of the Circular Functions: Basic Trigonometry

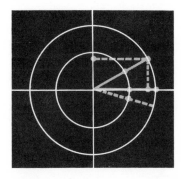

7.1 Simple Harmonic Motion

In §6.5 we considered circular functions defined by equations of the form $y = c \sin (ax + b)$ and $y = c \cos (ax + b)$, with particular attention being paid to their graphs. The principal objective of the present section is to see how such functions arise in the mathematical description of a type of motion of very frequent occurrence in nature. In applications involving motion, the role of the independent variable x is usually played by the "time" variable t.

It should be familiar by now that we have defined $\sin \theta$ and $\cos \theta$ of a real number θ to be, respectively, the ordinate and abscissa of the trigonometric point $P(\theta)$ on the unit circle—a Cartesian coordinate system being assumed for the plane as usual. Recall that θ is the measure of length of the arc from $P(0)$ to $P(\theta) = P$ on the circle. In Figure 58 we have shown the points $P(0)$ and $P(\theta)$, as well as the origin O and the point $Q(x, y)$ at which the extended radius OP intersects the circle of radius r concentric with the unit circle. A consideration of similar triangles shows that the abscissa and ordinate of Q are r times those of P, and we list this result as follows:

The coordinate pair of Q is (x, y), where $x = r \cos \theta$ and $y = r \sin \theta$.

Definition. *The points $M(x, 0)$ and $N(0, y)$, as shown in Figure 58, are the projections of Q on the x-axis and y-axis, respectively.*

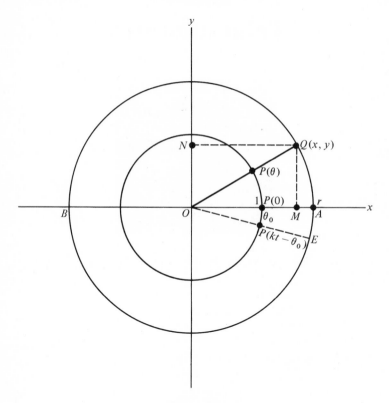

Figure 58

In the present context, we shall speak heuristically of a *particle* as an "atomic" entity whose position at any time may be identified with a single point. Let us then suppose that a particle p is moving in a counterclockwise (positive) direction around the circle of radius r, at a *uniform speed* of kr units of distance per unit of time, $k \in \mathbf{R}$. Our interest is not in p, but rather in the motions of two other "projective" particles p_x and p_y, whose positions at any time are the projections on the axes of the position of p: When p is at Q, p_x is at M and p_y is at N. For simplicity, let us suppose first that the movement of p starts at the point A where its circular path intersects the positive x-axis. Then, as p moves around the circle in the positive direction, p_x moves to the left from A along the x-axis with increasing speed until it reaches O and then with speed decreasing to zero when it reaches the point B where the circle intersects the negative x-axis; p_x then reverses its direction and moves with increasing speed to the right until it reaches O, at which time it begins to move more slowly until its speed at A is zero. The motion of p_x is then repeated indefinitely as p continues its circular motion. The motion of p_y on the y-axis is quite similar, being confined to the interval between the points where the circular path of p intersects the y-axis. In t units of time, the particle p will have traversed a circular arc of length krt, and if Q denotes the position of p at this time, the corresponding arc on the *unit* circle from $P(0)$ to P (which may include one or more complete circumferences), as shown in the figure, is kt units in length. If $P = P(\theta)$, this implies that $\theta = kt$, and the discussion in the preceding paragraph leads to the following descriptions of the motions of the "projective" particles p_x and p_y:

$$p_x\colon \; x = r \cos kt \qquad p_y\colon \; y = r \sin kt$$

These equations give the position of p_x and p_y, t units of time after the parent particle p left the point A on the x-axis.

In the mathematical descriptions that we have just given for the motions of the projective particles p_x and p_y, it was assumed that t was measured from some instant when p was at the point A on the x-axis. However, if t is measured from an instant when p is at some other point E, the (directed) length of the arc $\overset{\frown}{AE}$ being $-r\theta_0$, the corresponding point on the unit circle is $P(kt - \theta_0)$. It follows that, t units of time after p is at E, the positions of p_x and p_y may be described in mathematical terms as follows:

$$p_x\colon \; x = r \cos (kt - \theta_0) \qquad p_y\colon \; y = r \sin (kt - \theta_0)$$

Definition. *If a particle moves on a straight line in such a way that its distance x [or y] in time t from a given point on the line is given by $x = r \cos (kt - \theta_0)$ [or $y = r \sin (kt - \theta_0)$], for real numbers r (> 0), k, θ_0, the motion of the particle is said to be* simple harmonic.

A special case of simple harmonic motion occurs, of course, when $\theta_0 = 0$; this was the supposition in our initial discussion.

Our results have then shown that, if a particle moves with a uniform speed on the circumference of a circle, the motions of its projective particles on any diameter of the circle is simple harmonic. It is clear that motion of this kind is oscillatory and keeps repeating indefinitely—as may also be observed easily from the presence of the sine or cosine functions in its mathematical description. The time required for one cycle of the motion is called the *period* of the motion, and if we denote an appropriate measure of the period by T, it is clear that

$$T = \frac{2\pi}{k}$$

This may be seen to agree with our earlier definitions of the periods of the circular functions that appear in the descriptions of the motions of p_x and p_y. The number of cycles of the motion per unit of time is called its *frequency*, and if we denote the frequency by N, we have

$$N = \frac{1}{T} = \frac{k}{2\pi}$$

The positive number r in the definition measures the *amplitude* of the simple harmonic motion and is the maximum displacement of the moving particle from its central position. When either of the equations is used to describe the motion, the quantity $kt - \theta_0$ is called the *phase* of the motion at time t, and $-\theta_0$ is its *initial phase*. It should be emphasized, however, that the phase of a motion is not a characteristic of the motion itself, but rather of the equations that describe the motion.

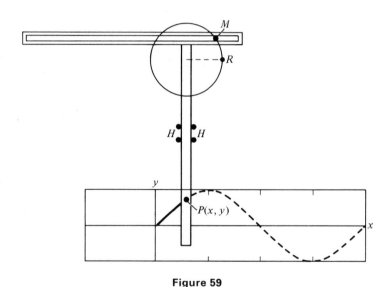

Figure 59

In Figure 59 we have shown a way in which simple harmonic motion can be generated by mechanical means. Let us suppose that the wheel, pictured in the diagram, is rotating uniformly in a positive (counterclockwise) direction, the wheel having a pin at M that fits into, and is free to move in, a slot of the indicated crossarm. If the vertical bar is restricted to vertical motion by the guides at H, any point P on the bar will execute a motion that is simple harmonic. If a tracing pencil is attached to the vertical bar at the point P, bearing upon a piece of paper moving to the left with constant speed, the pencil will trace out a graph of the motion of the point—its details depending on both the speed of the bar and the speed of the paper. The mathematical equation that describes the motion will also depend on the coordinate system used and the relative positions of the points P and M. If P is at the origin when M is on the horizontal diameter of the circle at R, the equation of the motion will be as simple as possible, its initial phase being zero.

If several simple harmonic motions are combined, it is not difficult to discover—either graphically or otherwise—that the result is also a periodic motion. It was shown by Fourier in 1822 that any periodic function f, satisfying certain conditions which we prefer not to detail here, can be decomposed so that $f(t) = a_0 + a_1 \cos h_1 t + b_1 \sin k_1 t + a_2 \cos h_2 t + b_2 \sin h_2 t + \cdots$, where we have used t to suggest time as the usual domain variable. The coefficients $a_0, a_1, b_1, a_2, b_2, \ldots$, as well as $h_1, k_1, h_2, k_2, \ldots$, are real numbers that depend on the characteristics—including the period—of the function f. In view of the presence of the simple harmonic components—the sine and cosine terms— in the expression for $f(x)$, any periodic motion that could be described by such a function is sometimes referred to as *harmonic*. A study of the methods of determining the sine and cosine components of f is called *harmonic analysis* and is the subject of more advanced courses in applied mathematics. We realize that the expression that we have given for $f(t)$ involves an infinite number of terms, and "series" of this kind are studied in a later chapter. However, it should be intuitively clear that our meaning is that, as more and more terms of the harmonic representation of $f(t)$ are included, the sum approaches the value $f(t)$.

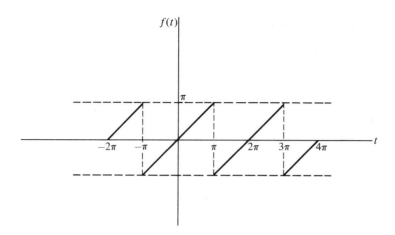

Figure 60

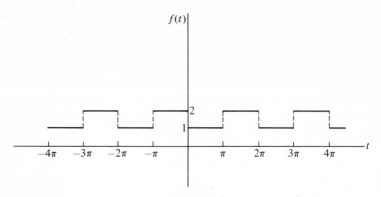

Figure 61

The type of periodic motion that is represented by the simplest Fourier series has period 2π, and, for such a case, $f(t) = a_0 + a_1 \cos t + b_1 \sin t + a_2 \cos 2t + b_2 \sin 2t + \cdots$. Two periodic wave forms of common occurrence in the mathematical description of impulses supplied to electronic equipment (and for each of which we have assumed that the period is 2π) are depicted in Figures 60 and 61. The graph shown in Figure 60—familiarly known as the *sawtooth* curve—is a portion of the graph of the periodic function f of period 2π such that $f(t) = t$ for $-\pi < t < \pi$, the function being undefined for odd multiples of π. The Fourier series that "represents" this function is given by

$$f(t) = 2 \sin t - \tfrac{2}{2} \sin 2t + \tfrac{2}{3} \sin 3t - \tfrac{2}{4} \sin 4t + \cdots$$

In Figure 61 we have shown the graph—known as a *square wave*—of the periodic *step function* f of period 2π and defined so that

$$f(t) = \begin{cases} 1 & 0 < t < \pi \\ 2 & \pi < t < 2\pi \end{cases}$$

The Fourier equation of this step function can be shown to be the following:

$$f(t) = \tfrac{3}{2} - \frac{2}{\pi} \sin t - \frac{2}{3\pi} \sin 3t - \frac{2}{5\pi} \sin 5t - \cdots$$

It is possible to prove that these expressions give adequate representations of the functions, except at those multiples of π where the graphs exhibit a break. At a point where a periodic function has a break, even a large number of terms of its Fourier series may not represent the function because of the presence of "Gibbs phenomenon." (See a book on Fourier Series for a discussion of it.) Although both of these illustrations of a Fourier series do not involve any cosine terms, it should be understood that this is due to the nature of the particular functions being considered. In Figure 62 we have given an indication of how a truncated portion of the Fourier series for a step function may approximate the actual function as more terms are included in its series representation. No attempt has been made in these figures to depict the presence of Gibbs phenomenon—mentioned above—and so the graphs in the vicinity of $t = 0$ should not be considered very accurate.

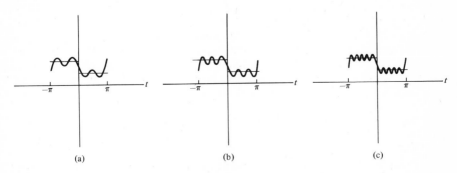

(a)   (b)   (c)

Figure 62

It may be fitting to close this section with a comment of a very general nature. Because $\cos kt = \sin (kt + \frac{1}{2}\pi)$, any motions defined by the equations $y = \sin kt$ and $y = \cos kt$ differ only in phase, the phase difference being $\frac{1}{2}\pi$. The presence of both sine and cosine terms in the analytical expression for a function is then not of particular significance, because either kind can be eliminated by the correct phase shift for these terms.

Problems 7.1

1. Determine the period and amplitude of the simple harmonic motion described by each of the following equations:
   (a) $y = 2 \sin 3t$; (b) $x = 3 \cos 4t$; (c) $y = 3 \sin (10t - \frac{1}{3}\pi)$.
2. Determine the period and amplitude of the simple harmonic motion described by each of the following equations:
   (a) $y = 4 \sin (\frac{2}{3}t + \frac{1}{4}\pi)$; (b) $x = 7 \sin 2\pi t$; (c) $x = 3 \sin \pi t$.
3. Determine the frequency and initial phase of each of the simple harmonic motions described in Problem 1.
4. Determine the frequency and initial phase of each of the simple harmonic motions described in Problem 2.
5. Explain the difference between the simple harmonic motion described by the equation $y = 3 \sin \pi t$ and that described by $y = 3 \sin (\pi t - \frac{1}{4}\pi)$.
6. Sketch a portion of the graph of the function f defined on **R** by $f(x) = 3 \cos 2\pi x$. Use our discussion of simple harmonic motion to express $f(x)$ in the form $r \sin (kx - \theta_0)$, and use Identity (12) of Chapter 6 to check your answer.

7. Explain any differences in the simple harmonic motions described by the equations $y = 3 \sin \pi t$, $y = 6 \sin \pi t$, and $y = 3 \sin (\pi t + \frac{1}{3}\pi)$.

8. With reference to Figure 58, assume that the particle p is initially at A and moves counterclockwise around the circle with a speed of 2 centimeters per second. If the radius of the circular orbit is 10 centimeters, write the equations of motion for the projective particles p_x and p_y.

9. Compare the simple harmonic motions defined by $y = 2 \sin 2t$ and $y = 3 \cos (2t - 2)$.

10. An object moves on a straight line in such a way that its distance x at time t from a given point on the line is given by $x = 4 \cos^2 t$. Show that the motion is simple harmonic, and determine its amplitude and period.

11. The period of a "seconds" pendulum is 2 seconds. If the bob swings a maximum of 3 centimeters on each side of its lowest position, write an equation of motion for the bob, assuming that it is approximately rectilinear and simple harmonic and that time is being measured from an instant when the bob is at its right extremity.

12. Write an equation for the motion of the bob of the pendulum described in Problem 11 if the bob is released $\frac{1}{2}$ second later than in that problem.

13. The period of a pendulum varies directly with the square root of its length. (That is, if the period of a pendulum of length L is T, the period of a pendulum of length bL is $\sqrt{b}T$, for $b > 0$.) Find the period of a pendulum four times as long as that described in Problem 11.

14. Use the information given in Problem 13 to determine the relative length of a pendulum compared with the "seconds" pendulum of Problem 11 if the new pendulum is to make one complete swing every 4 seconds.

15. Use a piece of string with a weight attached, and determine experimentally the ratio of lengths of pendulums having periods of 1 and 2 seconds. Check your result with the assertion in Problem 13.

7.2 Waves, Progressive and Stationary

Let us suppose that a progressive wave is present on the surface of a medium and that the surface particles in a plane perpendicular to the crests at any instant are located on the points of what is familiarly referred to as a *modified sine curve*. We are not assuming that the amplitude is 1 or that the period is 2π, and so the wave form may be appropriately called a "distorted" sine wave. An example of such a wave is an idealized ripple on the surface of a lake or pond, or the wave that travels along a flexible rope when one end is rapidly shaken. It should be pointed out, however, that the ordinary waves on a lake or ocean are not of this type, because their shape is not "sinusoidal." We wish to find an equation, called the *equation of the wave*, that gives the position at each instant of any surface particle that lies in the plane referred to above.

We choose Cartesian coordinate axes in the plane so that, at the instant from which we are measuring time, the equation of the wave—assumed to be momentarily fixed—is $y = a \sin hx$, with a (> 0), $h \in \mathbf{R}$. We know from the discussion in §6.5 on the effect of an additive term on a graph, that a replacement of x by $x - b$ in the equation of a curve effectively displaces the curve b units from its original position in the positive direction of x. *A progressive wave can be considered to be a "fixed" wave that is being continuously displaced in one direction.* Thus, if the velocity of the progressive wave is V, the equation of the wave form in the plane at time t can be given as $y = a \sin h(x - Vt)$, or if we replace hV by k, as $y = a \sin (hx - kt)$. The numbers x and y are the position coordinates in the xy-plane at time t of some particle on the surface of the medium. It is customary to use a terminology similar to that of simple harmonic motion and refer to a as the *amplitude* and to $hx - kt$ as the *phase* of the wave. As in the case of simple harmonic motion, the phase of a wave is dependent on the coordinate frame of reference rather than on the wave itself.

When a wave of the idealized type just described passes through a medium, the individual particles of the medium do not move in the direction of the wave but up and down. In order to study the nature of this vertical motion, let us put $x = c$ in the wave equation, the number c being the x coordinate of the particular particle under study. The vertical position of this particle is then given by $y = a \sin (hc - kt) = -a \sin (kt - hc) = a \sin (kt - hc - \pi)$, an equation that shows that the vertical motion is simple harmonic with period $2\pi/k$. The initial phase of the motion is $-hc - \pi$, this number varying with the particle under consideration. Thus, if a progressive sinusoidal wave passes through a medium with a horizontal surface, the surface particles will oscillate up and down in a motion that is simple harmonic.

The *wave length* of a progressive wave is the horizontal distance between corresponding points on successive cycles, and this distance is clearly the same as the corresponding distance of the basic fixed sine curve whose equation we have designated as $y = a \sin hx$. We shall denote the wave length of either kind of wave by L. Because the abscissa of each point on the curve defined by $y = a \sin hx$ is $1/h$ times the abscissa of the corresponding point on the locus of $y = \sin x$ (see §6.5) whose period is 2π, we conclude that

$$L = \frac{2\pi}{h}$$

It is worthy of note that we speak of the *period* of a *fixed sine curve* and the *wave length* of the associated *progressive sine wave*, but the two are equal. The *period* of a progressive wave is the time required for the wave to travel a distance of one wave length. Thus, if T and V are the period and velocity, respectively, of the progressive wave, we have $L = VT$ and so

$$T = \frac{L}{V} = \frac{2\pi}{hV} = \frac{2\pi}{k}$$

This result shows that the period of a progressive sine wave is equal to the period of the simple harmonic motion executed by any particle of the medium through which the wave is passing. The number of periods per unit of time is the *frequency* N of the progressive wave, whence

$$N = \frac{1}{T} = \frac{k}{2\pi}$$

Because $h = 2\pi/L$ and $k = 2\pi/T$, the equation of a progressive sine wave may be written in either of the two equivalent forms

$$y = a \sin 2\pi \left(\frac{x}{L} - \frac{t}{T} \right) \qquad y = a \sin \frac{2\pi}{L} (x - Vt)$$

In Figure 63 we have shown some wave forms with (*a*) different amplitudes, (*b*) different periods, and (*c*) different phases.

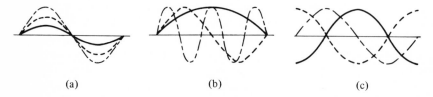

(a) (b) (c)

Figure 63

Let us now consider two progressive sinusoidal waves traveling in the same medium and in the same direction, the respective equations of which are $y = a \sin (2\pi/L)(x - Vt)$ and $y = a \sin (2\pi/L)(x - Vt - E)$, for some real number E. It may be noted that the waves represented by these equations have the same amplitude, same wave length, and same velocity, but at any instant the wave represented by the second equation is E units of distance ahead of the wave represented by the first equation. We refer to E as the *lead* or *lag* of the second wave, according as $E > 0$ or $E < 0$, and this wave characteristic may be considered the analogue of θ_0 introduced in §7.1 for simple harmonic motion.

We refer to the high points of a wave as its *crests*, and to the low points as its *troughs*; the points midway between successive crests and troughs are called *nodes*. If a violin string is vibrated, it takes on the appearance of a sine curve, but there is no progressive wave motion in visual evidence because the crests, troughs, and nodes appear to be stationary. It is only natural to refer to a wave of this kind as *stationary*. It is well known that when a violin string is set into vibration, the note emitted may be either the "fundamental" or a "harmonic." If the only nodes appear at the ends of the string, the note is the fundamental; but if the string vibrates "in segments" with additional nodes in evidence, the note is a harmonic. The manner in which a string is set into vibration determines whether it will be sounding its fundamental or a harmonic tone. In Figure 64 we have shown waves of the stationary kind: that in (*a*) illustrates a fundamental vibration frequency; that in (*b*) illustrates a harmonic.

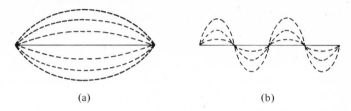

(a)   (b)

Figure 64

A stationary wave in a medium can always be considered the result of a progressive wave traveling in one direction with its "reflection" traveling in the opposite direction. If we assume ideal conditions, with no loss of energy in the reflection, the equations of such a pair of waves can be written—assuming the direction of motion is parallel to the x-axis—in the following form:

$$y = a \sin (hx - kt) \qquad y = a \sin (hx + kt)$$

We assume that the energy of each wave is imparted simultaneously to the particles of the medium through which the waves are passing, and the position (x, y) of an arbitrary particle on the surface of the medium in the vertical plane under consideration may then be described as follows:

$$y = a \sin (hx - kt) + a \sin (hx + kt) = a[\sin (hx - kt) + \sin (hx + kt)]$$
$$= 2a \cos kt \sin hx$$

(See Problem 10 of §6.7.) If we replace h and k by $2\pi/L$ and $2\pi/T$, respectively, the following alternative form for the equation of the stationary wave results:

$$y = 2a \cos \frac{2\pi t}{T} \sin \frac{2\pi x}{L}$$

It is instructive to consider that $|2a \cos (2\pi t/T)|$ is the continuously changing amplitude of the wave described analytically by the equation

$$y = 2a \cos \frac{2\pi t}{T} \sin \frac{2\pi x}{L}$$

In fact, as t increases from 0 to $T/2$, the amplitude of the wave changes from $2a$ to 0 and back to $2a$, at which time the cycle is repeated. It follows that, although a stationary wave has no horizontal motion, the amplitude at any point is changing so rapidly in a vertical direction that the eye does not detect the movement. It is for this reason, of course, that waves like this are called *stationary*.

It may be that the reader is a bit perplexed by our inclusion of these two sections on periodic motion. After all, this is material of interest principally to applied mathematicians! This is very true, but as our historical survey has intended to point out, the nature of trigonometric or circular functions has had a great change in emphasis in recent years, and that change has been in the transition of the domains of these functions to subsets of real numbers. It then seems only appropriate to include a few illustrations of physical situations in which circular functions play a role compatible with this modern emphasis. In the illustrations of these two sections, the circular functions that appeared were functions of the real "time" variable t. In the following and subsequent sections, we revert to a consideration of angles and the more traditional approach to trigonometry. Even though this so-called *basic trigonometry* is no longer as important as in former times, the student of mathematics should have some familiarity with it for historical—if for no other—reasons.

Problems 7.2

1. Find the amplitude and velocity of propagation of the progressive wave whose equation is:

   (a) $y = 2 \sin (5x - 3t)$ (b) $y = 10 \sin (x/3 - t/2)$

   (c) $y = 50 \sin \frac{2}{15}\pi(x - 15t - 3)$

2. Find the amplitude and velocity of propagation of the progressive wave whose equation is

   (a) $y = 100 \sin (5x + 3t)$ (b) $y = 0.25 \sin \frac{2}{3}\pi \dfrac{(x + 4t)}{3}$

   (c) $y = 40 \sin (0.75x + 100t)$

3. Determine the wave length and period of each of the waves described by the equations in Problem 1.

4. Determine the wave length and period of each of the waves described by the equations in Problem 2.

5. A sinusoidal wave is traveling with a velocity of 3 miles per hour, has a wave length of 15 feet, and reaches a maximum height of 3 feet. Write an equation for this progressive wave, assuming an appropriate coordinate system.

6. The velocity of sound in still air at 70°F is approximately 1130 feet per second. Determine approximations for the wave lengths of sound waves with respective frequencies of 128, 200, 300, and 600 cycles per second.

7. A string of length 20 centimeters is vibrating in two segments with a frequency of 150 cycles per second. If the amplitude of the resulting stationary wave is 1 centimeter, give its equation with appropriate assumptions with regard to coordinates.

8. If the string in Problem 7 is vibrating in three segments, write the equation of the resulting wave.

9. Describe the wave motions that are described in mathematical terms by the following equations:

   (a) $y = 10 \cos 3\pi t \sin \pi x$ (b) $y = 2 \cos \frac{1}{5}t \sin \frac{1}{6}x$

10. The surface of a landlocked body of water is sometimes set into vibration by natural causes, the stationary wave form that appears being called a *seiche*. In the case of a seiche, however, the shores—unlike the end points of a vibrating string—are not nodes but crests. If a uninodal (i.e., with one node) seiche observed on a small pond 200 meters wide has a period of 15 seconds and an amplitude of 10 centimeters, determine an equation for the wave form.

11. Determine an equation for a binodal (i.e., with two nodes) seiche on the pond in Problem 10 if the period of the wave is 10 seconds and its amplitude is 8 centimeters.

12. Draw rough sketches of the instantaneous appearance of two progressive waves that are identical except that (a) their amplitudes are in the ratio $1:2$; (b) their wave lengths are in the ratio $1:4$; (c) their phases differ by a quarter of a wave length.

13. The equation of a progressive wave is given as $y = 5 \sin (x/3 + 4t)$. Write the corresponding equation of a similar wave with (a) a lead of 10 units; (b) a lag of 5 units.

14. If a wheel of diameter 6 feet is rotating at the uniform rate of 25 revolutions per minute, find an equation that describes the *vertical* motion of a point (x, y) on the rim of the wheel at any time t, assuming that $t = 0$ when (x, y) is at its lowest point.

15. Let a wheel of radius r be considered to roll (without any slippage) along a straight line assumed to be the x-axis. Moreover, let us assume that $P(x, y)$ is the point on the rim of the wheel that originally passed through the origin. If θ is the length of arc on the wheel, as measured from the initial position of P at the origin, show that $x = r(\theta - \sin \theta)$ and $y = r(1 - \cos \theta)$. Eliminate the parameter θ, and show that the equation of the first arch of the curve (a *cycloid*) traced out by P can also be expressed in the form $x = r \operatorname{Arccos} (1 - y/r) \pm \sqrt{2ry - y^2}$.

7.3 Angles and Trigonometric Functions

Although angles and triangles have made their appearances in our development of the circular, or trigonometric, functions in preceding sections, the roles played by them have been very minor and in fact incidental to the main theory. Because the word "trigonometry" is derived from the latin word *trigonometria*— meaning *the measurement of triangles*—this lack of emphasis on triangles so far might have come as somewhat of a surprise had it not been for our historical discussion of the way in which the emphasis of trigonometry has changed in modern times. However, the remainder of this chapter will be devoted to a study of basic trigonometry—with angles and triangles—and we shall see that the results are corollary to the general theory in Chapter 6. Our point of view in these sections will be, of course, that of geometry.

The concepts of *point*, *line*, and *plane* are the undefined but intuitive ingredients of plane geometry. The only property of a point is *position*, but with any two distinct points there arises the notion of their *linear separation* or *distance apart*. This distance is the length of the line segment joining the points, and it can be measured with the help of an algebraic scale or familiar "ruler." Moreover, if we designate one of the points as *initial* and the other as *terminal*, and use the positive portion of the scale with its zero falling on the initial point, the distance measured will be *positive* and *unique*.

The concept of an *angle* is a difficult one to define, and so one is apt to find many different definitions of it. A person with an inclination toward geometry may be sympathetic with the definition of an angle as "a geometrical figure composed of two distinct rays or line segments emanating from a single point," or as the "opening" between two such rays or segments. However, it should be clear that neither of these could be acceptable as an accurate mathematical definition. Perhaps one can come closest to the idea of an angle by using analogy, and considering the concepts of angle and line segment as analogous. A line segment is the "linear separation" of two *points*, with its length a measure of this separation; an angle is the "rotational separation" of two intersecting *rays* or *line segments* (one considered to have been rotated about their point of intersection) and the size of the angle between them is a measure of the rotational separation of the rays or segments. In other words, the notion of "angle" can be considered to play a role in "rotational distance" that is analogous to that played by "line segment" in linear distance. But *both concepts remain essentially intuitive in* nature! We shall then regard line segments and angles as intuitively familiar and refrain from making any serious attempt to define either of them.

We have already used the terminology of "initial" and "terminal" point when referring to a line segment; such a segment may be considered *directed* from its initial to its terminal point. In an analogous way, with an angle regarded as an amount of rotation of one line segment about its point of intersection with another, one of the line segments may be designated the *initial* and the other the *terminal* segment. In harmony with our measurement of arc length on a unit circle, it is only natural to consider a counterclockwise rotation as generating a *positive* angle, whereas a clockwise rotation generates one that is *negative*. If we are indifferent to its mode of generation—as is usually the case in studies of Euclidean geometry—no direction will be assigned to the angle. For the purpose of diagrams, it is convenient to use a curved arrow to denote a directed angle; a curved double arrow will often denote one whose direction is unimportant. It is seldom of *geometric* interest to consider angles greater than one complete rotation, and those of most frequent occurrence are, in fact, less than half a rotation. No such limitation on the size of an angle is mandatory, and we shall not impose one in our discussions unless so specified. The language used to describe angles will reflect a geometric bias, and so we shall refer to the *vertex* and *sides* of an angle—the sides being *initial* and *terminal* if the angle is directed. In Figure 65 we have shown three angles, those in (*a*) and (*b*) being directed, and that in (*c*) without specific direction.

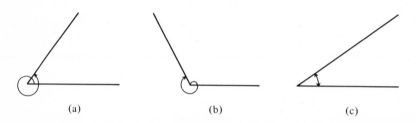

(a)   (b)   (c)

Figure 65

In our historical survey, we made an occasional reference to the familiar system of measuring angles in terms of degrees and their component parts. In this system, the "circle" (or one complete rotation of a line segment about an end point) is divided into 360 equal parts, each of which is called a *degree*. An angle of 1 degree may be subdivided into 60 equal parts called *minutes*, and a minute may be further subdivided into 60 equal parts called *seconds*. The symbolism used to denote an angle of, say, 60 degrees, 25 minutes, and 40 seconds is 60°25′40″. Although this is the familiar measuring system in which to denote angles, there is another system of much greater theoretical use and one that provides us with the measure that is essential for our study of the *analytic* trigonometry of angles.

Definition.   *The measure of an angle is* 1 radian *if its sides intercept on the unit circle with center at the vertex of the angle an arc of unit length.*

Because we have previously discussed the notion of arc length for a circle, this definition is quite meaningful. As a preliminary comment, it may be noted that a radian is a fairly large angle as compared with a degree. In Figure 66, we have depicted an angle of 1 radian (denoted 1 rad), and it may be seen to be "of the order" of 60°—although 57.3° is a closer approximation.

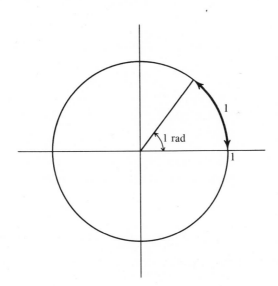

Figure 66

It may be worthwhile at this time to call attention to the fact that it is customary to be somewhat ambiguous in referring to angles, the ambiguity arising from our apparent identification of an angle with its measure. For example, we may refer to "an angle of 60°" or "an angle of $\frac{1}{3}\pi$ radians," when, if we insisted on absolute correctness of language, we should say "an angle whose measure is 60°"" or "an angle whose measure is $\frac{1}{3}\pi$ radians." However, this ambiguity is common practice and does not lead to any difficulty in understanding what is meant. In other words, *our symbolism will usually not distinguish an angle from its measure in either system of measurement*, and equalities such as $A = 60° = \frac{1}{3}\pi$ radians will be of frequent occurrence. In view of our definition above, it is immediate that π radians $= 180°$, and it is often useful to remember the following approximations relating the degree and radian units of angle measurement:

$$1 \text{ radian} = \left(\frac{180}{\pi}\right)^{\circ} \approx 57.3°$$

$$1° = \frac{\pi}{180} \text{ radians} \approx 0.01745 \text{ radian}$$

Example 1.   Determine (a) the radian measure of 90° and 45°; (b) the degree measure of 3 radians (an approximation) and $\frac{1}{3}\pi$ radians.

SOLUTION

(a) $90° = 90\left(\frac{\pi}{180}\right)$ radians $= \frac{\pi}{2}$ radians

$45° = 45\left(\frac{\pi}{180}\right)$ radians $= \frac{\pi}{4}$ radians

(b) 3 radians $= \left[3\left(\frac{180}{\pi}\right)\right]^{\circ} = \left(\frac{540}{\pi}\right)^{\circ} \approx 171.9°$

$\frac{1}{3}\pi$ radians $= \left[\left(\frac{\pi}{3}\right)\left(\frac{180}{\pi}\right)\right]^{\circ} = 60°$

Example 2.   Determine the approximate radian measure of 22° and the approximate degree measure of 3.2 radians

SOLUTION

$$22° = \left[22\left(\frac{\pi}{180}\right)\right] \text{ radians} = \frac{11}{90}\pi \text{ radians} \approx 0.3840 \text{ radian}$$

$$3.2 \text{ radians} = \left[3.2\left(\frac{180}{\pi}\right)\right]^{\circ} \approx 183°$$

The radian measure for an angle makes it a very suitable one to use in a determination of the length of a circular arc whose subtended central angle is known. It follows immediately from the definition of a radian that, if the angle between two radii on a unit circle is θ radians, the length of the intercepted arc is θ—assuming the length of a radius as the unit of length. This remains true, of course, regardless of how many complete circumferences of the circle (or complete angular rotations) are involved. It is of even greater importance that a simple relationship exists between a length of arc and its associated central angle on *any* circle of radius *r*—with *r* not necessarily equal to 1. The situation for an arc of less than half a circumference is depicted in Figure 67, but the

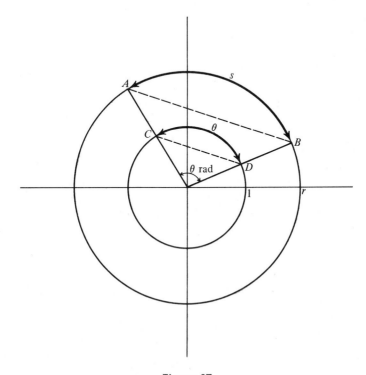

Figure 67

argument can easily be extended to an arc of arbitrary length. As recalled in §6.2, circular arcs are proportional in length to their subtended chords; and a consideration of similar triangles in the figure shows that $|AB|/|CD| = s/\theta = r/1$, in which an arc of length s subtends a central angle of θ radians, with AB and CD the indicated chords. It is important to note that the measure of length of the arc $\overset{\frown}{CD}$ on the unit circle is the same θ as the radian measure of the central angle. We have then obtained the following important result:

$$s = r\theta$$

At the risk of overlaboring the point, we emphasize that this formula is valid only if θ is the *radian* measure of the central angle.

Example 3. An arc 3 units in length is intercepted on a circle of radius 7 units by the sides of an angle. Determine the radian measure of the angle.

SOLUTION. Because $s = r\theta$, we have $3 = 7\theta$ and so we conclude that $\theta = \frac{3}{7}$. The desired measure of the angle is then $\frac{3}{7}$ of a radian.

Example 4. Find the length of the arc intercepted on a circle of radius 6 inches by a central angle of $22°$.

SOLUTION. By the result in Example 2, $22° \approx 0.3840$ radian. We now use the formula $s = r\theta$ to obtain the desired arc length as s inches, where $s \approx 6(0.3840) \approx 2.3$.

Whenever a motion is under study, the notion of *velocity* naturally arises. In the case of constant linear motion, as the reader knows, the (linear) velocity is the ratio of distance to time or, otherwise expressed, the *distance per unit of time*. If a particle moves with a constant velocity along the circumference of a circle, it is only natural also to consider the velocity of the particle for this type of nonlinear motion as the distance per unit of time—inasmuch as we have given precise meaning to the notion of distance on a circular arc. If the particle moves with a constant velocity v along the arc of a circle, we then let $v = s/t$, where the particle traverses s units of distance along the circle in t units of time. In view of the basic formula $s = r\theta$, introduced earlier, there is a natural connection between v and $\omega = \theta/t$, the latter being referred to as the associated *angular velocity* of the particle in radians per unit of time. The formula for the angular velocity ω of a particle associated with the velocity v of the particle along an arc of a circle of radius r is then

$$v = r\omega$$

In other words, the "ordinary" velocity of a particle moving uniformly along an arc of a circle of radius r is r times its angular velocity.

Example 5. A circular wheel of radius 6 inches is rotating at the rate of 100 revolution per minute. Determine the speed of a point on its rim.

SOLUTION. An angular velocity of 100 revolutions per minute is equivalent to $100(2\pi) = 200\pi$ radians per minute. Because $v = r\omega$, where $\omega = 200\pi$, we obtain $v = 6(200\pi) = 1200\pi$. The desired speed of a point on the rim is then $1200\pi \approx 3770$ inches per minute.

Problems 7.3

1. Determine an approximation in degree measure for each of the following angles: (a) 2.5 radians; (b) 1.6 radians; (c) 5 radians; (d) -3.2 radians; (e) -6 radians.
2. Determine an approximation in degree measure for each of the following angles: (a) $\frac{1}{7}\pi$ radians; (b) $\frac{2}{3}\pi$ radians; (c) $\frac{4}{3}\pi$ radians; (d) $-\frac{5}{6}\pi$ radians; (e) $\frac{6}{7}\pi$ radians.
3. Express each of the following angles in radian measure involving π: (a) $30°$; (b) $-225°$; (c) $135°$; (d) $-270°$; (e) $240°$; (f) $-315°$.

4. Determine a two-decimal approximation in radian measure for each of the following angles: (a) $34°$; (b) $162°$; (c) $26°36'$; (d) $35°24'$; (e) $-72°$; (f) $-132°42'$.

5. Give a sketch to denote an angle of (a) $90°$; (b) $-90°$; (c) $270°$; (d) $-270°$; (e) $450°$; (f) $-450°$.

6. Give a rough sketch to denote an angle of (a) $250°$; (b) $-250°$; (c) $590°$; (d) $-590°$; (e) $1000°$; (f) $-1000°$.

7. Take any radius of a unit circle as the initial side and give a rough sketch of a central angle of (a) 2 radians; (b) -2 radians; (c) 3 radians; (d) -3 radians; (e) 10 radians; (f) -10 radians.

8. If an arc on a circle of radius 12 inches is 3.2 inches in length, find the central angle subtended by the arc (a) in radians; (b) in degrees.

9. On a circle of radius r, what is the radian measure of the central angle subtended by an arc of length (a) $2r$, (b) $3r$; (c) $7r/2$; (d) πr?

10. The radius of a circle is 6 inches in length. Find the length of arc intercepted by two radii if the angle between them is (a) $\frac{1}{3}\pi$ radians; (b) $\frac{5}{6}\pi$ radians; (c) $\frac{7}{6}\pi$ radians.

11. The radius of a circle is 12 inches in length. Find (in terms of π) the length of arc intercepted by two radii if the angle between them is (a) $15°$; (b) $75°$; (c) $245°$; (d) $10°$.

12. What length of arc is intercepted on a circle of circumference 24 inches by a central angle of $32°36'$?

13. A circle has a 5-inch radius. Determine (in terms of π) the length of arc intercepted by a central angle of (a) $\frac{1}{6}\pi$ radians; (b) $\frac{2}{3}\pi$ radians; (c) $\frac{5}{6}\pi$ radians.

14. Determine the approximate length of arc intercepted on a circle of radius 10 inches by a central angle of (a) $30°$; (b) $43°$; (c) $73°36'$.

15. On a Cartesian plane, sketch two positive and two negative angles whose initial sides lie along the positive x-axis and whose terminal sides pass through the point (a) $(3, 5)$; (b) $(-1, 5)$; (c) $(-3, -4)$.

16. Decide which member of each of the following pairs of angles is the larger: (a) 2.1 radians, $150°$; (b) $140°$, 2.3 radians; (c) $\sqrt{2}$ radians, $81.5°$.

17. Using the familiar notation for a trigonometric point $P(\theta)$, find the central angle (in radians) subtended by the minimal positive arc from $P(0)$ to $P(\theta)$, where (a) $P(\theta) = (\sqrt{3}/2, \frac{1}{2})$; (b) $P(\theta) = (-1/\sqrt{2}, -1/\sqrt{2})$; (c) $P(\theta) = (0, -1)$.

18. Use the directions given in Problem 17, but with the arc assumed to be negative and $|\theta|$ of minimal length.

19. The speed of the wheel of a 5-horsepower steam turbine is 20,000 revolutions per minute. Find the angular velocity of the wheel in radians per second.

20. If a car traveled, at a constant speed, a distance of 252 miles in 4 hours, what was its speed? If the speed varied but the same total distance was covered in the same time, what was the average speed of the car? If the driver took a 30-minute coffee break during the trip, but covered the same distance in the same total elapsed time, what was the average speed of the car during its time in motion?

21. A diameter of the sun subtends, at a point on the earth, an angle of approximately 0.0093 radian. If we assume that the distance of the sun is 93,000,000 miles, determine the approximate length of its diameter.

22. If we assume that the earth is a sphere of diameter 8000 miles, find the approximate distance between two points on the equator located at $72°W$ longitude and $95°E$ longitude, respectively.

23. A wheel of radius 10 inches is rotating at the constant rate of 25 revolutions per minute. Determine (a) the angular velocity in radians per second of a spoke of the wheel; (b) the velocity in inches per second of a point on the rim of the wheel.

24. Determine, in degrees, the angle between the two hands of a clock at (a) 9:00; (b) 12:30; (c) 2:15.

25. Find the approximate acute angle between the positions of the hands of a clock when they are together near 2:10 and near 3:15.

26. How many times do the hands of a clock meet between noon and midnight of the same day? Use this result to do Problem 25.

27. Two angles have their initial sides along the positive x-axis and their vertices at the origin of a Cartesian plane. If the radian measure of one is θ and the other is $\theta - [\theta/2\pi]2\pi$, show that the terminal sides of the angles coincide.

28. Derive the formula $S = r^2\theta/2$ for the area S of a sector of a circle of radius r and central angle θ radians. (*Hint:* Observe that the area of a circular sector is proportional to the size of its central angle.)

29. Use the formula in Problem 28 to find the area of a sector of a circle of radius 10 inches with a central angle of 30°.

30. An arc of length s on a circle of radius $r(s < \frac{1}{2}\pi r)$ is bounded by two radii separated by an angle of θ radians. If a line segment is drawn tangent to the circle at the end of one radius until it intersects an extension of the other and if we denote the length of this segment by t, prove that $s < t$.

31. The earth orbits the sun in a path that is approximately a circle of radius 93,000,000 miles. Determine, approximately, how far the earth travels in its orbit in one day.

7.4   Trigonometric Functions of Angles

The circular functions have been defined in Chapter 6 in such a way that they share a common property with the other elementary functions of mathematics: their domains and ranges are both subsets of real numbers. In other words, for any element x in the domain of any elementary—possibly a circular—function f, both x and $f(x)$ are real numbers. It was pointed out in the historical interlude, however, that in its earlier development the subject of trigonometry was much more involved with angles and triangles than it is at the present time. It is our intention in the remaining sections of this chapter to examine this historical—but still important—application of the circular functions. The key to this geometric application will be to redefine the circular functions—which in this context will always be called *trigonometric*—so that their domains are sets of *angles* rather than real numbers. We shall retain the same names for these trigonometric functions of angles as those for the circular functions of real numbers, the ambiguity of terminology being removed with the knowledge of their domains.

Definition.   *If θ is a real number in the domain of a circular function T, and A is an angle whose radian measure is θ, we define the associated trigonometric function T such that $T(A) = T(\theta)$. The domain of the trigonometric function is clearly the subset of angles whose radian measures appear in the domain of the circular function with the same name.*

For example, because $\sin \frac{1}{2}\pi = 1$, our definition asserts the existence of another "sine" function such that $\sin A = 1$, where A is an angle of 90° or $\frac{1}{2}\pi$ radians. Similarly, because $\cos \frac{1}{3}\pi = \frac{1}{2}$, we are defining another "cosine" function such that $\cos B = \frac{1}{2}$, where B is an angle of 60° or $\frac{1}{3}\pi$ radians. In fact, the above definition defines *six* new basic functions called *sine, cosine, tangent, cotangent, secant,* and *cosecant* that are related in a very simple way to those with the same names defined in Chapter 6. In this section, however, we shall take a closer look at these trigonometric functions, in order to familiarize ourselves with them. All of our observations will be simple corollaries of results obtained earlier for circular functions.

Inasmuch as the trigonometric functions involve angles, and we have discussed two ways to measure angles—in the degree and the radian systems—the reader should observe that in Table 2 we have provided an automatic conversion from degree to radian measure for angles measured to the nearest tenth of a degree. We note, for example, that $20.4° \approx 0.3560$, but it should be emphasized that these conversion values are only approximations. Because the circular—and so also the trigonometric—functions are periodic, the table provides us with the domain coverage needed for any function of either kind. If one is interested in values not listed in the table, it will be necessary to use some sort of "interpolation" procedure, and "linear interpolation" is the one most commonly adopted. In this method—as we have seen earlier—the assumption is made that the two sets of values vary in a "linear" or "proportional" way. Even though the reader is already familiar with this procedure, we nevertheless include an example in the present context.

Example 1. Use Table 2 to approximate (a) 38.57° in radians; (b) 0.6115 radian in degrees.

SOLUTION

(a) Because 38.57° lies between 38.5° and 38.6°, the radian measure of 38.57° lies between 0.6720 and 0.6737. The latter two numbers differ by 0.0017, and so—*by linear interpolation*—we must increase the radian measure of 38.5° by $\frac{7}{10}(0.0017) = 0.00119 \approx 0.0012$. Hence $38.57° \approx (0.6720 + 0.0012)$ radians $= 0.6732$ radian.

(b) The radian value $\theta = 0.6115$ lies between the two table entries of 0.6109 and 0.6126, and so the desired degree value must lie between 35.0 and 35.1. The difference between the two radian values is 0.0017, and the given value exceeds the smaller by 0.0006. It then follows *by linear interpolation* that we must increase the degree value of 0.6109 radians by $[(0.0006/0.0017)(0.1)]° = [(6/17)(0.1)]° \approx 0.0353° \approx 0.04°$, and so 0.6115 radian $\approx 35.00° + 0.04° = 35.04°$.

We now return to the main theme of this section: the relationship between the circular and trigonometric functions with the same names. It was pointed out by a simple geometric argument that if trigonometric points $P(\theta)$ on the unit circle are symmetrically placed with respect to either coordinate axis or the origin, the circular functions of the various values of θ involved differ at most in sign. The matter of sign, moreover, can easily be decided from the quadrant in which $P(\theta)$ lies. These results—obtained geometrically in §6.2—were restated in part in §6.7 with the help of the addition formulas. It is useful at this time to reformulate this principle, which is of importance for both the circular and trigonometric functions, but first we need a couple of closely related definitions.

Definition. *If $P(\theta)$ is any trigonometric point on the unit circle, the length $(\leq \frac{1}{2}\pi)$ of the minimal arc between $P(\theta)$ and the x-axis is called the reference number for θ. (It should be noted that any reference number is nonnegative.)*

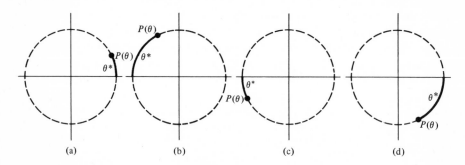

Figure 68

In Figure 68, we have shown the four possible situations that can arise depending on the quadrant in which $P(\theta)$ is located. It is now possible to state a general principle for circular functions that will include as special cases some of the identities given in §6.7.

Reduction Principle for Circular Functions. *If θ is any number in the domain of a circular function T, and θ^* is the reference number for θ, then $|T(\theta)| = T(\theta^*)$.*

In Chapter 6 we have seen many applications of what we have just called the Reduction Principle for Circular Functions, but we give a further illustration with the help of Table 2 and linear interpolation.

Example 2. Use the Reduction Principle and Table 2 to determine
(a) sin 9.1546; (b) tan 8.5966.

SOLUTION

(a) If $\theta = 9.1546$, the reference number $\theta^* = 9.1546 - \frac{5}{2}\pi \approx 1.3006$. We find by linear interpolation in Table 2 that sin 9.1546 $\approx$ 0.9637, having noted that the algebraic sign of sin 9.1546 is positive.

(b) If $\theta = 8.5966$, the reference number $\theta^* = 3\pi - 8.5966 \approx 0.8282$. We now find from Table 2, with linear interpolation, that tan 8.5966 $\approx$ -1.0895, the algebraic sign being negative because the point $P(8.5966)$ is in the second quadrant.

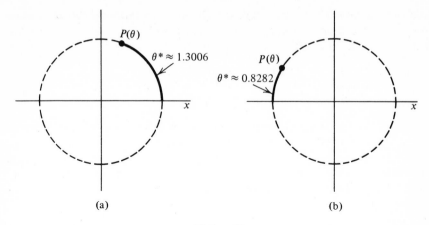

(a)   (b)

Figure 69

The geometric aspects of Example 2 are illustrated in Figure 69.

We are now in a position to define the notion of a *reference angle* and the related Reduction Principle for Trigonometric Functions.

Definition.   *If an angle A is in* standard position *on a Cartesian plane (i.e., its vertex is at the origin and its initial side lies along the positive x-axis), the positive acute angle A* between the terminal side of the angle and the x-axis is called the* reference angle *of A.*

It is clear that, if $A = \theta$ radians, the reference angle A^* intercepts on the unit circle, *between the terminal side of A and the x-axis, an arc of length θ^*—the reference number of θ.* This is depicted in Figure 70.

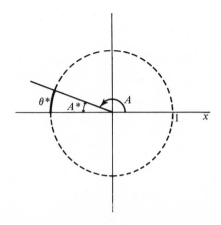

Figure 70

In view of the relationships between the circular and trigonometric functions, and between reference numbers and reference angles, we may now state the Reduction Principle for Trigonometric Functions.

Reduction Principle for Trigonometric Functions. *If A is an angle in the domain of a trigonometric function T, and A* is the reference angle for A, then* $|T(A)| = T(A^*)$.

As for circular functions, the sign of $T(A)$ can be determined from the quadrant through which the terminal side of the angle A passes.

Example 3.   Use the Reduction Principle and Table 2 to determine
(a) cos 245.62°; (b) csc 504.65°.

SOLUTION

(a) If $A = 245.62°$, we see easily that $A^* = 65.62°$. We observe that the terminal side of A passes through the third quadrant, and so we find from Table 2 (with linear interpolation) that cos 245.62° = $-\cos 65.62° \approx -0.4128$. (It should be noted that the cosine function is decreasing in the neighborhood of A^* in this problem, and so the interpolated quantity must be subtracted from cos 65.6°.)

(b) If $A = 504.65°$, we find without difficulty that $A^* = 35.35°$. The terminal side of A passes through the second quadrant, and so csc 504.65° = csc 35.35° ≈ 1.7284, from a simple linear interpolation in Table 2. (We note again in this case that, in the vicinity of this A^*, the cosecant function is decreasing, and so we must subtract the interpolated difference from csc 35.3°.)

The geometric aspects of both parts of this example are shown in Figure 71.

We have now reached the point in our development of the trigonometric functions (of angles) at which it is possible, with the help of Table 2, to find an

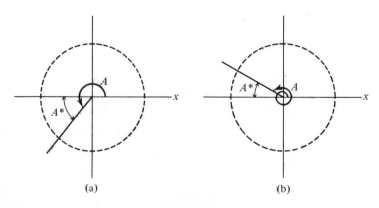

(a)   (b)

Figure 71

approximation for $T(A)$, for any trigonometric function T and any angle A in its domain. Before proceeding to our brief study of triangles in the two subsequent sections, the way in which the circular functions (of numbers) and the trigonometric functions (of angles) have been defined should make the following assertion clear: All identities, including the basic 20 derived in Chapter 6 for the circular functions, remain valid for the trigonometric functions, the number x (or θ) in the earlier identities being replaced by the angle A. For example, the very important Identity (6) could now be written as an identity for trigonometric functions in the form

$$\sin^2 A + \cos^2 A = 1 \qquad \text{for any angle } A$$

However, the two sets of identities should be considered equivalent, and it is not really necessary to change the variable x or θ—usually associated with real numbers—to an "angle" variable A. It will always be clear from the context whether the universe of a variable is to be regarded as a subset of real numbers or of angles. In spite of this, for the sake of clarity, we shall often prefer to use A to denote an angle variable. It is quite irrelevant, of course, whether angles are to be measured in degrees or radians—unless directions specify otherwise. The mathematical purist will probably deny the existence of what we have been referring to as the trigonometric functions (of angles) and will insist that only circular functions (of real numbers) are needed! However, anyone who makes real use of trigonometry will allow both kinds of functions and will adjust his thinking to whichever one best meets his needs of the moment.

Problems 7.4

Note: In this set of problems, it is assumed that full use is to be made of Table 2 along with any linear interpolation needed.

1. Find an approximate radian measure of each of the following angles:
   (a) 23.57°; (b) 48.28°; (c) 39.94°; (d) 18.37°; (e) 80.46°.
2. Find an approximate radian measure of each of the following angles:
   (a) $-26.47°$; (b) $-86.46°$; (c) $-49.92°$; (d) $-84.38°$; (e) $-74.78°$.
3. Find an approximate degree measure of each of the following angles:
   (a) 1.3548 radians; (b) 0.6395 radian; (c) 1.4629 radians; (d) 0.1957 radian;
   (e) 1.0136 radians.
4. Find an approximate degree measure of each of the following angles:
   (a) -1.5394 radians; (b) -1.4207 radians; (c) -0.9743 radian;
   (d) -0.2984 radian; (e) -0.1111 radian.
5. Use $\pi = 3.14159$ and find the approximate reference number associated with each of the following:
   (a) 1.9735; (b) 2.5693; (c) 5.7634; (d) 9.1046; (e) 15.1365.
6. Use $\pi = 3.14159$ and find the approximate reference number associated with each of the following:
   (a) -1.3659; (b) -3.6592; (c) -8.6539; (d) -12.546; (e) -21.654.

7. If $A = 90° = \frac{1}{2}\pi$ radians, what are the differences in *concept* between sin A, sin 90°, and sin $\frac{1}{2}\pi$? They are all considered to have the same value, but which of them involve(s) symbolism that is slightly inaccurate?

8. We know that sin $\frac{1}{2}\pi = 1$, but do we need to know anything about the nature of the quantity measured by $\frac{1}{2}\pi$? Generalize to $T(\theta)$, for any real number θ in the domain of any circular function T.

9. Determine an approximation for each of the following:
   (a) sin 2.5467; (b) cos 1.5397; (c) tan 5.3269; (d) sec 8.3546.

10. Determine an approximation for each of the following:
    (a) cos 13.472; (b) csc 10.643; (c) sin 21.54; (d) tan 6.7543.

11. Determine an approximation for each of the following:
    (a) sin (-3.4569); (b) cos (-13.6540); (c) cot (-9.1754); (d) sec 5.4300.

12. Determine an approximation for each of the following:
    (a) sin 4.327 radians; (b) cos 6.4392 radians; (c) cot 15.692 radians;
    (d) tan 15.15 radians.

13. Determine an approximation for each of the following:
    (a) sin $(-0.534$ radian); (b) tan $(-4.652$ radians); (c) sec $(-14.67$ radians);
    (d) cot $(-21$ radians).

14. Determine an approximation for each of the following:
    (a) sin 56.43°; (b) cos 69.52°; (c) tan 15.73°; (d) csc 48.64°.

15. Determine an approximation for each of the following:
    (a) sin 138.65°; (b) cos 239.76°; (c) sec 358.94°; (d) tan 448.62°.

16. Determine an approximation for each of the following:
    (a) sin 735.46°; (b) cos 439.62°; (c) cot 295.64°; (d) sec 1000.56°.

17. (a) sin $(-146.65°)$; (b) cos $(-538.62°)$; (c) csc $(-136.82°)$;
    (d) tan $(-600.65°)$.

18. Determine an approximation for each of the following:
    (a) sin 15°36′; (b) cos 138°24′; (c) tan $(-138°48′)$; (d) sec $(-34°12′)$.

19. Determine an approximation for each of the following:
    (a) sin 135°37′48″; (b) cos $(-217°49′36″)$; (c) tan $(-296°38′12″)$;
    (d) csc 700°52′54″.

20. Express, in terms of the appropriate trigonometric functions of an angle A (or angles A and B), the identities listed in Chapter 6 as
    (a) Elementary Identities (1) to (8)
    (b) Addition formulas (9) to (14)
    (c) Double-angle and half-angle formulas (15) to (20)

21. Sketch a graph of the trigonometric function f defined on the appropriate maximal subset of the *angle interval* $[-360°, 360°]$ by
    (a) $f(A) = 2 \sin A$; (b) $f(A) = -3 \cos A$; (c) $f(A) = -2 \tan A$.

22. Sketch a graph of the trigonometric function f defined on the appropriate maximal subset of the *angle interval* $[-360°, 360°]$ by
    (a) $f(A) = 2 + 3 \sin A$; (b) $f(A) = -2 + \cos A$; (c) $f(A) = -3 + \tan A$.

23. Sketch a graph of the trigonometric function f defined on the *angle interval* $[-360°, 360°]$ by
    (a) $f(A) = \sin 2A$; (b) $f(A) = 2 \sin 3A$; (c) $f(A) = 1 - 2 \cos 2A$.

24. Solve each of the following equations for $A \in [0°, 360°]$:
    (a) $2 \cos A - 1 = 0$ (b) $\sin A + \cos A = 1$

25. Solve each of the following equations for $A \in [-180°, 180°]$:
    (a) $\cos 2A + \sin A = 1$ (b) $\sin 2A + \cos 2A = 0$

26. Solve each of the following equations for $A \in [0°, 360°]$:

(a) $\cos 2A + \tan A = 1$ (b) $\tan \frac{1}{2}A - 2 \sin A = 0$

27. Establish the validity of the following identities:

(a) $\dfrac{\cot A + \tan A}{\csc 2A} = 2$ (b) $\dfrac{\cot A - \tan A}{\cot 2A} = 2$

28. Establish the validity of the following identities:

(a) $\dfrac{1 - \tan \frac{1}{2}A}{1 + \tan \frac{1}{2}A} = \sec A - \tan A$

(b) $\dfrac{1 - \sin 2A}{\sin A - \cos A} = \sin A - \cos A$

29. Find the solution subset of $[-360°, 360°]$ for A if

(a) $|\sin A| = |\cos A|$ (b) $\cos A < \sin A$

30. Solve the following systems of equations for angles A and B in the interval $[-360°, 360°]$:

(a) $\sin A + \cos A = 1$ (b) $4 \sin A + 2 \cos B = 3$

$\ \sin 2A - 2 \sin B = 0$ $\ \sin A - 3 \cos B = -1$

7.5 General Triangle Trigonometry

A triangle is a plane figure consisting of three sides and three angles, and it has been a familiar object for study since before the time of Euclid. The three sides and three angles of a triangle are known collectively as its *parts*, and a determination of those which remain after a certain subset of parts has been given is known as *solving* the triangle. Of course, one must exercise some care in supplying the "given" parts if there is to be any hope of solving the triangle, because it is intuitively clear that a triangle is not necessarily determined from a random subset of parts. However, if a triangle is determined, we shall see in this section that it can be completely solved with the help of one or more of the following three rules:

(1) $A + B + C = 180°$, where A, B, C are the interior angles of the triangle
(2) The Law of Cosines
(3) The Law of Sines

The reader will doubtless be quite familiar with (1), because it plays such a basic role in elementary Euclidean geometry. It is the objective of this section to derive the other two and to show how to use the three to solve any existing triangle. Although the theory of this section may be seen to include right triangles, we shall treat them in more detail in the subsequent section.

In our study of triangles, it will be convenient to be consistent—although again slightly ambiguous—in the matter of notation. In general, we shall be concerned with a triangle ABC, and A, B, C will be used with indifference to denote either its vertices or *interior* angles, the context making clear which meaning is intended. We shall also regularly use a, b, c to denote the lengths of the sides opposite the angles A, B, C, respectively. This notation is in line with common practice in books on trigonometry.

The important application of the circular—now called trigonometric—functions to problems in trigonometry is made possible by an elementary result noted in §7.1 but which we shall repeat here for emphasis. An angle is said to be in *standard position* on the Cartesian plane, if its vertex is at the origin and its initial side lies along the positive *x*-axis. We note in passing that this definition implies that an angle in standard position is always *considered* to be directed, whether the direction is of any importance or not. (It may also be observed that an arc on a unit circle is in standard position—as defined earlier—if and only if it subtends at the center of the circle an angle in standard position.) We now refer to Figure 72, in which an arbitrary point $Q(x, y)$ is shown on the terminal side of an angle A in standard position. *By definition of the circular functions*, the coordinate pair of the point $P(\theta)$ in which this terminal side intersects the *unit circle* is (cos θ, sin θ), where the real number θ is, of course, the length of the circular arc from the point $(1, 0)$ [i.e. $P(0)$] to $P(\theta)$. However, the most important interpretation of θ for our present purposes is that it is the radian measure of the angle A, so that

$$T(\theta) = T(A) \qquad \text{for any basic circular, or trigonometric, function } T$$

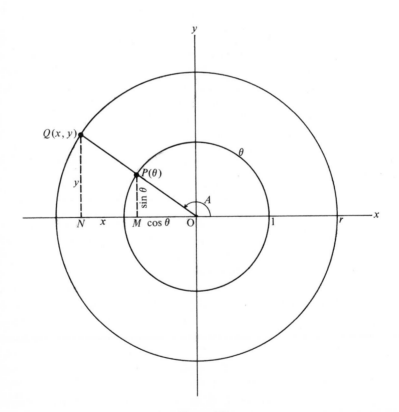

Figure 72

In particular, we see that $\sin \theta = \sin A$ and $\cos \theta = \cos A$, so that $P(\theta) = P = (\cos A, \sin A)$. The triangle with vertices at O, Q, N is certainly similar to the triangle with vertices at O, P, M, where M and N are the points at which perpendiculars from P and Q, respectively, intersect the x-axis. Because $|OQ| = r$, it follows from the geometry of similar triangles that

$$x = r \cos A$$
$$y = r \sin A$$

The coordinate pair of Q is then $(r \cos A, r \sin A)$, and this is the very important result to which we referred earlier. We are now in a position to derive both the Law of Cosines and the Law of Sines with very little difficulty.

In Figure 73 we have shown a general triangle in standard position and with which we are associating the usual notation—as introduced earlier. In view of the result just obtained, the coordinate pair of A is $(b \cos C, b \sin C)$ and we can use the distance formula (see §6.7) to determine c. Thus $c^2 = (b \cos C - a)^2 + (b \sin C - 0)^2 = b^2 \cos^2 C - 2ab \cos C + a^2 + b^2 \sin^2 C = b^2(\sin^2 C + \cos^2 C) + a^2 - 2ab \cos C = a^2 + b^2 - 2ab \cos C$. This is the *Law of Cosines*, and it is convenient to express it in three equivalent forms.

LAW OF COSINES

$$a^2 = b^2 + c^2 - 2bc \cos A$$
$$b^2 = c^2 + a^2 - 2ca \cos B$$
$$c^2 = a^2 + b^2 - 2ab \cos C$$

The Law of Cosines is useful in the solution of triangles for which either two sides and the included angle or all three sides are given. It should be intuitively clear that, in the *first* of these cases, a unique triangle is always determined by the given parts.

Example 1. In triangle ABC, find an approximation for a if $b = 10$, $c = 20$, and $A = 50°$.

SOLUTION. In this case, we use the Law of Cosines in the form

$$a^2 = b^2 + c^2 - 2bc \cos A$$

Hence,

$$a^2 = 100 + 400 - 400 \cos 50° = 500 - 400 \cos 50°$$
$$= 500 - 400(0.6428) = 500 - 257.12 = 242.88 \approx 243$$

whence $a \approx 16$.

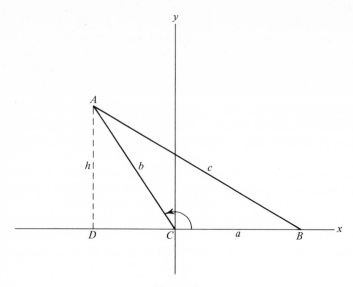

Figure 73

Example 2. In triangle ABC, find an approximation for B if $a = 5, b = 10$, and $c = 12$.

SOLUTION. The appropriate form of the Law of Cosines for this problem is $b^2 = c^2 + a^2 - 2ca \cos B$, and we transform it further into

$$\cos B = \frac{c^2 + a^2 - b^2}{2ca}$$

Hence,

$$\cos B = \frac{144 + 25 - 100}{120} = \frac{69}{120} = \frac{23}{40} \approx 0.5750$$

and we find from Table 2 that

$$B \approx 54.9° = 54°54'$$

We now come to the last of the three rules listed at the beginning of this section as aids in solving triangles: the Law of Sines. In Figure 74 we have shown a typical triangle ABC, with the usual symbolism and placed so that angle C is in standard position with respect to a Cartesian coordinate system of the plane. In Figure 75 we show the same triangle, but oriented so that the vertices at B and C have been interchanged—with B now appearing at the origin. If we consider the triangle in Figure 75 as resulting from a mere "flip" of the base CB of the triangle in Figure 74, it is intuitively evident that the altitudes AD and AE of the two triangles are the same. However, from the result derived just before the Law of Cosines, we know that the ordinate of A in

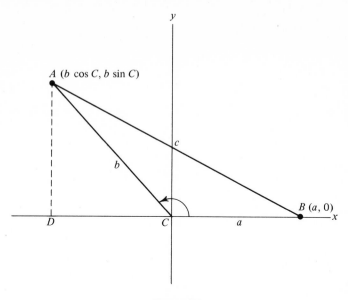

Figure 74

Figure 74 is $b \sin C$, and the altitude of A in Figure 75 is $c \sin B$. (Note that angle C in Figure 74 and angle B in Figure 75 are both in standard position.) Hence, $c \sin B = b \sin C$ and $b/\sin B = c/\sin C$. It is clear that the triangle could have been so oriented that angle A and side a would have become involved, in which case we would obtain either $a/\sin A = b/\sin B$ or $a/\sin A = c/\sin C$. In either case, we have obtained the desired result, known as the *Law of Sines*, and which we restate.

LAW OF SINES

$$\frac{a}{\sin A} = \frac{b}{\sin B} = \frac{c}{\sin C}$$

In words, this rule states that *the lengths of the sides of any triangle are proportional to the sines of the respectively-opposite angles.* In §7.6 we shall suggest an alternative proof of this result.

The Law of Sines can be used in solving triangles in cases for which the Law of Cosines is not applicable. But there is one difficulty: If we wish to determine an angle from its sine, there may be two solutions, one being an acute angle and the other obtuse. For example, if $\sin A = 0.5$, with A an interior angle of a triangle so that $0° < A < 180°$, we know that $A = 30°$ *or* $A = 150°$. However, this ambiguity causes no real trouble if a little common sense is applied!

The Law of Sines is useful whenever a "pair of opposites" is given, for example, A and a. If, in addition, another angle is given, the triangle has a unique

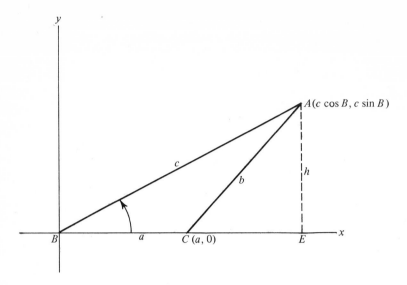

Figure 75

solution. On the other hand, if the additional part is a side, say c, then there are three possibilities that may arise in a determination of C from the equation $\sin C = (c/a) \sin A$:

(1) If $(c/a) \sin A > 1$, no solution for C is possible.
(2) If $(c/a) \sin A = 1$, there is one solution for C, and the triangle is right angled with $C = 90°$.
(3) If $(c/a) \sin A < 1$, there are two solutions for C, one an acute and the other an obtuse angle. Whether both are acceptable as angles for a triangle under the conditions of the problem can be determined from the fundamental geometric relation in any triangle that $A + B + C = 180°$.

These various possibilities are illustrated in the several parts of Figure 76, with a, A and c as the given parts. The left figure of (3) typifies the truly ambiguous case, with two triangle solutions, and the figure on the right illustrates a case with a single solution. We note then that a unique solution *may* exist under the conditions of (3), as well as under the conditions of (2) when the triangle is right-angled. The case when no triangle exists is illustrated in (1) of the figure.

Example 3.   If $a = 15$, $A = 55°$, $b = 10$, for a triangle ABC, use the Law of Sines to find an approximation for B.

SOLUTION. $\sin B = (b/a) \sin A \approx 10(0.8192)/15 \approx 0.5461$. Hence $B \approx 33°6'$ or $B \approx 146°54'$. However, we note that $55° + 146°54' > 180°$, and so the only acceptable solution is $B \approx 33°6'$. If c and C are also desired, c can be obtained with another application of the Law of Sines, whereas C is determined by the relationship $A + B + C = 180°$.

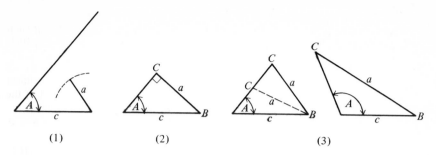

Figure 76

Problems 7.5

1. Use an *acute-angled* triangle to prove one form of the Law of Cosines.
2. Show that the Law of Cosines reduces to the familiar Pythagorean Theorem if the triangle is right-angled.
3. Determine the distance between the following points in the Cartesian plane: (a) $(-2, 3)$, $(1, 1)$; (b) $(3, -4)$, $(2, 2)$; (c) $(1, 1)$, $(-3, 5)$.
4. Interpret the Law of Sines for a right-angled triangle.
5. Find approximations for the remaining parts of triangle ABC if (a) $a = 15$, $b = 30$, $C = 40°$; (b) $b = 3.8$, $c = 6.4$, $A = 28°48'$; (c) $a = 16.5$, $c = 39.6$, $B = 69°36'$
6. If a triangle exists, determine approximations for all unknown parts of triangle ABC, subject to the given conditions: (a) $a = 15$, $c = 30$, $A = 67°18'$; (b) $b = 12$, $c = 8$, $B = 54°36'$; (c) $a = 38$, $b = 43$, $A = 58°$.
7. Two planes leave an airport together in directions that differ by 35°. If their respective speeds are 175 and 225 miles per hour, determine approximately their distance apart after 30 minutes of flight.
8. A force of 500 pounds is to be resolved into two components whose directions differ by 40°. If one of the components is 350 pounds, determine the approximate magnitude of the other component.
9. A ship sailing a straight course observes a lighthouse 22° to the left of its course. After sailing an additional 8 miles, the lighthouse is seen to bear 32° to the left of the ship's course. Determine approximately how close the ship will come to the lighthouse.
10. The weight of an object is the force of gravity acting vertically downward. If a 3500-pound automobile is resting on a 15° slope, find the approximate components of its weight acting parallel and perpendicular to the hill.
11. Prove the following rule in any triangle ABC:

$$\frac{a - b}{a + b} = \frac{\sin A - \sin B}{\sin A + \sin B}$$

(*Hint:* Let $a/\sin A = b/\sin B = k$, and substitute in the left member of the identity to be verified.)
12. Two military posts A and B are 300 feet apart. An observer in each post notices a shell burst in enemy territory at point C. If $\angle CAB = 60°$, and $\angle CBA = 72°$, determine the approximate distance of each post from C.

13. Three circles of radii 3, 4, and 5 inches are drawn on a plane to touch each other at an external point. Find approximations for the angles between their lines of centers.
14. Two observers in cities 8 miles apart observe the same object in the sky at the same time in the same general direction. If the angles of elevation of the object for the respective observers are 30° and 50°, find the approximate height of the object.
15. Prove that $a^2 = 2b^2(1 - \cos A)$ for an isosceles triangle ABC, in which $b = c$.
16. Prove that angle A in a triangle ABC is acute only if $b^2 + c^2 > a^2$.
17. Establish the validity of the expression $\frac{1}{2}ab \sin C$ for the area of a triangle ABC.
18. Use the appropriate form of the Law of Cosines to prove that

$$1 + \cos A = \frac{(b + c + a)(b + c - a)}{2bc}$$

19. A man hears the noon whistles of two factories 3 and 5 seconds after 12 noon. If the angle between the lines of sight to the factories is 39°, determine the approximate distance between the factories, assuming that both whistles blew accurately and that sound travels 1100 feet per second.
20. If D is a point on side AB of a triangle ABC such that CD bisects angle C, use the Law of Cosines to prove that $|AD|/|DB| = b/a$.
21. Assuming our usual notation for triangles, use the Law of Sines and the familiar inequality $a + b > c$ to deduce that $\sin A + \sin B > \sin C = \sin (A + B)$.
22. The base angles of an isosceles trapezoid are 75° and the length of the base is 10 feet. If the nonparallel sides are 8 feet long, determine the approximate length of a diagonal of the trapezoid.
23. Let r_1 and r_2 be the respective lengths of the line segments from the origin of the Cartesian plane to the points (x_1, y_1) and (x_2, y_2). If A is the angle between the segments, prove the validity of the following formula:

$$\cos A = \frac{x_1x_2 + y_1y_2}{r_1r_2}$$

24. Determine approximations for the angles of the triangle whose vertices are located at the following points of the Cartesian plane:
    (a) $(0, 0)$, $(3, 0)$, $(1, 4)$ (b) $(1, 2)$, $(-1, 3)$, $(3, -2)$

25. Assume the familiar formula $K = \frac{1}{2}bc \sin A$ for the area of the triangle ABC, and use the Law of Sines to prove that

$$K = c^2 \frac{\sin A \sin B}{2 \sin C}$$

26. Use the two formulas in Problem 25 to obtain Heron's Formula for the area K of the triangle ABC:

$$K = \sqrt{s(s - a)(s - b)(s - c)} \quad \text{where } s = (a + b + c)/2.$$

(*Hint:* Square both members of the formula derived in Problem 25, replace $\sin^2 A$ by $1 - \cos^2 A$, and use the Law of Cosines.)

27. If r is the radius of a circle inscribed in a triangle with each side tangent to the circle, use the definition of s given in Problem 26 and prove that

$$r = \sqrt{\frac{(s-a)(s-b)(s-c)}{s}}$$

28. Find a formula for the area common to two circles with the same radius and with the center of one located on the circumference of the other.

29. Find a formula for the area of a regular five-pointed star, inscribed in a circle of radius r.

30. Use Problem 11 above and Problem 10 of §6.7 to derive the Law of Tangents valid for any triangle ABC:

$$\frac{a-b}{a+b} = \frac{\tan\left[(A-B)/2\right]}{\tan\left[(A+b)/2\right]}$$

7.6 Trigonometry of a Right Triangle

In this final section of the chapter we shall see how to solve the simplest type of triangle—the right triangle. The reader will understand, of course, that every

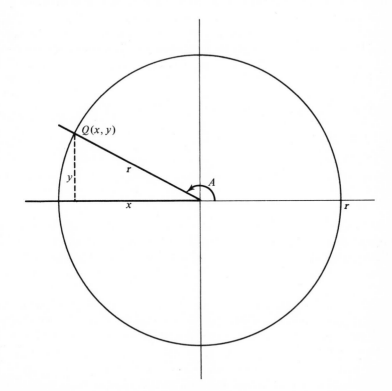

Figure 77

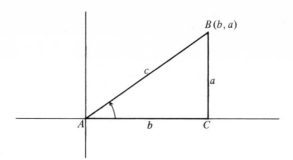

Figure 78

triangle of this kind has one of its angles equal to 90°. Even though the solution of any right-angle triangle can be accomplished by the methods of §7.5, we shall not make any direct use of either the Law of Cosines or the Law of Sines, but will show how to apply a general principle to take care of all possible triangles of this kind.

In Figure 77 we have reproduced a portion of Figure 72, showing an arbitrary point $Q(x, y)$ on the terminal side of an angle A in standard position in the Cartesian plane. It was shown in the discussion following Figure 72 that, if the distance of Q from the origin is r (> 0), the coordinates of Q satisfy the relations: $x = r \cos A$, $y = r \sin A$. It is now an elementary matter to express all the trigonometric functions of A in terms of the coordinates of the point Q as follows:

$$\sin A = \frac{y}{r} \qquad \csc A = \frac{r}{y}$$

$$\cos A = \frac{x}{r} \qquad \sec A = \frac{r}{x}$$

$$\tan A = \frac{y}{x} \qquad \cot A = \frac{x}{y}$$

The expressions for $\sin A$ and $\cos A$ are merely restatements of the above co-ordinate equations for Q, whereas the others follow directly from the elementary identities of §6.6 as applied to trigonometric functions (of angles). *These six expressions are often used in elementary textbooks to define the basic trigonometric functions.*

If A is an acute angle (that is, $0° < A < 90°$), as occurs when A is an interior angle of a right triangle, the above expressions may be simplified even further. In Figure 78 we have shown such a triangle with its interior angle A in standard position on the Cartesian plane. The sides and other two angles of the triangle are shown with their customary symbolism, so that the coordinate pair of the point B is (b, a) and its distance from the origin is r ($= c$). It then follows from the above formulation of the trigonometric functions of A that

$$\sin A = \frac{a}{c} \qquad \csc A = \frac{c}{a}$$

$$\cos A = \frac{b}{c} \qquad \sec A = \frac{c}{b}$$

$$\tan A = \frac{a}{b} \qquad \cot A = \frac{b}{a}$$

Inasmuch as a, b, c are the lengths of sides of the triangle, it is now possible and very helpful to restate the above expressions so that they are in terms of the sides and thus are *independent of our coordinate system*. It is clear that what we have done with A could be done just as easily with the other *acute* angle B, and so A should be regarded as *either* acute angle of a right triangle. Moreover, it is convenient to refer to a as the "side opposite" angle A or the "side adjacent" to angle B, to b as the "side opposite" angle B or the "side adjacent" to angle A, and to c as the "hypotenuse" of the right triangle. This language is slightly inexact, since a, b, c are actually *measures of length* of sides rather than the sides themselves, but this should cause no confusion. We now give the restatements referred to above, and with no reference to any coordinate system, but with the understanding noted above regarding terminology.

$$\sin A = \frac{\text{side opposite}}{\text{hypotenuse}} \qquad \csc A = \frac{\text{hypotenuse}}{\text{side opposite}}$$

$$\cos A = \frac{\text{side adjacent}}{\text{hypotenuse}} \qquad \sec A = \frac{\text{hypotenuse}}{\text{side adjacent}}$$

$$\tan A = \frac{\text{side opposite}}{\text{side adjacent}} \qquad \cot A = \frac{\text{side adjacent}}{\text{side opposite}}$$

In §6.7 we defined numbers as complementary if their sum is $\pi/2$, and so it is quite natural—in view of our association of the circular functions of numbers with the trigonometric functions of angles—to make the following definition.

Definition. *Two positive (acute) angles are* complementary *if their sum is 90°.*

For example, in view of a general assertion made in §6.7, $\sin 37° = \cos 53°$, $\tan 70° = \cot 20°$, and $\csc 15° = \sec 75°$. Although Table 2 is adapted to all acute angles, it is often more convenient to look up the cofunction of the complementary angle than to look up the desired functional value directly.

We are now ready to give the important rule, with the use of which it is possible to solve all *existing and determined* right triangles.

Use an appropriate trigonometric function of some angle of the triangle to involve the desired unknown part with two known parts, and solve the resulting equation for the unknown part.

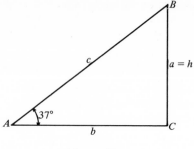

Figure 79

Example 1.   Find the approximate height of a tree if the length of its shadow
is 28 feet when the angle of elevation of the sun is 37°.

SOLUTION.   The situation in the problem is illustrated by Figure 79, in
which BC represents the tree and AC its shadow. If the unknown height
of the tree is denoted by h ($= a$) we use the tangent function to connect h
with the known (37°) angle A and the known (28) side AC. Thus, tan 37° $\approx$
$0.7536 = h/28$, whence $h \approx 28(0.7536) \approx 21.1$. The approximate height
of the tree is then 21 feet.

Example 2.   From a point on the level plain at the foot of a mountain, the
angle of elevation of the peak is observed to be 45°. If the angle
of elevation of the peak is 30°, as observed from a point 3000
feet farther away in the same plane, determine the approximate
height of the mountain peak above the plane.

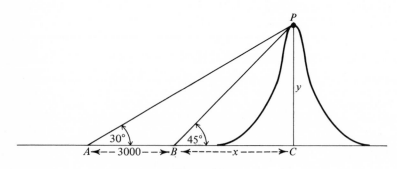

Figure 80

SOLUTION.   The situation in the problem is shown by Figure 80, in which P
is the peak of the mountain and A and B are the two points on the plane
from which the observations were made. We let y denote the desired un-

known height, and x the distance indicated in the figure. Both triangles APC and BPC are right-angled. Applications of our basic rule gives us the following equations:

$$\tan 45° = 1 = \frac{y}{x}$$

$$\tan 30° = \frac{1}{\sqrt{3}} = \frac{y}{x + 3000}$$

These equations yield $y = x$ and $x + 3000 = \sqrt{3}y$, from which we find easily that $y = 3000/(\sqrt{3} - 1) = 1500(\sqrt{3} + 1) \approx 4100$. The desired height is then approximately 4100 feet.

It may have been noted that the computational work involved in the solution of the two preceding examples was quite simple, because the required functional values were either known or read directly from Table 2. Of course, this pleasant situation does not always prevail, and it usually is the case with actual problems that an interpolation is needed. We have already encountered interpolation in connection with logarithms, the circular functions of real numbers, and also with conversions between the degree and radian measures of angles. The idea is always the same, the assumption being that the values vary in a linear or proportional fashion. However, we include a couple of examples that illustrate the interpolation procedure for both a direct and inverse use of the table. In Example 3 we also show—what is likely quite obvious—how to use the table when an angle is measured to the nearest minute rather than the nearest tenth of a degree—for which type of measurement the table is directly adapted.

Example 3. Use Table 2 to approximate $\sin 26°34'$.

SOLUTION. Because $34' = 0.566 \cdots °$, we round off the angle measurement to $26.57°$. From Table 2,

$$\sin 26.6° = \sin 26.60° \approx 0.4478$$
$$\underline{\sin 26.5° = \sin 26.50° \approx 0.4462}$$
$$0.0016$$

We note that 57 is $\frac{7}{10}$ of the way from 50 to 60 and so, by proportional parts,

$$\sin 26.57° \approx 0.4462 + \tfrac{7}{10}(0.0016) \approx 0.4462 + 0.0011 = 0.4473$$

In using the interpolation process it should be observed, of course, that whereas the sine, secant, and tangent functional values increase with increasing *acute* angles, the values of the reciprocal functions (cosecant, cosine, cotangent) decrease.

If Table 2 is to be used to determine an angle from a given functional value, it is necessary to use the table in reverse—a process similar to determining a number from its logarithm. We illustrate with an example.

Example 4. Determine angle A if sec $A = 1.9556$.

SOLUTION.   From Table 2 we note that the nearest listing *below* 1.9556 is:

$$\text{sec } 59.2° = \text{sec } 59.20° \approx 1.9530$$

$$0.0026$$

but also: $\text{sec } A = 1.9556$

$$0.0057$$

and: $\text{sec } 59.3° = \text{sec } 59.30° \approx 1.9587$

Because sec A exceeds sec 59.2° by 0.0026, and the excess of sec 59.3° over sec 59.2° is 0.0057, it follows by proportional parts that

$$A \approx 59.20° + \tfrac{26}{57}(0.10)° \approx 59.20° + 0.05° = 59.25°$$

Note: If an angle were to be determined from the value of a *decreasing* function (cosine, cotangent, or cosecant), we would work from the nearest table entry *above* the given value.

Problems 7.6

1. Use a protractor to construct the given angle, draw a right triangle of convenient size which contains the angle, and compute approximations for the following functional values from actual measurements of length of the sides of the triangle: (a) sin 35°24′; (b) sec 64°42′; (c) cot 39°12′; (d) tan 84°36′.
2. Use Table 2 and interpolation, if necessary, to approximate the acute angle A from each of the following conditions: (a) sin $A = 0.4221$; (b) sec $A = 1.5462$; (c) tan $A = 2.3456$; (d) cot $A = 1.8372$; (e) csc $A = 1.7563$.
3. Express each of the following as a functional value of a positive angle less than 45°: (a) cos 64°14′; (b) sec 86°30′; (c) csc 74°53′; (d) cot 83°55′; (e) tan 88°55′.
4. Express each of the following in terms of a *different* function of the *same* angle: (a) sin 66°; (b) cos 54°50′; (c) tan 37°45′; (d) cot 40°.
5. Use a different function *and* a different angle to express the values given in Problem 4.
6. Approximate the unknown parts of the right triangle ABC, with right angle at C, given that (a) $A = 44°50′$, $a = 15$; (b) $B = 53.6°$, $c = 25$; (c) $A = 48.5°$, $c = 41.6$.
7. The angle of elevation of the top of a cliff as seen from a small boat on a lake below is observed to be 36°40′. If the cliff is known to be 50 feet high, approximately how far is the boat from the base of the cliff?
8. Solve each of the following equations for the smallest *acute* angle A: (a) sin $(5A + 13°) = \cos 2A$;   (b) tan $\tfrac{1}{2}A = \cot A$;   (c) sin $(A + 60°) = \cos (3A + 12°)$. Find the other *acute* angles that are solutions of (a).
9. A pilot of a sea plane notes that his elevation is 6000 feet as he approaches a small island. According to his best estimate, the angle of depression of the farthest tip of the island is 40°, and the angle of depression of the closest point is 60°. Determine the approximate dimension of the island in the direction of flight.

10. Find an approximation for the acute angle between a diagonal and an adjacent edge of a cube.

11. If a 30-inch pendulum is moved from its vertical position by 15°, by approximately how much has the pendulum bob been raised?

12. A 20-foot ladder, with its base fixed at one spot in an alley, will reach 12 feet up the side of a building on one side and 15 feet up another building on the other side of the alley. What is the approximate width of the alley?

13. A microwave tower stands on top of a 200-foot building. From a spot on the ground 450 feet from the base of the building, the angle between the lines of sight to the top and bottom of the tower is 15°. Determine the approximate height of the tower.

14. From a certain spot on a plain, the angle of elevation of the top of a small mountain is 45°. If the angle of elevation is 60° from a spot at the same elevation but 2000 feet closer to the base of the mountain, determine the approximate height of the mountain.

15. Is it possible to construct a right triangle that contains an angle $A < 30°$ such that $\sin (30° + A) = \cos (30° - A)$?

16. A man standing on a ship at sea is h feet above the water level. If we assume that the radius of the earth is 3960 miles, show that his distance from the horizon is approximately $\sqrt{3h/2}$ miles.

17. Two airplanes circle the earth, one at a constant latitude of 30°N and the other at a constant latitude of 60°N. If they complete their trips in the same time, determine the ratio of their speeds.

18. A *segment* of a circle is the figure bounded by an arc of the circle and its subtended chord. If a radius is r units in length, and if the angle between the radii to the end points of the arc is θ radians, show that the area S of the associated segment is given by $S = \frac{1}{2}r^2(\theta - \sin \theta)$.

19. From two successive milestones on a straight level road, a man observes that the angles of elevation of the top of a hill directly ahead of him are 6.2° and 37.8°. Determine the approximate height of the top of the hill above the road level.

20. The centers of two circular pulleys are 14 inches apart, the radii of the pulleys being 3 and 10 inches, respectively. Determine the length of a belt running around the pulleys (a) if the belt is uncrossed; (b) if the belt is crossed once.

21. The fixed axis of a telescope mounting in the Northern Hemisphere must point toward the north celestial pole, the angle of elevation of this point being the latitude of the observer at this location. If the axis of a certain mounting is 9 feet in length, with its lower end 6 feet above the floor of the observatory located in a latitude of 30°, determine the height of the higher end above the floor.

8

Complex
Numbers

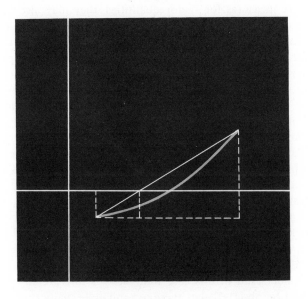

8.1 Introduction

The question "What is a number?" is quite
often asked, but somewhat less frequently
answered to one's complete satisfaction. In
Chapter 1 we gave a brief sketch of the
development of the system of real numbers,
from the viewpoint of a number as an
element of mensuration. One could also
pursue a parallel development from the
point of view of solving equations: The
integers, rational numbers, and real numbers are introduced so that successively
more complicated equations can be solved.
Within the real-number system, all the common practical and theoretical mensuration
problems are solvable; the operations
of addition, subtraction, multiplication,

division (except by 0), and root extractions for nonnegative numbers are (at least theoretically) possible. However, with only real numbers available, it is still not possible to make a suitable measurement of a so-called *vector quantity*, which possesses—along with a magnitude—something that can often be identified with a *direction*. Some of the most familiar quantities of this type are *directed distance, velocity,* and *acceleration*. A suitable measure of a vector quantity is a *vector*, and a study of the abstraction of this concept is the content of courses in linear algebra. In addition to the deficiency of the real numbers to give satisfactory measures for vector quantities, they may also be seen to be deficient in that such a simple equation as $x^2 + 1 = 0$ has no solution in **R**. It is these two deficiences that may be considered to provide at least partial motivation for an extension of **R** to include the system **C** of complex numbers. With these new numbers it is possible to give a satisfactory measure of any vector quantity representable in a plane and also to solve any polynomial equation with real coefficients. We now proceed to a development of this new number system.

A logical construction of integers is based on a prior knowledge of natural numbers; a development of the rational numbers is based on the integers and their known properties; and the usual developments of the real numbers are based on earlier studies of rational numbers. It is possible to regard a positive integer x as an ordered pair (a, b) of *natural numbers* ($b < a$), provided we understand that $a - b = x$, noting that there are infinitely many of these pairs that denote the same x. An extension of this idea—which we do not care to detail here—would lead us to the system **Z** of integers. In a somewhat similar way, a rational number r can be identified with an ordered pair (a, b) of *integers*, provided we understand in this case that (a, b) is interpreted as a/b, $b \neq 0$. Again it should be observed that there are infinitely many ordered pairs that denote the same rational number, but it would take us too far off our course to give any more details in connection with the development of this system **Q** of rational numbers. However, we do wish to emphasize the following point: The definition of an integer involves a *pair of natural numbers*, and the definition of a rational number involves a *pair of integers*. Although a very careful transition from the rationals to the reals involves the introduction of something much more subtle than mere *pairs* of rationals, it may still not be unreasonable to suspect that an extension of **R** can be based on ordered pairs of real numbers. This we do in our construction of the system **C** of complex numbers. Of course, it is inherent in the nature of any number system that an arithmetic structure must be introduced, and so we must make appropriate definitions of the operations of addition and multiplication in **C**. Although we have *always* associated the notion of *equality* with different names for the same thing, we include it— for the sake of completeness—in the following comprehensive definition.

Definition.   *A* complex *number is an ordered pair of real numbers such that the following hold:*

(a) *Equality.* $(a, b) = (c, d)$ *if and only if* $a = c$ *and* $b = d$.

(b) *Addition.* $(a, b) + (c, d) = (a + c, b + d)$.
(c) *Multiplication.* $(a, b)(c, d) = (ac - bd, bc + ad)$.

Before these ordered pairs with the given arithmetic structure should be accepted as "numbers," however, one should verify that they obey at least a substantial number of the usual laws of arithmetic and so resemble the more familiar real numbers. One of these laws is verified in Example 1, and the verification of others is suggested in the problems.

Example 1.   Verify the commutative law of addition for complex numbers.

SOLUTION

$$(a, b) + (c, d) = (a + c, b + d) = (c + a, d + b) = (c, d) + (a, b)$$

This establishes the commutative law of addition, and we note that the commutative law of addition for *real* numbers was used in the proof.

Since $(a, b) + (0, 0) = (a, b) = (0, 0) + (a, b)$ for any complex number (a, b), the number $(0, 0)$ is the zero of the new system, and we shall often denote it simply by 0. Also, because $(a, b)(1, 0) = (a, b) = (1, 0)(a, b)$ for any complex number (a, b), the number $(1, 0)$ is the multiplicative identity of the system and may be denoted by 1. The additive inverse $-(a, b)$ of (a, b) is $(-a, -b)$, because $(a, b) + (-a, -b) = 0 = (-a, -b) + (a, b)$, and it is easy to check that the multiplicative inverse $(a, b)^{-1}$ of (a, b) is

$$\left(\frac{a}{a^2 + b^2}, \frac{-b}{a^2 + b^2} \right)$$

provided $(a, b) \neq 0$. As for real numbers, we consider the operation of subtraction as inverse to addition, and so the subtraction of a complex number is the same as the addition of its additive inverse. Similarly, the operation of division is considered inverse to multiplication, and so dividing by a nonzero number is the same as multiplying by its multiplicative inverse. That is,

$$(a, b) - (c, d) = (a, b) + (-c, -d)$$

and

$$\frac{(a, b)}{(c, d)} = (a, b)(c, d)^{-1}$$

It is now a matter for routine checking that all the field properties listed in §1.4 are also properties of the system of complex numbers, and so this system is a field.

The complex numbers of the form $(a, 0)$, for any real a, behave "just like" the real numbers a in any computation involving the field properties, and so these special complex numbers are indistinguishable from real numbers—except in form. To use the technical term applied in such instances, we say that the subsystem of complex numbers $(a, 0)$, with $a \in \mathbf{Z}$, is "isomorphic" to the system of real numbers. In this sense the field of complex numbers contains the real numbers as a subset—just as the field of rational numbers contains the subset of numbers of the form $a/1$ as integers. The complex numbers then form an *extension* of $\mathbf{R}$, which we shall denote by $\mathbf{C}$, and so $\mathbf{N} \subset \mathbf{Z} \subset \mathbf{Q} \subset \mathbf{R} \subset \mathbf{C}$.

There is one important property possessed by the real numbers that is *not* shared by the complex numbers. This is the property of *order*. There is no way to order complex numbers so that the properties of §3.1 are preserved, and so the complex numbers comprise an "unordered" field. It is possible to introduce a type of "ordering" in this field, but not all of the usual properties of order are maintained, and so we do not have a *bona fide* order relation.

Example 2. Determine the product $(2, 3)(-1, 1)$, where the indicated pairs are regarded as complex numbers.

SOLUTION. By the definition for multiplication,

$$(2, 3)(-1, 1) = (-2 - 3, -3 + 2) = (-5, -1)$$

Example 3. Determine the quotient $(1, -2)/(2, -1)$, where the indicated pairs are regarded as complex numbers.

SOLUTION. By the formula for a multiplicative inverse, and the definition of multiplication, $(1, -2)/(2, -1) = (1, -2)(\frac{2}{5}, \frac{1}{5}) = (\frac{2}{5} + \frac{2}{5}, -\frac{4}{5} + \frac{1}{5}) = (\frac{4}{5}, -\frac{3}{5})$.

Inasmuch as we are identifying any complex number of the form $(a, 0)$ with the real number a, the rule for the multiplication of complex numbers makes the following definition quite natural.

Definition. *If $z = (a, b) \in \mathbf{C}$, then $rz = (ra, rb)$ for any $r \in \mathbf{R}$.*

Example 4. Solve the following equation for $z \in \mathbf{C}$:

$$2z + 3(1, -2) - 2(-1, 2) = 7(1, 0)$$

SOLUTION. Several applications of the definition just given yield $2z + (3, -6) + (2, -4) = (7, 0)$ so that $2z = (7, 0) - (3, -6) - (2, -4) = (2, 10) = 2(1, 5)$. Hence, on multiplying both members of the equality by $\frac{1}{2}$, we obtain $z = (1, 5)$.

Problems 8.1

1. Find the sum of the following complex numbers: (a) $(1, 3)$, $(-4, 2)$, $(0, 2)$; (b) $(-2, 5)$, $(3, 4)$, $(-2, -2)$; (c) $(1, 1)$, $(-2, 4)$, $(3, -6)$, $(5, 2)$.

2. Find the product of each of the following pairs of complex numbers: (a) $(1, 2)$, $(-2, -4)$; (b) $(5, 4)$, $(3, -2)$; (c) $(-1, -2)$, $(3, -2)$; (d) $(2, -5)$, $(1, 4)$.
3. With reference to Problem 2, subtract the second member of each pair from the first.
4. With reference to Problem 2, divide the first member of each pair by the second. Check your results by multiplication.
5. Solve each of the following equations for the indicated unknown x or y or both (as appropriate), where $x, y \in \mathbf{R}$ and where a, b, c, d are given real numbers: (a) $(x, 4) + (3, -4) = (6, y)$; (b) $(x, -3) - (2, y) = (3, 4)$; (c) $(3, -y) + (2x, 3) - (4, 3y) = (3, 1)$; (d) $(x, a) + (b, y) = (c, d)$.
6. Solve each of the following equations for $z \in \mathbf{C}$: (a) $2z + (3, -2) = (1, 1)$; (b) $3z + (2, -1) = z - (2, 1)$
7. Solve each of the following equations for $z \in \mathbf{C}$: (a) $3z - (1, -3)(2, -1) = (2, 1)(1, 2)$ (b) $(1, 2)^2 + z = (1, 1)^3 - 4z$
8. Simplify each of the following to a single complex number: (a) $2(3, -1) + (1, 2) - 4(2, -3)$ (b) $\frac{1}{2}(\frac{3}{4}, 2) + 2(\frac{1}{2}, 5) - \frac{3}{2}(2, \frac{7}{3})$
9. Solve each of the following equations for $z \in \mathbf{C}$: (a) $2z + 3(1, -1) = 2(2, 3) + 4(-2, 3)$ (b) $3z - \frac{1}{2}(\frac{2}{3}, -\frac{3}{4}) + 2z = 3(-\frac{1}{3}, 2)$
10. Simplify each of the following to a complex number as an ordered pair: (a) $(1, -2)^3$; (b) $(-2, 3)^4$; (c) $(0, 1)^5$.
11. Find $z = (x, y) \in \mathbf{C}$, where $(x, y) = (2, -1)/(1, -3)$.
12. Find $z = (x, y) \in \mathbf{C}$, where $(x, y) = (-\frac{1}{2}, \sqrt{3}/2)^3$.
13. Find $z = (x, y) \in \mathbf{C}$, where $(3, -2) = (x, y)/(2, -1)$.
14. How can you characterize the results if you perform additions, subtractions, multiplications, and divisions in the subset of complex numbers of the form $(a, 0)$, with $a \in \mathbf{R}$? Answer the question in general terms.
15. Verify that $(0, 1)^2 = (-1, 0)$. In view of our assertion about complex numbers of this form (see also Problem 14), what does this result suggest?
16. Verify that $(1, 0)$ is the multiplicative identity for the system of complex numbers. [That is, $(1, 0)z = z(1, 0) = z$, for any $z \in \mathbf{C}$.]
17. Decide whether the equalities $a0 = 0$ and $a(1) = a$, which are valid for any real number a, are also valid if a is a complex number. Consider the cases when 0 and 1 are real and when $0 = (0, 0)$ and $1 = (1, 0)$ are complex, noting in the latter case the result in Problem 16.
18. Derive a formula for the quotient $(a, b)/(c, d)$ of two complex numbers, where $(c, d) \neq 0$.
19. Name at least one other vector quantity not mentioned in this section.
20. List three pairs of natural numbers that, as indicated in this section, may denote the integer (a) 1; (b) 2; (c) 5.
21. Using the interpretation of positive integers as ordered pairs (a, b) of natural numbers, as given in this section, explain why an ordered pair (a, b) with $a < b$ would be meaningless.
22. Review two interpretations of ordered pairs (a, b) of real numbers, *different* from that given in this section. Does this imply that the notation (a, b) is an ambiguous one, meaningful only in a given context?
23. If f is a function defined on $\mathbf{C}$ so that $f(z) = 2z^2 + z - 1$, find (a) $f(1, 1)$; (b) $f(-2, 1)$; (c) $f(1, -3)$.

24. If f is a function defined on **C** so that $f(z) = z^3 + 2$, find (a) $f(0, 1)$; (b) $f(-1, 2)$; (c) $f(-1, -1)$.

25. Solve each of the following equations for $z = (x, y) \in \mathbf{C}$:
   (a) $z^2 + 2(0, 1) = 0$ (b) $(0, 1)z^2 + 2(1, 0) = 0$
   (c) $z^2 + 5z + 6 = 0$ (d) $z^2 + z - 6 = 0$

26. If $z \neq 1$, prove that

$$1 + z + z^2 + z^3 = \frac{1 - z^4}{1 - z}$$

27. Verify the associative law of addition for complex numbers.
28. Verify the associative law of multiplication for complex numbers.
29. Verify the commutative law of multiplication for complex numbers.
30. Verify the "usual" distributive laws for complex numbers.

8.2 The Normal or Rectangular Form of a Complex Number

In spite of what we have said by way of explanation in §8.1, it may seem a little strange to the student for us to define complex numbers as ordered pairs of real numbers. However, we repeat with emphasis that these pairs are "numbers" *only* after they have been given an arithmetic structure, with appropriate definitions of equality, addition, and multiplication. In this section, we shall give the more common way of representing complex numbers. This may be regarded for complex numbers as the analogue of expressing a *rational* number in the conventional form a/b, after a prior definition of a rational number as an ordered pair (a, b) of integers a and b, subject to certain rules of operation.

Our definition of addition allows us to write an arbitrary complex number (a, b) in the form $(a, b) = (a, 0) + (0, b)$, and our definition of multiplication lets us write $(0, b) = (b, 0)(0, 1)$. Hence,

$$(a, b) = (a, 0) + (b, 0)(0, 1)$$

The number $(0, 1)$ plays a very important role in complex analysis, and it is customary to designate it by i (physicists and engineers often use j for this purpose). We noted in §8.1 that the numbers of the form $(a, 0)$ may be identified with their first components a, and if we make this identification, the complex number (a, b) takes the form $a + bi$.

Definition. *The* normal *or* rectangular *form of the complex number* (a, b) *is* $a + bi$, *where we have designated* $(0, 1)$ *as* i, *and identified* $(a, 0)$ *with* a *and* $(b, 0)$ *with* b. *For historic reasons,* a *is sometimes called the* real *and* b *the* imaginary *component of the number, but no significance should be attached to the word "imaginary."*

If we square i, by the usual rule for multiplication, we find that $(0, 1)^2 = (0, 1)(0, 1) = (-1, 0)$ or, in the new symbolism,

$$i^2 = -1$$

It now is seen that in the system of complex numbers there is a number i whose square is -1. The equation $x^2 = -1$ (or $x^2 + 1 = 0$) is then solvable in this system, and herein lies an advantage of **C** over the system of real numbers.

If we reexamine our basic definitions, with the complex numbers written in normal form, the definitions assume the following appearance:

(1) *Equality.* $a + bi = c + di$ *if and only if $a = c$ and $b = d$.*
(2) *Addition.* $(a + bi) + (c + di) = (a + c) + (b + d)i$.
(3) *Multiplication.* $(a + bi)(c + di) = (ac - bd) + (bc + ad)i$.

In words, these rules are tantamount to the following:

1. Two complex numbers are *equal* if and only if their respective real and imaginary components are equal.
2. Two complex numbers are *added* by adding their respective real and imaginary components.
3. Two complex numbers are multiplied just like binomials in the symbol i, with i^2 replaced by -1 in the final result.

Some of the advantages arising from the normal form of complex numbers will be made apparent from the following examples.

Example 1.   Express $(2 + i)^4$ as a complex number.

SOLUTION

$$(2 + i)^2 = (2 + i)(2 + i) = 4 + 4i + i^2 = 4 + 4i - 1 = 3 + 4i$$

Hence,

$$(2 + i)^4 = (2 + i)^2(2 + i)^2 = (3 + 4i)^2 = 9 + 24i + 16i^2$$
$$= 9 + 24i - 16 = -7 + 24i$$

Example 2.   Express $(2 - i)/(1 + 3i)$ in the normal form of a complex number.

SOLUTION.   We multiply numerator and denominator of the given number by $1 - 3i$ and obtain

$$\frac{(2 - i)(1 - 3i)}{(1 + 3i)(1 - 3i)} = \frac{2 - 7i + 3i^2}{1 - 9i^2} = \frac{2 - 7i - 3}{1 + 9} = \frac{-1 - 7i}{10} = -\frac{1}{10} - \frac{7}{10}i$$

Two complex numbers of the forms $a + bi$ and $a - bi$, with $a, b \in \mathbf{R}$, are said to be *conjugates of* or *conjugate to* each other. It is then apparent from Example 2 that the following rule may be used for dividing one complex number by another:

Multiply numerator and denominator of the indicated quotient by the conjugate of the denominator; and simplify the multiplications.

It may be seen that the product of a complex number and its conjugate is always a real number, and so this procedure makes the denominator of the quotient real. The conjugate of $z = a + bi$ is denoted by $\bar{z} = a - bi$.

We have already noted that the complex number i is a solution of the equation $x^2 + 1 = 0$, an equation that is unsolvable in the field $\mathbf{R}$ of real numbers. It might be reasonable to expect that further extensions of the complex number system would be required if other more complicated equations are to be solved. However, it is a fact that any polynomial equation of the form

$$a_0 x^n + a_1 x^{n-1} + \cdots + a_{n-1} x + a_n = 0,$$

with n a positive integer and $a_0 (\neq 0)$, $a_1, \ldots, a_{n-1}, a_n$ real numbers, can be solved completely within the system of complex numbers. This result is a consequence of the following important theorem.

■**THEOREM 2.1** (*Fundamental Theorem of Algebra*). *Any polynomial equation, with real or complex coefficients, has a complex number for a solution.*

This theorem was first proved by Gauss in 1799. Since then many other proofs have been given, but they are all somewhat difficult and beyond the scope of this book. Inasmuch as no new numbers are needed to solve any polynomial equation, with coefficients in $\mathbf{C}$, we say that the field $\mathbf{C}$ is *algebraically closed.*

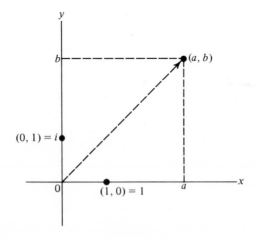

Figure 81

An ordered pair (a, b) of real numbers has a natural geometric representation as the point in a Cartesian plane whose coordinate pair is (a, b). There is a one-to-one correspondence between the points of this plane and the complex numbers, just as there is a one-to-one correspondence between the real numbers and the points of any algebraic scale drawn as a coordinate axis. Moreover, in this geometric environment, it is often convenient to speak of the complex numbers as if they are actual points of the plane. For example, we may speak of the "point" $z = x + yi$. The horizontal axis, which contains the (real) complex numbers of the form $(a, 0)$, is known as the *axis of reals*, and the vertical axis, which contains the numbers of the form $(0, b)$ or bi, is sometimes called the *pure imaginary axis*. We shall make more use of this geometric representation of the complex numbers in the following section.

The subject of vectors properly belongs in a book on linear algebra rather than in one of the present kind. However, because we did mention the fact that the measurement of vector quantities provides us with one of the several motivating factors for the introduction of complex numbers, it seems in order to make at least a brief pertinent comment along this line here. In Figure 81 we have graphed the geometric point (a, b) on the Cartesian plane, and *with the algebraic structure that we have imposed on such pairs in this and the preceding*

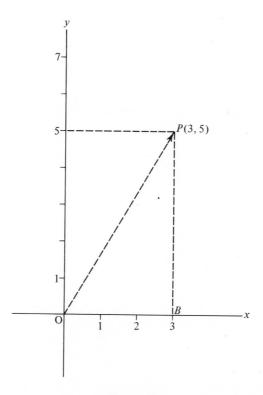

Figure 82

section, we may regard (a, b) as a *vector* with the alternative form of expression as $a + bi$. The vector (a, b), or $a + bi$, can then be considered to be a measure of a vector quantity, the magnitude of which is $\sqrt{a^2 + b^2}$ and whose direction may be identified with the direction of the line segment drawn from the origin to the point (a, b). Whether this direction is actual or symbolic depends on the manner in which the diagram was constructed. The "unit" vector i can then, of course, be identified with the point $(0, 1)$ on the vertical axis. For example, a measure of wind velocity can be represented by the vector $(3, 5)$, or $3 + 5i$, in Figure 82. We are able to conclude from the figure that the magnitude of the velocity is $\sqrt{3^2 + 5^2} = \sqrt{34}$ units, whereas its direction—relative to the coordinate axes—can be determined from a solution of the indicated triangle for $\angle POB$.

In order that the reader not be confused with what he may have read in books in which vectors are treated more extensively, it may be well to point out that the vector $(1, 0)$ is often denoted by **i** and $(0, 1)$ by **j**. In this notation the "wind" vector in our example would be $3\mathbf{i} + 5\mathbf{j}$. We shall not use this notation, however, but shall give the interpretation previously given to i. With this rather näive discussion of vectors, we drop the subject and refer the interested reader to books on linear algebra or vector analysis.

Problems 8.2

1. Write each of the following ordered pairs, regarded as complex numbers, in normal form: (a) $(-3, 5)$; (b) $(3, -2)$; (c) $(2, 6)$; (d) $(0, 1)$; (e) $(0, 0)$; (f) $(-1, -1)$.

2. Find the sum of each of the following pairs of complex numbers: (a) $2 + 3i$, $-2 - 5i$; (b) $2 + 4i$, $-2 - 6i$; (c) $6 - 5i$, $-3 - i$; (d) 5, $-2 + i$; (e) $4i$, $6i$; (f) $2i$, 6.

3. Find the product of each pair of complex numbers given in Problem 2.

4. With reference to the complex numbers given in Problem 2, express in normal form the quotient of the first number in each pair by the second.

5. Simplify each of the following: (a) $(2 + i)(-3 - 2i)(3 - 2i)$; (b) $\dfrac{(2 - 3i)^3}{(1 + 2i)}$; (c) $\dfrac{(3 - 2i)(1 + i)}{(1 + 2i)(3 - i)}$; (d) $\dfrac{2 + i - i^4}{i + i^2 + i^4}$.

6. Give the geometric representation of each of the following complex numbers: (a) $2 - 3i$; (b) $3 + i$; (c) $-4 - 3i$; (d) $3 + i/2$; (e) i; (f) $i/2$.

7. Verify that $y^3 = 1$, where $y = -\frac{1}{2} - \frac{1}{2}\sqrt{3}i$.

8. Simplify $(\frac{1}{2} + \frac{1}{2}\sqrt{3}i)^3$, and compare the result with that in Problem 7.

9. Solve each of the following equations for real x and y:
   (a) $(x + 2i) + (3 - yi) = -2 + 5i$ (b) $(2x - 3yi) + (-2 - 5i) = 1$
   (c) $(2x + i) - (3 - 4yi) = x - 2i$ (d) $3x + 2i = 2 + x - yi$

10. Prove for any positive integer n: (a) $i^{4n} = 1$; (b) $i^{2n+2} = 1$ if n is odd, and $i^{2n+2} = -1$ if n is even; (c) $i^{4n+3} = -i$.

11. Prove that the sum and the product of any two conjugate complex numbers are real numbers.

12. Prove that, if the sum and product of two complex numbers are real numbers, the two numbers are conjugates of each other.

13. Prove that $\bar{z} = z$, for a complex number z, if and only if $z \in \mathbf{R}$.

14. Prove that $\bar{\bar{z}} = z$ for any $z \in \mathbf{C}$.

15. If $u, v \in \mathbf{C}$, prove that $\overline{(u + v)} = \bar{u} + \bar{v}$ and $\overline{uv} = \bar{u}\,\bar{v}$.

16. If $u, v \in \mathbf{C}$, use the result in Problem 15 to prove that $uv = 0$ if and only if $u = 0$ or $v = 0$ (or both).

17. If $z = a + bi \in \mathbf{C}$ and $\bar{z} = -z$, prove that $a = 0$.

18. Show that $(z - \bar{z})/i$ is a real number for any $z \in \mathbf{C}$.

19. If z is a complex solution of the equation $3x^2 - 7x + 5 = 0$, show that $\bar{z}$ is a solution of the same equation. State the generalization of this result.

20. Check for $n = 0, 1, 2, 3, 4$ that $i^n = \cos \frac{1}{2}n\pi + i \sin \frac{1}{2}n\pi$. Would it be your conjecture that the result is true for all $n \in \mathbf{Z}$?

21. Use the complex number i to illustrate the fact that the complex number field does not satisfy the requirements of order as given in §3.1. (*Hint:* Consider the Trichotomy Law which would assert that $i = 0, i > 0$, or $i < 0$.)

22. Verify that $uv = 1$, where $u = -\frac{1}{2} + \frac{1}{2}\sqrt{3}i$ and $v = -\frac{1}{2} - \frac{1}{2}\sqrt{3}i$.

23. Solve each of the following equations for $z \in \mathbf{C}$:
(a) $3iz - 2 = 0$; (b) $(1 + i)z + 2 = 0$; (c) $(1 - 2i)z + i + 1 = 0$;
(d) $\dfrac{(1 - i)z}{1 + i} + \dfrac{3 + i}{2 - i} = 0$; (e) $z^2 + 4 = 0$; (f) $\dfrac{3z - 2i}{z + i} = 2$.

24. Use the method of factoring to solve each of the following equations with solutions in $\mathbf{C}$: (a) $x^2 - (2 - 3i)x - 6i = 0$; (b) $x^4 - 1 = 0$; (c) $x^3 - 5x^2i - 6x = 0$; (d) $ix^2 + 7x - 12i = 0$; (e) $2ix^2 - 5x - 2i = 0$. (Cf. Problem 16.)

25. Solve the following equation for real x and y:

$$\ln (x + y) + e^y i = 1 + 3i$$

26. Solve the following equation for real x and y:

$$x^2 + xi = y^2 - 2yi + 4i$$

27. If f is the function defined on $\mathbf{C}$ so that $f(z) = 2z - 1$, find (a) $f(i)$; (b) $f(-2i)$; (c) $f(1 - i)$.

28. If f is the function defined on $\mathbf{C}$ so that $f(z) = 2z^2 - z + i$, find (a) $f(i)$; (b) $f(-i)$; (c) $f(2i + 1)$.

29. If f is the function defined by $f(z) = iz$ on $\{z = a + bi \in \mathbf{C}|\, a = 0\}$, determine the range of f.

30. Let f be a function defined on the set of all complex numbers $\mathbf{C}$. Determine the complex zeros of f if:
(a) $f(x) = 3ix + 2$ (b) $f(x) = (1 + i)x - 2i$
(c) $f(x) = \dfrac{(1 - 2i)x}{1 + i}$ (d) $f(x) = \dfrac{2ix}{1 + i} + \dfrac{2 - i}{i}$

8.3 Trigonometric Form of Complex Numbers

We have pointed out in §8.2 that it is only natural to represent the complex number $z = (a, b) = a + bi$ by the *point* (a, b) in the Cartesian plane. In this geometric representation, the "real" part a is the abscissa and the "imaginary" part b is the ordinate of the point. This is illustrated in Figure 83.

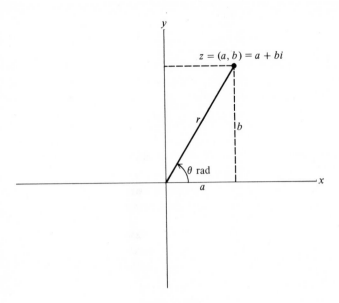

Figure 83

If $r \geq 0$ is the distance of the point z from the origin, this nonnegative number is called the *modulus* or *absolute value* of z and is designated by $|z|$. Thus $|z| = 0$ if and only if $z = 0$. If θ is the radian measure of any one of the angles in standard position whose terminal side passes through the point z, the real number θ is called an *argument* of z and is often designated as arg z. (It may be noted that (r, θ) constitutes a pair of *polar coordinates* of the point z.) There are, of course, an infinite number of positive and negative values for arg z, for any given z, but we select the one most convenient for our purpose at hand—and this is usually the one of smallest absolute value. It follows from elementary trigonometry that, if $z = a + bi = (a, b)$, then $a = r \cos \theta$ and $b = r \sin \theta$. Hence, we can write z in the following *trigonometric* form:

$$z = a + bi = r \cos \theta + (r \sin \theta)i = r(\cos \theta + i \sin \theta)$$

If so desired, the radian *measure* θ may be replaced by (or interpreted as) an *angle* with this measure. In line with this harmless ambiguity of symbolism—as discussed in §7.3—a complex number such as $2(\cos \frac{1}{4}\pi + i \sin \frac{1}{4}\pi)$ may also be written as $2(\cos 45° + i \sin 45°)$, and $\frac{1}{4}\pi$ in the first expression may be regarded as *either* a real number or an angle of $\frac{1}{4}\pi$ radians. In most cases, however, the argument of a complex number—like its absolute value—is considered to be a real number. It is often a convenience to abbreviate the number $r(\cos \theta + i \sin \theta)$ to $r \operatorname{cis} \theta$, and we shall make some use of this abbreviation.

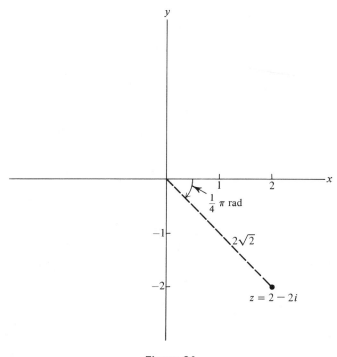

Figure 84

Example 1.   Express the complex number $z = 2 - 2i$ in trigonometric form.

SOLUTION.   The geometric representation of z is shown in Figure 84. It is clear from the figure that $r = |z| = 2\sqrt{2}$, and arg z may be taken to be $-\frac{1}{4}\pi$. Hence $z = 2\sqrt{2}[\cos(-\frac{1}{4}\pi) + i \sin(-\frac{1}{4}\pi)]$, which is the desired trigonometric form for z. It is clear that a more compact expression for z is $2\sqrt{2}(\cos \frac{1}{4}\pi - i \sin \frac{1}{4}\pi)$, but *this is not a standard trigonometric form for the number.*

Although the addition and subtraction of complex numbers is most easily effected if we leave the numbers in normal form, it is a consequence of the following theorem that it is easier to perform multiplications and divisions of complex numbers if they are in trigonometric form.

■ **THEOREM 3.1.** *If $z_1 = r_1(\cos \theta_1 + i \sin \theta_1)$ and $z_2 = r_2(\cos \theta_2 + i \sin \theta_2)$ are any two complex numbers, the product $z_1 z_2$ and quotient z_1/z_2 (if $z_2 \neq 0$) are given as follows:*

(a) $z_1 z_2 = r_1 r_2 [\cos (\theta_1 + \theta_2) + i \sin (\theta_1 + \theta_2)]$;

(b) $z_1/z_2 = (r_1/r_2)[\cos (\theta_1 - \theta_2) + i \sin (\theta_1 - \theta_2)]$.

PROOF

$$z_1 z_2 = [r_1(\cos \theta_1 + i \sin \theta_1)][r_2(\cos \theta_2 + i \sin \theta_2)]$$
$$= r_1 r_2 [(\cos \theta_1 \cos \theta_2 - \sin \theta_1 \sin \theta_2)$$
$$+ i(\sin \theta_1 \cos \theta_2 + \cos \theta_1 \sin \theta_2)]$$
$$= r_1 r_2 [\cos (\theta_1 + \theta_2) + i \sin (\theta_1 + \theta_2)]$$

If $z_2 \neq 0$, $\dfrac{z_1}{z_2} = \dfrac{r_1(\cos \theta_1 + i \sin \theta_1)}{r_2(\cos \theta_2 + i \sin \theta_2)}$

$$= \frac{r_1(\cos \theta_1 + i \sin \theta_1)[\cos (-\theta_2) + i \sin (-\theta_2)]}{r_2(\cos \theta_2 + i \sin \theta_2)[\cos (-\theta_2) + i \sin (-\theta_2)]}$$

$$= \frac{r_1[\cos (\theta_1 - \theta_2) + i \sin (\theta_1 - \theta_2)]}{r_2(\cos 0 + i \sin 0)}$$

$$= \frac{r_1}{r_2}[\cos (\theta_1 - \theta_2) + i \sin (\theta_1 - \theta_2)]$$

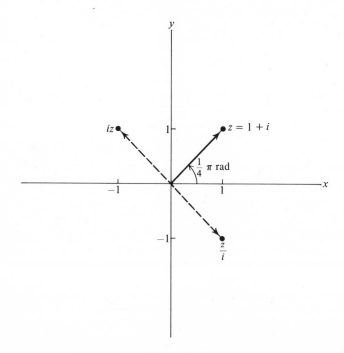

Figure 85

In words, the preceding theorem may be stated as follows:

The product (or quotient) of any two complex numbers may be effected by multiplying (or dividing) their absolute values and adding (or subtracting) their arguments, excluding division by zero.

Example 2.   If $z = 1 + i$, express iz and z/i in trigonometric form, and discuss both results from a geometric point of view.

SOLUTION.   The trigonometric form of z is $\sqrt{2}(\cos \frac{1}{4}\pi + i \sin \frac{1}{4}\pi)$, and the trigonometric form of i is $1(\cos \frac{1}{2}\pi + i \sin \frac{1}{2}\pi)$, as may be seen from Figure 85. Hence, by Theorem 3.1,

$$iz = \sqrt{2}[\cos (\tfrac{1}{4}\pi + \tfrac{1}{2}\pi) + i \sin (\tfrac{1}{4}\pi + \tfrac{1}{2}\pi)] = \sqrt{2}(\cos \tfrac{3}{4}\pi + i \sin \tfrac{3}{4}\pi)$$

Similarly,

$$\frac{z}{i} = \sqrt{2}[\cos (\tfrac{1}{4}\pi - \tfrac{1}{2}\pi) + i \sin (\tfrac{1}{4}\pi - \tfrac{1}{2}\pi)]$$
$$= \sqrt{2}[\cos (-\tfrac{1}{4}\pi) + i \sin (-\tfrac{1}{4}\pi)]$$

It appears from this example—and the result can be established in general—that the effect of multiplying or dividing a complex number by i is to rotate the line segment, joining the origin with the point representing the number, through an angle of 90°, counterclockwise in the case of multiplication and clockwise in the case of division.

Example 3.   If $z = 1 + i$, determine z^8.

SOLUTION.   Because $z = 1 + i = \sqrt{2}(\cos \frac{1}{4}\pi + i \sin \frac{1}{4}\pi)$, we may—for variety of notation—write $z = \sqrt{2}$ cis $\frac{1}{4}\pi$. Then $z^8 = (\sqrt{2}$ cis $\frac{1}{4}\pi)^8 = (\sqrt{2})^8$ cis $\frac{8}{4}\pi$, by successive applications of (a) of Theorem 3.1. Hence, $z^8 = 16$ cis $2\pi = 16(\cos 2\pi + i \sin 2\pi) = 16$.

This final example is illustrative of the ease with which integral powers of complex numbers can be determined when the numbers are expressed in trigonometric form.

Problems 8.3

1. Express each of the following complex numbers in trigonometric form:
   (a) $1 - i$; (b) $2 + 2i$; (c) $-\frac{1}{2} + \frac{1}{2}\sqrt{3}i$; (d) $\sqrt{3}/2 + \frac{1}{2}i$; (e) $-2i$.
2. Express each of the following complex numbers in trigonometric form:
   (a) 3; (b) -6; (c) $-2 - 2i$; (d) $\sqrt{3} - i$; (e) $-\sqrt{3} + i$; (f) $1 - \sqrt{3}i$.
3. Find the modulus and argument (of smallest absolute value) of each of the following complex numbers, and represent the number by a point on the Cartesian plane:
   (a) i; (b) $-i$; (c) $2 - 2i$; (d) $-1 - \sqrt{3}i$.

4. Find the modulus and argument (of smallest absolute value) of each of the following complex numbers, and represent the number by a point on the Cartesian plane:
    (a) $1 - \sqrt{3}i$; (b) $-1 + \sqrt{3}i$; (c) $\sqrt{2} - \sqrt{2}i$; (d) -1.

5. Express each of the following complex numbers in normal form, and represent it as a point on the Cartesian plane:
    (a) $2 \text{ cis } \frac{5}{6}\pi$; (b) $3 \text{ cis } \pi$; (c) $5 \text{ cis } (\frac{1}{3}\pi \text{ radians})$; (d) $2 \text{ cis } (\frac{1}{6}\pi \text{ radians})$; (e) $4 \text{ cis } 120°$; (f) $3 \text{ cis } (-300°)$.

6. Use Table 2 to find an approximate expression of each of the following complex numbers in normal form:
    (a) $2 \text{ cis } 2$; (b) $4 \text{ cis } 1$; (c) $3 \text{ cis } 1.42$; (d) $2 \text{ cis } 200°$; (e) $5 \text{ cis } (-100°)$.

7. Use Table 2 to find an approximate expression of each of the following complex numbers in trigonometric form:
    (a) $2 - 3i$; (b) $-2 - 3i$; (c) $1 + 3i$; (d) $-1 - 3i$; (e) $3 + 4i$; (f) $-3 - 4i$.

8. Simplify to a complex number in normal form:
    (a) $\dfrac{2 \text{ cis } \frac{5}{6}\pi \text{ cis } \frac{1}{5}\pi}{4 \text{ cis } \frac{1}{3}\pi \text{ cis } \frac{1}{6}\pi}$ (b) $\dfrac{(2 \text{ cis } \frac{3}{4}\pi)^3}{4 \text{ cis } \frac{1}{4}\pi}$ (c) $\dfrac{(3 \text{ cis } \frac{1}{6}\pi)^4}{(2 \text{ cis } \frac{1}{3}\pi)^2}$

9. Simplify to a complex number in trigonometric form:
    (a) $[3(\cos 2 + i \sin 2)]^3$ (b) $[2(\cos 3 + i \sin 3)]^4$

10. Simplify to a complex number in trigonometric form with positive argument:
    (a) $\dfrac{[2 \text{ cis } (-\frac{1}{3}\pi)]^2}{2 \text{ cis } (-\frac{3}{4}\pi)}$ (b) $\dfrac{5 \text{ cis } (-\frac{2}{5}\pi)}{2 [\text{cis } (-\frac{3}{4}\pi)]^2}$ (c) $\dfrac{[4 \text{ cis } (-\frac{5}{4}\pi)]^5}{[2 \text{ cis } (-\frac{1}{3}\pi)]^3}$

Use the trigonometric form of complex numbers to simplify each of the expressions in Problems 11–14 to a complex number in normal form:

11. $\dfrac{(\sqrt{3} + i)(-1 + i)}{(1 + \sqrt{3}i)(\sqrt{3} - i)}$

12. $(1 + i)(1 + \sqrt{3}i)(-\frac{1}{2} - \frac{1}{2}i)$

13. $(-\sqrt{3} - i)^3/(1 + \sqrt{3}i)^2$

14. $\dfrac{[10(\cos 15° + i \sin 15°)]^5}{[3(\cos 120° + i \sin 120°)]^2}$

15. Find z^{10}, where $z = 2(\cos 10° + i \sin 10°)$.

16. Use Table 2 to approximate z^5 where:
    (a) $z = 2(\cos 20° + i \sin 20°)$ (b) $z = 2(\cos 2 + i \sin 2)$

17. Use the trigonometric form of $z = \frac{1}{2} + \frac{1}{2}\sqrt{3}i$ to verify that $z^3 = 1$ (cf. Problem 7 of §8.2).

18. Use the trigonometric form of a complex number to simplify each of the following: (a) $(1 - i)^5$; (b) $(2 + 2i)^{10}$; (c) $(\sqrt{3}/2 - \frac{1}{2}i)^5$; (d) $(\frac{1}{2} - \frac{1}{2}\sqrt{3}i)^8$; (e) $(-2i)^{11}$; (f) $(\sqrt{3} + i)$; (g) $(1 - \sqrt{3}i)^9$.

19. Use Table 2 to approximate each of the following as a complex number in trigonometric form: (a) $(3 - i)^6$; (b) $(2 + 3i)^5$; (c) $(1 - 5i)^{10}$.

20. Prove that $(r \text{ cis } \theta)^2 = r^2 \text{ cis } 2\theta$ and $(r \text{ cis } \theta)^3 = r^3 \text{ cis } 3\theta$. Conjecture a generalization and refer to §8.4.

21. Prove, for any complex numbers u, v, that $|uv| = |u| |v|$ and (if $v \neq 0$) that $|u/v| = |u|/|v|$.

22. Prove that $z\bar{z} = |z|^2$, for any complex number z.

23. Prove that $|z| = |-z| = |\bar{z}| = |iz| = |z/i| = |z \text{ cis } \theta|$, for any $z \in C$ and any $\theta \in R$.

24. Prove that two complex numbers u and v are equal if and only if $|u| = |v|$ and $\arg u - \arg v = 2n\pi$, for some $n \in \mathbf{Z}$.
25. If $z_1 = a + bi$ and $z_2 = c + di$ are complex numbers, verify that $|z_1 - z_2|$ is equal to the distance between the geometric points of the Cartesian plane that represent z_1 and z_2.
26. Give a geometric characterization of the points representing the following sets of complex numbers: (a) $\{z \in \mathbf{C} |\, |z| < 1\}$; (b) $\{z \in \mathbf{C} |\, |z| = 2\}$; (c) $z \in \mathbf{C} |\, |z| \leq 1\}$; (d) $\{z \in \mathbf{C} |\, |z| > 2\}$.
27. Give a geometric characterization of the points representing the following sets of complex numbers: (a) $\{z \in \mathbf{C} |\, |2z| \leq 3\}$; (b) $\{z \in \mathbf{C} |\, z + \bar{z} < 1\}$; (c) $\{z \in \mathbf{C} |\, z + \bar{z} > 1\}$; (d) $\{z \in \mathbf{C} |\, z - \bar{z} = 2i\}$.
28. If we attempt to "order" the complex numbers by the rule that $z_1 < z_2$ if and only if $|z_1| < |z_2|$, which of the requirements of an order relation, given in §3.1, fail(s) to be satisfied?
29. Prove, for any complex number $z = a + bi$, that $a \leq |z|$ and $b \leq |z|$.
30. Prove that the absolute value of the sum of two complex numbers is less than or equal to their absolute values. (*Hint:* Write $|z_1 + z_2|^2 = (z_1 + z_2)(\overline{z_1 + z_2})$ and use the fact that $z_1\bar{z}_2 + z_2\bar{z}_1$ is twice the real component of $z_1\bar{z}_2$.)

8.4 Mathematical Induction

The topic to be discussed in this section belongs in Chapter 1 from a purely logical point of view, because it is a property of numbers—the natural numbers. However, the notion of mathematical induction is not an easy one for the average person whose mathematical maturity is at the approximate level of this book. Inasmuch as Chapter 1 already contains considerable material of an abstract nature, it seemed pedagogically feasible to postpone any discussion of induction until now. Moreover, although many—in some cases most—of the proofs in books on advanced mathematics are inductive in nature, there are very few occasions in a book on elementary algebra or trigonometry when it is propitious to use this type of proof. There were one or two places in the earlier chapters where we *could* have used induction (for example, in extending the laws of exponents), but it would not have been used often enough for the reader to have become thoroughly familiar with it. However, we do plan to use it in the next section to derive an important result and again—to a greater extent —in Chapter 10. It is then our hope that the reader will understand our pedagogical and utilitarian reasons for the location in the text of this most important but rather subtle topic. An early attempt was made by G. Peano (1858–1932) to reduce the theory of natural numbers to a minimal set of postulates and undefined terms. Although his set has been shown by later investigators not to be minimal, nor even to define the natural numbers uniquely, these so-called "Peano postulates" have nonetheless been regarded as standard characterizing postulates for the natural numbers. We shall not list all the postulates here, but shall be content with giving the one of present interest to us—the postulate of *Induction*. It should be recalled that we have not included 0 in the set $\mathbf{N}$ of natural numbers—contrary to the practice of some mathematicians.

The Postulate of Induction.   Let S be a subset of $\mathbf{N}$ with the following properties:

(1) $1 \in S$
(2) $k + 1 \in S$ provided $k \in S$

Then $S = \mathbf{N}$.

From the Postulate of Induction, we are able to derive quite easily

The Principle of Mathematical Induction.   Let P_n be a statement involving an arbitrary natural number n. Then if

(1) P_1 is true, and
(2) P_{k+1} is true whenever P_k is true,

it follows that P_n is true for every natural number n. [We often refer to (2) as our "inductive assumption."]

PROOF.   Let S be the subset $\{n \in \mathbf{N} | \ P_n \text{ is true}\}$. By (1), we know that P_1 is true, and so $1 \in S$. From (2) we know that $k + 1 \in S$ whenever $k \in S$, for any natural number k. But then the Postulate of Induction asserts that $S = \mathbf{N}$, which is to say that P_n is true for every natural number n.

It should be pointed out that some people prefer not to distinguish between what we have called the "Postulate" and "Principle" of induction. In the language that we have adopted it is clear that the Principle of Induction is an immediate consequence of the Postulate, but it is our personal preference to keep the identity of each distinct: The *Postulate* is an axiom in the context of set theory, whereas the *Principle* embodies a method of proof for theorems. It may also be fitting to make the remark that there are *two* Principles of Mathematical Induction, and the person who does more advanced work in mathematics will most certainly encounter the Second Principle at least as often as the one we have stated. In this elementary book, however, we shall make no further mention—except in Problem 33—of this other type of induction. For *our* purposes, the Principle of Induction is the one described above. However, we shall resume our practice in the sequel of referring to *positive integers* rather than to *natural numbers*, even though the latter language was used in our introduction above to the Postulate of Induction.

A word of caution should possibly be given that mathematical induction is quite different from empirical induction—frequently called "induction"—in the natural sciences. Empirical induction is a type of reasoning which allows one to proceed from a number of observations to a statement of a physical law, the degree of certainty of the "law" depending on the frequency of the observations on which it was based. This kind of "inductive" reasoning is often quite convincing—as, for instance, the prediction that the sun will rise in the east tomorrow—but the statement has its origin in experience rather than logic. The proof of an assertion by mathematical induction, on the other hand, follows essentially from the inductive postulate of Peano—the accepted truth of which lies at the very foundation of mathematics.

It is often the case that even the *mathematical* novice feels that, if enough examples of a certain proposition are established, the truth of the general proposition must follow. But in reality this is equivalent to empirical induction. It can happen that many cases of a proposition are true, but the proposition is not true in its complete generality. The mathematical statement $n^2 - 40n - 41 \neq 0$ is true for $n = 1, 2, 3, \ldots, 40$, but it is easily seen to be false for $n = 41$. We now illustrate the use of the Principle of Mathematical Induction with a few examples.

Example 1. If $a\,(> 1)$ is a real number, use mathematical induction to prove that $a^n > 1$ for every positive integer n.

PROOF. The assertion P_n to be established for every natural number n is: $a^n > 1$, for any real number $a\,(> 1)$.

(1) Because $a^1 = a > 1$, P_1 is true.
(2) Let us assume that P_k is true for an *arbitrary but fixed* natural number k; that is, $a^k > 1$. Then $a^{k+1} = (a^k)a > 1$ (because $a^k > 1$ and $a > 1$) whence P_{k+1} is true.

It follows, by the Principle of Mathematical Induction, that P_n is true; that is, $a^n > 1$ for any natural number n.

Example 2. The sum of the interior angles of a convex polygon of $n + 2$ sides is $180n$ degrees.

PROOF. We shall let P_n stand for the assertion to be proved.

(1) If $n = 1$, the polygon is a triangle, and it is well known from elementary geometry that the sum of the interior angles of any triangle is $180°$. Hence, P_1 is true.
(2) Let us assume that P_k is true for an *arbitrary, but fixed*, natural number k; that is, a polygon of $k + 2$ sides has interior angles that total $(180k)°$. Now any convex polygon of $k + 3$ sides may be broken up into a triangle and a convex polygon of $k + 2$ sides, by joining the first and third of any three consecutive vertices of the given polygon. By our inductive assumption, the sum of the angles of the polygon with $k + 2$ sides is $(180k)°$, whereas the sum of the angles of the triangle is $180°$. The sum of the angles of both—which make up the angles of the given polygon of $k + 3$ sides—is then $[180(k + 1)]°$. But this means that P_{k+1} is true. By the Principle of Mathematical Induction, it then follows that P_n is true for every natural number n, and the assertion has been verified.

It may appear to the somewhat careless reader that our proofs by mathematical induction are circular. Our inductive assumption that P_k is true for an arbitrary natural number k seems to differ only in notation from the assertion to be proved—that P_n is true for every natural number n. However, the inductive assumption is not that P_k is in fact true, but rather that *if P_k is true then P_{k+1} is also true*. This is quite different from the *statement* that P_n *is* true for every natural number n.

Example 3.   Use mathematical induction to prove that $x^n - y^n$ is divisible by $x - y$, for every natural number n.

SOLUTION.   We let P_n be the proposition to be established.

(1) Because $x^1 - y^1 = x - y$ is certainly divisible by $x - y$, P_1 is true.
(2) Let us assume that P_k is true, for an *arbitrary but fixed* natural number k; that is, $x^k - y^k$ is divisible by $x - y$. But $x^{k+1} - y^{k+1} = x^{k+1} - xy^k + xy^k - y^{k+1} = x(x^k - y^k) + y^k(x - y)$, where both terms are divisible by $x - y$. Hence, $x^{k+1} - y^{k+1}$ is divisible by $x - y$, which means that P_{k+1} is true. It follows by mathematical induction that P_n is true for any natural number n, as desired.

Problems 8.4

Use the Principle of Mathematical Induction to establish the truth of the assertions in Problems 1–21, in which n should be assumed to be an arbitrary positive integer—unless stated otherwise. (Problems involving sums of series—usually handled by induction—are being postponed until Chapter 10)

1. $1! + 2! + \cdots + n!$ is an integer.
2. $n + 1 = 1 + n$
3. $n(a + b) = na + nb$, for arbitrary real numbers a, b.
4. If z is any complex number, the conjugate of z^n is equal to the nth power of the conjugate of z (that is, $\overline{z^n} = \bar{z}^n$).
5. $x^{2n} - y^{2n}$ is divisible by $x - y$.
6. $2^n \geq 2n$.
7. $|A_1A_2| + |A_2A_3| + \cdots + |A_{n-1}A_n| \geq |A_1A_n|$ for arbitrary points A_1, A_2, $\ldots$, A_n of a plane.
8. Any set of $n + 1$ points in a plane, no three of which are collinear, determines $\frac{1}{2}n(n + 1)$ lines in the plane.
9. $n^3 + 2n$ is divisible in **Z** by 3.
10. The product of any three consecutive positive integers n, $n + 1$, $n + 2$ is divisible in **Z** by 6.
11. The product of any four consecutive positive integers n, $n + 1$, $n + 2$, $n + 3$ is divisible in **Z** by 24. (*Hint:* Use the result in Problem 10.)
12. $n^2 - n + 2$ is an even integer.

13. $2n^3 + 3n^2 + n$ is divisible in $\mathbf{Z}$ by 6.

14. $m + n = n + m$, for arbitrary positive integers m and n. (*Hint:* Assume either m or n arbitrary but *fixed*, and use induction on the other; also use Problem 2.)

15. $a^m a^n = a^{m+n}$, for a real number a and arbitrary positive integers m and n. [*Hint:* Assume powers have been defined so $a^1 = a$ and $a^{k+1} = (a^k)a$, for any k (> 0) $\in \mathbf{Z}$. Then consider either m or n fixed and use induction on the other.]

16. $(a^m)^n = a^{mn}$, for raeal number a and any positive integers m and n. (See Hint in Problem 15; see Problem 18.)

17. $(m + n) + r = m + (n + r)$, for any positive integers m, n, and r. (*Hint:* Assume two of m, n, r arbitrary but *fixed*, and use induction on the third; also use Problem 2.)

18. $(mn)r = m(nr)$, for any positive integers m, n, and r (see Hint in Problem 17).

19. If n lines divide a plane into k regions, $k \le 2^n$.

20. $(n + 1)^n < n^{n+1}$, for any n (≥ 3) $\in \mathbf{Z}$. (*Hint:* Replace n by $m + 2$ and use induction on m.)

21. $2^n < n! < n^n$, for n (≥ 4) $\in \mathbf{Z}$. (*Hint:* Replace n by $m + 3$ and use induction on m.)

22. It is well known that there exists an integer n such that $x + n = y$, for arbitrary integers x and y. Can one use mathematical induction to prove this assertion? If so, give the proof; if not, explain why such a proof is not possible.

23. Find the error in the following "proof" by induction that "All numbers in a set of n numbers are equal."

PROOF. Let P_n be the given assertion.

(1) Because every number is equal to itself, it is clear that P_1 is true.

(2) Let us assume that P_k is true, and consider an arbitrary set of $k + 1$ numbers $a_1, a_2, \ldots, a_k, a_{k+1}$. Then, because $a_1, a_2, \ldots, a_k$ and $a_2, a_3, \ldots, a_{k+1}$ are both sets of k numbers, our inductive assumption implies that $a_1 = a_2 = \cdots = a_k$ and also $a_2 = a_3 = \cdots = a_{k+1}$. Because "things equal to the same thing are equal to each other," it follows that $a_1 = a_2 = \cdots = a_{k+1}$, which is to say that P_{k+1} is true.

It then follows (!) by the Principle of Mathematical Induction that P_n is true for all positive integers n, as asserted.

24. Find the error in the following "proof" by induction that the following assertion P_n is true:

P_n: If r and s are positive integers such that max $\{r, s\} = n$, then $r = s$.

PROOF. (1) It is clear that P_1 is true, because, of necessity in this case, $r = s = 1$.

(2) Suppose P_k is true for any k (> 0) $\in \mathbf{Z}$. Then, if r and s are such that max $\{r, s\} = k + 1$, consider the numbers $a = r - 1$ and $b = s - 1$. It is clear that max $\{a, b\} = k$, and so, by our inductive assumption, $a = b$ and $r = s$. Hence, P_{k+1} is true.

It then follows (!) by the Principle of Mathematical Induction that P_n is true for all positive integers n.

25. If a ($\in \mathbf{R}$) > 1, use induction on n to prove that $(a + 1)^n \ge 1 + na$ for any n (> 0) $\in \mathbf{Z}$.

26. Extend the proof that you have given in Problem 25 to include any real number $a < -1$.

27. Use induction to prove that $|\sin nx| \le n|\sin x|$, for $x \in \mathbf{R}$ and n (> 0) $\in \mathbf{Z}$.

28. It was a conjecture of Fermat that there do not exist natural numbers x, y, z such that $x^n + y^n = z^n$, for any natural number $n > 2$. Prove that the conjecture is true if $x = 1$. (Even though the conjecture has been established for $n \leq 4000$, no proof exists that the conjecture is true for any positive integer n. The conjecture is known familiarly as "Fermat's Last Theorem.")

29. If a line segment of unit length is given, used the Principle of Mathematical Induction to prove that a segment of length $\sqrt{n}$ can be constructed with straight-edge and compass, for any $n\ (> 0) \in \mathbf{Z}$.

30. Give an argument that would make it permissible to use induction to prove a proposition P_n that is true only for $n \geq k$, for some fixed $k\ (> 0) \in \mathbf{Z}$ (cf. Problems 20 and 21).

31. The "Well-ordering Principle" asserts the following: If S is any nonempty collection of natural numbers, there exists a number $m \in S$ such that $m \leq s$ for all $s \in S$. Prove that this and the mathematical induction principles are equivalent; that is, each one implies the other.

32. Use the principle in Problem 31 to prove the following: For every integer $n \geq 0$, there exist nonnegative integers q and r such that $n = qb + r, 0 \leq r < b$.

33. Use the result in Problem 31 to establish the *Second Principle of Induction:*
    Let P_n be an assertion involving a positive integer n. Then if P_m is true provided P_k is true for every $k < m$, then P_n is true for any $n\ (> 0) \in \mathbf{Z}$.

34. Use the result in Problem 33 to establish the *Fundamental Theorem of Arithmetic:*
    Any positive integer n is either 1, a prime, or a product of prime numbers, this expression being unique except for the order of the factors. (A *prime* is a positive number p that is divisible in $\mathbf{Z}$ by only $\pm p$ and ± 1.)

8.5 DeMoivre's Theorem and Root Extraction

We have noted in §8.2 that the Fundamental Theorem of Algebra assures us of the existence of a complex number solution of any polynomial equation with complex coefficients. In particular, the equation $x^n - a = 0$, with $a \in \mathbf{C}$ and $n\ (> 0) \in \mathbf{Z}$ has a solution in $\mathbf{C}$. There then exists in the field of complex numbers an nth root of any complex number, and in particular (recalling that $\mathbf{R} \subset \mathbf{C}$) of any positive *or negative* real number. It was suggested in Problem 20 of §8.3 that the reader use the theorem in that section to prove that $(r \text{ cis } \theta)^2 = r^2 \text{ cis } 2\theta$ and $(r \text{ cis } \theta)^3 = r^3 \text{ cis } 3\theta$, for $r\ (> 0)$, $\theta \in \mathbf{R}$, but we now see that these results are special cases of DeMoivre's Theorem, which we now prove.

■ **THEOREM 5.1.** (*DeMoivre*).   *For any positive integer n, and any $\theta \in \mathbf{R}$,*

$$(\cos \theta + i \sin \theta)^n = \cos n\theta + i \sin n\theta.$$

PROOF.   The truth of this theorem is quite evident from the definition that we gave in §8.3 for the multiplication of complex numbers. However, in order to give a substantial foundation to the result, we use the Principle of Mathematical Induction. It is only natural to let $z^1 = z$, for any $z \in \mathbf{C}$, and we now let P_n denote the assertion of the theorem.

(1) P_1 asserts that $(\cos \theta + i \sin \theta)^1 = \cos \theta + i \sin \theta$, and this is true from the identification of z^1 with z. That is, P_1 is true.

(2) Let us suppose that P_k is true for any fixed but arbitrary integer $k \geq 1$, and consider P_{k+1}. Again, the concept of a natural number exponent implies that $(\cos \theta + i \sin \theta)^{k+1} = (\cos \theta + i \sin \theta)^k(\cos \theta + i \sin \theta)$, and by our inductive assumption, this latter expression equals $(\cos k\theta + i \sin k\theta)(\cos \theta + i \sin \theta)$. But now, a simple application of Theorem 3.1 shows that $(\cos \theta + i \sin \theta)^{k+1} = \cos (k + 1)\theta + i \sin (k + 1)\theta$, which is to say that P_{k+1} is true. It then follows from the Principle of Mathematical Induction that P_n is true for any positive integer n, and the proof of the theorem is complete.

As for real numbers, we *define* $z^0 = 1$ and $z^{-n} = 1/z^n$, for any $z \ (\neq 0) \in \mathbf{C}$ and any $n \ (> 0) \in \mathbf{Z}$, and the following corollary follows.

■ **COROLLARY.**   *The laws of exponents hold for m, n nonnegative integers and z, z_1, z_2 complex numbers arbitrary except as indicated:*

$$z^m z^n = z^{m+n}$$

$$(z^m)^n = z^{mn}$$

$$(z_1 z_2)^n = z_1^n z_2^n$$

$$z^m/z^n = z^{m-n} = 1/z^{n-m} \qquad \text{if } z \neq 0$$

$$(z_1/z_2)^n = z_1^n/z_2^n \qquad \text{if } z_2 \neq 0$$

We now proceed to a very important consequence of DeMoivre's Theorem.

■ **THEOREM 5.2.**   *If* $z = r(\cos \theta + i \sin \theta)$ *is an arbitrary complex number, there are exactly n distinct complex nth roots of z, and these may be expressed in the form*

$$\sqrt[n]{r}\left(\cos \frac{\theta + 2k\pi}{n} + i \sin \frac{\theta + 2k\pi}{n}\right) \qquad where \ k = 0, 1, 2, \ldots, n - 1$$

PROOF.   Let $z = r(\cos \theta + i \sin \theta)$, with n an arbitrary positive integer. By an nth root of z, we mean a number w such that $w^n = z$. Hence, if w exists as a complex number, $w = s(\cos \alpha + i \sin \alpha)$ and, by DeMoivre's Theorem, we have $w^n = s^n(\cos n\alpha + i \sin n\alpha) = z = r(\cos \theta + i \sin \theta)$. If two complex numbers are equal, their absolute values must be equal, and so $s^n = r$. Because s must be a positive real number, $s = \sqrt[n]{r}$ where, as always, $\sqrt[n]{r}$ indicates the positive nth root of the real number r. Moreover, from the equation connecting w and z, it also follows that

$$\cos n\alpha = \cos \theta$$

and

$$\sin n\alpha = \sin \theta$$

These equations can be satisfied only if $n\alpha$ differs from θ by some integral multiple of 2π (the period of both the basic sine and cosine functions), so that $n\alpha = \theta + 2k\pi$ and $\alpha = (\theta + 2k\pi)/n$, for some integer k. If we let $k = 0, 1, 2, \ldots, n - 1$ in the above formula for α, we obtain n distinct possibilities for α, whereas any other integral substitution for k will result in a repetition of a value previously obtained. These n distinct values of α are then the only possible ones, and we have obtained the desired result.

From the point of view of geometry, the nth roots of z are n points equally spaced around a circle with center at the origin and radius $\sqrt[n]{r}$. This is illustrated in Figure 86 for the case $n = 3$.

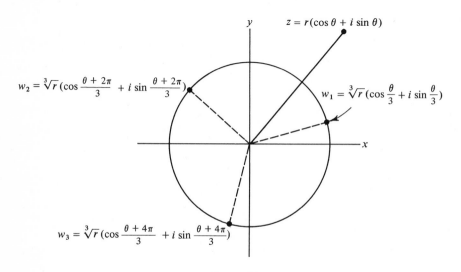

Figure 86

We have emphasized in an earlier chapter that, if a is a real number, $\sqrt[n]{a}$ is a well-defined real number—the principal nth root—if a real nth root of a exists. However, except for special cases, if z is an arbitrary complex number, it is not generally the case that $\sqrt[n]{z}$ designates a *particular* nth root of z. If we wish to do so, of course, we could let this symbol designate, say, the nth root whose real component is positive and minimal, but there is no generally accepted usage of this symbol. In the case of square roots of a negative number a, however, it is customary to let $\sqrt{a}$ denote the number $\sqrt{|a|}i$, so that $\sqrt{-4} = 2i$. In the case of the nth roots of unity, we usually let the one with the smallest positive argument be ω, and the complete set of nth roots of unity is then

$$\{\omega, \omega^2, \omega^3, \ldots, \omega^n = 1\}.$$

Example 1.   Find the three cube roots of -1.

SOLUTION.   The trigonometric form of -1, considered as a complex number, is $1(\cos \pi + i \sin \pi)$ or, more generally, $1[\cos (\pi + 2k\pi) + i \sin (\pi + 2k\pi)]$, where k is an arbitrary positive integer. Hence, by Theorem 5.2 the three cube roots are $\cos (\frac{1}{3}\pi + \frac{2}{3}k\pi) + i \sin (\frac{1}{3}\pi + \frac{2}{3}k\pi)$, where $k = 0, 1, 2$. In more simple form, these three cube roots are

$$\cos \tfrac{1}{3}\pi + i \sin \tfrac{1}{3}\pi, \quad \cos \pi + i \sin \pi, \quad \cos \tfrac{5}{3}\pi + i \sin \tfrac{5}{3}\pi$$

Because

$$\cos \tfrac{1}{3}\pi = \cos \tfrac{5}{3}\pi = \tfrac{1}{2}, \quad \text{and} \quad \sin \tfrac{1}{3}\pi = \tfrac{1}{2}\sqrt{3}, \quad \sin \tfrac{5}{3}\pi = -\tfrac{1}{2}\sqrt{3}$$

the three desired cube roots, in rectangular form, are

$$\tfrac{1}{2} + \tfrac{1}{2}\sqrt{3}i, \quad -1, \quad \tfrac{1}{2} - \tfrac{1}{2}\sqrt{3}i$$

In Figure 87, we have given a graphical representation of these three cube roots, which we note are equally spaced on the unit circle.

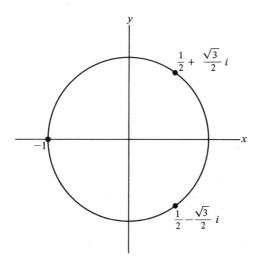

Figure 87

Example 2.   Find the two square roots of $2 + 2i$.

SOLUTION.   The trigonometric form of $2 + 2i$ is $2\sqrt{2}(\cos \frac{1}{4}\pi + i \sin \frac{1}{4}\pi)$. Hence the two square roots of the given number are

$$\sqrt[4]{8}(\cos \tfrac{1}{8}\pi + i \sin \tfrac{1}{8}\pi), \quad \sqrt[4]{8}(\cos \tfrac{9}{8}\pi + i \sin \tfrac{9}{8}\pi)$$

Now $\cos \frac{9}{8}\pi = -\cos \frac{1}{8}\pi$ and $\sin \frac{9}{8}\pi = -\sin \frac{1}{8}\pi$, whereas

$$\cos \tfrac{1}{8}\pi = \sqrt{\frac{1 + \cos \frac{1}{4}\pi}{2}} = \sqrt{\frac{1 + \sqrt{2}/2}{2}} = \frac{\sqrt{2 + \sqrt{2}}}{2}$$

and

$$\sin \tfrac{1}{8}\pi = \sqrt{\frac{1 - \cos \frac{1}{4}\pi}{2}} = \frac{\sqrt{2 - \sqrt{2}}}{2}$$

Hence, the two square roots of $2 + 2i$ are

$$\sqrt[4]{8}\left(\frac{\sqrt{2 + \sqrt{2}}}{2} + \frac{\sqrt{2 - \sqrt{2}}}{2}\,i\right)$$

and

$$-\sqrt[4]{8}\left(\frac{\sqrt{2 + \sqrt{2}}}{2} + \frac{\sqrt{2 - \sqrt{2}}}{2}\,i\right)$$

Example 3.   Find the five fifth roots of $1 + \sqrt{3}i$.

SOLUTION.   The trigonometric form of $1 + \sqrt{3}i$ is $2(\cos \frac{1}{3}\pi + i \sin \frac{1}{3}\pi)$. Hence the five fifth roots of $1 + \sqrt{3}i$ may be expressed as

$$\sqrt[5]{2}\left[\cos\left(\frac{\frac{1}{3}\pi + 2k\pi}{5}\right) + i \sin \frac{\frac{1}{3}\pi + 2k\pi}{5}\right] \qquad \text{for } k = 0, 1, 2, 3, 4$$

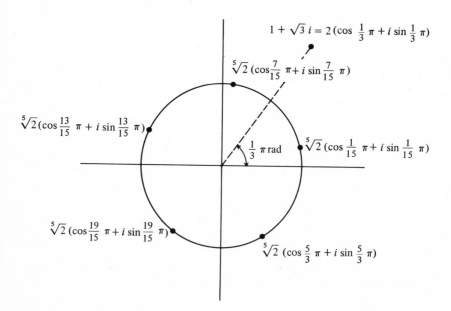

Figure 88

These roots may be expressed as $\sqrt[5]{2}(\cos \frac{1}{15}\pi + i \sin \frac{1}{15}\pi)$, $\sqrt[5]{2}(\cos \frac{7}{15}\pi + i \sin \frac{7}{15}\pi)$, $\sqrt[5]{2}(\cos \frac{13}{15}\pi + i \sin \frac{13}{15}\pi)$, $\sqrt[5]{2}(\cos \frac{19}{15}\pi + i \sin \frac{19}{15}\pi)$, and $\sqrt[5]{2}(\cos \frac{5}{3}\pi + i \sin \frac{5}{3}\pi)$. The geometric representation of these numbers is given in Figure 88. If we need to know the rectangular form of the numbers, it is a simple matter to convert them with the help of Table 2. For example, $\frac{1}{15}\pi \approx 0.2094$, and from Table 2, $\cos 0.2094 \approx 0.9781$ whereas $\sin 0.2094 \approx 0.2079$. Hence, $\sqrt[5]{2}(\cos \frac{1}{15}\pi + i \sin \frac{1}{15}\pi) \approx (1.1487)(0.9781 + 0.2079i) \approx 1.124 + 0.239i$. The other fifth roots could be converted to decimal form in a similar manner, with an application of the Reduction Principle.

Problems 8.5

1. If ω is the nth root of unity with smallest positive argument, verify that the other nth roots are $\omega^2, \omega^3, \ldots, \omega^n = 1$.
2. Use the symbolism of Problem 1 (with $n = 5$) to express the five fifth roots of 32.
3. Find, in normal form, the four fourth roots of -1.
4. Find the four fourth roots of $-i$ and express them in normal form.
5. Find the three cube roots of $\sqrt{3} + i$, and represent this number and its cube roots on a graph.
6. Find the five fifth roots of i, and represent this number and its fifth roots on a graph.
7. Use Table 2 to approximate in normal form the three cube roots of $2 - 3i$.
8. Use Table 2 to approximate in normal form the three cube roots of $3 + 4i$.
9. Determine the five complex solutions of the equation $x^5 = 1$.
10. Without any arithmetic analysis, use a diagram to construct the sixth roots of z, where (a) $z = -1$; (b) $z = -i$; (c) $z = 64$; (d) $z = 1 + i$.
11. Write each of the following numbers in the form bi, where b is real, interpreting the radical sign as is done in the text: (a) $\sqrt{-16}$; (b) $\sqrt{-36}$; (c) $\sqrt{-12}$.
12. If we designate one square root of a complex number as $\sqrt{z}$, would it be correct to designate the other one as $-\sqrt{z}$? Give a reason for your answer.
13. Decide whether the following indicated equalities are true or false:
    (a) $|z|^2 = |z^2|$, for any $z \in \mathbf{C}$
    (b) $\sqrt{|a|} = |\sqrt{a}|$, where $a (\in \mathbf{R}) < 0$ and $\sqrt{a}$ may denote *either* complex square root of a
14. Use Table 2 to compute an approximation for $(\cos 1 + i \sin 1)^{10}$.
15. Find the solution set in $\mathbf{C}$ of the equation
    (a) $2x^4 = 1 - \sqrt{3}i$ (b) $x^2 - (3 - i)x - 3i = 0$
16. Use Table 2 to approximate three distinct cube roots of
    (a) $64 \text{ cis } 165°$ (b) $27 \text{ cis } 75°$
17. Solve the equation $(x + \bar{x})x = 2 + 4i$ for all solutions in $\mathbf{C}$.
18. Find the zeros of the function f defined on $\mathbf{C}$ by (a) $f(x) = x^2 - 2i$; (b) $f(x) = 4x^4 + 1$; (c) $f(x) = ix^3 + 1$.
19. If $g(z)$ is defined to be the real component of $\bar{z}$, for any $z \in \mathbf{C}$, determine (a) $g(2 + i)$; (b) $g(z + w)$, where $z = 1 - i$ and $w = 2 + 3i$; (c) $g(zw)$, with z and w as given in (b).
20. Solve the equation $x^3 + i = 0$ in $\mathbf{C}$, and express each solution in both rectangular and trigonometric form. Locate the three solutions on an appropriate diagram.

21. Factor the polynomial $x^3 - 64$ into linear factors with coefficients in **C**.

22. Describe the geometric effect of multiplying a complex number by either square root of i.

23. Let $z^5 = 1$, with $z \ (\in \mathbf{C}) \neq 1$. Then, if $y = 1 + z + z^2 + z^3 + z^4$, show that $yz = y$ and so conclude that $y = 0$. Give a verbal statement of this conclusion.

24. If $\sqrt{a}$ is defined (as in the text) to be $\sqrt{|a|}\,i$, for $a \ (\in \mathbf{R}) < 0$, show that the rule $\sqrt{ab} = \sqrt{a}\,\sqrt{b}$ is not valid for negative numbers a, b.

25. Verify that the rules for multiplication and division of "numbers" of the form $re^{i\theta}$, with r and θ real, are analogous to the corresponding rules for complex numbers in the form $r(\cos \theta + i \sin \theta)$, provided we assume the usual laws for complex exponents.

26. If we were to identify the "number" $re^{i\theta}$ with $r(\cos \theta + i \sin \theta)$, what would be the trigonometric form of $e^{\pi i}$. (This identification is justified in more advanced courses.)

27. Prove that $1 + \cos \theta + \cos 2\theta + \cos 3\theta = \frac{1}{2} + (\sin \frac{7}{2}\theta)/(2 \sin \frac{1}{2}\theta)$. [*Hint:* If $z \ (\neq 1) \in \mathbf{C}, 1 + z + z^2 + z^3 = (1 - z^4)/(1 - z)$.]

28. Extend DeMoivre's Theorem to the case where (a) n is negative integer; (b) n is any rational number.

29. Give a proof of the corollary to Theorem 5.1.

30. Comment on some of the difficulties that you would encounter in an attempt to define z^π for arbitrary $z \in \mathbf{C}$. Would $(-1)^\pi$ be any easier?!

31. How would *you* now answer the question "What is a number"?

9

Theory of Equations

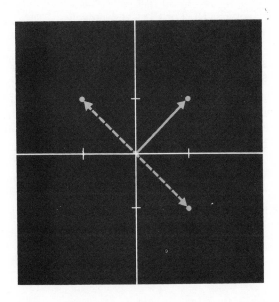

9.1 Polynomials

We have previously used the word "polynomial" to refer to an expression of the form $a_0 x^n + a_1 x^{n-1} + \cdots + a_{n-1} x + a_n$. Although the nature of x depends on the context, the *coefficients* $a_0 \ (\neq 0), a_1, \ldots,$ a_{n-1}, a_n are from some number system (usually a field), and the nonnegative integer n is called the *degree* of the polynomial. In our discussions, the coefficient field will be either the field $\mathbf{R}$ of real numbers or the field $\mathbf{C}$ of complex numbers. We note that nonzero elements from the field of coefficients are themselves considered to be polynomials of degree 0, because we define $x^0 = 1$ for every nonzero interpretation of x; and so $a = ax^0$ for any field element a. The number 0 is also considered to be polynomial, but either no degree or (in some contexts) the degree $-\infty$ is assigned to it. Note that "no degree" and "degree 0" have very different meanings! The additive parts of a polynomial (that is, a_0x^n, a_1x^{n-1}, ..., $a_{n-1}x$, and a_n) are called its *terms*. We shall always use $p(x)$ to denote an arbitrary polynomial in x, and deg $p(x)$ to denote its degree. Other symbols, like $q(x)$ and $r(x)$, will be used when more than one general polynomial is under consideration. On occasion, it may be convenient to refer to the set of all *real* or *complex polynomials* (i.e., with real or complex coefficients) as $\mathbf{R}[x]$ or $\mathbf{C}[x]$, respectively.

If the rule of mapping of a function f is given by an equation of the form $f(x) = p(x)$, for any x in the domain of f, then f is said to be a *polynomial function*. For example, the function f, defined on $\mathbf{R}$ by $f(x) = 3x^4 - x + 4$, is a polynomial function.

The algebraic operations of a number system are the operations of addition, subtraction, multiplication, division, and the extraction of roots. We have already seen that, in the field $\mathbf{C}$, it is possible to perform all these operations except division by 0. (We recall, however, that, to make sure an expression such as $\sqrt[n]{1 - i}$ has an unambiguous meaning, we must make clear which one of the nth roots is to be understood.) If we include along with the set of complex numbers a symbol x, and *formally* perform any sequence of these operations in the enlarged system, we obtain what are called *algebraic expressions* in x. Examples of such algebraic expressions are

$$2x - 1, \quad \sqrt{3 + 2x}, \quad \frac{1 - 3x}{1 + 2x}, \quad (2i - 1)x^2 + \frac{1}{(i - 1)x}$$

It may be worthwhile to point out that, if other processes are permitted, it is possible to obtain nonalgebraic or "transcendental" expressions such as $e^{\sin x}$, $\cos(1 + x)$, and $\ln(2x - 1)$. A polynomial in x is, of course, a particular kind of algebraic expression, and it is with polynomials—in which x has a special interpretation—that we are to be mostly concerned in this chapter.

There is an arithmetic of polynomials, just as there is for any number system and for functions. As a matter of fact, the arithmetic of polynomials in x with coefficients in a field is much like the arithmetic of integers. In both of these systems, it is possible to perform addition, subtraction, and multiplication without exceptions. However, in order to obtain a system closed under division (except by 0), it was necessary to extend the integers to the field of rational numbers; the same motivation leads us to extend the system of polynomials to the field of all "rational functions" of x, which means that we include all quotients $p(x)/q(x)$ of polynomials $p(x)$ and $q(x)$ ($\neq 0$). In order to obtain root extractions, it would be necessary to extend the field of rational functions still further to fields of so-called "algebraic functions," but we shall not discuss this type of field extension here.

The student is probably familiar with the pertinent definitions of the relations and operations in the system $\mathbf{C}[x]$ of complex polynomials in x. However, we

shall review them briefly, using the polynomials $p_1(x) = a_0x^n + a_1x^{n-1} +$
$\cdots + a_{n-1}x + a_n = \sum_{k=0}^{n} a_kx^{n-k}$ and $p_2(x) = b_0x^m + b_1x^{m-1} + \cdots +$
$b_{m-1}x + b_m = \sum_{k=0}^{m} b_kx^{m-k}$, where $n \geq m$ and $a_0b_0 \neq 0$. We use the Greek letter
$\sum$ to denote "summation," a usage that is probably familiar to the reader; if
not, the above equations should make the meaning of the symbol clear. In the
expression for a polynomial, we *assume that any coefficients that do not appear
explicitly are zero*, and this is a convenience for the phrasing of some of our
pertinent definitions.

Equality. $p_1(x) = p_2(x)$ *if* $m = n$ *and* $a_k = b_k$, *for* $k = 0, 1, 2, \ldots, n$.

This is our usual interpretation for the notion of equality, and we include it
merely for the sake of completeness. That is, two polynomials are *equal* if
corresponding coefficients are equal. For example, if $ax^3 + bx^2 + cx + d =$
$3x^2 - 2x - 1$, it follows that $a = 0$, $b = 3$, $c = -2$, $d = -1$.

Addition and Subtraction

$$p_1(x) \pm p_2(x) = \sum_{k=0}^{n} (a_k \pm b_k)x^{n-k}$$

This means that we add (or subtract) polynomials by formally adding (or
subtracting) corresponding coefficients of the polynomials. For example,

$$(3x^3 + 2x - 5) + (x^3 - 2x^2 + x + 4) = 4x^3 - 2x^2 + 3x - 1$$

Multiplication

$$p_1(x)p_2(x) = \sum_{k=0}^{n+m} c_kx^{n+m-k}$$

where

$$c_k = \sum_{i+j=k} a_ib_j \qquad 0 \leq i \leq n, \, 0 \leq j \leq m$$

This means, in effect, that we multiply two polynomials by multiplying each
term of one by each term of the other, according to the rule that $(ax^r)(bx^s) =$
abx^{r+s}, and then collect terms having like powers of x. For example,

$$(2x^2 - x + 1)(3x^2 + 2) = 6x^4 + 4x^2 - 3x^3 - 2x + 3x^2 + 2$$
$$= 6x^4 - 3x^3 + 7x^2 - 2x + 2$$

Division. We have already pointed out that, even though the division of one
polynomial by another can always be formally indicated, the quotient is not
always a polynomial. In the system of integers it is what is known loosely as
the *Division Algorithm* that asserts that for two integers m, $n > 0$, there exist
integers q and r, $0 \leq r < n$, such that $m = nq + r$ or $m/n = q + r/n$. In

this division process, q is the quotient and r is the remainder. In the system of polynomials with complex coefficients, there is a similar "algorithm" which we now state as a theorem without proof.

■ **THEOREM 1.1.** *If $p(x)$ and $d(x)$ are polynomials (in either $\mathbf{R}[x]$ or $\mathbf{C}[x]$), with $d(x) \neq 0$, there exist polynomials $q(x)$ and $r(x)$ of the same kind such that $p(x) = d(x)q(x) + r(x)$ where $r(x) = 0$ or $0 \leq \deg r(x) < \deg d(x)$.*

It is sometimes useful to express the polynomial equation of the theorem in the form $p(x)/d(x) = q(x) + r(x)/d(x)$, in which the *quotient* $q(x)$ predominates rather than the remainder $r(x)$—as in the statement of the theorem. The actual procedure for determining the quotient and remainder for two polynomials is much like long division in ordinary arithmetic, and we merely illustrate it with an example.

Example. Find the quotient and remainder when $3x^4 + x^2 - x + 1$ is divided by $x^2 - 2$.

SOLUTION

$$
\begin{array}{r}
x^2 - 2 \enclose{longdiv}{3x^4 + x^2 - x + 1} \quad \underline{\left| 3x^2 + 7 \right.} \\
\underline{3x^4 - 6x^2} \\
7x^2 - x \\
\underline{7x^2 - 14} \\
- x + 15
\end{array}
$$

Thus,

$$3x^4 + x^2 - x + 1 = (x^2 - 2)(3x^2 + 7) + (15 - x)$$

or

$$\frac{(3x^4 + x^2 - x + 1)}{x^2 - 2} = 3x^2 + 7 + \frac{15 - x}{x^2 - 2}$$

In this case, $q(x) = 3x^2 + 7$ and $r(x) = 15 - x$.

In a later section we shall give an abbreviated method, known as "synthetic division," which is applicable for a very special type of divisor.

Our principal concern in this chapter is with *polynomial equations* of the form $p(x) = 0$. In such an equation x is no longer to be considered a formal symbol but is understood to be a variable whose universe is the field $\mathbf{C}$. Hence, a polynomial equation does not express an equality of polynomials, as discussed earlier, but is rather an open sentence that becomes an equality between complex numbers after a proper replacement of x from $\mathbf{C}$. The two notions of equality become the same in case the polynomial equation is in fact an identity—and is then true for any complex substitution for x. By a "solution" of a polynomial equation we mean, of course, a complex number c that, when substituted for x in the equation, reduces it to a true equality. We then write that $p(c) = 0$. The *complete solution,* or the *solution set,* of the equation is then the set of all such complex-number solutions. It is easy to see that 2 is a solution of the equation $x^4 - 2x^3 + x^2 - 4 = 0$, because $2^4 - 2(2^3) + 2^2 - 4 = 0$. It is a much more difficult job to start with the equation and discover that 2 is a solution! However, the theory of equations is for the most part devoted to this project of discovery for a given polynomial equation.

Problems 9.1

1. Express each of the indicated sums in the form of an ordinary polynomial:

   (a) $\sum_{k=0}^{5} (k+1)x^k$; (b) $\sum_{k=1}^{7} (2k-1)x^k$; (c) $\sum_{k=1}^{5} \frac{k-1}{k+1} x^k$.

2. Express each of the indicated sums in the form of an ordinary polynomial:

   (a) $\sum_{k=0}^{7} 2a_k x^{7-k}$, $a_k = 2k+1$; (b) $\sum_{k=0}^{3} 3b_k x^{3-k}$, $b_k = (1+i)^k \in \mathbf{C}$;

   (c) $\sum_{k=1}^{5} (a_k + b_k)x^{5-k}$, $a_k = (-1)^k \in \mathbf{R}$, $b_k = (-i)^k \in \mathbf{C}$.

3. Use an illustration to distinguish between the meanings of "no degree" and "degree 0."

4. Explain why $\mathbf{R}[x] \subset \mathbf{C}[x]$. Give an example of a polynomial $p(x) \notin \mathbf{C}[x]$, where $p(x) \in \mathbf{R}[x]$.

5. Find the sum of the given polynomials: (a) $x^3 - 2x + 3$, $2x - 4$; (b) $3x^4 + x^2 - 2x + 1$, $3x^3 - 3x^2 + x - 5$; (c) $2x + 3$, $x^3 - 2x^2 + 5x + 2$.

6. In the case of each pair of polynomials in Problem 5, subtract the first polynomial from the second.

7. Find the product of each pair of polynomials given in Problem 5.

8. With reference to the polynomials in Problem 5, use the long-division process to divide the one of lesser degree in each pair into the other.

9. If $p(x) = 2x^2 - (1-i)x + 1$ and $q(x) = (1-i)x^3 + 3ix - 4$, find (a) $p(x) + q(x)$; (b) $q(x) - p(x)$; (c) $p(x)q(x)$.

10. Find the quotient and remainder when $q(x)$ is divided by $p(x)$ for the polynomials given in Problem 9.

11. Give the degree of each of the following polynomials: (a) $3x^4 - 1$; (b) $2x^3 - 3x + 2$; (c) $ix^2 + (1+i)x - 2$; (d) $ix^5 - ix + 2$.

12. Use the long-division process to divide $3x^4 - 2x^2 + 2x - 5$ by $x^2 + x - 1$.

13. Classify each of the following expressions as algebraic or nonalgebraic in x: (a) $1 + 2x$; (b) $(1 - x^2)/(1 + x^2)$; (c) $2^{\sin x}$; (d) 3^x; (e) $2 + 3x - x^2$; (f) $\sqrt{2} - x + x^2$; (g) $(1 + x)^{2/3}$.

14. By $np(x)$ we mean $p(x) + p(x) + \cdots + p(x)$, with n summands. If $p(x) = 2x^3 + 3x - 2$, $q(x) = x^2 - 1$, and $r(x) = 2x - 1$, express each of the following in polynomial form: (a) $p(x) + 2q(x)$; (b) $3p(x) + 2r(x)$; (c) $[p(x)]^2[q(x)]^2$; (d) $p(x) + 2q(x) - 4r(x)$.

15. With reference to the polynomials in Problem 14, find the degree of each of the following: (a) $[p(x)]^3 r(x)$; (b) $2p(x) - 3[q(x)]^2$; (c) $q(x) + 3[p(x) - 2]^2$.

16. Determine integers q, $r (0 \le r < d)$, such that $p = qd + r$, if (a) $p = 17$, $d = 4$; (b) $p = 435$, $d = 13$; (c) $p = 146$, $d = 39$.

17. If $p(x) = d(x)q(x) + r(x)$, with $r(x) = 0$ or $\deg r(x) < \deg d(x)$, determine $q(x)$ and $r(x)$ where (a) $p(x) = 4x^3 - 2x + 1$, $d(x) = 2x - 1$; (b) $p(x) = x^6 + 4x^4 - 3x^2 + 6$, $d(x) = x^2 + 2$; (c) $p(x) = 3x^4 - 2x^3 + x^2 + x - 2$, $d(x) = x - 3$.

18. If a polynomial function f is defined on $\mathbf{R}$ by $f(x) = 3x^3 - 2x^2 + x + 1$, determine (a) $f(1)$; (b) $f(-1)$; (c) $f(2)$; (d) $f(c), c \in \mathbf{R}$; (e) $f(x + h)$, with $h \in \mathbf{R}$; (f) $[f(x + h) - f(x)]/h$, with $h \, (\neq 0) \in \mathbf{R}$; (g) $[f(3 + h) - f(3)]/h$, with $h \, (\neq 0) \in \mathbf{R}$.

19. If a polynomial function g is defined on $\mathbf{C}$ by $g(x) = 3x^3 - 2x + 1$, determine (a) $g(-1)$; (b) $g(i)$; (c) $g(1 + i)$; (d) $g(\frac{1}{2})$; (e) $g(-\frac{1}{2} + i)$.

20. If g is a polynomial function defined on $\mathbf{C}$ by $g(x) = ix^3 - 2ix + 1$, determine (a) $g(-1)$; (b) $g(1)$; (c) $g(1 - i)$; (d) $g(1 + 2i)$; (e) $g(1/i)$.

21. Explain why it is immediately evident that the equation $2x^4 + x^2 + 6 = 0$ has no real solution.

22. If $ax^2 + bx + c = 0$, with $a, b, c \in \mathbf{C}$ and with x merely a symbol, it must be the case that $a = b = c = 0$. However, if $a = 2, b = 1, c = -1$, and $x = -1$, we find that the expressed equality is true. Explain the difference in the two interpretations of x.

23. If $p(x) = 3x^3 - 3x^2 - x + 1$, with x interpreted as a symbol, we know that $p(x) \neq 0$. However, interpret x as a real variable and try to find—by mere inspection—a solution of the equation $p(x) = 0$.

24. Review the exact meaning to be attached to the words "variable" and its "universe."

25. Give an example of a polynomial equality in a symbol x such that the equality is also an identity—in the sense of Chapter 6—if x is interpreted as a real variable in some universe.

26. If we attempt to solve a polynomial equation $p(x) = 0$ for complex-number solutions, explain the difference between this usage of the equals ($=$) sign and its usage in the definition of equality for polynomials in a symbol x—as given in this section.

27. If $p(x) = 2x^4 - 5x^3 + 4x^2 - 5x + 2 = (2x - 1)(x - 2)(x^2 + 1)$, find the solution set of the equation $p(x) = 0$ if x is regarded as a variable with universe (a) $\mathbf{Z}$; (b) $\mathbf{Q}$; (c) $\mathbf{R}$; (d) $\mathbf{C}$.

28. If $(x - 2)(x + 2) = 0$ and x is a real variable, we may conclude that $x - 2 = 0$ or $x + 2 = 0$. On the other hand, if $(x - 2)(x + 2) = 1$, why may we not conclude that $x - 2 = 1$ or $x + 2 = 1$? What property of $\mathbf{R}$ are we using in the first case?

29. If f is the function defined on $\mathbf{R}$ by $f(x) = x^3 + 2x + 47$, use a rough sketch of f to determine an approximation to the real-number solution of the equation $f(x) = 0$.

30. Determine the real-number solution set of each of the following inequalities: (a) $x^2 - 2x - 1 < 0$; (b) $x^2 - 2x + 4 > 0$; (c) $|2x + 3| \leq \frac{1}{2}$; (d) $x^2 + 6 > 5x$.

9.2 Linear and Quadratic Equations

In this section our concern will be with equations of the form $ax^2 + bx + c = 0$, where the coefficients a, b, c are most frequently real numbers. If $a \neq 0$, the equation is *quadratic*; if $a = 0$ and $b \neq 0$, the equation is *linear*. We have already used these words in connection with functions in Chapter 4, and it is likely that the student is familiar with equations of these two types. If not, a brief review is included in the Appendix, but in addition, it may be in order at this time to take a somewhat more critical look at these types of equations.

It should not be implied that our use of the notation $p(x)$ for a polynomial means that we are necessarily thinking of p as a function, although we have already noted that $f(x) = p(x)$ does define f as a polynomial function. However, we shall find it convenient in the context of this chapter to use some functional notation and let $p(r)$ denote the numerical result of replacing x in the polynomial $p(x)$ by the number r. Our first use of this notation occurs in the first theorem below.

The most general equation of the first degree in x, with either real or complex coefficients, has the form $bx + c = 0$, with $b \neq 0$. Its only solution—real or complex—is given by $x = -c/b$, and this leads us to a theorem that is a very simple case of a more general result to be given in the next section. We remark in passing, however, that whether the solution $-c/b$ is an acceptable one, in any given case, depends on the nature of the solution desired. For example, if our interest is only in integral solutions and $-c/b = \frac{2}{3}$, the equation effectively has no solution.

■ **THEOREM 2.1.** *If $p(x) = bx + c \in \mathbf{C}[x]$, with $b \neq 0$, and $p(r) = 0$ for $r \in \mathbf{C}$, then $p(x) = b(x - r)$.*

PROOF. We have already noted that $r = -c/b$. Hence $b(x - r) = b[x - (-c/b)] = b(x + c/b) = bx + c = p(x)$, as asserted.

If f is a function defined on $\mathbf{R}$ by $f(x) = bx + c$ with $b, c \in \mathbf{R}$, we have seen in Chapter 4 that the graph of f is a straight line. It was also pointed out in §4.3 that, although such a function is frequently called "linear" for the obvious graphical reason, we have decided to use this terminology for *functions* only if $c = 0$. In other words, we shall refer to an *equation* $bx + c$ as *linear* in x, regardless of the values of b or c—except that $b \neq 0$—but a *function* f is *linear* only if its graph is a *straight line that includes the origin as one of its points*. In a more geometric environment, it is customary to replace $f(x)$ by y, and refer to $y = bx + c$ as "the equation of the line" described as the graph of f. We are then emphasizing that the line consists of all points (x, y) such that $y = bx + c$. The solution $-c/b$ (if $b \neq 0$) is the abscissa of the point where the line crosses the x-axis. It is not difficult to show that any equation of the form $ax + by + c = 0$ (with a and b not both 0) is the equation of some straight line in the Cartesian plane.

Example 1. Express $2x - 3$ in the factored form of Theorem 2.1.

SOLUTION. If $2x - 3 = 0$, then $2x = 3$, and so $x = \frac{3}{2}$. Hence, by Theorem 2.1,

$$2x - 3 = 2(x - \tfrac{3}{2})$$

We now turn to quadratic equations of the form $ax^2 + bx + c = 0$, where $a \neq 0$, and all coefficients are considered to be real numbers. In the Appendix Review we have outlined two methods of solving such equations: (a) factoring; (b) completing the square. The method of factoring is based on the property that the product of two field elements can be 0 only if at least one of them is 0. The method of completing the square leads us to the Quadratic Formula, and because we shall be referring to this formula again, we repeat the result in the form of a theorem.

■ **THEOREM 2.2.**   *If* $p(x) = ax^2 + bx + c$, *with* a ($\neq 0$), b, c *real, the equation* $p(x) = 0$ *has two solutions* r_1, r_2 *(which may be equal) given by*

$$r_1 = \frac{-b + \sqrt{b^2 - 4ac}}{2a} \qquad r_2 = \frac{-b - \sqrt{b^2 - 4ac}}{2a}$$

The number $b^2 - 4ac$ appearing under the radical sign is called the *discriminant* d of the equation, and it is this number that determines the nature of the solutions r_1, r_2. In terms of d, these solutions may be expressed in the form

$$r_1 = \frac{-b + \sqrt{d}}{2a} \qquad r_2 = \frac{-b - \sqrt{d}}{2a}$$

We recall that, if d is a negative number, the symbol $\sqrt{d}$ has been defined as $\sqrt{|d|}\,i$, but we have not established any such convention if the coefficients of the equation or d (or both) are allowed to be general complex numbers. It is possible to establish a convention for this and derive a result which corresponds to Theorem 2.2 for the cases where a, b, c are complex numbers. However, we shall not pursue this matter here. It is now easy to see the validity of the relationship between d and the solutions of a general quadratic equation $ax^2 + bx + c = 0$, with a, b, c, integers as described in the following table:

$d = b^2 - 4ac$	*Solutions*
$d = p^2 \neq 0$, p an integer	real, rational, unequal
$d = 0$	real, rational, equal
$0 < d \neq p^2$, p an integer	real, irrational, unequal
$d < 0$	complex conjugates

Example 2.   Describe the nature of the solutions in **C** of the equation

$$2x^2 + 2x + 5 = 0$$

SOLUTION.   In this case, $a = 2$, $b = 2$, $c = 5$. Hence, $d = 2^2 - 4(2)(5) = -36$, and we see that the solutions of the equation are complex conjugates. Because $\sqrt{-36} = 6i$, the actual solutions are $(-2 \pm 6i)/4$ or, more simply, $-\frac{1}{2} \pm \frac{3}{2}i$.

If a function f is defined on $\mathbf{R}$ by $f(x) = ax^2 + bx + c$, with a ($\neq 0$), b, c real, we have seen in Chapter 4 that the graph of f is called a *parabola*, which opens up or down according as $a > 0$ or $a < 0$. The real solutions of $ax^2 + bx + c = 0$ are the abscissas of the points where the parabola crosses the x-axis. (If the parabola touches the axis at only one point, the equation has a *unique* real solution.) It is customary to refer to $y = ax^2 + bx + c$ as *the equation* of the parabola, the curve being regarded as the set of points (x, y) that satisfy the equation—a geometric viewpoint referred to before.

If r_1 and r_2 are the two solutions of $ax^2 + bx + c = 0$ where $a \neq 0$, it is a matter of elementary computation to verify that

$$r_1 + r_2 = \frac{-b}{a} \qquad r_1 r_2 = \frac{c}{a}$$

It is now possible to obtain the result analogous to Theorem 2.1 for quadratic equations.

■ **THEOREM 2.3.** *If r_1 and r_2 are the complex (possibly real) solutions of* $p(x) = ax^2 + bx + c = 0$, *with $a, b, c \in \mathbf{C}$, then $p(x) = a(x - r_1)(x - r_2)$.*

PROOF. By direct multiplication, we see that $a(x - r_1)(x - r_2) = a[x^2 - (r_1 + r_2)x + r_1 r_2] = a[x^2 - (-b/a)x + c/a] = ax^2 + bx + c = p(x)$.

Example 3. Factor the polynomial $2x^2 - 3x + 1$.

SOLUTION. Because $a = 2, b = -3, c = 1$, it follows that $d = 9 - 8 = 1$. Hence, $r_1 = (3 + 1)/4 = 1$ and $r_2 = (3 - 1)/4 = \frac{1}{2}$. It then follows, by Theorem 2.3, that

$$2x^2 - 3x + 1 = 2(x - \tfrac{1}{2})(x - 1) = (2x - 1)(x - 1)$$

Example 4. Factor the polynomial $2x^2 + 2x + 5$.

SOLUTION. We discovered in Example 2 that the two complex solutions of the equation $2x^2 + 2x + 5 = 0$ are $r_1 = -\frac{1}{2} + \frac{3}{2}i$ and $r_2 = -\frac{1}{2} - \frac{3}{2}i$. By Theorem 2.3 we then have

$$2x^2 + 2x + 5 = 2(x + \tfrac{1}{2} - \tfrac{3}{2}i)(x + \tfrac{1}{2} + \tfrac{3}{2}i)$$
$$= \tfrac{1}{2}(2x + 1 - 3i)(2x + 1 + 3i)$$

In Example 4, we note that the coefficients of the factors are not all real numbers, although the original polynomial has only real coefficients. It is only because we now accept complex (and not necessarily real) coefficients that the given polynomial can be factored into linear factors.

Even though the subject of "extraneous" solutions does not arise directly when either linear or quadratic equations of the type under discussion are being solved, such "solutions" do arise sometimes when equations involving radicals or exponents are being solved. Moreover, it is often convenient to solve such equations by linear or quadratic methods—after the radicals or fractional exponents have been eliminated. A very brief discussion of "extraneous" solutions is given in §9 of Appendix A, which the student is invited to consult. We shall be content *here* with the remark that, after an equation has been "rationalized" by various squaring procedures, the equation that results is frequently not equivalent to (that is, does not have the same solutions as) the original equation. The solutions of the final equation that are *not* solutions of the original are the "extraneous" ones, and it is these which should be discarded. The only way to distinguish them from the true solutions is by actual checking.

Problems 9.2

Note: Unless otherwise stated, the universe of each variable x, y, z in any equation to be solved will be assumed to be **C**.

1. Solve each of the following linear equations for x: (a) $3x - 2 = 0$; (b) $4x + 3 = 0$; (c) $kx + t = 0$, with $k(\neq 0)$, $t \in$ **C**; (d) $sx - t = 0$, with s $(\neq 0)$, $t \in$ **C**; (e) $3x - 2 = x + 5$; (f) $x - 2 = -5x + 7$; (g) $2x/3 = \frac{7}{2}$; (h) $3x/2 - \frac{5}{3} = 0$.
2. Factor each of the following polynomials in the manner described in Theorem 2.1: (a) $3x + 2$; (b) $5x - 3$; (c) $7x + 2$; (d) $kx + t$, with k $(\neq 0)$, $t \in$ **C**; (e) $3x/2 + \frac{5}{3}$; (f) $\frac{2}{5} - x/3$.
3. Solve each of the following quadratic equations for x: (a) $2x^2 - 3x + 1 = 0$; (b) $3x^2 + x - 3 = 0$; (c) $4x^2 + 2x + 3 = 0$; (d) $x^2 - 5x + 1 = 0$.
4. Use the method described in Theorem 2.3 as an aid to factor the left member of each of the equations given in Problem 3.
5. Without solving the equations, determine the sum and product of the solutions of each of the following equations: (a) $3x^2 - 2x + 1 = 0$; (b) $4x^2 + x + 3 = 0$; (c) $2x^2 - 3x + 1 = 0$; (d) $x^2 - 3x + 9 = 0$; (e) $3x^2 + px + q = 0$; (f) $rx^2 - 2x + t = 0$, with r $(\neq 0)$, $t \in$ **C**.
6. Find an equation with coefficients in **Z** the sum and the product of the solutions of which, respectively, are (a) $\frac{2}{3}$, $-\frac{3}{4}$; (b) 2, $-\frac{2}{3}$; (c) $\frac{3}{2}$, $\frac{3}{4}$; (d) -4, 3; (e) π, $\frac{1}{4}\pi$; (f) π/c, $2\pi/c$, with c $(\neq 0) \in$ **C**.
7. Solve each of the following equations for x:

    (a) $\dfrac{x - 2}{2} + \dfrac{x - 1}{3} = \dfrac{3x + 1}{6} - 5$

    (b) $t^2 - bx = a^2 + cx$, with $a, b, c, t \in$ **C** and $b + c \neq 0$
    (c) $xy + ix - (y + 1) = 2 + 3i$
8. Make a graph of the straight line whose equation is given below, and use it to approximate the solution (if any) of the equation that results if $y = 0$:
    (a) $2x - 3y + 1 = 0$ (b) $3x + y - 6 = 0$
    (c) $2x + y = 0$ (d) $3y + 7 = 0$
9. Use a graph of the related parabola to approximate the real solutions of each of the following quadratic equations:
    (a) $2x^2 + 3x - 1 = 0$; (b) $x^2 - 5x + 5 = 0$; (c) $x^2 + 3x + 1 = 0$.

10. Solve for x in terms of y and (if necessary) z;
    (a) $x^2 + xy - y^2 = 0$ (b) $2x^2 - x + 2xy + y = 0$
    (c) $x^2 + xy - xz + 2yz = 0$

11. Decide (without actually graphing) how many times the graph of the function f crosses the x-axis if (a) $f(x) = x^2 + 2x + 5$; (b) $f(x) = x^2 + x - 1$; (c) $f(x) = 2x - 1 - 4x^2$.

12. Determine the limitations on $k \in \mathbf{R}$ if the following equation is to have only real solutions: (a) $x^2 + kx - 1 = 0$; (b) $2x^2 + x - k = 0$; (c) $kx^2 - 3x + 5k = 0$.

13. Use the directions given in Problem 12 for the following equations: (a) $2x^2 + kx + 4 = 0$; (b) $x^2 - 3kx + 3 = 0$; (c) $kx^2 - 2x + 9 = 0$.

14. Explain why the solution $x = 0$ is "lost" when both members of the equation $x^2 - x = 0$ are divided by x. Because $x^2 - x = x(x - 1)$, what happens if you divide the members of the original equation by *both* x and $x - 1$?

15. Use the method of linear equations (at least in part) to solve each of the following equations for x: (a) $2x^2 + 5 = 0$; (b) $4x^2 - 3t = 0$, with $t (> 0) \in \mathbf{R}$; (c) $x^2 + k^2t^2 = 0$, with $k, t \in \mathbf{R}$.

16. Use the method of linear equations (at least in part) to approximate any existing solution for x in each of the following equations: (a) $2 \ln x - 3 = 7$; (b) $\ln x^2 - 2 = 0$; (c) $\ln x^4 = 16$; (d) $(3^x - 1)/2 = (3^x + 1)/3$; (e) $2(10^x) - 3 = 5(10^x - 2)$.

17. Use a method for quadratic equations to solve each of the following equations for x: (a) $x^4 - x^2 - 6 = 0$; (b) $x^4 - 2x^2 - 8 = 0$; (c) $x^6 - 9x^3 + 8 = 0$

18. Use a linear or quadratic method (at least in part), as appropriate, to find any real solutions for x in the following equations:
    (a) $2(\ln x - 1) = 1 - \ln x$ (b) $(\ln x)^2 - 3 \ln x + 2 = 0$

19. Solve each of the following equations for the indicated unknown, all symbols that appear being assumed to denote numbers in $\mathbf{C}$: (a) $S = (a - rh)/(1 - r)$ for h if $r \neq 1$; (b) $S = n(a + b)/2$ for b if $n \neq 0$; (c) $R = v_0 t + gt^2/2$ for v_0 if $t \neq 0$; (d) $y/\sin \alpha = (2 + y)/\sin \beta$ for y if $\sin \beta \neq \sin \alpha$, $\sin \alpha \neq 0$, $\sin \beta \neq 0$.

20. If $p(x) = ax^2 + bx + c = 0$, with $a (> 0)$, $b, c \in \mathbf{R}$, determine the conditions on the coefficients for (a) both solutions to be real and positive; (b) both solutions to be real and negative; (c) the solutions to be real and opposite in sign.

21. Solve the following equations for x, being sure to discard any extraneous "solutions" that may arise: (a) $x^4 - 2x^2 + 1 = 0$; (b) $x^4 + 2x^2 - 15 = 0$; (c) $3x + 2\sqrt{x} = 5$.

22. Solve the following equations for x, being sure to discard any extraneous "solutions" that may arise: (a) $x^2 - 4 + 3/x^2 = 0$; (b) $3x^{2/3} + 5 = 8x^{1/3}$; (c) $\sqrt{x - 1} = \sqrt{2x - 1} + 1$; (d) $\sqrt{5x + 1} = \sqrt{2x + 3} + 1$.

23. Solve the equation $4 \sin^2 2x + 2 \cos^2 2x - 3 = 0$ for all x such that $0 \leq x \leq 2\pi$.

24. Solve the equation $2 \sin^2 x + 3 \cos x = 0$ for all x such that $0 \leq x \leq 2\pi$.

25. If $p(x) = 2x^2 - 3x - (k - 2)$, determine $k \in \mathbf{C}$ such that (a) $p(2) = 0$; (b) the two solutions of $p(x) = 0$ are reciprocals of each other; (c) the product of the solutions of $p(x) = 0$ is -5.

26. Solve the following inequalities for $x \in \mathbf{R}$: (a) $x(3 - x) < 2$; (b) $x^3 < 2x^2 + x$; (c) $5 + 3x < 2x^2$.

27. Solve each of the following equations for $x \in \mathbf{R}$: (a) $2x^2 + 5|x| - 3 = 0$; (b) $2x|x| + 5x + 18 = 0$; (c) $2[x]^2 + 5[x] - 3 = 0$.
28. A jug contains 12 pints of a solution that is 30 per cent alcohol by volume. How much alcohol (as a percentage of the original volume) should be added to obtain a solution that is 40 per cent alcohol, assuming the capacity of the jug is ample?
29. It takes Jones 3 hours and Smith 4 hours to do a certain job. If both men work at the job together (with neither interfering with the other), how long will it take for the job to be completed?
30. A man 40 years of age has a son aged 14. In how many years will the son be half as old as the father?
31. A plane takes $1\frac{1}{2}$ hours to fly against a constant head wind to a certain spot, whereas the return flight takes only 1 hour. If the wind speed is 30 miles per hour, determine the air speed (assumed to be constant) of the plane during the flight.

9.3   The Remainder and Factor Theorems

We now consider several theorems that will be of use in determining the solution set of a polynomial equation $p(x) = 0$, the coefficients of $p(x)$ being complex (or real) numbers. It will be convenient sometimes to speak of the *zeros* of the polynomial rather than the *solutions* of the polynomial equation, but the two notions are the same. The first theorem is a consequence of the Division Algorithm discussed in §9.1.

■**THEOREM 3.1.** (*Remainder Theorem*). *If a polynomial $p(x)$ is divided by a binomial of the form $x - a$ (where a is any complex number) until a remainder r free of x is obtained, then $r = p(a)$.*

PROOF.   Theorem 1.1 implies the existence of a polynomial $q(x)$ and a complex number r such that $p(x) = (x - a)q(x) + r$. This equation is an identity, valid for every real number x, and is valid in particular if $x = a$. Hence, on substituting a for x we obtain $p(a) = 0 + r = r$.

Example 1.   Use the Remainder Theorem to determine the remainder when $p(x) = 3x^4 - x^2 + x - 2$ is divided by $x + 2$.

SOLUTION.   Because $x + 2 = x - (-2)$, the desired remainder is $p(-2) = 3(-2)^4 - (-2)^2 + (-2) - 2 = 48 - 4 - 2 - 2 = 40$. This result can be verified by actual division.

■**THEOREM 3.2.** (*Factor Theorem*). *If a is a zero of the polynomial $p(x)$, then $x - a$ is a factor of $p(x)$.*

PROOF.   The assertion that a is a zero of $p(x)$ implies that $p(a) = 0$, and so, by the Remainder Theorem, $r = p(a) = 0$. It is then a consequence of Theorem 1.1 that there exists a polynomial $q(x)$ such that $p(x) = (x - a)q(x)$, and so $x - a$ is a factor of $p(x)$.

It is an immediate consequence of this theorem that linear factors of $p(x)$ are determined as zeros of $p(x)$ are discovered. The converse of the Factor Theorem is also immediate: If $x - a$ is a factor of the polynomial $p(x)$, it is quite clear that a is a zero of $p(x)$. That every polynomial of degree $n \geq 1$ has a complex zero is the statement of the following theorem, which we have previously listed as Theorem 2.1 of Chapter 8.

■ **THEOREM 3.3.** (*Fundamental Theorem of Algebra*). *Any polynomial equation $p(x) = 0$ of degree $n \geq 1$, with complex coefficients, has a complex numbers as a solution.*

As indicated earlier, many proofs of this theorem are available, but they are all beyond the scope of this book.

It is now easy—at least theoretically—to use the Fundamental Theorem and the Factor Theorem to find the complete solution set of any polynomial equation. The Fundamental Theorem asserts the existence of *one* solution for such an equation, but the proof of the following theorem illustrates a procedure for finding *all* solutions—i.e., the procedure actually terminates. By the "multiplicity" of a zero a of $p(x)$, we shall mean the number of times $x - a$ occurs as a factor of $p(x)$.

■ **THEOREM 3.4.** *The number of zeros of a polynomial $p(x)$ of degree n is s, where $s \leq n$. If n_i is the multiplicity of the zero a_i, then $\sum_{i=1}^{s} n_i = n$.*

PROOF. The Fundamental Theorem asserts the existence of a zero a_1 of $p(x)$, and by the Factor Theorem we may write $p(x) = (x - a_1)q_1(x)$, where $q_1(x)$ is a polynomial of degree $n - 1$. If we apply the Fundamental Theorem to $q_1(x)$, we know there exists a zero a_2 of $q_1(x)$ and by the Factor Theorem $q_1(x) = (x - a_2)q_2(x)$, where $q_2(x)$ is a polynomial of degree $n - 2$. But then $p(x) = (x - a_1)(x - a_2)q_2(x)$. This procedure may be continued, and it is clear that it must terminate after n stages, for otherwise the degree of the product of the factors would exceed n. Hence, $p(x) = (x - a_1)(x - a_2) \cdots (x - a_n)a_0$, where a_0 is some complex number (a polynomial of degree 0). By multiplication, it is evident that a_0 must be the leading coefficient of $p(x)$, i.e., the coefficient of x^n. It may happen, of course, that not all of $a_1, a_2, \ldots, a_n$ are distinct, but if s of these solutions are distinct, it must be the case that $s \leq n$, as stated in the theorem. Moreover, the manner in which the zeros were obtained implies that, if a_i occurred n_i times, then $\sum_{i=1}^{s} n_i = n$.

Theorem 3.4 is the generalization of Theorems 2.1 and 2.3 that was promised in §9.2.

Example 2. Find a real polynomial equation of degree 3 whose solution set is $\{-1, 2, -3\}$.

SOLUTION.   The Factor Theorem implies that $x + 1$, $x - 2$, and $x + 3$ are factors of the desired polynomial, and no more than three linear factors are permitted by Theorem 3.4. Hence, $p(x) = a_0(x + 1)(x - 2)(x + 3)$, where a_0 ($\neq 0$) may be chosen at random. If we let $a_0 = 1$, we obtain $(x + 1)(x - 2)(x + 3) = 0$ or, equivalently, $x^3 + 2x^2 - 5x - 6 = 0$ as a satisfactory polynomial equation.

The converse of the Factor Theorem (referred to above) along with Theorem 3.4 leads us to an important result in the solution of polynomial equations: Each linear factor of $p(x)$ provides us with a zero of $p(x)$ and Theorem 3.4 guarantees that no more zeros are possible. Hence, we obtain the complete solution set of a polynomial equation by determining the set of zeros of the various linear factors of the polynomial.

Example 3.   Solve the equation $x^3 - 27 = 0$ for $x \in \mathbf{C}$.

SOLUTION.   Because 3 is clearly a solution of the equation, $x - 3$ is a factor of $x^3 - 27$. By division, we find that $x^3 - 27 = (x - 3)(x^2 + 3x + 9)$. We can use the Quadratic Formula to find the zeros of $x^2 + 3x + 9$, and we find them to be $(-3 \pm \sqrt{9 - 36})/2$, that is, $(-3 \pm 3\sqrt{3}i)/2$. The desired set of solutions is then $\{3, (-3 \pm 3\sqrt{3}i)/2\}$.

Example 4.   Determine the complete complex solution set of the equation $(2x - 1)(x - 1)(x^2 + 1) = 0$.

SOLUTION.   Because the complex zeros of the individual factors are $\frac{1}{2}$, 1, $\pm i$, the solution set of the given equation is $\{\frac{1}{2}, 1, \pm i\}$.

We remark that the Quadratic Formula makes it unnecessary to factor every quadratic factor of a polynomial into *linear* factors in order to obtain the zeros of the polynomial. It is clear that this can be done, however, if we so desire.

Problems 9.3

In Problems 1–4, use long division to divide $p(x)$ by $d(x)$ and then express $p(x)$ in the form $d(x)q(x) + r(x)$, for polynomials $q(x), r(x) \in \mathbf{R}[x]$.

1. $p(x) = x^5 + 2x + 1, d(x) = x + 3$
2. $p(x) = x^6 + 3x^2 - 6, d(x) = x - 2$
3. $p(x) = 2x^3 - 3x^2 + 2, d(x) = 2x - 5$
4. $p(x) = x^4 + 3x^3 - 5x^2 + 2x - 24, d(x) = x - 2$

5. Check that the solution set of $p(x) = x^3 - 2x^2 - x + 2 = 0$ is $\{-1, 1, 2\}$, and then express $p(x)$ as a product of three linear factors.
6. Use the directions given in Problem 5 if $p(x) = x^3 - 4x = 0$ and the solution set is $\{-2, 0, 2\}$.

7. Use the directions given in Problem 5 if $p(x) = x^4 - 5x^2 + 4 = 0$ and the solution set is $\{-2, -1, 1, 2\}$.

8. Verify that 3 is a zero of $x^2 - 4x + 3$, and find the second real zero of the polynomial.

9. Verify that 2 is a zero of $3x^3 - 4x^2 - 2x - 4$.

10. Determine the real polynomial with lowest degree and leading coefficient 1, that has the following zeros: (a) $1, -2, 3$; (b) $0, 3, -3$; (c) $3, 2$; (d) $-1, 3, -2, 4$; (e) $0, 1, 2, -3, 4$.

11. Use the directions of Problem 10 for the following: (a) $2, i, -i, 1$; (b) $1 + i$, $1 - i, 3, 2$; (c) $2 - 3i, 2 + 3i, i, -i$; (d) $\frac{1}{2} + i, \frac{1}{2} - i, \frac{2}{3}$.

12. Use the directions of Problem 10 for the following: (a) $1 + i, i, -2$; (b) $3 - i$, $2 + i, 4, -2$; (c) $0, i, 1 + i, -2$; (d) $0, 2 + 3i, 3 - 2i$. (*Note:* In these cases, additional zeros will be present.)

13. Determine the complex polynomial with leading coefficient 1, having the following zeros, each of multiplicity 1 except as indicated: (a) $0, -1, 2$, with 2 a zero of multiplicity 3; (b) $-1, 2$, with 2 a zero of multiplicity 2; (c) $i, -1, 1$, with i a zero of multiplicity 3 and 1 a zero of multiplicity 2; (d) $1 - i, i$, with $1 - i$ a zero of multiplicity 2.

14. If $p(x) = 4x^3 - 2x^2 + x - 5$, use the Remainder Theorem to find (a) $p(-2)$; (b) $p(1)$; (c) $p(i)$; (d) $p(-\frac{1}{3}i)$.

15. If $p(x) = 2x^4 + x^2 - i$, use the Remainder Theorem to find (a) $p(i)$; (b) $p(1 - 2i)$; (c) $p(\frac{1}{2}i)$.

16. Determine the complete solution set (in **C**) of each of the following equations:
(a) $(x - 2)(x + 3)(x^2 + x + 1) = 0$; (b) $(x - 3)(x + 2)(x - 7)(x + 4) = 0$;
(c) $(x^2 - 5x + 6)(x^2 - x + 2) = 0$; (d) $(x - 4)(x^2 + x - 30)(x^2 - 1) = 0$.

17. Determine the complete solution set (in **C**) of each of the following equations:
(a) $(x - 2)(x + 5)^3(x - 3) = 0$ (b) $(x^2 + x + 1)^2(x^2 + 1)^3 = 0$
(c) $(x - 3)^2(x + 2)^3(x^2 - 1)^3(x^2 + 4)^2 = 0$

18. With reference to Problem 17 and Theorem 3.4, in each case determine n, s, and n_i, and check that $\sum_{i=1}^{s} n_i = n$.

19. Determine the solution set (in **C**) of each of the following equations: (a) $3x^2 - 2ix + 3 + i = 0$; (b) $2ix^2 - 3x + 2 - i = 0$; (c) $x^2 - (1 - i)x - 1 = 0$; (d) $x^2 + ix - i = 0$.

20. Use the Remainder Theorem to find the remainder when (a) $2x^3 - 3x + 1$ is divided by $x - 3$; (b) $2x^4 + x^2 - 5$ is divided by $x - \sqrt{2}$; (c) $x^3 - ix^2 + 3x - 1 + 2i$ is divided by $x + \frac{1}{2}i$.

21. Use the Factor Theorem to verify that $x - a$ is a factor of $x^n - a^n$, for any positive integer n.

22. Use the Factor Theorem to verify that $x + y$ is a factor of $x^n + y^n$, for any odd positive integer n.

23. Determine the number k if (a) $x + 1$ is a factor of $3x^3 - kx + 5$; (b) $x - 2$ is a factor of $2x^4 + k^2x^2 + 1$; (c) $x + 2$ is a factor of $2x^2 - 3k^2x + 3k$.

24. Determine the number $k \in \mathbf{R}$ if (a) $x - 1$ is a factor of $2x^3 - x^2 + 2kx + 1$; (b) $x + 1$ is a factor of $3x^3 + 5x^2 - 3kx + 7$; (c) $x - k$ is a factor of $3x^2 + 2x - 1$.

25. Determine $a, b \in \mathbf{R}$ such that (a) $3x^3 + ax^2 - 5x + b$ is divisible by $x + 1$ and $x - 2$; (b) $x^4 + ax^3 + bx^2 - x + 2$ is divisible by $x^2 - 1$.

26. Express each of the following polynomials as a product of linear factors with coefficients in **C**: (a) $x^4 - 16$; (b) $16x^4 - 1$; (c) $x^3 + x^2 - x - 1$; (d) $3x^3 - 2x^2 + x - 2$, given that 1 is a zero.

27. Find the polynomial of degree 6 with leading coefficient 1 that has 1 and -2 as its only zeros, each occurring with the same multiplicity.

28. Is $x - 2$ a factor of $x^9 - 4x^6 + 48x^3 - 64x^2$? If so, give the multiplicity of 2 as a zero of the polynomial.

29. Find the complete solution set of $4x^3 - x - 3 = 0$, and express the left member of the equation as a product of linear factors.

30. Use Theorem 3.4 to show that, if $p(x)$ is a polynomial of formal degree n, but with $n + 1$ complex numbers as zeros, all of its coefficients must be 0.

31. Use the result in Problem 30 to show that, if the zeros of $p(x)$ and $q(x)$ are the same, and each with the same multiplicity, then $q(x) = cp(x)$ for some complex number c.

32. If $p(x)$ and $q(x)$ are polynomials in **C**$[x]$ such that $c \in $ **C** is a common zero, prove that $x - c$ is a factor of the remainder when $p(x)$ is divided by $q(x)$.

9.4 Synthetic Division

The division of a polynomial by a binomial of the form $x - c$ can be abbreviated to a simple process known as *synthetic division*. The process is basically that of ordinary long division, but with the omission of all but the essential numbers. Although it is possible to use the method with nonreal coefficients, we shall restrict our illustrations to polynomials with real—and usually integral—coefficients. We shall demonstrate the method by means of an example. If the polynomial $2x^5 - x^4 + 12x^2 - 10x + 2$ is divided by $x + 2$, the steps of the long-division process are shown below.

$$
\begin{array}{r}
2x^4 - 5x^3 + 10x^2 - 8x + 6 \\
x + 2 \overline{\big)\ 2x^5 - x^4 + 0x^3 + 12x^2 - 10x + 2} \\
\underline{2x^5 + 4x^4} \\
-5x^4 + 0x^3 \\
\underline{-5x^4 - 10x^3} \\
10x^3 + 12x^2 \\
\underline{10x^3 + 20x^2} \\
-8x^2 - 10x \\
\underline{-8x^2 - 16x} \\
6x + 2 \\
\underline{6x + 12} \\
-10
\end{array}
$$

Thus,

$$2x^5 - x^4 + 12x^2 - 10x + 2 = (2x^4 - 5x^3 + 10x^2 - 8x + 6)(x + 2) - 10.$$

In the above arithmetic process, the powers of x play no important role except to keep the coefficients in order. It is then possible to omit the powers of x from the computation provided we are careful to keep the coefficients of these powers in distinct vertical columns. This has been done in the display below, *where we have been careful to include the coefficients* 0 *and* 1.

$$
\begin{array}{l}
\underline{1+2|} \quad 2 \quad -1 \quad\ \ 0 \quad\ \ 12 \ \ -10 \quad\ \ 2 \quad\ \ |2 \ \ -5 \quad 10 \ \ -8 \quad\ 6 \\
\phantom{\underline{1+2|}} \quad \underline{2 \quad\ \ 4} \\
\phantom{\underline{1+2|}} \quad\quad -5 \quad\ \ 0 \\
\phantom{\underline{1+2|}} \quad\quad \underline{-5 \ \ -10} \\
\phantom{\underline{1+2|}} \quad\quad\quad\quad\quad 10 \quad\ \ 12 \\
\phantom{\underline{1+2|}} \quad\quad\quad\quad\quad \underline{10 \quad\ \ 20} \\
\phantom{\underline{1+2|}} \quad\quad\quad\quad\quad\quad\quad -\ 8 \ \ -10 \\
\phantom{\underline{1+2|}} \quad\quad\quad\quad\quad\quad\quad \underline{-\ 8 \ \ -16} \\
\phantom{\underline{1+2|}} \quad\quad\quad\quad\quad\quad\quad\quad\quad\quad 6 \quad\ \ 2 \\
\phantom{\underline{1+2|}} \quad\quad\quad\quad\quad\quad\quad\quad\quad\quad \underline{6 \quad\ \ 12} \\
\phantom{\underline{1+2|}} \quad\quad\quad\quad\quad\quad\quad\quad\quad\quad\quad\quad -10
\end{array}
$$

The above array of numbers can be simplified still further, because there are needless duplications. Two occurrences each of $2, -5, 0, 10, 12, -8, -10, 6$, and 2 may be observed in the same vertical column (and with no intervening numbers as we examine the array of columns from left to right) and in each case the lower number can safely be omitted. If we then "project" the remaining numbers into three horizontal rows, the result will be as follows:

$$
\begin{array}{l}
\underline{1+2|} \quad\ 2 \quad -1 \quad\ \ 0 \quad\ \ 12 \ \ -10 \quad\ \ 2 \quad\ \ |2 \ \ -5 \quad 10 \ \ -8 \quad 6 \\
\phantom{\underline{1+2|}} \quad\quad\quad\ \ 4 \ \ -10 \quad 20 \ \ -16 \quad 12 \\
\phantom{\underline{1+2|}} \quad\quad \underline{-5 \quad\ 10 \quad -\ 8 \quad\ \ 6 \ \ -10}
\end{array}
$$

The coefficient 1 of x in the divisor is always 1, *for the type of division under consideration*, and so it may be omitted. If we include the leading 2 of the dividend on the third row, the numbers on this row will be the coefficients of the quotient in their proper order, followed by the remainder -10. The original listing of the quotient may then be omitted, and we have simplified the arithmetic process to the abbreviated display below:

$$
\begin{array}{l}
\underline{2|} \quad\ \ 2 \quad -1 \quad\ \ 0 \quad\ \ 12 \ \ -10 \quad\ \ 2 \\
\phantom{\underline{2|}} \quad\quad\quad\quad\ 4 \ \ -10 \quad 20 \ \ -16 \quad 12 \\
\phantom{\underline{2|}} \quad \underline{2 \quad -5 \quad 10 \quad -\ 8 \quad\ \ 6 \ \ -10}
\end{array}
$$

In this simplified form, we note that any number on the second row can be obtained by multiplying by 2 (the "divisor") the number on the third row in the column preceding it on the left; the numbers on the third row can be obtained by subtracting, in order, those on the second row from those on the first. Hence, by starting with the first number on the third row—which was merely copied from the first row—we can alternately produce the successive numbers of the second and third rows. After one further slight change we obtain the process known as *synthetic division*: We replace the "divisor" 2 by −2 (in general, change the sign of the "divisor"), and obtain the third row by the orderly *addition* of the numbers on the second row and those on the first. (It is clear that the subtraction of any number is equivalent to the addition of its negative!) The final computation would then have the following appearance:

$$
\begin{array}{r|rrrrrr}
-2 & 2 & -1 & 0 & 12 & -10 & 2 \\
   &   & -4 & 10 & -20 & 16 & -12 \\
\hline
   & 2 & -5 & 10 & -8 & 6 & -10
\end{array}
$$

Example 1.   Use synthetic division to divide $3x^4 - 2x^2 + x - 5$ by $x - 1$.

SOLUTION.   In this case, $c = 1$, and the computation by synthetic division will have the indicated form.

$$
\begin{array}{r|rrrrr}
1 & 3 & 0 & -2 & 1 & -5 \\
  &   & 3 & 3 & 1 & 2 \\
\hline
  & 3 & 3 & 1 & 2 & -3
\end{array}
$$

The quotient is then $3x^3 + 3x^2 + x + 2$ and the remainder is -3.

The process of synthetic division can be used to advantage in the checking of a possible zero of a polynomial. For if c is a zero of $p(x)$, the remainder, when $p(x)$ is divided by $x - c$, must be 0 as a consequence of the Remainder Theorem.

Example 2.   Use synthetic division to show that -2 is a zero of

$$
x^5 - 3x^3 + 4x^2 - 8
$$

SOLUTION.   The synthetic-division computation, for the division of the polynomial by $x + 2$ [i.e., by $x - (-2)$] is

$$
\begin{array}{r|rrrrrr}
-2 & 1 & 0 & -3 & 4 & 0 & -8 \\
   &   & -2 & 4 & -2 & -4 & 8 \\
\hline
   & 1 & -2 & 1 & 2 & -4 & 0
\end{array}
$$

Because the remainder is 0, the number -2 is a zero of the given polynomial.

In the process just outlined, our major interest has been in whether a certain number is a zero of a given polynomial. If $p(x)$ is the polynomial and r is the number, we have pointed out that *the final entry in the third row of the synthetic-division process gives us the remainder when $p(x)$ is divided by $x - r$* and that *this entry is 0 if r is a zero of $p(x)$*. It is clear that we *may* be interested in the value $p(r)$ of the polynomial when $x = r$, regardless of whether r is a zero, and the Factor Theorem tells us that $p(r)$ is the remainder when $p(x)$ is divided by $x - r$. In other words, *the final entry in the third row of the above computational array is always $p(r)$ and is 0 if r happens to be a zero of $p(x)$*.

The motivation for our above procedure was supplied by ordinary long division, but the *rule* for the results of the synthetic-division process can be put on a more theoretic basis. Although the validity of the rule can be established by induction for a general polynomial of degree n, we shall be content with illustrating the theoretical formalism for a general polynomial $p(x)$ of degree 4, with $p(r)$ desired for a fixed number r. We let $p(x) = a_0x^4 + a_1x^3 + a_2x^2 + a_3x + a_4$ and the quotient $q(x) = b_0x^3 + b_1x^2 + b_2x + b_3$, for numbers $a_0, a_1, a_2, a_3, a_4, b_0, b_1, b_2, b_3$, when $p(x)$ is divided by $x - r$. The formalism of the synthetic-division process, as outlined above, would then have the following appearance:

$$
\begin{array}{c|ccccc}
r & a_0 & a_1 & a_2 & a_3 & a_4 \\
  &   & a_0r & b_1r & b_2r & b_3r \\
\hline
  & b_0 & b_1 & b_2 & b_3 & R
\end{array}
$$

where $b_0 = a_0, b_1 = a_1 + a_0r, b_2 = a_2 + b_1r, b_3 = a_3 + b_2r$, and $R = p(r) = a_4 + b_3r$. Inasmuch as the given polynomial $p(x)$ can be expressed in the form

$$p(x) = \{[(a_0x + a_1)x + a_2]x + a_3\}x + a_4$$

it is easy to *see again* that the *rule* for the computation of $p(r)$, for a general polynomial $p(x)$ of degree n, can be put in a systematic form as follows:

1. Rewrite the leading coefficient a_0 of $p(x)$ as b_0.
2. Multiply b_0 by r and add the result to the next coefficient a_1 to obtain b_1.
3. Multiply b_1 by r and add the result to the next coefficient a_2 to obtain b_2.

. . . .

This routine procedure is now continued and terminates after $n + 1$ stages, if the degree of the polynomial $p(x)$ is n. The next-to-the-last stage results in our obtaining b_{n-1}, which is the "constant" term of the quotient polynomial. The final or $(n + 1)$st stage will then appear in the form given below.

$n + 1$. Multiply b_{n-1} by r and add the result to the next (last) coefficient a_n to obtain $R = p(r) = a_n + b_{n-1}r$.

The advantage in having a computational rule in this form is that it can be very easily programmed for—and the result obtained by—a computer.

Although the verification is not really necessary, it is a simple exercise to check that the above rule for obtaining the coefficients of the quotient polynomial and the remainder does give correct results. For this checking, we shall again assume the fourth-degree polynomial $p(x)$ and its third-degree quotient as given earlier, so that $p(x) = (x - r)q(x) + R$ with R the numerical remainder. If we replace $p(x)$ and $q(x)$ by their expressions as polynomials, the preceding identity—after the usual association of like terms—becomes

$$a_0x^4 + a_1x^3 + a_2x^2 + a_3x + a_4$$
$$= b_0x^4 + (b_1 - b_0r)x^3 + (b_2 - b_1r)x^2 + (b_3 - b_2r)x + R - b_3r$$

Because this is an *identity* in the symbol x (and not merely an equation in which x is considered to be a real variable), our definition of polynomial equality allows us to equate the coefficients of like powers of x, and the result is the following system of equalities:

$$a_0 = b_0 \quad a_1 = b_1 - b_0r \quad a_2 = b_2 - b_1r \quad a_3 = b_3 - b_2r \quad a_4 = R - b_3r$$

It is seen immediately that these equalities are equivalent to the following ones, which were given earlier in our *rule*:

$$b_0 = a_0 \quad b_1 = a_1 + b_0r \quad b_2 = a_2 + b_1r \quad b_3 = a_3 + b_2r \quad R = a_4 + b_3r$$

This completes the theoretical verification of our synthetic division procedure for the case of a polynomial $p(x)$ of degree 4. The process may be applied to a polynomial of arbitrary degree, and, as indicated earlier, the proof of this remark can be accomplished by means of the Principle of Mathematical Induction. We shall assume the result, however, without further comment.

Problems 9.4

1. Use synthetic division to divide $2x^3 - x^2 + 5x - 10$ by (a) $x - 1$; (b) $x + 1$; (c) $x - 2$; (d) $x + 2$.
2. Use synthetic division to divide $4x^4 - 2x^2 + 5x - 2$ by (a) $x - 3$; (b) $x + 3$; (c) $x - 4$; (d) $x + 4$.
3. Use synthetic division to divide $3x^3 - x^2 + 2x + 5$ by (a) $x - \frac{1}{2}$; (b) $x + \frac{1}{2}$; (c) $x - \frac{2}{3}$; (d) $x + \frac{2}{3}$.
4. Use synthetic division to divide $4x^4 + x^2 - 8$ by (a) $x - \frac{2}{3}$; (b) $x + \frac{1}{3}$; (c) $x - \frac{1}{2}$.
5. If $p(x) = 2x^3 + x - 5$, use synthetic division to compute (a) $p(1)$; (b) $p(-1)$; (c) $p(2)$; (d) $p(-3)$.
6. If $p(x) = x^4 + x^2 + 6$, use synthetic division to compute (a) $p(-3)$; (b) $p(-2)$; (c) $p(\frac{1}{2})$; (d) $p(-\frac{1}{3})$.

7. A polynomial function f is defined on **R** by $f(x) = 2x^4 - 3x + 5$. Use the process of synthetic division to determine (a) $f(1)$; (b) $f(-1)$; (c) $f(2)$; (d) $f(-\frac{1}{2})$.

8. Apply the directions given in Problem 7 if $f(x) = x^3 + x^2 - 2x + 1$.

9. Verify that the complete solution set in **C** of the equation $2x^3 - 5x^2 - 4x + 3 = 0$ is $\{-1, 3, \frac{1}{2}\}$. Apply the process of synthetic division to *successive quotients* rather than reverting to the original polynomial each time. (That is, if c is a zero of $p(x)$ so that $p(x) = (x - c)q(x)$ for some polynomial $q(x)$, examine $q(x)$ for the remaining zeros of $p(x)$. Explain why this procedure is valid.

10. Apply the directions given in Problem 9 (omitting the explanation of the procedure) to the equation $2x^4 + 3x^3 - 4x^2 - 3x + 2 = 0$ and the solution set $\{-2, -1, 1, \frac{1}{2}\}$.

11. If $2x^2 - 3x + 1$ is divided by $x - r$ and the remainder is 3, what are the possible values for $r \in \mathbf{R}$?

12. If $3x^2 - 8x - 1$ is divided by $x - r$ and the remainder is 2, what are the possible values for $r \in \mathbf{R}$?

13. Determine $k \in \mathbf{R}$ if the remainder is (a) 5 when $3x^3 - x^2 + kx + 2$ is divided by $x - 2$; (b) 2 when $kx^4 - x^3 + x - 6$ is divided by $x + 1$; (c) -4 when $x^4 - 2kx^2 + x - 2$ is divided by $x + 2$.

14. Use synthetic division with all integral x such that $-2 \le x \le 4$ to compute a table of values of the function f, where f is defined on **R** by $f(x) = 2x^3 - 9x^2 + x + 1$. Use these values to sketch a graph of the function.

15. Apply the directions given in Problem 14 if $f(x) = 2x^4 - 10x^2 + x - 8$, and $-3 \le x \le 3$.

16. If $x^3 - 2x^2 + kx - 4$ yields the same remainder when divided by $x - 2$ and $x + 2$, determine $k \in \mathbf{R}$.

17. Apply the directions given in Problem 16 to the polynomial $2x^4 + kx - 3x + 2$.

18. Make a slight modification of the synthetic-division process to divide $3x^3 - x^2 + x - 6$ by (a) $2x - 1$; (b) $3x + 2$; (c) $4x - 3$.

19. Use the "computer" *rule* for synthetic division to verify that, if $ax^2 + bx + c$ is divided by $x - 1$, the remainder is $a + b + c$. Check this result with the Remainder Theorem.

20. Use synthetic division in **C**[x] to divide $3x^4 + x^3 + 2x^2 + x - 1$ by $x - i$.

21. Use synthetic division in **C**[x] to divide the polynomial in Problem 20 by $x + i$. Use a property of complex numbers to check this result with that in Problem 20.

22. Use synthetic division in **C**[x] to divide $x^5 + 3x^3 + x^2 - 4x + 4$ by $x - 2i$.

23. Use synthetic division to divide $2x^4 + 6x^3 + 6x^2 - 12x - 20$ by $x - \sqrt{2}$.

24. Use synthetic division to divide $x^5 + x^4 - 6x^3 - 4x^2 + 5x - 5$ by $x - \sqrt{5}$.

25. If $p(x) = 2x^4 - x^3 + x^2 + 3x - 1$, use synthetic division in **C**[x] to determine $p(i)$.

26. If $p(x) = 3x^3 - 2x^2 + x + i$, use synthetic division in **C**[x] to determine $p(i + 1)$.

27. Use a general polynomial of degree 5, and repeat the process that we used with a general polynomial of degree 4, to obtain anew the rule for synthetic division as it applies to this case.

28. Try to establish the validity, by the Principle of Mathematical Induction, of the rule for synthetic division as it applies to a general polynomial of degree n in **C**[x] on division by $x - c$, $c \in \mathbf{C}$.

9.5 Real Polynomial Equations

In the remaining sections of this chapter, we shall be considering the general problem of finding the complete (complex) solution set of any polynomial equation with real coefficients. We shall find in general that the problem is a very difficult one.

It is possible, of course, that every complex number is a solution of an equation and in such a case the equation is an *identity* on $\mathbf{C}$, a notion that we have discussed quite carefully at an earlier time. For example, the equation $(x + 1)(x - 1) = x^2 - 1$ is such an identity, its solution set being the set $\mathbf{C}$. (It should be recalled that our earlier definition of an identity permitted certain possible exclusions—those substitutions for which one or both sides of the equation are meaningless.) Our first theorem is of interest in connection with identities.

■ **THEOREM 5.1.** *If a polynomial $p(x) \in \mathbf{C}[x]$ of degree n has more than n complex zeros, the coefficient of each power of x in $p(x)$ is* 0, *and so the polynomial is identically* 0.

PROOF. Let $p(x) = a_0 x^n + a_1 x^{n-1} + \cdots + a_{n-1} x + a_n$. We know from Theorem 3.4 that $p(x)$ has n complex zeros (possibly not all distinct), which we may designate as $c_1, c_2, \ldots, c_n$, and the Factor Theorem allows us to write

$$p(x) = a_0(x - c_1)(x - c_2) \cdots (x - c_n)$$

If $c \in \mathbf{C}$ is a zero of $p(x)$, with $c \neq c_i$ $(i = 1, 2, \ldots, n)$, then

$$a_0(c - c_1)(c - c_2) \cdots (c - c_n) = 0$$

But $c - c_i \neq 0$ $(i = 1, 2, \ldots, n)$, and so the absence of any divisors of zero in the field $\mathbf{C}$ requires that $a_0 = 0$. Hence, $p(x) = a_1 x^{n-1} + a_2 x^{n-2} + \cdots + a_{n-1} x^{n-1} + a_n$, whereas our hypothesis is that $p(x)$ has more than n zeros—and so *a fortiori* more than $n - 1$ zeros. A repetition of the preceding argument would show that $a_1 = 0$, and in like manner we can find that $a_2 = a_3 = \cdots = a_n = 0$. The proof is now complete.

■ **COROLLARY.** *If the equation formed by equating two polynomials of formal degree n or less has more than n complex solutions, the two polynomials are identical. (A polynomial in x has* formal degree n *if its degree does not exceed n and the coefficient a_n of x^n is included even though a_n may be equal to* 0.

PROOF. Let the two polynomials be $a_0 x^n + a_1 x^{n-1} + \cdots + a_{n-1} x + a_n$ and $b_0 x^n + b_1 x^{n-1} + \cdots + b_{n-1} x + b_n$, where we are assuming that either a_0 or b_0 is not 0. Then any zero of both polynomials is also a solution of

$$(a_0 - b_0)x^n + (a_1 - b_1)x^{n-1} + \cdots$$
$$+ (a_{n-1} - b_{n-1})x + (a_n - b_n) = 0$$

and so this equation has more than n complex solutions. It follows from the theorem that $a_0 - b_0 = a_1 - b_1 = \cdots = a_n - b_n = 0$, so that $a_0 = b_0$, $a_1 = b_1$, ..., $a_n = b_n$, and the polynomials are identical.

Example 1.   Prove that

$$\frac{(x - a)(x - b)}{(c - a)(c - b)} + \frac{(x - b)(x - c)}{(a - b)(a - c)} + \frac{(x - c)(x - a)}{(b - c)(b - a)} = 1$$

is an identity for distinct—but otherwise arbitrary—complex numbers a, b, c.

PROOF.   The given equation has degree 2 in x, but it is clear that a, b, c are three solutions. It is then a consequence of Theorem 5.1 that the equation is an identity (and its solutions set is **C**).

Example 2.   Without any simplification of either, show that the polynomials
$$(x - 1)^2 + 3(x + 1)^2 \quad \text{and} \quad 4(x + 1)^2 - 4x \quad \text{are identical.}$$

PROOF.   If $x = 0$, both polynomials equal 4; if $x = 1$, both equal 12; if $x = -1$, both equal 4. Because the degree of both polynomials is 2 and the polynomials have the same values for at least three distinct numerical replacements of x, it follows from the Corollary that the two polynomials are identities on **C**.

Example 3.   Determine real numbers A and B such that $A(2x + 1) + B(x - 2) = 5x - 5$ is an identity on **C**.

SOLUTION.   The given equation can be expressed in equivalent form as $(2A + B)x + A - 2B = 5x - 5$, and so, by the Corollary, $2A + B = 5$ and $A - 2B = -5$. If we solve these two equations for A and B, we find at once that $A = 1$ and $B = 3$.

It is clear that, if an equation is known to be an identity, the problem of its solution presents no difficulty! Hence, let us return to a consideration of equations that are not identities—otherwise known as *conditional equations*. Because we have precise methods for determining the (real or complex) solutions of any linear or quadratic equation with its coefficients in **C**, it is clear that we can solve any polynomial equation $p(x) = 0$ if we can express $p(x)$ as a product of linear or quadratic polynomials in **C**[x]. That such a factorization is (at least theoretically) possible is the result of the two following theorems.

■ **THEOREM 5.2.** *Nonreal complex zeros of a polynomial* $p(x) \in \mathbf{R}[x]$ *occur in conjugate pairs: if* $a + bi$ *is a zero, so is* $a - bi$.

SOLUTION.   We first assume that $a + bi$ is a nonreal zero of $p(x)$, and form the product $(x - a - bi)(x - a + bi) = x^2 - 2ax + a^2 + b^2$. We designate this real polynomial as $d(x)$. If we now apply Theorem 1.1 to $p(x)$, with $d(x)$ as divisor, we obtain $p(x) = d(x)q(x) + r(x)$, for real polynomials $q(x)$ and $r(x)$, where $r(x) = sx + t$ is of the first degree in x. Because $p(a + bi) = 0 = d(a + bi)$, it follows that $r(a + bi) = 0 = s(a + bi) + t = sa + t + sbi$, whence $sa + t = 0 = sb$. Inasmuch as $a + bi$ was assumed to be nonreal, $b \neq 0$, and so $s = 0 = t$. Hence, $r(x) = 0$ and $p(x) = d(x)q(x)$. But $a + bi$ and $a - bi$ are the two conjugate complex zeros of $d(x)$, and so these numbers also appear as zeros of $p(x)$. This completes the proof of the theorem.

■ **THEOREM 5.3.** *Any real polynomial can be written as a product of real linear and quadratic factors.*

PROOF.   By Theorem 5.2, the nonreal zeros of a real polynomial $p(x)$ occur in conjugate pairs, and there is a quadratic real factor of $p(x)$ associated with each such pair of zeros. The zeros of any remaining factor must be real, and, if these are $r_1, r_2, \ldots, r_k$, this factor may be written (according to the Factor Theorem) as $a_0(x - r_1)(x - r_2) \cdots (x - r_k)$ with $a_0 \in \mathbf{R}$. Hence, if $q_1(x), q_2(x), \ldots, q_t(x)$ are the quadratic factors previously obtained, it is possible to express $p(x)$ in the following factored form—in which all the factors are real:

$$p(x) = a_0(x - r_1)(x - r_2) \cdots (x - r_k)q_1(x)q_2(x) \cdots q_t(x)$$

The two preceding theorems give us information about the nature of the zeros of a real polynomial, but they are of little practical use in the actual determination of these zeros. No algorithm is available for the factoring of $p(x)$, as asserted in Theorem 5.3, and it is quite possible that some or all of the coefficients of the real factors are irrational. Although we could cope with the second situation, however disagreeable it might be, the difficulties associated with the first are unsurmountable for us. However, the above theorems are still of interest, and in the final two sections of the chapter we shall attack the *practical* problem of determining the rational and irrational (real) zeros of a real polynomial, with the help of several very practical rules.

Problems 9.5

1. Review the definition given in §6.6 for an *identity*. In particular, what numbers— if any—are to be excluded from the universe of a variable in an identity?
2. Give an illustration of (a) a polynomial identity on $\mathbf{R}$; (b) an identity on $\{x \in \mathbf{R} \mid x \neq 1, 2\}$; (c) an identity on $\{x \in \mathbf{C} \mid x \neq i, -1\}$.

3. What do we mean by the statement that "two polynomials are identical"?

4. If $p(x)$ is a polynomial in a symbol x, review the distinction between the *equation* $p(x) = 0$ and the *identity* $p(x) = 0$. Describe $p(x)$ if $p(x) = 0$ is an identity.

5. Find two polynomial equations $p_1(x) = 0$ and $p_2(x) = 0$ with $\{1, 2, 3\}$ as the common solution set and with the polynomials having the same degree, but such that $p_1(x)$ and $p_2(x)$ are not identical polynomials.

6. We have stated that the problem of solving an identity "presents no difficulty." What is the *only* matter to investigate before being able to exhibit the complete solution set?

7. Explain why every *real* cubic (third-degree) polynomial has at least one real zero. Give the generalization of this statement.

8. Find a real polynomial equation of degree n and with $\{c_1\}$ or $\{c_1, c_2\}$ as a solution subset where (a) $n = 2$, $c_1 = 1 - i$; (b) $n = 3$, $c_1 = 1$, $c_2 = i$; (c) $n = 4$, $c_1 = 1 + i$, $c_2 = 3 - i$; (d) $n = 4$, $c_1 = i$, $c_2 = 2 + 2i$.

9. Apply the directions in Problem 8 but with the solutions subset $\{c_1, c_2\}$ or $\{c_1, c_2, c_3\}$, as indicated.
(a) $n = 4$, $c_1 = 1$, $c_2 = 2 - 3i$
(b) $n = 4$, $c_1 = -1$, $c_2 = 3 - i$
(c) $n = 5$, $c_1 = 0$, $c_2 = 1 - i$, $c_3 = 2 - i$
(d) $n = 6$, $c_1 = i$, $c_2 = 2i$, $c_3 = 1 + i$

10. Factor the following polynomial into *real* linear or quadratic factors, with the understanding that the number given is a zero: (a) $2x^3 + 5x^2 - 2x - 15$, $-2 + i$; (b) $x^4 - 7x^3 + 21x^2 - 37x + 30$, $1 - 2i$.

11. Apply the directions in Problem 10 to the polynomial and given number:
(a) $x^3 - 5x^2 + 9x - 5$, $2 - i$ (b) $2x^4 - 3x^3 + 3x^2 - 3x + 1$, i

12. Use DeMoivre's Theorem to express the following polynomials as products of real linear or quadratic factors: (a) $x^4 + 1$; (b) $x^4 + 16$; (c) $x^3 - 1$.

13. If $a + bi$ is a solution of $x^3 + bx^2 + cx + d = 0$, with $b, c, d \in \mathbf{R}$, use actual substitution to verify that $a - bi$ is also a solution.

14. Explain why it is evident on inspection that the equation $2x^4 + 5x^2 + 1 = 0$ has no real solutions.

15. Find all complex solutions of the equation $x^4 + x^3 - 2x^2 - 6x - 4 = 0$, given that one solution is $-1 + i$.

16. Determine the complex numbers a and b such that $-2i$ is a zero of the polynomial $x^3 + 3x^2 + bx + c$.

17. Explain why it is not possible for a straight line to intersect the graph of a polynomial function on $\mathbf{R}$ in more than n points if n is the degree of the defining polynomial.

18. Determine real numbers A, B, C, D so that the following equations are identities on $\mathbf{C}$:
(a) $(A - 1)x^3 + (B + 2)x^2 + Cx - D = x^3 + x^2 + x - 2$
(b) $Ax^3 + B(x - 1)^2 + C(x + 1)^2 + D(x - 2) = 3x^2 + x + 5$

19. Determine real numbers A, B so that the following equations are identities on $\mathbf{C}$:
(a) $A(x - 1)^2 - B(x - 2)^2 = 2(2x - 3)$
(b) $A(x - 2)^2 + B(x + 2)^2 = x^2 + 6x + 4$

20. Determine real numbers A, B, C so that the following equations are identities on $\mathbf{C}$:
(a) $A(x - 1)(x + 2) + B(x + 1)(x - 1) + C(x - 2)(x + 1) = x^2 + x + 1$
(b) $A(x - 1)^2 + B(x - 2)^2 + C(x + 2)^2 = 4x^2 + 2x + 13$

21. Verify that the following is an identity on **C**, for distinct $a, b, c \in$ **C**:

$$\frac{(x-a)(x-b)}{(c-a)(c-b)}c^2 + \frac{(x-b)(x-c)}{(a-b)(a-c)}a^2 + \frac{(x-c)(x-a)}{(b-c)(b-a)}b^2 = x^2$$

22. Verify, without any expansion, that the following are identities on **C**:
  (a) $(x+1)(x+2)(x-1) = (x-2)^3 + 8x(x-1) - 5x + 6$
  (b) $(x-2)(x+1) - (x-1)^2 = x - 3$

23. Verify, without any expansion, that the following are identities on **C**:
  (a) $2(x-1)(x+2) - 3(x+1)(x-2) + (x-1)^2 = 3(x+1)$
  (b) $(x+1)(x-2)(x+2) = (x+1)^3 - 2(x+1)^2 - 3(x+1)$

24. Find a polynomial of the same degree, but with zeros the negatives of those of
  (a) $2x^3 - 3x^2 + 5x - 2$; (b) $3x^4 - 2x^3 + x^2 - 5x + 1$; (c) $x^4 + 2x^2 + 6$;
  (d) $x^4 - 2x^3 + x^2 + 1$.

25. Explain why no polynomial $p(x) \in$ **R**$[x]$ can exist such that $p(x) = \sin x$ is an identity on **R**.

26. Does the Fundamental Theorem of Algebra give any information about the solutions of the equation $2\sin^3 x - \sin^2 x - \sin x = 0$? Use any method you know to solve the equation for x such that $0 \leq x \leq 2\pi$.

27. If r $(\neq 0)$ is a zero of the real polynomial $p(x) = x^3 + bx^2 + cx + d$, show that the other two (real or complex) zeros of $p(x)$ are also zeros of $x^2 + (b+r)x - d/r$.

28. With $p_1(x), p_2(x) \in$ **C**$[x]$, prove that $p_1(x)$ divides $p_2(x)$ if and only if the zeros of $p_1(x)$ form a subset of the zeros of $p_2(x)$.

29. Prove that

$$p(x) = a\frac{(x-r_2)(x-r_3)}{(r_1 - r_2)(r_1 - r_3)} + b\frac{(x-r_1)(x-r_3)}{(r_2 - r_1)(r_2 - r_3)} + c\frac{(x-r_1)(x-r_2)}{(r_3 - r_1)(r_3 - r_2)}$$

is the only real polynomial in x of the second degree such that $p(r_1) = a$, $p(r_2) = b$, $p(r_3) = c$, for arbitrary distinct real numbers r_1, r_2, r_3, and any $a, b, c \in$ **R**. What is the graphical significance of this fact?

30. Use the formula given in Problem 29 to find the real polynomial $p(x)$ of the second degree such that the graph of the function f on **R**, where $f(x) = p(x)$, contains the points $(0, 5)$, $(1, 4)$, $(2, 7)$.

9.6 Rational Zeros of Rational Polynomials

Although the discussions in the two preceding sections may be useful in solving polynomial equations, the results given there are largely theoretical in nature and often of little help in the actual solving of a given equation. Thus we are still faced with the practical problem of finding the solution subset in **C** of a general polynomial equation with complex coefficients. It may be well to make it clear immediately that *this general problem will not be solved*! In view of the difficulty of the problem, we shall make a simplification *in this section* and assume most of the time that the coefficients are rational numbers. For this simplified problem, there is a finite—though sometimes tedious—procedure for finding all existing *rational* solutions of the equation. In many instances, we shall see that the method actually gives us the complete complex solution set. It is clear that the solutions of an equation are unchanged if each coefficient is multiplied by the same nonzero number. There is then no loss in generality in our assumption that the coefficients of a *rational* polynomial equation have been "cleared" of fractions, so that the resulting equation has only *integral* coefficients.

In our search for the *real* solutions of a polynomial equation, it is clear that the establishment of upper and lower bounds to these solutions may be of help. The process of synthetic division, as described in §9.4, provides us with two results that are very useful in this connection, and these results are valid whether the coefficients of the equation are rational—or arbitrary real—numbers.

■ **THEOREM 6.1** (*Upper Bound*).   *Let $p(x)$ be a polynomial with real co-efficients (not all 0), and c any positive real number. Then, in the process of synthetic division of $p(x)$ by $x - c$, if the numbers on the third row—with a suitable sign for any 0 that appears—are all of the same sign, the number c is an upper bound of the set of real zeros of $p(x)$.*

> PROOF.   We can write $p(x) = (x - c)q(x) + r$, where $q(x)$ is the quotient polynomial and r is the real-number remainder. The uniformity in signs of the numbers on the third row of the synthetic-division computation implies that r and $q(x)$ have the same sign for any $x > 0$. Moreover, if $x > c$, the number $x - c > 0$ and so $p(x)$ will exceed r in absolute value, whence $p(x) \neq 0$. Hence every real positive zero of $p(x)$ must be less than c, which is to say that c is an upper bound of the set of real zeros of $p(x)$.

■ **THEOREM 6.2** (*Lower Bound*).   *Let $p(x)$ be a polynomial with real coefficients (not all 0), and c any negative real number. Then, in the process of synthetic division, if the numbers on the third row—with a suitable sign given to any 0 that appears—alternate in sign, the number c is a lower bound to the set of real zeros of $p(x)$.*

> PROOF.   The proof of this theorem resembles that of Theorem 6.1 and depends on the fact that the alternating nature of the signs in the third row implies that $q(x)$ and r are of opposite sign for *any* real $x < 0$. If $x < c$, we then note that $x - c < 0$ and so $|p(x)| > |r|$, whence $p(x) \neq 0$ for any $x < c$. We leave any further details of the proof to the student.

Example 1.   Use synthetic division to show that 4 is an upper bound and -2 is a lower bound to the set of real zeros of $x^4 - 3x^3 - 4x^2 + 3x - 7$.

SOLUTION.   The computation below shows the synthetic division of the given polynomial by $x - 4$ and $x + 2$.

$$
\begin{array}{r|rrrrr}
4 & 1 & -3 & -4 & 3 & -7 \\
  &   & 4 & 4 & 0 & 12 \\
\hline
  & 1 & 1 & 0 & 3 & 5
\end{array}
\qquad
\begin{array}{r|rrrrr}
-2 & 1 & -3 & -4 & 3 & -7 \\
   &   & -2 & 10 & -12 & 18 \\
\hline
   & 1 & -5 & 6 & -9 & 11
\end{array}
$$

Because all numbers on the third row in the left computation are positive (with 0 being assigned a positive sign) and $4 > 0$, it follows from Theorem 6.1 that 4 is an upper bound to the set of real zeros of the polynomial. Because $-2 < 0$ and the numbers on the third row in the computation on the right alternate in sign, it is a consequence of Theorem 6.2 that -2 is a lower bound to the set of real zeros. Hence *any* real zero t of the polynomial must be such that $-2 < t < 4$.

When the two preceding theorems are used to discover bounds for the real zeros of a real polynomial, it should be clear that the bounds so obtained are not unique. Of course, there always *exist* unique least upper and greatest lower bounds for these zeros, but it is unfortunately the case that these "best" bounds are not necessarily obtainable by the above procedures—and this is true even if they happen to be integers. In the proper mathematical language, the conditions stated in Theorems 6.1, and 6.2 are *sufficient* but *not necessary* for bounds to the set of real zeros of a real polynomial.

There is another theorem of quite general validity that is sometimes of help in discovering the solutions of a real polynomial equation. This result is known informally as Descartes' Rule of Signs, and we state it without proof. If the terms of a polynomial are arranged in order of descending (or ascending) powers of the variable, with all 0 terms omitted, we say there is a *variation in sign* when two adjacent coefficients are of opposite sign. For example, there are three variations in sign in $2x^5 - 4x^4 + 2x^2 - x - 2$ and one variation in sign in $2x^4 - x^2 - 5$.

■ **THEOREM 6.3** (*Descartes' Rule of Signs*). *The number of positive real zeros of a polynomial $p(x)$ is equal to the number of variations in sign of the coefficients of $p(x)$, or less than this by a positive even integer.*

It should be noted that the rule gives information about *positive* real zeros only, and no precise information even then! However, because $p(c) = p[-(-c)]$, it follows that a number c is a negative real zero of $p(x)$ if and only if $-c$ is a positive real zero of $p(-x)$. Hence, we are able to apply the rule for information about the negative zeros of $p(x)$ by considering the positive zeros of $p(-x)$. In addition to positive and negative zeros, a polynomial may, of course, have the number 0 as one of its real zeros to some multiplicity—but this fact may be observed from a mere inspection of the polynomial.

Example 2.   Use Descartes' Rule of Signs to examine the real solutions of the equation $3x^5 - 2x^3 + x^2 + 5x - 2 = 0$.

SOLUTION.   There are three variations in sign in the ordered coefficients of the given polynomial, and so the number of positive real solutions is either three or one. If we replace x by $-x$ in the polynomial, the resulting equation is $-3x^5 + 2x^3 + x^2 - 5x - 2 = 0$. Because there are two variations in sign in the ordered coefficients of the polynomial on the left, there are either two or no negative real solutions of the original equation. The various solution possibilities (noting that 0 is not a solution) may then be listed as follows:

3 positive, 2 negative, no nonreal
3 positive, no negative, 2 complex conjugates
1 positive, 2 negative, 2 complex conjugates
1 positive, no negative, 2 pairs of complex conjugates.

It is often important to note—as a result of Theorem 5.2—that any polynomial with real coefficients and of *odd* degree has *at least one* real solution.

We stated near the beginning of this section that we are to be concerned primarily with polynomial equations with *rational* coefficients. The three results listed as theorems up to this point apply to general real polynomial equations—if we wish so to apply them—but our final theorem is applicable only to the rational case. It should also be recalled that we may assume the coefficients of this type of polynomial to be integers.

■ **THEOREM 6.4.** *Let* $p(x) = a_0 x^n + a_1 x^{n-1} + \cdots + a_{n-1} x + a_n$, *where* $a_0, a_1, \ldots, a_{n-1}, a_n$ *are integers. Then, if* p/q *is a rational zero of* $p(x)$, *where* p/q *is a fraction in reduced form,* p *is an integral divisor of* a_n *and* q *is an integral divisor of* a_0.

PROOF.   Because p/q is a zero of $p(x)$,

$$a_0 \left(\frac{p}{q}\right)^n + a_1 \left(\frac{p}{q}\right)^{n-1} + \cdots + a_{n-1} \left(\frac{p}{q}\right) + a_n = 0$$

If we multiply both members of this equality by q^n, we obtain

$$a_0 p^n + a_1 p^{n-1} q + \cdots + a_{n-1} p q^{n-1} + a_n q^n = 0$$

or, in an equivalent form,

$$a_0 p^n + a_1 p^{n-1} q + \cdots + a_{n-1} p q^{n-1} = -a_n q^n.$$

Because p is a common factor of all terms of the left member of the equation, p must be an integral divisor of the right member. The assumption that p and q are relatively prime now requires that p must be an integral divisor of a_n, as asserted. If we write the above equality in the form

$$a_0 p^n = -a_1 p^{n-1} q - \cdots - a_{n-1} p q^{n-1} - a_n q^n$$

it may be seen by a similar argument that q is an integral divisor or factor of a_0. The proof of the theorem is now complete.

This theorem provides us with a complete set of possibilities for the rational zeros of a polynomial from a simple inspection of its first and last coefficients.

It is clear, of course, that if the leading coefficient a_0 of the polynomial in the theorem is 1, all of its rational zeros (if any) are integers.

Example 3. From an inspection of its coefficients, determine a set of rational numbers that includes all the rational zeros of the polynomial $2x^5 - 4x^3 + 2x - 9$.

SOLUTION. Using the symbolism of the general polynomial in Theorem 6.4, we see that $a_0 = 2$ and $a_5 = -9$. Hence, the possible choices for q (as integral divisors of 2), are ± 1 and ± 2; the possibilities for p (as integral divisors of -9) are ± 1, ± 3, and ± 9. After duplicates have been eliminated, we see that the remaining possibilities for zeros of the polynomial lie in the set $\{\pm 1, \pm 3, \pm 9, \pm\frac{1}{2}, \pm\frac{3}{2}, \pm\frac{9}{2}\}$.

After we have obtained a set that contains all possible rational zeros of a polynomial, there remains the problem of checking the numbers in the set. Of course, it may be that there are no rational zeros, but it is not difficult to do the checking by means of synthetic division. It may be useful to note, in the checking process, that if a proper fraction appears on the third row of a synthetic-division computation, the rational number being checked may be immediately discarded. (Why?) On the other hand, a number should not be removed from further consideration just because it has been found to be a zero: It is possible that this number occurs as a zero with multiplicity greater than 1. Thus, if a has been discovered to be a zero of the polynomial $p(x)$, we should write $p(x) = (x - a)q(x)$, for some polynomial $q(x)$; and the number a should now be checked as a possible zero of $q(x)$—and so a multiple zero of $p(x)$— in addition to the other candidates for zeros.

It then appears, from what has just been said, that the complete set of rational zeros of a rational polynomial can be obtained with the sole use of Theorem 6.4 plus a finite number of checks by synthetic division. However, it is usually the case that the work can be reduced by making use of the other results given earlier in this section. Our final example will illustrate this composite usage.

Example 4. Determine all rational solutions of the equation

$$2x^4 - 5x^3 + 7x^2 - 10x + 6 = 0$$

SOLUTION. An application of Theorem 6.4 shows that the rational solutions of the equation comprise a subset of $\{\pm 1, \pm 2, \pm 3, \pm 6, \pm\frac{1}{2}, \pm\frac{3}{2}\}$. However, instead of checking each of these 12 solution "candidates," we can use Descartes' Rule (Theorem 6.3) to advantage. If we denote the left member of the equation by $p(x)$, we note that $p(-x) = 2x^4 + 5x^3 + 7x^2 + 10x + 6$. It follows that $p(-x) = 0$ has no positive solutions and so the given equation $p(x) = 0$ has no negative solutions. The set of rational solution possibilities is then immediately reduced to $\{1, 2, 3, 6, \frac{1}{2}, \frac{3}{2}\}$. At this point there is generally no one "best" order in which to begin the checking of the solution possibilities. It may be done in a random manner or by checking the numbers in ascending or descending order, but in any case it often happens that a useful application of either Theorem 6.1 or Theorem 6.2 can be made. For example, if one makes a first "random" check of $x = 3$, the synthetic-division computation yields the following:

$$\begin{array}{r|rrrrr} 3 & 2 & -5 & 7 & -10 & 6 \\ & & 6 & 3 & 30 & 60 \\ \hline & 2 & 1 & 10 & 20 & 66 \end{array}$$

Because the numbers in the third row all have the same (positive) sign, it follows from Theorem 6.1 that 3 is an upper bound to the real solutions, and our subset of solution possibilities has been reduced to $\{1, 2, \frac{1}{2}, \frac{3}{2}\}$. In this particular example, however, one would have been led more directly to the solution subset if we had considered first the positive-integer solution possibilities in ascending order. The computation for $x = 1$ is portrayed as follows:

$$\begin{array}{r|rrrrr} 1 & 2 & -5 & 7 & -10 & 6 \\ & & 2 & -3 & 4 & -6 \\ \hline & 2 & -3 & 4 & -6 & 0 \end{array}$$

We see immediately that $x = 1$ is a solution and that the original polynomial can be factored into $(x - 1)(2x^3 - 3x^2 + 4x - 6)$, so that our problem is now reduced to solving $2x^3 - 3x^2 + 4x - 6 = 0$. We find easily that $x = 1$, $x = 2$, and $x = \frac{1}{2}$ are not solutions of this cubic equation, but the computation for $x = \frac{3}{2}$ yields the following:

$$\begin{array}{r|rrrr} \frac{3}{2} & 2 & -3 & 4 & -6 \\ & & 3 & 0 & 6 \\ \hline & 2 & 0 & 4 & 0 \end{array}$$

This shows that $x = \frac{3}{2}$ is a solution and so $2x^3 - 3x^2 + 4x - 6 = (x - \frac{3}{2})(2x^2 + 4)$ and $2x^4 - 5x^3 + 7x^2 - 10x + 6 = (x - 1)(x - \frac{3}{2})(2x^2 + 4)$. Because the remaining factor $2x^2 + 4$ is quadratic, it is not necessary to make any further checks for rational solutions of the original equation: Any additional solutions of the original equation are solutions of $2x^2 + 4 = 0$ or, more simply, of $x^2 + 2 = 0$. It is clear that this equation has no rational solutions, and so we conclude that the *rational* solution set of the given equation is $\{1, \frac{3}{2}\}$. If the complete (complex) solution set is of interest, we have found it to be $\{1, \frac{3}{2}, \pm\sqrt{2}i\}$. If we now consider the checking part of this problem from the advantage of "hindsight," it will be observed that we would have reached our rational solutions with a minimum of checking if we had done it in strictly increasing order of magnitude: we would have discarded $\frac{1}{2}$, but the next two checks would yield 1 and $\frac{3}{2}$ as the remaining rational solutions. It may be safely assumed that there is no one way of ordering the checks that will always lead most directly to the desired solutions. However, it is usually the preferred custom to check the positive integers first, and follow these with the negative integers and nonintegers in this order.

We close this section with a very modest appraisal of what we have accomplished. The *practical* problem of solving a general polynomial equation with real coefficients has remained unsolved, because our attention has been directed to the rational solutions of rational equations. If we have been able to obtain the complete complex solution set of an equation, we may consider ourselves to have been "lucky" because of the low degree of the "reduced" equation— as in Example 4. As a matter of plain fact, however, the occurrence of polynomial equations with rational solutions is quite rare outside of "textbook" problems: Most equations that are encountered in practice have only irrational or nonreal solutions! There do exist methods, which we have not covered, for attacking the more general problem, but many are beyond the scope of this book. (One method that is somewhat common is known as "Newton's Method," but it requires a knowledge of differential calculus and is of use only for the real solutions of an equation.) With the advent of modern high-speed computers, however, it is now possible to set up "programs" for the solution of polynomial equations—at least to a high degree of approximation—and so the importance of these longhand methods of solution appears to have diminished. In the final section of the chapter we shall include a brief descriotion of the common graphical method of finding approximations to the real solutions of both polynomial and nonpolynomial equations.

Problems 9.6

1. Write each of the following as an equivalent equation with integral coefficients:
   (a) $x^5/2 + 3x^3/5 - x^2 + x/2 - \frac{1}{3} = 0$; (b) $x^6/4 - x^4/2 + x^2/3 + 1 = 0$;
   (c) $3x^3/5 - 2x^2/3 + x/4 - \frac{1}{3} = 0$.
2. Write each of the following as an equivalent equation with integral coefficients:
   (a) $\sqrt{2}x^3 - \sqrt{2}x^2/3 + x/\sqrt{2} - 3\sqrt{2} = 0$;
   (b) $3\sqrt{3}x^5 - 2x^2/\sqrt{3} + \sqrt{3}x = 0$.
3. Use synthetic division to verify that 5 is an upper bound and -3 is a lower bound of the real zeros of $x^4 - 2x^3 - 9x^2 + 2x + 8$.
4. Use synthetic division with random "divisors" to discover integral bounds for the real zeros of (a) $2x^3 - 5x^2 + 6$; (b) $4x^4 + 2x^2 - 6x - 5$; (c) $3x^4 - 2x^2 + 8$; (d) $x^4 - 5x^2 + 6x - 9$.
5. Use synthetic division with random "divisors" to discover integral bounds for the real zeros of (a) $4x^5 - x^2 + 2x - 6$; (b) $x^4 - 3x^3 + 2x^2 - x - 6$; (c) $x^3 + 16x - 29$.
6. Without actually finding the solution sets, what can you say about the real solutions of (a) $3x^4 + 5x^2 - 2 = 0$; (b) $x^6 - 4x^4 + x^2 + 2 = 0$?

7. Use Descartes' Rule of Signs to obtain information about the real zeros of the following polynomials:
   (a) $2x^3 - 3x^2 + 5x - 2$ (b) $3x^4 - 2x^3 + x^2 - 5x + 1$
   (c) $x^4 + 2x^2 + 6$ (d) $x^4 - 2x^3 + x^2 + 1$
8. Use Descartes' Rule of Signs to obtain information about the real zeros of the following polynomials:
   (a) $3x^3 - x^2 + 2x - 5$ (b) $4x^4 + x^2 - 3x + 1$
   (c) $4x^4 + 2x^2 + 5$ (d) $-3x^6 - 6x^4 + x^2 + 2x - 1$
9. Without solving, verify that the real solutions (if any) of the equation $3x^4 - 2x^3 + x^2 - 2x + 4 = 0$ must lie between 0 and 1.
10. Use any of the theorems of this section to find a set of rational numbers that includes all rational solutions (if any) of:
    (a) $2x^4 - 4x^3 + x - 6 = 0$ (b) $4x^3 - 3x^2 + 2x + 3 = 0$
    (c) $3x^5 - 3x^3 + 4x^2 - 2x + 8 = 0$ (d) $8x^4 - 3x^2 + 5x - 8 = 0$
11. Apply the directions given in Problem 10 to the following equations:
    (a) $3x^5 - 2x^4 + x^3 - 5x + 9 = 0$ (b) $5x^4 + 2x^2 + 12 = 0$
    (c) $5x^4 - 3x^2 + 6x - 8 = 0$ (d) $2x^4 + x^3 + x^2 + 1 = 0$
12. Apply the directions given in Problem 10 to the following equations:
    (a) $3x^4 + 2x^3 + x^2 + 5 = 0$ (b) $5x^5 - 7x^3 + 2x - 1 = 0$
    (c) $2x^4 - 5x^2 + 8 = 0$ (d) $x^5 + 4x^3 + 3x^2 + 2x + 1 = 0$
13. Verify that $\sqrt{3}$ is an irrational number by trying to discover any rational zeros of the polynomial $x^2 - 3$.
14. Verify that the polynomial $x^3 + 3x - 5$ has no rational zeros.
15. Find the rational solutions of each of the following equations, and, if the associated reduced equation is quadratic, complete the complex solution set:
    (a) $2x^4 - 5x^3 + 4x^2 - 5x + 2 = 0$ (b) $6x^4 - x^3 - 8x^2 + x + 2 = 0$
    (c) $x^4 - 2x^3 + x^2 + 2x - 2 = 0$
    (d) $3x^6 - 16x^5 + 26x^4 + 2x^3 - 33x^2 + 10x = 0$
16. Apply the directions given in Problem 15 to each of the following equations:
    (a) $6x^3 - 35x^2 + 19x + 30 = 0$ (b) $3x^3 + 13x^2 + 2x - 8 = 0$
    (c) $x^4 + 2x^3 - 13x^2 + 10x = 0$ (d) $x^4 - 9x^3 + 30x^2 - 44x + 24 = 0$
17. Determine all rational zeros of each of the following polynomials, or show that none exist:
    (a) $x^4 - x^3 + 5x^2/9 + 4x/9 - \frac{4}{9}$ (b) $x^4 + 3x^3/2 + x^2 - \frac{1}{2}$
    (c) $x^6 + 3x^3/2 + x/2$
18. Write an equation of degree 4 that will have (a) no positive solutions; (b) no negative solutions; (c) no real solutions.
19. A polynomial equation with rational coefficients may have irrational solutions. Explain why a polynomial with only rational zeros may always be expressed as a polynomial with only rational or only irrational coefficients, as desired.
20. Determine the complete complex solution set of the equation (a) $4x^3 - 3x^2 + 4x - 3 = 0$; (b) $x^3 + 3x^2/2 + x + 3/2 = 0$.
21. There is at least one real zero of the polynomial $p(x)$ between a, $b \in \mathbf{R}$ if $p(a)$ and $p(b)$ are of opposite sign. Use this fact to isolate between consecutive integers the nonintegral real zeros of (a) $x^3 - 3x + 1$; (b) $x^3 + 2x^2 - 6x + 2$; (c) $x^3 - x^2 - 11x + 14$.
22. Use the method suggested in Problem 21 to isolate between consecutive integers the real zeros of (a) $x^4 - 11x - 50$; (b) $x^4 - 2x^3 - 3x^2 + 2x + 1$; (c) $2x^3 - 5x^2 + x + 1$.

23. For what values of k will $2x^2 + x - k$ and $x^2 + 3x + 2$ have a common factor?

24. If c_1 and c_2 are the zeros of $x^2 + bx + c$, find (a) $c_1^2 + c_2^2$; (b) $c_1^4 + c_2^4$; (c) $1/c_1 + 1/c_2$.

25. When the process of synthetic division is being used to check a given rational number as a possible zero of a polynomial with integral coefficients, explain why the presence of a rational fraction on the third row of the computation shows immediately that the number being tested is not a zero of the polynomial.

26. Use the method suggested in Problem 21 to isolate between consecutive integers the real solutions of the equation $x^3 - x^2 - 11x + 14 = 0$, and continue the same procedure to show that approximations to the three solutions of the equation are 1.324, 3.093, and -3.417.

27. Find a polynomial whose zeros are the reciprocals of the zeros of

$$(1 - i)x^4 + \pi x^3 - \sqrt{2}x + 3$$

28. Determine all positive zeros less than 2π of the equation

$$\cos^4 x - 4\cos^3 x + 4\cos x - 1 = 0$$

29. Fill in the details of the proof of Theorem 6.2.

30. If $p(x) = x^n + a_1 x^{n-1} + \cdots + a_{n-1}x + a_n$ and $M = \max |a_i|, i = 1, 2, \ldots, n$, show that $1 + M$ is an upper bound to the real zeros of $p(x)$.

9.7 Real Zeros of Real Polynomials

The procedures in §9.6 have provided us with a foolproof method for a determination of all *rational* solutions of a polynomial equation with *integral* (or *rational*) coefficients. We have remarked, however, that our method gives us no help in finding solutions that are irrational or nonreal even for this kind of equation—except for certain very special cases. Of course, the method does not apply at all to nonpolynomial equations or to polynomial equations with at least one coefficient that is not rational! Although we make no attempt here to solve a general equation of any type, it is our objective in this section to present a method—largely graphical in nature—that may be used to approximate the *real* solutions of a real polynomial equation and of other simple equations of a nonpolynomial—but real—nature. It will be convenient to denote a general real equation in a variable x by $f(x) = 0$, and $f(x)$ may be considered the value of a function f at some point x of its domain. The method to be described is an extension of the result in Problem 21 of §9.6 and depends for its validity on the two following facts:

1. The real solutions of the real equation $f(x) = 0$ are the abscissas of the points of intersection of the graph of the function f [or equation $y = f(x)$] with the x-axis, assuming the domain of f to be maximal.

2. Let a and b be real numbers in the domain of the function f, with $a < b$ and such that $f(a)$ and $f(b)$ have opposite signs. Then, if the graph of f is "smooth" for the interval $[a, b]$, there is a real number r between a and b such that $f(r) = 0$. In other words, under the conditions assumed, the equation $f(x) = 0$ has a real solution r where $a < r < b$.

The first of the above facts is an obvious one and is in immediate consequence of what we mean by a "solution" of an equation. The second fact is a more subtle one, the "smoothness" of the graph of f depending on the "continuity" of f in the interval $[a, b]$. The proof of this result is usually found in books on the calculus, and we shall merely make the blanket assertion that *all the elementary functions*—including the polynomial functions—have this property.

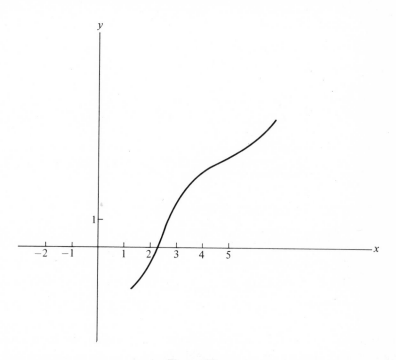

Figure 89

In Figure 89 we have shown a portion of the graph of a real function, and it should be noted that the graph crosses the x-axis. Although this graph was not drawn to represent any specified function, its point of crossing of the x-axis is clearly between 2 and 3, and one may *guess* that a slightly better approximation to this point is 2.3. The procedure of Problem 21 in §9.7, previously referred to (and further extended in Problem 26 of the same problem set), is quite laborious but could be used to obtain the desired point of crossing of the graph to any desired degree of accuracy—at least in the case of a polynomial function.

However, for general purposes it is usually better to use the method of linear interpolation, and although we have described it before in the use of the various tables at the back of the book, we repeat the details in the present context. In brief, one assumes that the portion of the curve in the neighborhood of its crossing the x-axis is a line segment and we approximate the crossing point under this assumption. This interpolation procedure can, of course, be used as often as desired, but if nonpolynomial functions are involved and tables are needed for computational purposes, there is always a limit to the accuracy of our results by this method.

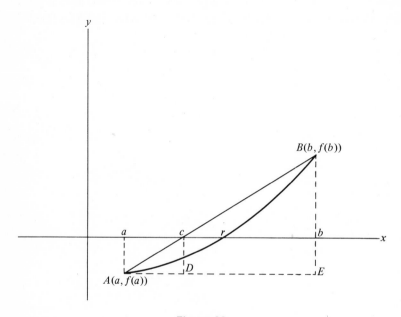

Figure 90

In order to review the method of linear interpolation, we have shown in Figure 90 an enlargement of the neighborhood of crossing the x-axis of the graph of a function f, whose domain includes the interval $[a, b]$. The portion of the actual graph of f shown is curved, and we are interested in the point r where the graph intersects the x-axis. However, we replace the curve by the line segment joining the points $(a, f(a))$ and $(b, f(b))$ and use the point c at which this segment intersects the x-axis as an approximation for r. In order to find the number c, we observe from the figure that the similarity of the triangles ACD and ABE that $\dfrac{f(b) - f(a)}{b - a} = \dfrac{0 - f(a)}{c - a}$. If we now solve this equation for c, we find that $c = \dfrac{af(b) - bf(a)}{f(b) - f(a)}$. Hence, because we are regarding c as an approximation for r, we have obtained the following approximation formula:

$$r \approx \frac{af(b) - bf(a)}{f(b) - f(a)}$$

As we have said earlier, this formula may be used as many times as desired to obtain better approximations: All that is necessary is to find a sequence of diminishing intervals $[a, b] \supset [a', b'] \supset [a'', b''], \ldots$ in each of which the signs of $f(a), f(a'), f(a''), \ldots$ differ, respectively, from the signs of $f(b), f(b')$, $f(b''), \ldots$. If the function is not polynomial, however, the inadequacy of our tables may limit the number of times it is expedient to repeat the process. Before giving an example, it may be well to caution that difficulties may be encountered in using the above procedure in case the graph of f crosses the x-axis at more than one point in the original interval $[a, b]$, because the approximations may not always tend toward the same crossing point. It is then important to be sure that a *single* zero has been isolated in the initial interval $[a, b]$, before beginning the linear interpolation procedure. Our first example is with a polynomial equation, the type of equation for which the method is best adapted.

Example 1.   Approximate the real zeros of the polynomial $2x^3 + x - 4$.

SOLUTION.   Our first observation is that, as a result of Descartes' Rule of Signs, there is exactly one real zero for the polynomial. Thus any possible confusion arising from more than one real zero in an interval does not occur in this case. We then note that, if we let $2x^3 + x - 4 = f(x)$, the graph of f crosses the y-axis at -4 and the functional values become arbitrarily large as x increases without bound. Hence, the desired zero is positive—a fact that could also be deduced from a consideration of the positive zeros of $f(-x)$. A little checking by synthetic division now yields the following results:

$$f(1) = -1 \qquad f(2) = 14$$

The real zero r is then in the interval $[1, 2]$, as indicated in the rough sketch shown in Figure 91. An application of the formula developed in this section for a first approximation r_1 of r, with $a = 1$ and $b = 2$, gives

$$r_1 = \frac{f(2) - 2f(1)}{f(2) - f(1)} = \frac{14 - 2(-1)}{14 + 1} = \frac{16}{15} \approx 1.07 \approx 1.1$$

Further computation reveals that $f(1.1) = -0.238$ and $f(1.2) = 0.656$, so that the real zero of the polynomial lies in $[1.1, 1.2]$. Another application of the same formula, in which $a = 1.1$ and $b = 1.2$, now yields r_2 as a second approximation to r, where

$$r_2 = \frac{(1.1)f(1.2) - (1.2)f(1.1)}{f(1.2) - f(1.1)} \approx \frac{(1.1)(0.656) - (1.2)(-0.238)}{0.656 + 0.238}$$

$$\approx \frac{0.7216 + 0.2856}{0.894} = \frac{1.0072}{0.894} \approx 1.127 \approx 1.13$$

A check shows that $f(1.13) \approx 0.0158$, and this verifies that 1.13 is indeed an approximation to the desired zero. It would be possible to continue this process indefinitely, but it is surely clear that the computation—at least by hand—becomes very tedious. We then accept 1.13 as a satisfactory approximation, and the solution of the problem is completed.

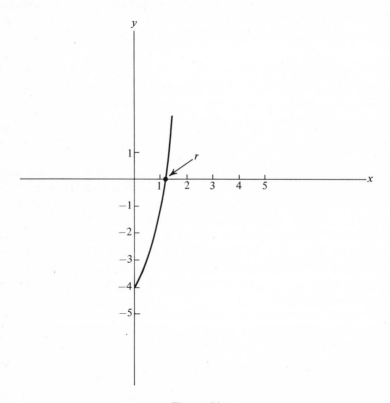

Figure 91

We have remarked earlier that the linear interpolation method under discussion in this section is valid—at least in theory—for nonpolynomial equations, but the absence of adequate tables for the elementary functions that may arise limits its use. It may also be worthwhile to point out that, if interpolations are required in the use of a table, we are actually using the formula in this section in an intuitive fashion for these interpolations. Our second and final example will illustrate the procedure—and also the difficulty—in dealing with non-polynomial equations.

Example 2.   Find an approximate real solution of the equation

$$\sin 2x + 2x - 1 = 0$$

SOLUTION.   If we let $\sin 2x + 2x - 1 = f(x)$, it is clear that $f(0) = -1$ and $f(\frac{1}{4}\pi) = \frac{1}{2}\pi$, so that a zero lies in the interval $[0, \frac{1}{4}\pi]$. Moreover, any solution of the equation $\sin 2x + 2x - 1 = 0$ is the abscissa of a point of intersection of the line $y = 1 - 2x$ and the curve $y = \sin 2x$, and it is clear graphically that there is only one such point of intersection. Hence, as in Example 1, our search is for a unique solution. Some computation, involving interpolation in Table 2, shows that $f(0.25) = \sin 0.5 + 0.5 - 1 \approx -0.021$ and $f(0.26) = \sin 0.52 + 0.52 - 1 \approx 0.017$. Hence, we may use the formula developed in this section, with $a = 0.25$ and $b = 0.26$, to obtain the desired first approximation r_1 as follows:

$$r_1 = \frac{(0.25)f(0.26) - (0.26)f(0.25)}{f(0.26) - f(0.25)} \approx \frac{(0.25)(0.017) - (-0.26)(-0.021)}{0.017 + 0.021}$$

$$= \frac{0.00425 + 0.00546}{0.038} = \frac{0.00971}{0.038} \approx 0.256$$

Because $f(0.256) = \sin 0.512 + 0.512 - 1 \approx 0.490 + 0.512 - 1 = 0.002$, it is clear that 0.256 is a close approximation to the real zero of the given equation. Whether it is close enough depends upon our needs, but we shall not attempt a closer approximation here.

If the method discussed here for finding the real solutions of a real equation does not have great appeal, we are in sympathy with such a feeling. However, as we said earlier, better—but more sophisticated methods—do exist, but they are more suited for coverage in an advanced course. Even some of the calculus methods—such as Newton's—previously mentioned determine only the real solutions of a real equation, and it is often the case in electrical engineering and elsewhere that the nonreal solutions are also required. One of the best procedures for a determination of both the real and nonreal solutions of an equation is due to Graeffe, and his name is used to refer to the method. The basic idea of the method is to form a new equation, the solutions of which are some high power of the solutions of the original equation. If the power is high enough, the solutions of the new equation will be widely separated, and they may be obtained by a simple—but tedious—process. From these solutions, we then obtain readily the solutions of the given equation. For a fuller discussion of this and other methods of solving equations, the reader is invited to consult other more advanced books on the theory of equations. We close this section, however, with a repetition of one of our opening remarks: The advent of modern computing machines has made the problem of solving equations of all kinds much less important than in former times, and for this and other reasons we do not emphasize it here.

Problems 9.7

1. Determine the real intervals of unit length in each of which is contained exactly one real zero of each of the following polynomials:
   (a) $x^4 + 6x^2 + 3x - 1$ (b) $x^3 - 9x^2 - 3x + 1$
   (c) $x^3 + 3x^2 - x - 1$ (d) $x^5 + 3x^3 + x - 2$

2. Determine one or more real intervals of unit length that together contain all of the real zeros of each of the following polynomials:
   (a) $x^3 - x^2 + 2x - 5$ (b) $x^3 - 3x^2 - 2x + 5$
   (c) $x^4 - 5x^3 - x^2 - 5x - 2$ (d) $x^4 - 2x^3 + 3x^2 - 6x + 3$

3. Let $f(x) = 4x^3 - 12x^2 + 8x - 1$, and verify that the equation $f(x) = 0$ has two real zeros in the interval $[0, 1]$ even though $f(0)$ and $f(1)$ have the same (negative) sign.

4. Use the method outlined in this section to find a two-decimal approximation to
   (a) $\sqrt[3]{7}$; (b) $\sqrt[4]{3}$; (c) $\sqrt[5]{10}$; (d) $\sqrt[3]{-9}$.

   In Problems 5–8, find a two-decimal approximation of the smallest positive real zero of the polynomial given.

5. $x^3 + 3x + 1$ 6. $x^3 - 4x^2 + 2x + 2$
7. $x^3 - 33x + 20$ 8. $x^4 - 2x^3 + 3x^2 - 11x + 10$

   In Problems 9–10, find a two-decimal approximation of the negative zero of largest absolute value for the polynomial given.

9. $x^3 - 3x^2 - 2x + 5$ 10. $3x^3 + 13x^2 + 2x - 2$

   In Problems 11–20 find a two-decimal approximation of each of the real zeros of the polynomials given, first observing whether the polynomial under study has appeared in one of the earlier problems.

11. $x^3 - 3x^2 + 2x - 11$ 12. $4x^4 - 4x^3 - 3x^2 - 7x + 1$
13. $x^4 - 5x^3 - x^2 - 5x - 2$ 14. $x^4 - 2x^3 + 3x^2 - 11x + 10$
15. $3x^3 + 13x^2 + 2x - 2$ 16. $4x^3 - 12x^2 + 8x - 1$
17. $8x^3 + 12x^2 - 50x + 29$ 18. $x^3 - 3x^2 - 2x + 5$
19. $x^3 - 33x + 20$ 20. $3x^5 + 8x^4 - 24x^3 + 16x^2 + 81x - 28$

21. If f and g are functions defined on $\mathbf{R}$, explain why the real solutions of the equation $f(x) - g(x) = 0$ are the abscissas of the points of intersection of the graphs of f and g.

22. Explain why it would be appropriate to write the interpolation formula, developed in this section, in the form:

   (a) $r \approx \dfrac{a|f(b)| + b|f(a)|}{|f(b)| + |f(a)|}$ (b) $r \approx a + (b - a) \dfrac{|f(a)|}{|f(a)| + |f(b)|}$

The form in (b) is especially desirable if $0 < a < b$, as was tacitly implied in our formal development.

23. Use rough sketches to determine the number of real solutions of each of the following equations:
(a) $e^x - 3x - 2 = 0$; (b) $e^x - \sin x = 0$; (c) $e^x + \sin x = 0$.

24. Use rough sketches to determine the number of real solutions of each of the following equations:
(a) $4 - 2x - \ln x = 0$; (b) $e^{2x} + 3 \ln x + 5 = 0$; (c) $3 + 8x - 4 \sin x = 0$.

In Problems 25–28, use a graphical sketch to determine the number of real solutions of the given equation, and use the method of this section to compute a two-decimal approximation of the smallest of the positive solutions.

25. $e^x - 4x = 0$ 26. $\tan x + x - 1 = 0$

27. $\cos x - e^x + 1 = 0$ 28. $\sin x + x - 1 = 0$

29. If $p(x)$ is any polynomial and $a \in \mathbf{R}$, we may write $p(x) = (x - a)q(x) + r$, with $r \in \mathbf{R}$; moreover $(c - a)q(c) + r = 0$, for any zero c of $p(x)$. If a is "close" to c, then deduce the following approximation formula:

$$c \approx a - \frac{p(a)}{q(a)}$$

30. Use the polynomial in Example 1 and the approximation formula given in Problem 29 to find an approximation to the real zero if $a = 1.1$. Compare with the result obtained in the example.

10

The Binomial Theorem and Sequences

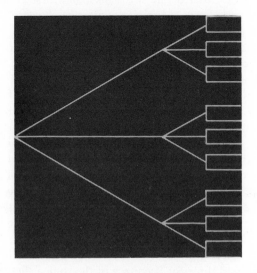

10.1 The Fundamental Counting Principle

The topics to be discussed in this chapter are of importance in many different areas of mathematics, as well as being of interest in themselves. In many of the modern applications of mathematics, there is an increasing use of probability and statistics, and although we shall discuss neither of these subjects, the concepts that are basic to both of them *will* be introduced. The student may have observed that even weather forecasts are now being made in terms of probabilities! Many of our discussions in the early part of the chapter will involve the matter of discovering efficient means of counting the members of some given set. For example, the question of the number of possible hands in a game of bridge will arise in one of the later problem sets, and it would clearly be hopeless to list all such hands and count them! The fundamental principle enunciated in this section will be very useful when a problem such as this one arises, and we shall see then how to answer the question—and others of more importance—with some simple computations.

Let us introduce the principle in this section with an example. If a college student has two pairs of shoes, two pairs of slacks, and four sport shorts, in how many different outfits can he appear on the campus? He can wear any one of the four shirts with either of the two slacks, and these two articles can then be selected in 4 · 2 or 8 ways. Moreover, with *any* choice of shirt and slacks, he may wear either of two pairs of shoes. Because his shoes can be selected in two ways, it is clear that his three-piece outfit can be selected in 8 · 2 or 16 ways. It is sometimes helpful to use a diagram—called a *tree*—in which to portray the various possibilities for a multiple-choice situation. In Figure 92 we have drawn the tree associated with the example just discussed. Each line segment of the diagram is called a *branch*, the branches corresponding to the various immediate choices, and it may be noted that all *paths* or joins of line segments through the tree emanate from the point *S*—the "student." The four line segments drawn from *S* correspond to the four choices for a shirt, the two segments drawn from the end of each of the first four correspond to the choices for a pair of slacks, and the terminal segments correspond to the choices for a pair of shoes. The number of paths from *S*—which is clearly the same as the number of terminal branches of the tree—may then be counted and found to be 16.

As another example, suppose there are three candidates for President, two for Vice-President, and three for Secretary of the student body of your college.

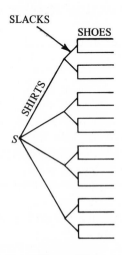

SLACKS

SHOES

SHIRTS

S

Figure 92

In how many ways can the three offices be filled? Because any one of the three candidates for President can be associated with either of the two candidates for Vice-President, these two offices together can be filled in $3 \cdot 2$ or 6 different ways. The Secretary can be chosen in three ways and may be associated with any one of the six choices for the other two offices, and so the three positions can be filled in $6 \cdot 3$ or 18 ways. We do not include the tree diagram for this example, but it is suggested as a problem at the end of the section.

The two examples that we have just given are illustrative of the following basic principle which, in reality, is just a matter of "common sense."

Fundamental Counting Principle. *If there are m possible outcomes of one operation or "event" and after any one of them has occurred, there are n possible outcomes of a second event, there are mn possible outcomes for the composite event consisting of the first followed by the second. There is, of course, the obvious extension of the principle to the composite of any finite number of events.*

We remind the reader that a composite of two operations or events presumes that an ordering of their occurrence has been understood. Although the order of the events in the two examples given above was clearly of no importance, we shall see later that order does matter in some cases.

Example 1. How many three-letter code words can be formed from the letters of our alphabet?

SOLUTION. In this problem, three events are involved: the selection of a first letter, the selection of a second letter, and finally the selection of a third letter. There are 26 letters in our alphabet, and so there are 26 possible outcomes to the event of selecting one of the letters. In this problem, the letters are not "used up" as a result of a previous selection, and so the possible outcomes of the three events are independent of each other. In other words, each of the three events has 26 possible outcomes, and the Fundamental Counting Principle assures us that the possible number of three-letter code words is $26 \cdot 26 \cdot 26$ or 17,576.

It was pointed out, in the discussion of Example 1, that the possible outcomes of the events occuring there were quite independent of the outcomes of any preceding events. In general this is not the case, however, and our next example illustrates a case in which there is a dependency on the outcomes of earlier events.

Example 2. Three men wish to stay overnight in a certain city, but for business reasons, each wishes to locate in a hotel in which neither of the other two is staying. If five hotels are available to accommodate them, in how many ways is it possible for the men to take up satisfactory quarters for the night?

SOLUTION. For the purposes of the problem, let us identify the men as A, B, and C, and it is clear that the "events" in the problem are the selection of a satisfactory hotel by each of these three men. It is possible for A to select any one of the five hotels, but after his selection has been made, B must select one of the remaining four, whereas a choice of only three hotels remains for C. It follows from the Fundamental Counting Principle that the three men can be housed in $5 \cdot 4 \cdot 3$ or 60 ways that are satisfactory to all of them.

In our solution of the problem in Example 2, it may have appeared that we favored A by allowing him to make his choice first and that B also had an advantage over C. If we are to suppose that the hotels are not of the same quality, this would indeed be true. However, for the purposes of our problem here, *we are merely counting the number of distinct possibilities* without prejudice to any other matters, and it is clear that the answer to the problem would be the same *regardless of the order* in which A, B, and C make their selections. In our next example, however, we shall consider a case in which the ordering of the events does make a difference to the number of composite outcomes.

Example 3. Let M and N designate two urns, with M containing two white balls and one black ball and N containing two white and two black balls, all the balls assumed to be distinguishable. If a ball is drawn from either urn, and, *provided the ball drawn is white*, a ball is drawn from the other urn, compare the number of distinct possible outcomes, according as M or N is selected first.

SOLUTION. For convenience, let us denote by (M, N) the composite event of a drawing from M followed by a drawing from N—provided the latter is permitted—with (N, M) denoting the composite event with the reverse order of the drawings.

(1) In the case of (M, N), a white ball can be drawn from M in two ways, and there are four possible outcomes for the subsequent drawing of a ball from urn N. There are then eight possible ways in which two balls can be drawn, according to the rules of the drawings. If we now include the case in which a black ball is drawn from urn M, the total number of possible outcomes of the composite event is 9.

(2) In the case of (N, M), a white ball can be drawn from N in two ways, and there are three possibilities for the subsequent drawing from urn M. There are then 6 possible outcomes involving two drawings, and if we include the two cases in which an initial black ball is drawn from urn N, it is seen that the total number of distinct outcomes of this composite event is 8.

We note that the number of outcomes for the ordering (M, N) is different from the number for the ordering (N, M).

Example 4. If $S = \{a, b, c, d\}$ and $T = \{x, y, z\}$, find the number of elements in $S \cup T$ and in $S \times T$.

SOLUTION.   Because $S \cap T = \emptyset$, the number of elements in $S \cup T$ is the sum of the numbers in S and T separately, and this number is clearly $4 + 3 = 7$. The elements of $S \times T$, on the other hand, are ordered pairs of elements from S and T *in this order*, and the "events" are the selections of these pairs. The first member of a pair can be selected from S in four ways, and the second member can be selected from T in three ways. It then follows from the Fundamental Counting Principle that the two members can be selected in $4 \cdot 3 = 12$ ways, and so there are 12 elements in the product set $S \times T$.

Problems 10.1

1. If $S = \{1, 2, 3, 4\}$ and $T = \{3, 5, 7\}$, determine the number of elements in (a) $S \cup T$; (b) $S \times T$.
2. How many four-letter code words can be made if the first and fourth letters must be consonants and the second and third must be vowels?
3. If four colors are available, in how many ways can a map of four countries be colored if no two countries are to have the same color?
4. How many five-digit numerals can be written if 0 is excluded as a first digit for any number except the number $0\ (= 00000)$?
5. Draw a tree diagram to represent the possibilities for the student offices, as discussed in the third paragraph of this section.
6. In Example 2, if A requires a hotel with an elevator and only three of the available hotels have this service, determine the number of ways in which the men can be satisfactorily accommodated. Does the order in which the men are considered to choose their hotels alter the answer to *this* problem?
7. Draw tree diagrams to illustrate Example 2 and its variation as suggested in Problem 6.
8. Suppose that urn N in Example 3 has two black balls and one white ball and that M remains the same as in the example. Now follow the same directions, and compare your answer with that worked out in the example. Does the order in which the urns are considered to be selected make any difference in *this* case?
9. Draw a tree diagram for each of the orderings in Problem 8.
10. If the boy in Example 1 has three shirts, three pairs of slacks, and two pairs of shoes, find the number of possible combination outfits available to him and illustrate the count with a tree diagram.
11. Alter the conditions given in Example 3 so that a second ball may be drawn only if the first ball drawn is black. Compare your answer with that in the example.
12. If two dice are tossed, in how many different ways can they fall, the two dice being considered distinguishable?
13. If a mathematics class is offered at periods 1, 3, 4, 5, an English class at periods 3, 4, 6, and a physics class at periods 4, 5, 6, 7, how many different class schedules are possible for a student taking one course in each of these three subject areas? (*Hint:* Construct a tree diagram.)

14. In a certain college, mathematics courses are offered at periods 1, 2, 6, physics at periods, 2, 5, 7, and English at periods 1, 7, 9. In how many different ways can a college student make up his class schedule if he wishes to take one course from each of the three subject areas? (See hint in Problem 13.)

15. A menu has a choice of soup, orange juice, or tomato juice for an appetizer, a choice of chicken, beef, or fish for entree, and a choice of pie or ice cream for dessert. How many different three-course dinners are possible? Use a tree to portray the various possibilities.

16. If a diner, selecting from the menu in Problem 15, must have fish as his entree, how many different complete dinners are available to him? Draw a tree diagram to represent his possible choices.

17. In how many ways can five girls and six boys be seated on a row of 11 chairs if each of the girls is to be positioned between two boys?

18. A student has six shirts and three ties, the colors of three of the shirts and two of the ties being shades of green, and the colors of the other articles are various shades of blue. How many shirt-tie combinations are possible for him if (a) all color combinations are acceptable; (b) blue and green combinations are not acceptable?

19. If there are three major routes from Jacksonville to Atlanta, three from Atlanta to Chicago, and two from Chicago to Minneapolis, how many major routings are possible for a trip from Jacksonville to Minneapolis?

20. Use a tree diagram to illustrate how many three-digit numerals can be formed from the digits 3, 4, 6, 8 if the number represented is to exceed 600?

21. In how many different ways can the letters of the word MONDAY be arranged?

22. The inscriptions on car license plates of a certain state consist of two letters of the alphabet followed by a four-digit nonzero number. How many different license plates are possible if (a) the letters may not be repeated on any one plate, and the first digit of the number may not be 0; (b) no further restrictions are imposed on the choice of letters and digits?

23. Determine how many four-digit numbers can be formed out of the digits 1, 2, 3, 4 if (a) no digit is repeated; (b) repetitions of digits are permitted.

24. If there are six chairs in a reception room, in how many ways can four people be seated?

25. A signal device consists of three rows of lights, each with a red, a green, and an amber light. Determine how many signals can be sent from this device, if at least one light is to be lit in each row for every signal.

26. It is possible to record information on "punched" cards by punching holes at the proper locations. If a card has 80 columns and 12 locations in each column, how many theoretically different lines of information can be punched on any one card if exactly one hole is to be punched in each column?

27. A signalman can hold a flag in each hand, and each flag can be put in any one of four positions. If each pattern represents a signal, how many different signals can be sent? If two successive patterns are needed for a signal, how many signals are available to the signalman?

28. Three arithmetic operations may be defined on a number as follows: (a) add three; (b) multiply by itself (i.e., square); (c) divide by two. Draw a tree diagram to show the various orders in which these three operations may be applied to a given number, and use the tree to find the maximal number of distinct numerical results. Is it possible for two of these results to be equal for some given initial number?

29. Use the tree constructed in Problem 28 to find the results of applying the operations in their various orders to the number 1.

30. With reference to Problem 29, examine each of the ordered sets of operations and discover if there exists a number that is left invariant by any one of them. Does there exist a number that is independent of the order in which the three operations are applied?

10.2 Permutations and Combinations

A special application of the Fundamental Counting Principle arises when we consider the different possible *ordered arrangements* or *permutations* of a finite set of elements. Such arrangements can be broken down into subpatterns, each of which is equivalent to a permutation of elements either in a straight line or on a circle. These basic permutations are called *linear* or *circular*, according to the type of arrangement. It sometimes happens that, even though the elements of a set may be all distinct in one sense, they are nonetheless indistinguishable from each other. For example, the four letters A, A, A, A that appear in the word ALABAMA are indistinguishable from each other, but they are distinct letters in the sense that they occupy distinct positions in the word. In this section, we shall be concerned only with *distinguishable* elements and all permutations will be *linear*, which may then be considered arranged in a linear (or straight line) array.

The basic problem in permutations is the following: In how many ways can n objects be arranged in a straight line? If we think of the objects as occupying the first, second, third, ..., nth positions in the linear array, the arranging of the objects can be broken down into the primary events of filling the first position, filling the second position, filling the third position, etc. Because there are n objects, the first position can be filled in n ways, the second in $n - 1$ ways, the third in $n - 2$ ways, etc., with only one way of filling the final position. Hence, by the Fundamental Counting Principle, the n positions can be filled in $n(n - 1)(n - 2) \cdots 3 \cdot 2 \cdot 1$ ways. *This is then the number of permutations of n objects in a linear arrangement.*

Products of the form $n(n - 1)(n - 2) \cdots 3 \cdot 2 \cdot 1$ occur frequently in mathematics and are designated $n!$ (read "n factorial"). Thus $n!$ is the product of all integers from 1 to n, inclusive. We also make the *definition* that $0! = 1$. If we designate the number of permutations of n objects in a linear array by $P(n)$, we have shown above that

$$P(n) = n!$$

Example 1. Express $8 \cdot 7 \cdot 6 \cdot 5$ in terms of factorials.

SOLUTION. $8 \cdot 7 \cdot 6 \cdot 5 = \dfrac{8 \cdot 7 \cdot 6 \cdot 5 \cdot 4 \cdot 3 \cdot 2 \cdot 1}{4 \cdot 3 \cdot 2 \cdot 1} = \dfrac{8!}{4!}$

Example 2. In how many ways can six students be seated on a row of six chairs?

SOLUTION. This is precisely the number of permutations of six objects in a linear array, and so the desired number is 6! or 720.

A slightly different problem arises if we ask for the number of ways in which r objects can be selected from a set of n objects ($r \leq n$) and then arranged in a linear array. This is called *the number of permutations of n objects taken r at a time* and is designated $P(n, r)$. Because the first position can be filled in n ways, the second in $n - 1$ ways, ..., and the rth in $n - r + 1$ ways, we obtain the following formula for $P(n, r)$:

$$P(n, r) = n(n - 1)(n - 2) \cdots (n - r + 1) = \frac{n!}{(n - r)!}$$

In case $r = n$, this formula gives $P(n) = P(n, n) = n!$, as before.

If the order of the objects in an array is of no interest, we are concerned with mere *subsets* or *combinations* of objects. *The number of combinations of n objects taken r at a time*, designated $C(n, r)$ or $\binom{n}{r}$, is then the number of ways in which r objects can be selected from a set of n ($\geq r$) objects, or, alternatively, as the "number of r-subsets of an n-set." Both notations $C(n, r)$ and $\binom{n}{r}$ are useful and will be used. The notation $C(n, r)$ is more suggestive if the elements of the subsets are being "combined" in some way, whereas $\binom{n}{r}$ is probably to be preferred in purely set-theoretic circumstances; but we emphasize that both symbols have the same meaning. Inasmuch as order is not of importance in subsets, it follows immediately that $C(n, r) = \binom{n}{r} \leq P(n, r)$. In fact, because each subset of r (≥ 1) objects can be permuted in $r!$ ways, there are $r!$ times as many permutations of r objects as there are r-subsets or combinations of r objects. Hence, $P(n, r) = r!C(n, r) = r! \binom{n}{r}$, and so

$$C(n, r) = \binom{n}{r} = \frac{P(n, r)}{r!} = \frac{n!}{(n - r)!r!} \qquad \text{if } r > 0$$

Because $0! = 1$, this formula remains valid even when $r = n$. In this case $C(n, n) = \binom{n}{n} = 1$, which is simply the assertion that there is only 1 subset of n elements in a set of n elements. It is convenient to include the case $r = 0$ and to *define* $C(n, 0) = \binom{n}{0} = 1$, for any positive integer n.

Example 3. How many five-digit integers can be formed from the numbers of the set $\{1, 2, 3, 4, 5, 6, 7, 8\}$.

SOLUTION. This is a matter of choosing five of the eight given digits, and arranging them to form numbers. Symbolically, this can be done in $P(8, 5)$ ways, and so the desired number is $8!/3!$ or 6720.

Example 4. In how many ways can a committee of three boys and two girls be chosen from a class of twelve boys and eight girls?

SOLUTION. Because order is not involved in committee membership, this is a problem involving subsets of a set. There are $\binom{12}{3}$ possible subsets of three boys and $\binom{8}{2}$ possible subsets of two girls, obtainable from the given class. An application of the Fundamental Counting Principle then gives us $\binom{12}{3} \cdot \binom{8}{2} = \dfrac{12!}{3!9!} \cdot \dfrac{8!}{2!6!} = \dfrac{12 \cdot 11 \cdot 10}{3 \cdot 2 \cdot 1} \cdot \dfrac{8 \cdot 7}{2 \cdot 1} = 6160$ ways of forming the committee.

Example 5. The directions of an examination specify that the student is to answer four of the first six, and six of the remaining nine questions. In how many ways can a student complete the examination?

SOLUTION. The student may select four questions from the first six, and this can be done in $C(6, 4)$ ways. He must then select six from the remaining nine questions, and this can be accomplished in $C(9, 6)$ ways. By the Fundamental Counting Principle, the student can do his examination in

$$[C(6, 4)][C(9, 6)] = \frac{6!}{4!2!} \cdot \frac{9!}{6!3!} = \frac{6 \cdot 5}{2 \cdot 1} \cdot \frac{9 \cdot 8 \cdot 7}{3 \cdot 2 \cdot 1} = 15 \cdot 84 = 1260 \text{ ways.}$$

Problems 10.2

1. Determine the positive integer represented by each of the following symbols:
   (a) 3!; (b) 8!; (c) 5!; (d) 0!; (e) 10!
2. Express each of the following as a positive integer:
   (a) 3(4!); (b) 6(5!); (c) 2(5!) + 3!; (d) 4(5!) − 2(3!); (e) 3(4!) + 4(5!) + 6(2!).
3. Express each of the following as a positive integer:
   (a) 5!/3!; (b) 10!/5!; (c) 7!/4!; (d) (12!6!)/(7!3!).
4. Find the positive integer represented by each of the following symbols: (a) $\binom{5}{3}$;
   (b) $\binom{10}{5}$; (c) $\binom{12}{10}$.

5. Find the positive integer represented by each of the following symbols: (a) $\binom{8}{2}$;

(b) $\binom{10}{3}$; (c) $\binom{20}{5}$.

6. Find the positive integer represented by each of the following symbols:
(a) $P(6, 3)$; (b) $P(8, 6)$; (c) $P(6)$; (d) $P(9)$.

7. Find the positive integer represented by each of the following symbols:
(a) $C(5, 2)$; (b) $C(7, 3)$; (c) $C(10, 4)$; (d) $C(20, 3)$.

8. Express each of the following numbers as a multiple of the largest possible factorial: (a) $9(8!)$; (b) $10(6!) - 7(5!)$; (c) $3!6! + 6!$.

9. In how many different ways can a six-man working party be selected from a platoon of 15 soldiers?

10. How many different "singles" tennis matches (i.e., involving two players) can be arranged with a group of (a) ten players; (b) six players? For the purposes of the problem, assume that not all matches are to be played simultaneously.

11. A plane is determined by three noncollinear points in space. How many distinct planes can be determined by five points, no three of which are collinear and no four of which are coplanar?

12. If there are two possible catchers but only one pitcher in a group of nine ball players, how many baseball teams can be formed, assuming that all positions other than catcher and pitcher can be filled by any player?

13. In how many different ways can ten books be arranged on a shelf if the books of a certain three-volume set are to be kept together in the proper order?

> For Problems 14–15 the following information is relevant. A deck of playing cards has four suits, each suit containing an ace, nine cards numbered from 2 to 10, and three "face" cards (king, queen, jack). Two cards with the same number or picture are said to have the same "rank."

14. A poker hand consists of five cards; a "pair" is a set of two cards with the same rank; a "full house" is a hand consisting of three cards of equal rank and a "pair" of some other rank.
(a) How many different poker hands are possible from a deck of playing cards?
(b) How many different poker hands are possible with at least one pair in each?
(c) In how many different ways is it possible for a poker player to get a hand consisting of a full house?

15. A bridge "deal" is four hands of 13 cards from one deck of playing cards, the order of the hands relative to the dealer being of importance.
(a) How many different bridge deals are possible from a deck of playing cards?
(b) How many different bridge deals are possible from a deck of playing cards, if the dealer gets all the aces, kings, and queens?

16. A man has one penny, one nickel, one dime, one quarter, and one half-dollar in his pocket. If he reaches into his pocket and pulls out three coins, how many different sums are possible?

17. Three civic clubs have memberships of 40, 50, and 60 people. In how many different ways can a steering committee for a certain drive be constituted if three members are to be selected from each club?

18. In Problem 17, if the 60-member club consists of 30 couples, and man-wife combinations are not to be permitted on the committee, in how many ways can the committee be formed?

19. A baseball squad of 15 men is to make a trip in two conveyances—a station wagon and a car. If the station wagon will take ten and the car will take five players, in how many different ways can the squad make the trip?

20. In how many ways can the wife of a college President entertain (a) 3, (b) 4, (c) 3 or more, of a select group of 10 faculty wives at tea?

21. Solve the following equation for n: $\binom{n+2}{4} = 6\binom{n}{2}$.

22. Solve the following equation for n: $\binom{n}{n-2} = 6$.

23. Solve the following equation for n: $\binom{n}{3} = 2\binom{n-1}{2}$.

24. Solve the following equation for n: $\binom{n+3}{n+1} = 2\binom{n+2}{n}$.

25. For positive integers $n, r \ (\leq n)$, prove that $\binom{n}{n-r} = \binom{n}{r}$.

26. For positive integers $n, r \ (\leq n)$, prove that $\binom{n}{r} + \binom{n}{r-1} = \binom{n+1}{r}$.

27. For positive integers $n \ (> 1), r \ (\leq n)$, prove that $r\binom{n}{r} = n\binom{n-1}{r-1}$.

28. Prove that $C(n, 1) + C(n, 2) + \cdots + C(n, n) = 2^n - 1$, for any positive integer n.

29. Prove that the number of terminal zeros in $n!$ is $[n/5]$, and check your answer with $n = 10$ and $n = 20$.

30. Decide—with a proof—whether $(mn)!$ or $m!n!$ is the larger, for arbitrary positive integers m and n greater than 1.

10.3 More on Permutations and Combinations

Our primary purpose in discussing permutations and combinations in this chapter is to provide a foundation for a proof of the simplest case of the Binomial Theorem. The preceding two sections are adequate for this purpose, but we are inserting one more section on permutations and combinations to round off this study more satisfactorily. We shall now relax the assumption that our permutations are always linear and that the elements are always distinguishable.

If the elements of a set are considered arranged in a circular array, we have called the arrangement a *circular* permutation. (It is of no consequence, of course, whether the geometric form of the array is actually a circle, but the ordered set must be closed with no "first" or "last" member.) For such a permutation, a displacement of each element the same number of positions in either direction (i.e., all clockwise or all counterclockwise), will produce a permutation that is indistinguishable from the original. These indistinguishable permutations are said to be *cyclic* permutations of the given array. For example, the beads on a string or the keys on a ring may be displaced in this way without effecting any essential change in the arrangement.

If there are n distinguishable objects in a circular array, there are n possible cyclic permutations that are not to be distinguished from the original. (It should be noticed that any cyclic permutation in a counterclockwise direction is equivalent to a certain cyclic permutation in a clockwise direction, and so both types do not have to be considered.) Inasmuch as the *linear* permutations of the same n objects are all distinguishable, the number of linear permutations of these objects is n times as great as the number of circular permutations. There are $P(n)$ or $n!$ permutations of n objects in a linear array, and so there must be $n!/n$ or $(n - 1)!$ permutations of n objects in a circular array. A similar argument will show that the number of permutations of n distinguishable objects, taken r at a time, in a circular array, is $P(n, r)/r$ or

$$\frac{n!}{(n - r)!r}$$

We repeat these two results for the sake of emphasis.

(1) *The number of distinct circular permutations of n objects is* $(n - 1)!$
(2) *The number of distinct circular permutations of n objects, taken r at a time, is*

$$\frac{n!}{(n - r)!r}$$

Example 1. In how many ways can eight people be seated at a round table?

SOLUTION. The solution to this problem is a direct application of the above result for circular permutations. Hence, the desired number is $7!$ or 5040.

Let us now return to linear permutations, but we shall no longer insist that the objects be all distinguishable. If we permute n objects, s of which are indistinguishable, the permutations that arise from these s objects will not be distinguishable. Because there are $s!$ possible arrangements of this kind, there will be $s!$ times as many permutations of n distinguishable objects as there are if s of the objects are indistinguishable. It follows that the number of permutations of n objects, s of which are indistinguishable, is $n!/s!$. If there are an additional t objects distinct from the first s objects but that are not to be distinguished from each other, a similar argument will give the number of distinguishable permutations as $n!/(s!t!)$, and it is easy to extend the argument. In general, the following result holds:

If, in a set of n objects, there are subsets of s, t, . . . , v objects that are indistinguishable (but distinguishable between subsets), the number of distinguishable permutations of the n objects is

$$\frac{n!}{s!t! \cdots v!}$$

There is no *general* formula for the number of permutations of n objects, taken r at a time ($r < n$) if some of the objects are indistinguishable.

Example 2.   How many distinguishable permutations can be made of the letters of the word MISSISSIPPI?

SOLUTION.   The word contains 11 letters, four of which are I, four are S, and two are P. Hence, the number of distinguishable permutations is $11!/(4!4!2!)$ or 34,650.

Many problems that arise in permutations and combinations cannot be solved by the direct application of any formula. Such problems must be broken down into basic subproblems in some way consistent with common sense. The following problem illustrates the method for one such problem.

Example 3.   From a group of four Americans, three Canadians, and two Mexicans, a committee is to be formed. Find the number of different committees possible if (a) any number of people may comprise a committee; (b) each of the three nationalities must be represented on a committee.

SOLUTION

(a) For this case, there are two possibilities that confront each person: Either he is selected or he is not selected. Because there are nine persons involved, the number of possible outcomes of this selection process is 2^9, or 512. This includes the possibility that none are selected, however, and so there are 511 committees of one or more persons.

(b) In this case, there may be selected one, two, three, or four Americans, one, two, or three Canadians, and one or two Mexicans. The Americans can be selected in $\binom{4}{1} + \binom{4}{2} + \binom{4}{3} + \binom{4}{4} = 4 + 6 + 4 + 1 = 15$ ways; the Canadians can be selected in $\binom{3}{1} + \binom{3}{2} + \binom{3}{3} = 3 + 3 + 1 = 7$ ways; and the Mexicans can be selected in $\binom{2}{1} + \binom{2}{2} = 2 + 1 = 3$ ways. Hence, by the Fundamental Counting Principle, the number of possible committees under the given circumstances is $15 \cdot 7 \cdot 3 = 315$.

A problem of the type illustrated in Example 3 can sometimes be more easily solved with the help of a tree diagram, provided the numbers involved are not large. In particular, in this example, if the numbers of Americans, Canadians, and Mexicans are two each but only one Mexican can be on the committee, the solution to this variant of part (b) of the example is illustrated in Figure 93. It can be seen from the figure—or otherwise—that the answer to the modified problem is 18. In the figure, we have used A_1, A_2 to denote the two Americans, with C_1, C_2 and M_1, M_2 denoting the available Canadians and Mexicans, respectively. In the construction of the tree in Figure 93, we have assumed that the American, Canadian, and Mexican members of the committee were selected *in this* order, but the answer to the problem is clearly independent of the order of selection. In one of the problems below, it is suggested that the reader construct a tree for this same problem but with the members of the committee considered chosen in a different order of nationalities.

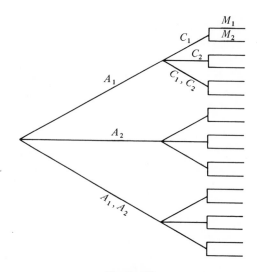

Figure 93

Problems 10.3

1. Compute and give a possible "counting" interpretation for each of the following: (a) $7!/(3!3!)$; (b) $10!/(7!2!)$; (c) $12!/(8!4!)$.
2. Compute and give a possible "counting" interpretation for each of the following: (a) $8!/(4!2!2!)$; (b) $10!/(6!2!2!)$; (c) $15!/(10!3!2!)$.
3. In how many ways can six keys be arranged on a key ring?
4. In how many ways can six keys be selected from a collection of ten keys and arranged on a key ring?
5. A party of six men and six women are to be seated in equal numbers at two (indistinguishable) round tables. In how many ways can this be done if (a) the men and women are to be at different tables; (b) no two men or women are to sit together; (c) any arrangement of men and women is permissible?
6. How many distinguishable permutations are possible with all letters of the word (a) SYZYGY; (b) ALABAMA; (c) ARRANGEMENT; (d) LLAMA?
7. A selection of fruit is to be made from three apples, four oranges, and two grapefruit. If we assume that all pieces are distinguishable, how many selections are possible with (a) at least one piece taken; (b) at least one piece of each kind of fruit taken? Illustrate the result in (b) with a tree diagram.

8. Draw a tree diagram to portray a situation similar to that shown by Figure 93, but in which the Canadian member of the committee is considered to be chosen first, followed by the American and then the Mexican.

9. In how many ways can a committee of at least two and not more than four people be chosen from a group of eight people?

10. If $P(n, r) = 24$ and $\binom{n}{r} = 4$, determine n and r.

11. In how many ways can a man make up a party of one or more of his six local friends?

12. How many different numbers can be formed by using all of the six following digits, those that are indistinguishable being considered distinct: 1, 1, 2, 2, 3, 3?

13. In how many ways can five prizes be given away to eight boys, if each boy is eligible for all of the prizes?

14. A jeweler wishes to make a bracelet by linking together six different sections of linkages. In how many ways can he do this if he has ten different kinds of linkages available?

15. Determine the number of ways in which it is possible to (a) select and (b) select and then arrange four letters (assumed to be distinct but not necessarily distinguishable) from the word PARALLEL?

16. Use the directions of Problem 15 for the letters of the word KENNEDY.

17. A squad of baseball players consists of seven outfielders, six infielders, three pitchers, and five catchers. How many baseball teams of nine men can be chosen? (A team has one pitcher, one catcher, four infielders, and three outfielders.)

18. In how many ways can three men and three women be seated at a round table if (a) there are no restrictions on seating; (b) men and women are to be seated on alternate chairs?

19. The families of Smith, Jones, and Robinson are to be seated on a bench. If there are five members to each family, how many arrangements of family names are possible after they have been seated?

20. In how many ways can a committee of five be chosen from a group of ten people if two particular people agree to serve only if both are chosen?

21. An urn contains two red, two blue, two green, and one white ball. Determine how many distinct color combinations of two balls can be drawn from the urn— including the possibilities of two balls of the same color.

22. Construct a tree diagram for Problem 21, and use it to check the result obtained.

23. The Senate of a certain country consists of 27 men from the party in power and 20 men from the opposition party. Determine an expression for the number of five-man senate committees that may be formed without regard to party.

24. If the committees in Problem 23 are to consist of at least three men from the party in power, how many five-man committees are possible to form?

25. Illustrate and further verify the result in Problem 24 with a tree diagram.

26. In how many ways is it possible to distribute two nickels, four dimes, three quarters, and four silver dollars among 13 people, if it is understood that each person is to receive a coin?

27. In how many ways can the coins in Problem 26 be distributed if only six of the people are eligible to receive a silver dollar?

28. Use a tree diagram to show the number of ways in which four quarters and three silver dollars can be distributed among three people, with each person receiving at least one coin.

29. Construct a tree diagram to portray the result in Problem 28 if we impose the condition that no one person may receive more than one silver dollar.

30. If $r_1, r_2, \ldots, r_p$ are positive integers such that $r_1 + r_2 + \cdots + r_p = n$, show that
$$\binom{r_1 + \cdots + r_p}{r_1}\binom{r_2 + \cdots + r_p}{r_2}\cdots\binom{r_{p-1} + r_p}{r_{p-1}} = \frac{n!}{r_1!r_2!\cdots r_p!}.$$

10.4 The Binomial Theorem for Positive Integral Exponents

If a and b are arbitrary numbers, it is well known that $(a + b)^2 = a^2 + 2ab + b^2$, $(a + b)^3 = a^3 + 3a^2b + 3ab^2 + b^3$, and $(a + b)^4 = a^4 + 4a^3b + 6a^2b^2 + 4ab^3 + b^4$. The corresponding formal sum of products of powers of a and b equal to $(a + b)^n$, for any real number n ($\neq 0$), is known as its *binomial expansion*. The theorem which establishes its validity is known as the *Binomial Theorem*.

The various terms in the expansion of $(a + b)^2 = (a + b)(a + b)$ arise from the multiplication of each term of the first factor by each term of the second factor. The expansion then consists of the four terms a^2, ab, ba, and b^2, and on combining ab with ba, we obtain the familiar result $a^2 + 2ab + b^2$. In a similar way, if we consider $(a + b)^3 = (a + b)(a + b)(a + b)$, there are eight terms that arise from the multiplication of one and only one term from each factor. These eight products are a^3, a^2b, ab^2, bab, b^2a, aba, ba^2, and b^3, and on combining equal terms, we obtain $a^3 + 3a^2b + 3ab^2 + b^3$.

More generally, the terms of the expansion of $(a + b)^n$, where n is any *positive integer*, arise from the multiplication together of exactly one term from each of the n factors of $(a + b)^n$. There is a choice of either a or b as a multiplier from each factor, and if we select b from r ($\leq n$) of the factors and a from the remaining $n - r$ factors, each such product will be $a^{n-r}b^r$. But the r choices of b (and automatically the associated $n - r$ choices of a) can be made in $C(n, r)$ or $\binom{n}{r}$ ways, and so there are $\binom{n}{r}$ products equal to $a^{n-r}b^r$. If we allow r to assume all integral values from 0 to n, inclusive, this analysis allows us to write the complete expansion of $(a + b)^n$.

■ **THEOREM 4.1** (*The Binomial Theorem*). If n (> 0) $\in \mathbf{Z}$ and a, b are arbitrary real numbers, then $(a + b)^n = a^n + \binom{n}{1}a^{n-1}b + \binom{n}{2}a^{n-2}b^2 + \cdots + \binom{n}{n-1}ab^{n-1} + b^n$.

The coefficients 1, $\binom{n}{1}$, $\binom{n}{2}$, $\ldots$, $\binom{n}{n-1}$, 1 on this expansion are known as the *binomial coefficients*. It is clear that, if we know these coefficients for any positive integer n, we can write down the corresponding binomial expansion.

It is possible to obtain the coefficients from what is known as "Pascal's Triangle," displayed in the configuration below. If the 1 at the vertex is excepted, the rows of the "Triangle" (each of which is formed from the preceding in an obvious way) are the binomial coefficients for successive positive integral exponents n, beginning with $n = 1$. Although it has some interest, Pascal's Triangle has little practical value, because all rows prior to a given row must be reproduced before this row can be obtained. The theoretical basis for the Triangle is contained in Problem 27.

$$
\begin{array}{ccccccccccc}
 & & & & & 1 & & & & & \\
 & & & & 1 & & 1 & & & & \\
 & & & 1 & & 2 & & 1 & & & \\
 & & 1 & & 3 & & 3 & & 1 & & \\
 & 1 & & 4 & & 6 & & 4 & & 1 & \\
1 & & 5 & & 10 & & 10 & & 5 & & 1
\end{array}
$$

. . . .

Example 1. Write out the complete binomial expansion for $(\frac{1}{2} + 2x)^5$.

SOLUTION. This expansion is the case of the general result with $a = \frac{1}{2}$, $b = 2x$, $n = 5$. Hence,

$$
\begin{aligned}
(\tfrac{1}{2} + 2x)^5 &= (\tfrac{1}{2})^5 + \binom{5}{1}(\tfrac{1}{2})^4(2x)^1 + \binom{5}{2}(\tfrac{1}{2})^3(2x)^2 + \binom{5}{3}(\tfrac{1}{2})^2(2x)^3 \\
&\quad + \binom{5}{4}(\tfrac{1}{2})^1(2x)^4 + (2x)^5 \\
&= \tfrac{1}{32} + 5(\tfrac{1}{16})(2x) + 10(\tfrac{1}{8})(4x^2) + 10(\tfrac{1}{4})(8x^3) + 5(\tfrac{1}{2})(16x^4) + 32x^5 \\
&= \frac{1}{32} + \frac{5x}{8} + 5x^2 + 20x^3 + 40x^4 + 32x^5
\end{aligned}
$$

If we examine the $(r + 1)$st term of the binomial expansion of $(a + b)^n$, we notice that this term involves the number r in a conspicuous way. For this term is $\binom{n}{r} a^{n-r}b^r$, that is,

$$
\frac{n!}{r!(n - r)!} a^{n-r}b^r
$$

or, more simply,

$$
\frac{n(n - 1)(n - 2) \cdots (n - r + 1)}{r!} a^{n-r}b^r
$$

and we make the following general observations concerning the $(r + 1)$st term:

1. The numerator of the coefficient formally contains the product of r consecutive descending integers, beginning with n.
2. The denominator of the coefficient formally contains the factor $r!$.
3. The exponent of b is r and the exponent of a is $n - r$.

With these three observations as a mnemonic device, it is easy to write any particular term of a binomial expansion without having to write the complete expanion or even the terms that precede it. This is often useful in problems in probability and statistics.

Example 2. Determine the fifth term of the binomial expansion of

$$\left(\frac{1}{\sqrt{2}} - \frac{x^2}{3}\right)^{10}$$

SOLUTION. The conspicuous number formally associated with the fifth term is 4. Hence, an application of the above mnemonic device gives us the fifth term as

$$\frac{10 \cdot 9 \cdot 8 \cdot 7}{4!}\left(\frac{1}{\sqrt{2}}\right)^{10-4}\left(\frac{-x^2}{3}\right)^4 = \frac{10 \cdot 9 \cdot 8 \cdot 7}{4 \cdot 3 \cdot 2 \cdot 1}\left(\frac{1}{2^3}\right)\left(\frac{x^8}{81}\right) = \left(\frac{35}{108}\right)x^8$$

Perhaps we should emphasize that, in this section, we have obtained the binomial expansion *only* for any positive integral exponent. While we do nothing further with this expansion insofar as proofs are concerned, we do direct our attention in the following section to the binomial expansion in which the exponents are more general real numbers. A alternative proof of the Binomial Theorem for positive integral exponents is suggested in Problem 22 as an application of the Principle of Mathematical Induction.

Problems 10.4

In Problems 1–8 write out the complete binomial expansion as indicated:

1. $(3x + 5)^3$
2. $(1 - 3x^2)^5$
3. $(\frac{1}{2} - 2x)^4$
4. $(x - \frac{3}{2})^5$
5. $(1 + 2x^2)^6$
6. $(\frac{2}{3} + 3x)^6$
7. $(1 - x)^8$
8. $(2 - xy)^5$

9. Find the sixth term of the binomial expansion of $(2x - 3y/2)^{12}$.
10. Find the seventh term of the binomial expansion of $(1 + 2x^3)^{10}$.
11. Find the two middle terms of the binomial expansion of $(\sqrt{2} + x^2/2)^9$.
12. Find the term involving x^6 in the binomial expansion of $(y - x^2/2)^8$.
13. Find the term that is independent of x in the binomial expansion of $(2x - 3/x)^{12}$.
14. Indicate the general binomial expansion of $(x + h)^n$, for a positive integer n.

15. Write out the complete binomial expansion for each of the following (with $i \in C$), and then express the result as a complex number in normal form:
    (a) $(1 - i)^5$ (b) $(1 + 2i)^4$
16. Write out the complete binomial expansion for each of the following:
    (a) $(1 - \sin x)^5$; (b) $(\sec x - 1)^3$.
17. Write out the complete binomial expansion for $(2x^3 - 1/2\sqrt{x})^9$.
18. Use a binomial expansion to obtain an expression for $\sin^{10} x + \cos^{10} x$ as a polynomial of degree 8 in $\sin x$.
19. Prove that $1 - \binom{n}{1} + \binom{n}{2} - \cdots + (-1)^n \binom{n}{n} = 0$. (Cf. Problem 28 of §10.2.)
20. Use DeMoivre's Theorem and the square of the binomial $\cos x + i \sin x$ to obtain the familiar identities for $\sin 2x$ and $\cos 2x$ in terms of $\sin x$ and $\cos x$. (*Note: $i \in C$*) Use the same method to obtain a formula of the same kind for $\sin 4x$.
21. Verify that the binomial expansion of $(a - b)^n$, for any positive integer n, can be expressed in the form $\sum_{r=0}^{n} (-1)^r \binom{n}{r} a^{n-r}b^r$.
22. Use the Principle of Mathematical Induction to obtain the binomial expansion of $(a + b)^n$, for any positive integer n. [*Hint:* Assume the expansion valid for $n = k$, and multiply both members of the equality by $a + b$. Then compute the $(r + 1)$st term of this product and show that it is $\dfrac{(k + 1)!}{r!(k + 1 - r)!} a^{k+1-r}b^r$, which may be seen to be the $(r + 1)$st term of the expansion of $(a + b)^{k+1}$. On observing that the expansion is valid for $n = 1$, the induction is complete.]
23. Use parentheses to write each of the expressed trinomials as binomials and give the complete expansion by the Binomial Theorem:
    (a) $(1 + x - y)^3$ (b) $(x - y + z)^2$ (c) $(\cos x + \sin x + 1)^2$
24. Use parentheses to write each of the expressed polynomials in the form of a binomial, and give the complete expansion by the Binomial Theorem (assuming that $i \in C$):
    (a) $(\cos x + \sin x + 1 + i)^2$ (b) $[(a - ib) + (c - id)]^3$
25. Prove that $\binom{n}{r + 1} = \dfrac{n - r}{r + 1} \binom{n}{r}$, for integers r, n such that $n > 0$, $0 \le r < n$. This is a *recursive* formula for obtaining one binomial coefficient (not the first) from the one that immediately precedes it.
26. Use the formula in Problem 25 and $\binom{20}{0} = 1$ to determine $\binom{20}{r}$ for $r = 1, 2, 3, 4$. Then write the first five terms of the expansion of $(x + y)^{20}$.
27. The identity given in Problem 26 of §10.2 is known as *Pascal's Rule*. Show why this rule checks the validity of the results that may be obtained from Pascal's Triangle.
28. If $a + b = 1$, show that $\sum_{r=0}^{n} \binom{n}{r} a^{n-r}b^r = 1$, for any positive integer n.
29. Solve the following equations for $x \in Z$:
    (a) $\sum_{r=0}^{5} \binom{5}{r} x^{5-r}2^r = 0$ (b) $\sum_{r=0}^{15} \binom{15}{r} x^r = 0$
30. Solve the following equation for $x \in Z$: $\sum_{r=0}^{7} (-1)^r \binom{7}{r} x^{7-r}5^r = 1$.

10.5 Extension of the Binomial Theorem

Although the principal use of the Binomial Theorem is directed toward binomials, we have already pointed out in Problems 23 and 24 of §10.4 how to extend it to include more general polynomials. The general theorem that establishes the validity of an expansion of an expression of the type $(a + b + c)^n$, for numbers a, b, c, is sometimes known as the Trinomial Theorem, and its extension to powers of polynomials with an arbitrary number of terms is called the Multinomial Theorem. We shall not develop these general expansions, however, but shall be content with the method of reducing such expansions to the binomial type.

The statement and proof that we gave for the Binomial Theorem in the preceding section is based on the theory of permutations and combinations, and we have tried to emphasize that the exponent n in the theorem must be a positive integer. The alternative proof by induction, as suggested in Problem 22 of that section, also assumes that n is a positive integer, and so no extension of the theorem results from this inductive proof. It is clear, of course, that if anything resembling the expansion in Theorem 4.1 is to be valid for an n that is not a positive integer, we must discard the notation and ideas of subsets and replace the symbols $\binom{n}{r}$ by the quotients $n(n-1)\cdots(n-r+1)/r!$ to which they are equivalent when n *is* a positive integer. If we do this, it can be shown by methods of more advanced mathematics that *under certain circumstances* a type of Binomial Expansion is valid, but the number of terms in the expansion is necessarily infinite—except for the trivial case when $n = 0$. In this trivial case, of course, we know that $(a + b)^0 = 1$ for any numbers a, b, not both equal to zero. (If so desired, this case may be associated with the 1 at the vertex of Pascal's triangle, inasmuch as this number was left without any interpretation in §10.4). However, if $n\ (\neq 0)$ is not a positive integer, the more advanced methods show that the validity of the (infinite) expansion of $(a + b)^n$ depends on what is known as the "convergence" of the expansion—a matter to be discussed briefly in §10.8. For our present purposes, the following result— for which we omit the proof—will be sufficient.

■ **THEOREM 5.1.** *If n is an arbitrary real number and x is a real number such that $|x| < 1$, then*

$$(1 + x)^n = 1 + a_1 x + a_2 x^2 + \cdots + a_r x^r + \cdots$$

is valid where

$$a_r = \frac{n(n-1)(n-2)\cdots(n-r+1)}{r!} \qquad r = 1, 2, \ldots$$

If n is a positive integer, it is clear that the expansion outlined in this theorem terminates with the $(n + 1)$st term, and the result is in agreement with that of the Binomial Theorem in §10.4. Moreover, the case $n = 0$ is also correctly included in the above expansion. If n is neither 0 nor a positive integer, however, it is clear that this expansion does not terminate and so we are faced with the problem of summing an infinite number of terms! By the remark in the theorem that the expansion as given is "valid," we mean that it is possible to approximate $(1 + x)^n$ *to any desired degree of accuracy* by taking a sufficiently large (but finite) number of terms. The various problems connected with the number of terms necessary for a given accuracy of an expansion, or the error introduced by the truncation of an infinite number of terms to a finite number in any given case, are left for more advanced books on the general subject of infinite series.

The form of the binomial in Theorem 5.1 appears to be rather restricted, but it is possible to adapt a power of a general binomial to this form. In particular, because $(a + b)^n = [a(1 + b/a)]^n = a^n(1 + b/a)^n$ if $a \neq 0$, it is possible to use the above theorem for this general situation, provided $|b/a| < 1$.

Before giving illustrations of our extended binomial expansion, it may be useful to rewrite the expansion in Theorem 5.1 in its more familiar form and to include one important special case of it:

$$(1 + x)^n = 1 + nx + \frac{n(n - 1)x^2}{2!} + \frac{n(n - 1)(n - 2)x^3}{3!} + \cdots$$

$$(1 + x)^{-1} = 1 - x + x^2 - x^3 + x^4 - \cdots$$

(The second of these two expansions can also be obtained by using long division to divide 1 by $1 + x$.) It must be emphasized, of course, that both expansions require that $|x| < 1$ if any meaning is to be attached to them—except when n is a nonnegative integer in the case of $(1 + x)^n$.

Example 1. Find the first four terms of the binomial expansion of

$$(1 + 2x)^{1/2}$$

SOLUTION. This the case of $(a + b)^n$ where $a = 1$, $b = 2x$, $n = \frac{1}{2}$. Hence,

$$(1 + 2x)^{1/2} = 1^{1/2} + \tfrac{1}{2}(1)^{-1/2}(2x) + \frac{\tfrac{1}{2}(-\tfrac{1}{2})}{2!}(1)^{-3/2}(2x)^2$$

$$+ \frac{\tfrac{1}{2}(-\tfrac{1}{2})(-\tfrac{3}{2})}{3!}(1)^{-5/2}(2x)^3 + \cdots = 1 + x - \frac{x^2}{2} + \frac{x^3}{2} - \cdots$$

As more terms are included, this will approximate $(1 + 2x)^{1/2}$, provided $|2x| < 1$, that is, $|x| < \frac{1}{2}$.

Example 2. Use a binomial expansion to find a three-decimal approximation for $\sqrt[3]{65.1}$.

SOLUTION

$$\sqrt[3]{65.1} = (65.1)^{1/3} = (64 + 1.1)^{1/3} = \left[64\left(1 + \frac{1.1}{64}\right)\right]^{1/3}$$

$$= 4\left(1 + \frac{1.1}{64}\right)^{1/3} = 4\left[1 + \left(\frac{1}{3}\right)\left(\frac{1.1}{64}\right) + \frac{(\frac{1}{3})(-\frac{2}{3})}{2!}\left(\frac{1.1}{64}\right)^2 + \cdots\right]$$

$$= 4(1 + 0.0057 - 0.00003 + \cdots) \approx 4(1.00567) \approx 4.023$$

It may be well to point out, in connection with binomial approximations such as that in Example 2, that the number of terms required for a given degree of accuracy depends upon the magnitude of $|x|$ in $(1 + x)^n$, as well as upon n.

Problems 10.5

In Problems 1–8 write out the first four terms of the indicated binomial expansions, and state in each case the condition necessary if the truncated expansion is to approximate the given expression.

1. $(1 + 3x)^{1/2}$ **2.** $(1 - 3/x)^{2/3}$

3. $(2 + 5x^2)^{1/3}$ **4.** $(5 - 3/x)^{-2}$

5. $(1 - 2x)^{-1}$ **6.** $(4 + 2x^3)^{-1/2}$

7. $(4 + 5a)^{1/3}$ **8.** $(2 + 3/x)^{-2/3}$

9. Apply the expansion given in Theorem 5.1 to the case where $x = 3$ and $n = \frac{1}{2}$, and observe that the sum of the terms does not approach the number $(1 + 3)^{1/2} = 2$. What is wrong?

10. Apply the expansion given in Theorem 5.1 to the case where $x = 1$ and $n = -1$, and observe that the sum of the terms does not approach $(1 + 1)^{-1} = \frac{1}{2}$. What is wrong?

11. Use a "binomial" expansion to expand $(1 + a - b)^3$.

12. Use a "binomial" expansion to expand $(2x - 2 + x^2)^4$.

In Problems 13–18, use a binomial expansion to find a (rounded) three-decimal approximation of each of the indicated quantities.

13. $(1.01)^{-2}$ **14.** $(8.63)^{1/3}$ **15.** $1/\sqrt{2.2}$

16. $1/(1.05)^3$ **17.** $\sqrt[3]{120}$ **18.** $\sqrt[4]{17}$

19. Establish the validity of the following approximation formulas, where $|x| < 1$: (a) $\sqrt{1 + x} \approx 1 + x/2$; (b) $(1 + x)^{-2/3} \approx 1 - 2x/3$; (c) $(1 - x)^{-1} \approx 1 + x$.

20. Determine the approximate percentage increase in (a) the surface area and (b) the volume of a sphere, if its radius is increased from 100 to 101 inches.

21. The period of a simple pendulum of length L inches is T seconds where $T \approx 0.3198\sqrt{L}$, and it may be calculated that the pendulum beats seconds ($T = 2$) if $L \approx 39.10$. If the length of the pendulum is increased by 0.16 inch, determine the approximate increase in period. (*Hint:* Apply the binomial expansion to $\sqrt{L + h}$, where $h = 0.16$.)

22. Determine the approximate change in period if the pendulum in Problem 21 is decreased in length to 38.5 inches.

23. Assume the earth is a sphere of radius 3960 miles, and find an approximation formula for the maximum range of unobstructed vision from a point h feet above the surface of the earth.

24. Use the formula that was found in Problem 23 to determine the maximum range of unobstructed vision from a point 50 yards above the surface of the earth.

25. If n and r ($\leq n$) are positive integers, prove that $\binom{n}{r}\left(\frac{1}{n}\right)^r \leq \frac{1}{r!}$, and then deduce that $(1 + 1/n)^n \leq \sum_{r=0}^{n} \frac{1}{r!}$. It can be shown by more advanced techniques that the two members of this inequality approach equality as n gets larger and that both approach the number e (the base for natural logarithms).

10.6 Sequences

If the elements of a set are arranged in a definite order, this ordered set may be called a *sequence*. If the set is finite (but not too large), it is customary simply to list the elements of the sequence in their proper order and possibly enclose them in parentheses rather than braces—our custom for (unordered) sets. If the set is infinite, a descriptive subset of the first few elements may be listed followed by an ellipsis (a triplet $\cdots$ of dots) to indicate the unending nature of the sequence. Thus, for example, $a_1, a_2, a_3, \ldots$ or $(a_1, a_2, a_3, \ldots)$ is a sequence whose first element or *term* is a_1, whose second term is a_2, whose third term is a_3, etc. It is also convenient sometimes to denote such a sequence by (a_n), $n = 1, 2, 3, \ldots$, or even to abbreviate the notation to (a_n), with a_n being understood as the "general" or nth term. We shall usually prefer to use this latter simplified symbolism for sequences. In earlier chapters we have referred to a *finite* sequence $(a_1, a_2, \ldots, a_n)$ as an *n-tuple*, and if $n = 2$, as an *ordered pair*, and so n-tuples and ordered pairs may be regarded as special kinds of sequences. The sequences to be discussed in this section will usually be infinite, the terms of each being in a one-to-one correspondence with the natural numbers.

We saw in Chapter 4 that a function is basically a mapping of the members of one set—the *domain*—onto the members of another set—the *range* of the function. It is then natural to regard a sequence as a function on the set **N** of natural numbers. For the sequence $(a_1, a_2, \ldots, a_n, \ldots)$ is essentially a mapping $n \rightarrow a_n$ of the natural numbers **N**, where each number n is mapped onto the nth term a_n of the sequence. The domain of the sequence (regarded as a function) is **N**, and its range is the set of terms. However, even though we may consider a sequence as a special kind of function, it is usually preferred not to use the notation f of functions, but rather to write a_n instead of $f(n)$ for the nth term of the sequence (a_n).

One common method of defining a sequence (a_n) is to write a formula for a_n in terms of n.

Example 1.   Write the first three terms of the sequence (a_n) where

$$a_n = 3n^2 - 2n + 1$$

SOLUTION.   A replacement of n by 1, 2, 3, respectively, in the formula for a_n, gives the following:

$$a_1 = 3 \cdot 1^2 - 2 \cdot 1 + 1 = \ 3 - 2 + 1 = \ 2$$
$$a_2 = 3 \cdot 2^2 - 2 \cdot 2 + 1 = 12 - 4 + 1 = \ 9$$
$$a_3 = 3 \cdot 3^2 - 2 \cdot 3 + 1 = 27 - 6 + 1 = 22$$

Another method of describing a sequence is by means of a *recursion* formula, which allows us to determine any term from the preceding term. If such a formula is to be adequate, it is necessary, of course, to be given the first—or some other—term.

Example 2.   Let (a_n) be a sequence for which $a_1 = 1$, and $a_n = 2a_{n-1} + 3$, $n = 2, 3, 4, \ldots$. Find the first three terms of the sequence.

SOLUTION.   Because $a_1 = 1$, $a_2 = 2a_1 + 3 = 2 \cdot 1 + 3 = 5$, $a_3 = 2a_2 + 3 = 2 \cdot 5 + 3 = 13$. The desired terms are than 1, 5, 13.

It is sometimes possible to manipulate a recursion formula and either derive or guess from it an expression for the nth term in terms of n. For example, it is easy to verify by mathematical induction that $a_n = 2^{n+1} - 3$, for the sequence in Example 2. If we let P_n represent the statement of this formula, it is immediate that $a_1 = 2^2 - 3 = 1$, and so P_1 is true. Now let us assume that P_k is true, for an arbitrary positive integer k. Then $a_{k+1} = 2a_k + 3 = 2(2^{k+1} - 3) + 3 = 2^{k+2} - 6 + 3 = 2^{k+2} - 3$, and we have shown that P_{k+1} is true. Hence, P_n is true for every positive integer n.

Although most sequences are defined by either an explicit formula for a_n or by means of a recursion formula, there are other ways to formulate such a definition. For example, we can define the sequence (a_n) to be the sequence whose terms in order are the digits in the decimal representation of $e = 2.71828 \cdots$. Thus, $a_1 = 2$, $a_2 = 7$, $a_3 = 1$, $a_4 = 8$, etc., and although it is possible to obtain any desired term, there is no formula available for the nth term.

On many occasions we wish to know the sum of certain or all terms of a sequence. However, it should be recognized that what we mean by the *sum* of a sequence (with an infinite number of terms) must be clarified before it is possible to perform the addition. For example, if we attempt to determine the "sum" of the terms of the sequence $(1, -1, 1, -1, \ldots)$, by adding *pairs* of terms in the order of occurrence, the result is consistently 0, and we might conclude that the sum of the sequence is then 0. However, if we try to obtain the sum by adding the terms individually in their natural order, the successive partial sums that we encounter are 1, 0, 1, 0, 1, 0, . . . , and so we obtain no definite answer. Different methods of summation are used for different purposes, but the most common method is the one that we now describe.

Definition. *The sum S_n of n terms of the sequence (a_n) is defined so that*

$$S_1 = a_1$$
$$S_n = S_{n-1} + a_n, \, n > 1$$

This method of summation requires that we start with the first term, add the second to it, and successively add each term to the sum of the preceding terms as already computed. Hence, $S_1 = a_1$, $S_2 = a_1 + a_2$, $S_3 = (a_1 + a_2) + a_3$, $S_4 = [(a_1 + a_2) + a_3] + a_4$, etc. It can be shown that this recursion formula does define S_n, the sum of n terms of the sequence, for any positive integer n. (See Problem 16.) The sequence (S_n), associated in this way with (a_n), is called the *sequence of partial sums* of (a_n). When we write $S_n = a_1 + a_2 + \cdots + a_n$, it will be understood that the addition is to be performed in the manner described above, but the sum of a *finite* number of terms is, of course, independent of the manner of summation. The manner of summation is of importance only when we are trying to obtain a "sum" for the terms of an infinite sequence. We touch on this topic very briefly in §10.8, for a very special type of sequence.

Problems 10.6

1. Find the first five terms of the sequence (a_n) where (a) $a_n = 2n + 1$; (b) $a_n = 3 - (-1)^n$; (c) $a_n = 2(\frac{1}{2})^n$; (d) $a_n = (-1)^{n^2}$.

2. Find the first five terms of the sequence (a_n) where (a) $a_n = n^2 + 1/n$; (b) $a_n = 5(\frac{1}{2})^n$; (c) $a_n = (-1)^{n(n+1)/2}$; (d) $a_n = \sin \frac{1}{4}\pi$.

3. Find the first five terms of the sequence (a_n) where (a) $a_n = (1/n) \ln e^{2n}$; (b) $a_n = (1/n) \log 10^{3n}$; (c) $a_n = (1 \cdot 2 \cdot 4 \cdots 2n)/(2n)!$.

4. Use the sigma (Σ) notation to express each of the following sums: (a) $1 + 2 + 4 + \cdots + 128$; (b) $1 + \frac{1}{2} + \frac{1}{4} + \cdots + \frac{1}{128}$; (c) $1 - 2 + 4 - \cdots - 128$; (d) $1 - \frac{1}{2} + \frac{1}{4} - \cdots - \frac{1}{128}$.

5. Find a formula for a_n such that the first few terms of the sequnce (a_n) are (a) $1, -1, 1, -1, 1, \ldots$; (b) $1, 0, 1, 0, 1, \ldots$; (c) $1, 0, -1, 0, 1, 0, -1, 0, \ldots$; (d) $3, 3^{1/2}, 3^{1/4}, 3^{1/8}, \ldots$. Are these formulas necessarily unique?

6. Find the first five terms of the sequence (a_n) where (a) $a_1 = 2$ and $a_n = 3a_{n-1} + 1$ for $n > 1$; (b) $a_1 = -1$ and $a_n = -a_{n-1}$ for $n > 1$.

7. Find the first five terms of the sequence (a_n) where (a) $a_1 = 3$ and $a_n = (n/2)a_{n-1}$ for $n > 1$; (b) $a_1 = 0$ and $a_n = a_{n-1}^2 + 2$ for $n > 1$.

8. Find the first five terms of the sequence (a_n) where (a) $a_1 = 1$ and $a_n = 3a_{n-1} + 2$ for $n > 1$; (b) $a_1 = 1$, $a_2 = 3$, and $a_n = (a_{n-1} + a_{n-2})/2$ for $n > 2$.

9. Find the first five terms of the sequence (a_n) where (a) $a_1 = 1$, $a_2 = 2$, and $a_n = a_{n-2}a_{n-1}$ for $n > 2$; (b) $a_1 = 1$ and $a_n = n \sin \pi(a_{n-1} + \frac{1}{2})$ for $n > 1$.

10. Find the next two terms of the sequence (a_n) if (a) $a_1 = -1$, $a_2 = 1$, and $a_n = 2a_{n-1} - 3a_{n-2}$ for $n > 2$; (b) $a_1 = 2$, $a_2 = 5$, and $a_n = 3a_{n-1} + 2a_{n-2}$ for $n > 2$.

11. A *Fibonacci sequence* may be defined as one in which the first two terms are 1 and each successive term is obtained by adding the two that immediately precede it. Find the first ten terms of this sequence.

12. Find the first four terms of the sequence (S_n) of partial sums of the sequence (a_n) where (a) $a_n = (-1)^n$ for $n \geq 1$; (b) $a_n = 3 - (-1)^{n+1}$ for $n \geq 1$.

13. Find the first four terms of the sequence (S_n) of partial sums of the sequence (a_n) where (a) $a_1 = 1$ and $a_n = 2a_{n-1}/(n-1)$ for $n > 1$; (b) $a_1 = -2$ and $a_n = 2^n - 3a_{n-1}$ for $n > 1$.

14. If a_n is the nth digit in the decimal expansion of $\frac{1}{4}\pi$, determine the first three terms of (a_n) and of its associated sequence of partial sums.

15. Apply the directions in Problem 14 to the case for which a_n is the nth digit in the decimal expansion of $\frac{3}{7}$.

16. Let (S_n) denote the sequence of partial sums of (a_n). Then, if S_1 is given and $S_k = S_{k-1} + a_k$ for $k > 1$, use mathematical induction to prove that S_n is defined for every positive integer n. (There is a theoretical difficulty of a subtle nature in such recursive definitions. For a brief discussion of it, see Moore [*Elements of Abstract Algebra*, 2nd ed., pp. 20–21, Macmillan, New York (1967)].)

17. Let a sequence (S_n) of partial sums of (a_n) be defined so that $S_1 = a_1 + a_2$, $S_2 = (a_1 + a_2) + (a_3 + a_4)$, $S_3 = [(a_1 + a_2) + (a_3 + a_4)] + (a_5 + a_6)$, etc.; that is, the terms are paired off in order, and each *pair* is added in succession to the sum of the preceding pairs. Determine the first five terms of (S_n) if $a_n = 2n - 1$ for $n \geq 1$.

18. Apply the directions in Problem 17 to the case for which $a_n = 2n^2 - 3n$ for $n \geq 1$.

19. If $a_1 = 2$ and $a_n = a_{n-1}^2$ for $n > 1$ in a sequence (a_n), use mathematical induction to prove that $a_n = 2^{2^{n-1}}$ for every positive integer n.

20. Determine the first five terms of the sequence of partial sums of (a_n), where

$$a_n = \frac{1}{n(n+1)} \text{ for } n \geq 1.$$ Make an "educated" guess for S_n, and try to prove it correct by mathematical induction.

21. If $a_2 = 6$ and $a_n = na_{n-1}$ for $n > 2$ in a sequence (a_n), use mathematical induction to prove that $a_n = 3n!$ for any integer $n \geq 2$. [In this case, it is appropriate to ignore a_1 and define the proposition P_n to be established as follows: $a_{n+1} = 3(n+1)!$ for every positive integer n.]

22. Use mathematical induction to prove that $\sum_{k=1}^{n} k = n(n+1)/2$ for every positive integer n.

23. Use mathematical induction to prove that $\sum_{k=1}^{n} k^2 = n(n+1)(2n+1)/6$ for every positive integer n.

24. Use mathematical induction to prove that $\sum_{k=1}^{n} 2^k = 2(2^n - 1)$ for every positive integer n.

25. Each of the sums in Problems 22–24 denotes the nth term of the sequence of partial sums of another sequence. Identify the nth term of this other sequence in each case, and check the relationship between the terms for $n = 5$.

26. If P_n is the proposition that $1 + 3 + 5 + \cdots + (2n - 1) = n^2 + 1$, show that P_{k+1} is true if P_k is true, whereas the proposition is actually false. Where does the induction "proof" fail?

10.7 Arithmetic Sequences

Among the many types of sequences there are two of common occurrence. These are the *arithmetic* and *geometric* sequences, also known as *progressions*. In this section we shall discuss arithmetic sequences.

An arithmetic sequence is distinguished by the fact that successive terms differ by the same amount—called the *common difference*. For example, $(1, 2, 3, 4, \ldots)$ is an arithmetic sequence with common difference 1, because $2 - 1 = 3 - 2 = 4 - 3 = \cdots = 1$. Another arithmetic sequence is $(1, 3, 5, \ldots)$, the common difference in this case being $3 - 1 = 5 - 3 = \cdots = 2$. More generally, if the common difference of an arithmetic sequence (a_n) is d, we must have $a_2 - a_1 = a_3 - a_2 = \cdots = d$, so that $a_2 = a_1 + d$, $a_3 = a_2 + d = a_1 + 2d$, $a_4 = a_3 + d = a_2 + 2d = a_1 + 3d$, etc. It is easy to see in general —and we suggest an induction proof of this in Problem 2—that $a_n = a_1 + (n - 1)d$, for any positive integer n. We restate this result as a defining characteristic of this type of sequence.

Definition. *A sequence (a_n) is called* arithmetic *if* $a_n = a_1 + (n - 1)d$

for every positive integer n and some fixed number d.

Example 1. Find the first five terms of the arithmetic sequence (a_n) where $a_1 = 8$ and $d = -3$.

SOLUTION. From the formula for a_n, we obtain $a_2 = a_1 + d = 8 + (-3) = 5$, $a_3 = a_2 + d = 5 + (-3) = 2$, $a_4 = a_3 + d = 2 + (-3) = -1$, $a_5 = a_4 + d = -1 + (-3) = -4$.

Example 2. Find the nineteenth term of the arithmetic sequence whose first three terms, in order, are 3, $4\frac{1}{2}$, 6.

SOLUTION. We see from the basic "difference" property of an arithmetic sequence that $d = 4\frac{1}{2} - 3 = 6 - 4\frac{1}{2} = \frac{3}{2}$. Because $a_1 = 3$, $a_n = a_1 + (n - 1)d = 3 + (n - 1)\frac{3}{2}$, and so $a_{19} = 3 + 18(\frac{3}{2}) = 30$.

Example 3. If the third and seventh terms of an arithmetic sequence are 1.4 and 2.2, respectively, determine the twentieth term.

SOLUTION. Because $a_n = a_1 + (n - 1)d$, we have $a_3 = a_1 + 2d = 1.4$ and $a_7 = a_1 + 6d = 2.2$. If we solve these two equations simultaneously, the result is $a_1 = 1$ and $d = 0.2$. Hence, $a_{20} = a_1 + 19d = 1 + 19(0.2) = 1 + 3.8 = 4.8$.

It is easy to find a formula for the sum of n terms of an arithmetic sequence (a_n) if we notice that $a_{n-1} = a_n - d$, $a_{n-2} = a_n - 2d$, etc., where d is the common difference. A derivation of this formula is suggested in Problem 1, but we shall establish its validity by mathematical induction.

■ **THEOREM 7.1.** *The sum S_n of n terms of the arithmetic sequence (a_n) is given by the following formula:*

$$S_n = a_1 + a_2 + \cdots + a_n = n\frac{a_1 + a_n}{2}$$

PROOF. Let P_n denote the formula to be established.

(1) If we let $n = 1$, the formula becomes $S_1 = 1(a_1 + a_1)/2 = a_1$, which is clearly the "sum" of the first n terms where $n = 1$. Hence, P_1 is true.

(2) Let us suppose that the formula is valid for $n = k$; that is, $S_k = k(a_1 + a_k)/2$, for an arbitrary fixed natural number k. Then $S_{k+1} = S_k + a_{k+1} = k(a_1 + a_k)/2 + a_{k+1} = k(a_1 + a_{k+1} - d)/2 + a_{k+1} = k(a_1 + a_{k+1})/2 - kd/2 + a_{k+1}$. But $a_{k+1} = a_1 + kd$, and so $kd/2 = (a_{k+1} - a_1)/2$. Hence, $S_{k+1} = k(a_1 + a_{k+1})/2 + (a_1 - a_{k+1})/2 + a_{k+1} = k(a_1 + a_{k+1})/2 + (a_1 + a_{k+1})/2 = (k + 1)(a_1 + a_{k+1})/2$. Hence P_{k+1} is true, and, by mathematical induction, P_n is true for any positive integer n.

■ **COROLLARY.** *If d is the common difference in the arithmetic sequence (a_n), we also have the alternate formula*

$$S_n = \frac{n}{2}[2a_1 + (n - 1)d]$$

PROOF. We know that $a_n = a_1 + (n - 1)d$. If we now replace a_n in the formula of the theorem by the expression equal to it, we obtain $S_n = n[a_1 + a_1 + (n - 1)d]/2 = \frac{n}{2}[2a_1 + (n - 1)d]$, as asserted.

Example 4. Find the sum of the first 50 odd positive integers.

SOLUTION. The odd positive integers comprise a sequence (a_n) for which $a_1 = 1$ and $d = 2$. Hence, for this sequence, $S_{50} = \frac{50}{2}[2(1) + (50 - 1)2] = 25(2 + 98) = 2500$.

The *arithmetic mean* $(x + y)/2$ of two numbers x and y is probably a familiar notion. If we observe that x, $(x + y)/2$, y are three successive terms of an arithmetic sequence, it is easy to extend the notion of *one* mean to include any number of arithmetic means. Thus, if one or more numbers are inserted between any two given numbers so that the augmented ordered set comprises the terms of an arithmetic sequence, the numbers inserted are called *arithmetic means* of the given numbers.

Example 5. Insert three arithmetic means between 4 and 16.

SOLUTION. The given numbers and the three means must comprise five ordered terms of an arithmetic sequence (a_n) for which $a_1 = 4$ and $a_5 = 16$. Then, $a_5 = a_1 + 4d = 4 + 4d = 16$, and so $4d = 12$, $d = 3$. Hence, $a_2 = 7$, $a_3 = 10$, $a_4 = 13$, and these numbers are the desired arithmetic means.

Problems 10.7

1. Using the suggestion given immediately above Theorem 7.1, write $S_n = a_1 + a_2 + \cdots + a_{n-1} + a_n$ as a sum in reverse order, and, by adding the two expressions, obtain the formula for S_n as given in the theorem.
2. Use mathematical induction to prove that $a_n = a_1 + (n-1)d$ for a sequence (a_n) whose successive terms increase by d.
3. Find the twelfth term and the sum of the first 12 terms of the arithmetic sequence whose first term is 2 and common difference is 3.
4. The second term of an arithmetic sequence is 5 and the seventh term is 20. Determine the first term and the sum of the first seven terms.
5. Find the twentieth term of the arithmetic sequence whose first three terms are $-2, -5, -8$, in this order.
6. If the first term of an arithmetic sequence is 19 and its common difference is -2, find the sixty-first term and the sum of the first 61 terms.
7. For an arithmetic sequence (a_n), determine (a) S_7 if $a_1 = 3$ and $d = -4$; (b) S_9 if $a_1 = -6$ and $d = 3$.
8. For an arithmetic sequence (a_n), determine (a) S_{10} if $a_7 = 13$ and $a_{12} = 28$; (b) S_{15} if $a_4 = 15$ and $d = 2$.
9. Use the method of Problem 1 to discover a formula for the sum of the first n odd positive integers.
10. Use the method of Problem 1 to discover a formula for the sum of the first n even positive integers.
11. Determine the indicated sums: (a) $\sum_{r=1}^{10} 5r$; (b) $\sum_{r=1}^{27} (2r + 1)$; (c) $\sum_{r=1}^{50} (r + 3)$; (d) $\sum_{r=1}^{60} (5 - r)$.
12. Insert three arithmetic means between 3 and -17.
13. Insert six arithmetic means between 2 and 23.
14. Find the first term of an arithmetic sequence whose fifteenth term is 59 and common difference is 4.
15. If \$300 is invested at 6 per cent simple interest, *use a formula from this section* to determine the amount of the investment after 10 years.
16. For how many years must \$100 be invested at 6 per cent simple interest if the final amount is to exceed \$500?
17. Find a_1 and a_8 for the arithmetic sequence (a_n) where $d = -2$ and $S_8 = 72$.
18. A function f is defined on the set of positive integers so that $f(n) = a_n$, for some arithmetic sequence (a_n). Find the first four terms of the sequence if (a) $f(n) = 2n + 3$; (b) $f(n) = 3n + 2$; (c) $f(n) = 1 - 3n$.
19. If the domain of each function in Problem 18 is extended to **R** but with no change in the rule of mapping, use graphs of the extended functions to interpret the earlier results.

20. How many feet of rung material are required for the construction of a ladder of 31 rungs, if the rungs taper from 29 inches in length at the bottom to 19 inches at the top?

21. If logs are stacked in a vertical pile so that there are 20 logs on the bottom row and 1 less on each successive row, how many rows are needed to stack 155 logs?

22. A slide of uniform slope is to be built on a level piece of land. If there are to be 15 equally spaced supports, the lengths of the longest and shortest being 47 and 5 feet, respectively, find the length of each intermediate support.

23. The force of gravity causes a body near the surface of the earth to fall (in a vacuum) so that its approximate velocity at the end of 1 second is 32.2 feet per second and its approximate increase in velocity for each successive second is also 32.2 feet per second. *Use a formula from this section* to approximate its theoretical velocity after 10 seconds of fall.

24. A new piece of machinery costs $30,000. If the machinery depreciates 5 per cent of its original cost each year, determine its value at the end of 10 years.

25. A man buys a car for $3000, making a down payment of $1000. If he agrees to pay the remainder in 20 equal monthly payments of $100 plus 6 per cent of the previously unpaid balance, determine the total amount of his interest payments.

10.8 Geometric Sequences

A sequence whose successive terms are 1, 2, 4, 8, . . . has the characteristic that each term (after the first) may be found from the preceding by multiplying the latter by 2. This is an example of a type of sequence that we now define.

Definition. *A sequence (a_n) is said to be* geometric *if $a_n = a_{n-1}r$ for every positive integer $n > 1$, some fixed real number $r \neq 0$, and a nonzero first term a_1.*

The number r is called the *common ratio* and gives the ratio of any term (not the first) to the preceding, r for a geometric sequence being loosely comparable to d of the arithmetic type. It is customary to express the successive terms of a geometric sequence, with first term a_1 and common ratio r, in the form a_1, $a_1r, a_1r^2, \ldots$. As was the case with an arithmetic sequence, we are interested in formulas for the nth term and for the sum of n terms of a geometric sequence.

It is clear from the preceding array of terms that the nth term of that general sequence has the following form:

$$a_n = a_1 r^{n-1}$$

A formal proof of this result can be given quite easily by mathematical induction, and this proof is suggested in Problem 2.

Example 1. Find the tenth term of the geometric sequence whose first term is 2 and common ratio is $\frac{3}{2}$.

SOLUTION

$$a_{10} = 2\left(\frac{3}{2}\right)^9 = \frac{3^9}{2^8} = \frac{19,683}{256}$$

If we let $S_n = a_1 + a_2 + \cdots + a_n$, in Problem 1 we suggest an elementary method (similar to that in Problem 1 of §10.7) for obtaining a formula for S_n, provided $r \neq 1$. If $r = 1$, it is clear that $S_n = na_1$, but the following theorem establishes the validity of the formula for the more important cases by mathematical induction.

■ **THEOREM 8.1.** *If S_n is the sum of n terms of the geometric sequence (a_n) whose common ratio is $r(\neq 1)$, then*

$$S_n = a_1(1 - r^n)/(1 - r)$$

PROOF.   We let P_n denote the assertion of the formula.

(1) If $n = 1$, the formula gives $S_1 = a_1(1 - r^1)/(1 - r) = a_1$, which is a true statement and so P_1 is true.

(2) Let us assume P_k is true, so that $S_k = a_1(1 - r^k)/(1 - r)$, for an arbitrary but fixed positive integer k. Then

$$S_{k+1} = S_k + a_{k+1} = \frac{a_1(1 - r^k)}{1 - r} + a_1 r^k = \frac{a_1(1 - r^k) + a_1 r^k(1 - r)}{1 - r}$$

$$\frac{a_1(1 - r^k + r^k - r^{k+1})}{1 - r} = \frac{a_1(1 - r^{k+1})}{1 - r}$$

Hence, P_{k+1} is true, and it follows by mathematical induction that P_n is true for every natural number n.

For convenience if $r > 1$, it should be observed that the formula can also be expressed in the form

$$S_n = \frac{a_1(r^n - 1)}{r - 1}$$

Example 2.   Find the sum of the first 12 terms of the geometric sequence whose first term is 2 and common ratio is $\frac{1}{2}$.

SOLUTION

$$S_{12} = \frac{2[1 - (\frac{1}{2})^{12}]}{1 - \frac{1}{2}} = 4\left(1 - \frac{1}{2^{12}}\right)$$

$$= 4 - \frac{1}{2^{10}} = 4 - \frac{1}{1024} = \frac{4095}{1024}$$

With geometric sequences it is sometimes possible to define what we call the *sum* of all terms of the sequence, even when the number of these terms is infinite. It is in connection with such infinite sums that the manner of summation becomes critical, and we use the summation convention adopted for S_n in §10.7. But first we must introduce the concept of a *limit*, a notion of basic importance in the calculus.

Intuitively, the *limit* of a sequence (a_n) or *lim a_n* is a number L—if such a number exists—to which the terms of the sequence get arbitrarily close if a sufficiently large number of terms are considered. Thus, for sufficiently large index n—say $n > M$ for some real number M—the number $|a_n - L|$ will be arbitrarily close to 0. Our definition below makes the concept mathematically precise.

Definition. *lim $a_n = L$, if, for arbitrary $\epsilon > 0$, there exists a real number M such that $|a_n - L| < \epsilon$, provided $n > M$.*

To illustrate the notion of limit, consider the sequence $(1, \frac{1}{2}, \frac{1}{3}, \ldots, 1/n, \ldots)$. It should be apparent that $1/n$ is arbitrarily close to 0 if n is sufficiently large. To be precise, if $\epsilon > 0$ is given, it is sufficient to choose $M = 1/\epsilon$, and we are then able to assert that $1/n - 0 = 1/n < 1/(1/\epsilon) = \epsilon$, provided $n > 1/\epsilon = M$. Hence, by our definition of the limit of a sequence, the limit of this sequence is 0.

As another—and rather "homey"—illustration, consider the case of an easily tired frog that jumps halfway to the opposite bank of a 30-foot creek in each of a sequence of jumps. If $d_1, d_2, d_3, \ldots$ designates the *total* distance jumped by the frog in $1, 2, 3, \ldots$ jumps, respectively, it is evident that d_n will get as close to 30 as we wish. Indeed, although d_n never equals 30 for any index n, d_n will actually exceed any real number less than 30. Under these circumstances, we state that lim $d_n = 30$.

We now adopt the summation convention for S_n, as we did in §10.7, for the sum of the first n terms of a sequence (a_n). If the sequence (S_n) of partial sums, associated with (a_n), has a limit, we *define* this limit to be the *sum S_∞* of the whole sequence. That is, to restate this definition,

$$S_\infty = \lim S_n$$

In particular, let us consider the geometric sequence (a_n) and the formula for S_n given in the theorem above. We may write $S_n = a_1/(1 - r) + a_1 r^n/(1 - r)$, and note that n occurs only in the second term of this expression. If $|r| < 1$, it is reasonably clear (because a_1 and r are fixed) that the numerator of this second term gets arbitrarily close to 0 for an n sufficiently large, whereas the denominator is independent of n. Hence, the limit of the second term is 0, and so lim $S_n = a_1/(1 - r)$. We have obtained the following correct result by a slightly intuitive argument:

$$S_\infty = \frac{a_1}{1 - r} \qquad \text{provided } |r| < 1$$

Example 3. Determine the sum of the infinite geometric sequence whose terms in order are $1, \frac{1}{2}, \frac{1}{4}, \frac{1}{8}, \ldots, 1/2^{n-1}, \ldots$.

SOLUTION. In this case, the sequence is geometric with $a_1 = 1$ and $r = \frac{1}{2}$. Hence, $S_\infty = 1/(1 - \frac{1}{2}) = 1/(\frac{1}{2}) = 2$.

Example 4. Express the rational number $0.7121212 \cdots$ as the quotient of two integers.

SOLUTION. Let $t = 0.7121212 \cdots$. Then $t = 0.7 + 0.012 + 0.00012 + 0.0000012 + \cdots = 0.7 + (0.012 + 0.00012 + 0.0000012 + \cdots) = 0.7 + 0.012/(1 - 0.01) = 0.7 + 0.012/0.99 = \frac{7}{10} + \frac{12}{990} = \frac{7}{10} + \frac{4}{330} = \frac{235}{330} = \frac{47}{66}$.

If we insert between two numbers x and y other numbers so that the augmented set of numbers forms an ordered portion of a geometric sequence, the inserted numbers are called *geometric means* of x and y.

Example 5. Insert four geometric means between 2 and $-\frac{1}{16}$.

SOLUTION. If four geometric means are inserted as desired, $-\frac{1}{16}$ is the sixth term of a geometric sequence whose first term is 2. Then $a_6 = 2r^5 = -\frac{1}{16} = -2^{-4}$ and so $r^5 = -2^{-5} = (-\frac{1}{2})^5$. Hence, $r = -\frac{1}{2}$, and the desired means are $a_2 = -1$, $a_3 = \frac{1}{2}$, $a_4 = -\frac{1}{4}$, $a_5 = \frac{1}{8}$.

Problems 10.8

1. Derive the formula obtained in the theorem of this section, by expressing S_n and rS_n as sums of n terms, subtracting the latter from the former and solving the resulting expression for S_n.
2. Use mathematical induction to verify that the nth term of a geometric sequence (a_n) with common ratio r is given by $a_n = a_1 r^{n-1}$.
3. With reference to a geometric sequence (a_n), find (a) a_5 if $a_1 = 2$ and $r = 3$; (b) a_4 if $a_1 = 1$ and $r = -0.01$; (c) a_{10} if $a_3 = 8$ and $r = 0.2$.
4. With reference to a geometric sequence (a_n), find (a) a_8 if $a_2 = 2$ and $a_5 = \frac{16}{27}$; (b) a_7 if $a_2 = \frac{3}{4}$ and $a_5 = \frac{81}{256}$.
5. Find the sum of 10 terms of the geometric sequence whose first term is 2 and common ratio is $\frac{2}{3}$.
6. Insert two geometric means between 56 and 875.
7. Insert three geometric means between 18 and $\frac{2}{9}$.
8. With the usual notation for sequences, find (a) S_6 if $a_1 = \frac{1}{8}$ and $r = 2$; (b) S_8 if $a_1 = 6$ and $r = -2$.
9. If $a_1 = 3$ and $a_3 = 48$, for a geometric sequence (a_n), determine r.
10. Express each of the following rational numbers as the quotient of two integers; (a) $0.314314 \cdots$; (b) $0.237237 \cdots$; (c) $1.56717171 \cdots$.
11. Determine S_∞, for each of the indicated infinite geometric sequences: (a) $(2, \frac{4}{3}, \frac{8}{9}, \ldots)$; (b) $(1, \frac{1}{3}, \frac{1}{9}, \ldots)$; (c) $(\frac{2}{3}, \frac{1}{6}, \frac{1}{24}, \ldots)$.
12. If \$1000 is invested for 5 years at 4 per cent interest compounded annually, determine the amount of the investment in 5 years.
13. How many years are necessary for \$20, invested at 8 per cent interest compounded annually, to exceed \$50?
14. Explain why the formula for S_∞ is meaningless if $|r| \geq 1$.
15. Evaluate each of the following sums: (a) $\sum_{k=0}^{\infty} (\frac{1}{2})^k$; (b) $\sum_{k=0}^{\infty} (-\frac{1}{3})^k$.

16. The bob of a pendulum travels 20 inches during its first swing. If each swing thereafter is four fifths as long as the preceding, determine the theoretical distance traveled by the bob "before" it comes to rest.

17. An elastic ball is dropped from a height of 50 feet, the ball rebounding three fifths of its height of fall for each subsequent descent. Determine the theoretical distance traveled by the ball "before" coming to rest.

18. A sequence of equilateral triangles is constructed, starting with a triangle with sides 2 feet in length and joining midpoints of these sides, and continuing this process indefinitely. Determine the theoretical sum of the perimeters of "all" the triangles of the infinite sequence constructed.

19. Find the theoretical sum of the areas of "all" triangles in Problem 18, ignoring the fact that the triangles overlap.

20. It is estimated that the enrollment of a certain university will increase 8 per cent per year. If the present enrollment is 2000 students, in how many years will the enrollment have more than doubled?

21. A chemist has 10 gallons of alcohol. If he drains off 2 gallons of alcohol and replaces it with water, stirs the resulting mixture thoroughly, and then repeats the operation ten times, how much alcohol will there be in the final mixture?

22. The half-life of a radioactive substance is the time required for the natural decomposition of half of any given amount of it. If the half-life of a certain isotope is 6 years, how many of $3(10^{12})$ original isotopes will remain after 36 years?

23. Find all possible ordered triplets of real numbers such that the numbers are consecutive terms of both an arithmetic and a geometric sequence.

24. A sequence (a_n) is called *harmonic* if $a_n = 1/b_n$, where (b_n) is an arithmetic sequence.
    (a) Find the first five terms of (a_n) if $b_1 = 5$ and $b_2 = 3$.
    (b) Find the first four terms of (a_n) if $b_1 = \frac{1}{3}$ and $b_2 = \frac{1}{2}$.
    (c) Make a reasonable definition for the harmonic mean of two numbers, and find a suitable formula.

25. If $r \neq 1$ and n is positive integer, use synthetic division to show that $\dfrac{r^n - 1}{r - 1} = \displaystyle\sum_{k=0}^{n-1} r^k$. Compare this result with the summation formula derived in this section.

26. An exponential function is defined on **R** in such a way that $f(n) = a_n$ for a geometric series (a_n). If $a_1 = 2$ and $r = \frac{1}{3}$ for the sequence, sketch a graph of f and give a graphical interpretation for the numbers of the sequence.

Appendix A
Review of
High School Algebra

In this very brief review, we shall merely recall the pertinent rules, give several examples of their use, and include a fairly large collection of problems. The letters used in this Appendix should be regarded as real numbers that are arbitrary—except when the context or statements require them to be otherwise.

1. Arithmetic of Fractions

In this section, the letters a, b, c, d are to be regarded as integers.

(a) *Equality.* $a/b = c/d$ if and only if $ad = bc$. A consequence of this definition of equality is the following *basic principle*: If both numerator and denominator of a fraction are multiplied or divided by the same nonzero integer, the fraction is unchanged except in form. In the case of division, we refer to the new form as a "reduction" of the original form.

Example

$$\frac{2}{3} = \frac{2 \cdot 4}{3 \cdot 4} = \frac{8}{12}$$
$$= \frac{2 \cdot 5}{3 \cdot 5} = \frac{10}{15}$$
$$\frac{8}{10} = \frac{\frac{8}{2}}{\frac{10}{2}} = \frac{4}{5}$$

(b) *Addition and Subtraction.* $a/b \pm c/d = (ad \pm bc)/bd$. The gist of this rule is that the principle in (a) is used to express the fractions of an indicated sum or difference in a form that will exhibit the same denominator in each case. Then perform the indicated operations on the numerators, and reduce if possible.

Example

$$\frac{1}{2} - \frac{3}{4} + \frac{2}{3} = \frac{6}{12} - \frac{9}{12} + \frac{8}{12} = \frac{6 - 9 + 8}{12} = \frac{5}{12}$$

(c) *Multiplication.* $(a/b)(c/d) = ac/bd$. In this way the multiplication of fractions can be accomplished by the formal multiplication of the respective numerators and denominators, followed or accompanied by any possible reductions.

Example

$$\left(\frac{2}{5}\right)\left(\frac{3}{4}\right)\left(\frac{5}{6}\right) = \frac{2 \cdot 3 \cdot 5}{5 \cdot 4 \cdot 6} = \frac{\overset{1}{2} \cdot \overset{1}{3} \cdot \overset{1}{5}}{\underset{1}{5} \cdot \underset{2}{4} \cdot \underset{2}{6}} = \frac{1 \cdot 1 \cdot 1}{1 \cdot 2 \cdot 2} = \frac{1}{4}$$

(d) *Division.* $(a/b)/(c/d) = ad/bc$. Hence, to divide one fraction by another, we invert the divisor and multiply.

Example

$$\frac{\frac{2}{3}}{\frac{5}{6}} = \left(\frac{2}{3}\right)\left(\frac{6}{5}\right) = \frac{2 \cdot 6}{3 \cdot 5} = \frac{2 \cdot \overset{2}{6}}{\underset{1}{3} \cdot 5} = \frac{2 \cdot 2}{1 \cdot 5} = \frac{4}{5}$$

Exercises*

1. Explain the process of "cancellation" in terms of the basic principle enunciated in (a) above.
2. Express each of the following numbers as a prime power product: (a) 64; (b) 36; (c) 72; (d) 160; (e) 42; (f) 18; (g) 125; (h) 60; (i) 80; (j) 90; (k) 102.
3. Determine the greatest common divisor of the integers in each of the following collections: (a) 8, 12, 15; (b) 21, 15, 42; (c) 2, 4, 8, 18; (d) 30, 45, 105, 120; (e) 3, 7, 13.
4. Reduce each of the following fractions by dividing numerator and denominator by the same number; (a) $\frac{4}{12}$; (b) $\frac{32}{48}$; (c) $\frac{7}{21}$; (d) $\frac{70}{21}$; (e) $\frac{90}{24}$; (f) $\frac{120}{260}$.
5. Replace each of the following fractions by an equivalent fraction after multiplying its numerator and denominator by 5: (a) $\frac{2}{3}$; (b) $\frac{3}{4}$; (c) $\frac{5}{3}$; (d) $\frac{4}{6}$; (e) $\frac{4}{9}$.
6. Replace each of the following fractions by an equivalent fraction after multiplying its numerator and denominator by 10: (a) $\frac{4}{3}$; (b) $\frac{2}{7}$; (c) $\frac{5}{8}$; (d) $\frac{5}{6}$; (e) $\frac{3}{4}$.
7. Find the sum of the numbers in each of the following collections: (a) $\frac{2}{3}, \frac{3}{4}, \frac{5}{8}, \frac{1}{2}$; (b) $\frac{1}{2}, \frac{2}{3}, \frac{3}{4}, \frac{4}{5}$; (c) $\frac{1}{3}, \frac{3}{7}, \frac{1}{15}, \frac{3}{10}$.
8. In each of the following pairs of fractions, subtract the second member from the first: (a) 5, $\frac{2}{3}$; (b) $\frac{3}{4}, \frac{2}{3}$; (c) $\frac{5}{7}, \frac{3}{8}$; (d) 4, $\frac{3}{7}$; (e) $\frac{12}{5}$, 2.
9. Simplify each of the following expressions: (a) $\frac{3}{2} + \frac{2}{3} - \frac{1}{8} - \frac{1}{4}$; (b) $\frac{3}{5} - \frac{2}{3} + \frac{5}{8} - \frac{1}{3} + \frac{5}{6}$; (c) $\frac{3}{7} + \frac{8}{3} - \frac{3}{5} + \frac{2}{9}$.
10. Simplify each of the following expressions: (a) $(\frac{2}{3})(\frac{1}{4})(\frac{3}{8})(\frac{4}{3})$; (b) $(\frac{4}{5})(\frac{10}{3})(\frac{2}{5})(\frac{3}{10})$; (c) $(\frac{5}{8})(\frac{4}{3})(\frac{2}{3})(5)(\frac{1}{2})$.
11. Divide the first member of each of the following pairs of numbers by the second: (a) $\frac{3}{4}, \frac{2}{3}$; (b) $\frac{1}{2}, \frac{4}{5}$; (c) $\frac{3}{8}, \frac{4}{5}$; (d) $\frac{3}{7}$, 6; (e) 8, $\frac{1}{4}$; (f) $\frac{4}{3}$, 6.

---

* The sets of exercises in this review have been taken, with the kind permission of the publisher, from *Fundamental Principles of Mathematics* by John T. Moore (New York: Holt, Rinehart and Winston, 1960).

12. Simplify each of the following expressions: (a) $\frac{3}{4} + (\frac{2}{3})(\frac{1}{4})$; (b) $(\frac{5}{6})(\frac{2}{3}) + (\frac{1}{4})(\frac{2}{3}) - (\frac{1}{3})(\frac{1}{8})$; (c) $(\frac{2}{3})(\frac{4}{5}) - (\frac{3}{8})(\frac{1}{2})$; (d) $[(\frac{5}{6})(\frac{2}{3})] \div [(\frac{3}{7})(\frac{2}{9})]$; (e) $\frac{3}{4} \div [(\frac{2}{3})(\frac{1}{2}) - \frac{1}{8}]$.

13. From the sum of $7 + \frac{7}{8}$ and $3 + \frac{3}{4}$ subtract the sum of $2 + \frac{1}{5}$ and $4 + \frac{1}{2}$.

14. Subtract $5 + \frac{7}{8}$ from $16 + \frac{3}{4}$; subtract $15 + \frac{5}{12}$ from $27 + \frac{3}{4}$.

15. In building a fence, a man used steel posts $6\frac{1}{2}$ feet long. If he drove each post $2\frac{1}{4}$ feet into the ground, how much of each post was above ground?

16. What is the cost (to the nearest cent) of $55\frac{1}{2}$ feet of sash cord at $\frac{3}{4}$ cents per foot?

17. A filling station advertised $6\frac{1}{4}$ gallons of gasoline for \$1.00. What was the exact price per gallon?

18. Find the sum of $\frac{5}{2}$ and its reciprocal; find the sum of $3 + \frac{2}{3}$ and its reciprocal.

2. Arithmetic of Signed Numbers

(a) *Addition.* If the numbers to be added have the same signs, add their absolute values and attach the common sign.

Example

$$(+\tfrac{2}{3}) + (+\tfrac{4}{5}) = +(\tfrac{2}{3} + \tfrac{4}{5}) = +(\tfrac{10}{15} + \tfrac{12}{15}) = +\tfrac{22}{15}$$
$$(-\tfrac{1}{2}) + (-\tfrac{2}{3}) + (-\tfrac{1}{4}) = -(\tfrac{1}{2} + \tfrac{2}{3} + \tfrac{1}{4})$$
$$-(\tfrac{6}{12} + \tfrac{8}{12} + \tfrac{3}{12}) = -\tfrac{17}{12}$$

If two numbers to be added have unlike signs, subtract the smaller absolute value from the larger and attach the sign of the larger.

Example

$$(+\tfrac{1}{4}) + (-\tfrac{2}{3}) = -(\tfrac{2}{3} - \tfrac{1}{4}) = -(\tfrac{8}{12} - \tfrac{3}{12}) = -\tfrac{5}{12}$$

(b) *Subtraction.* To subtract a signed number, change its sign and add.

Example

$$(-\tfrac{2}{5}) - (+\tfrac{1}{3}) = (-\tfrac{2}{5}) + (-\tfrac{1}{3}) = -(\tfrac{6}{15} + \tfrac{5}{15}) = -\tfrac{11}{15}$$

(c) *Multiplication and Division.* For any compound product or quotient of signed numbers, perform the indicated operations on the absolute values, and attach a positive sign if the number of negative signs is even and a negative sign if the number of negative signs is odd.

Example

$$\left(\frac{-1}{3}\right)\left(\frac{+2}{5}\right)\left(\frac{-6}{7}\right) = +\left(\frac{1}{3}\right)\left(\frac{2}{5}\right)\left(\frac{6}{7}\right) = +\frac{4}{35}$$
$$\left(\frac{-1}{2}\right)\left(\frac{+2}{3}\right)\left(\frac{+1}{5}\right) = -\left(\frac{1 \cdot 2 \cdot 1}{2 \cdot 3 \cdot 5}\right) = -\frac{1}{15}$$
$$\frac{(\frac{2}{3})(-\frac{1}{2})}{(-\frac{1}{4})(+\frac{5}{2})} = +\frac{(\frac{2}{3})(\frac{1}{2})}{(\frac{1}{4})(\frac{5}{2})} = +\frac{\frac{1}{3}}{\frac{5}{8}} = +\frac{8}{15}$$

Note: Although we have included the $+$ sign in the above examples, this sign is usually omitted (as the sign of a number) unless it is needed for emphasis.

Exercises

1. Give the absolute value of each of the following: (a) 6; (b) -7; (c) -4; (d) $\frac{3}{5}$; (e) $-\frac{5}{7}$.
2. Find the sum of the numbers in each of the following collections: (a) 7, 4, 5, 1; (b) -3, -5, -2, -8, -3; (c) $-\frac{2}{3}$, $-\frac{3}{4}$, $-\frac{1}{6}$, $-\frac{5}{12}$, $-\frac{3}{8}$; (d) $\frac{3}{5}$, $\frac{2}{3}$, $\frac{3}{8}$.
3. Find the sum of the numbers in each of the following collections: (a) 6, 3, -8, -4; (b) 12, -7, 6, -33, 5; (c) -4, 12, -9, -3, 5; (d) -5, 8, 14, -3, -16.
4. Find the sum of the numbers in each of the following collections: (a) $\frac{2}{3}$, $-\frac{3}{4}$, $\frac{5}{8}$, $-\frac{1}{8}$; (b) $\frac{3}{2}$, $-\frac{5}{7}$, $\frac{7}{8}$, $-\frac{1}{2}$, $\frac{6}{7}$; (c) $\frac{3}{4}$, $-\frac{2}{5}$, $\frac{4}{7}$, $\frac{7}{8}$, $-\frac{1}{2}$, $\frac{3}{4}$.
5. Subtract the second number from the first in each of the following pairs: (a) $\frac{3}{4}$, $-\frac{2}{7}$; (b) $-\frac{5}{3}$, $\frac{2}{5}$; (c) 5, $-\frac{3}{4}$; (d) $-\frac{2}{7}$, 3; (e) $-\frac{4}{3}$, $-\frac{2}{5}$; (f) $\frac{3}{5}$, -4; (g) -1, $-\frac{5}{4}$.
6. Multiply together the numbers in each of the following collections, and reduce the result to lowest terms: (a) $\frac{2}{3}$, $-\frac{4}{5}$, $-\frac{3}{4}$; (b) -2, $-\frac{4}{5}$, -5; (c) $\frac{3}{5}$, $-\frac{6}{7}$, -3, $-\frac{5}{2}$.
7. Divide the first number by the second in each of the following pairs: (a) $\frac{3}{4}$, $-\frac{3}{4}$; (b) $-\frac{2}{3}$, $-\frac{6}{5}$; (c) 5, $-\frac{4}{5}$; (d) $\frac{6}{5}$, -4.
8. Simplify each of the following expressions: (a) $(\frac{2}{3})(-\frac{5}{2})(-\frac{3}{4})(-6)$; (b) $[(-4)(-\frac{2}{3})(-\frac{6}{7})] \div [(-\frac{5}{2})(\frac{7}{4})]$; (c) $(\frac{6\frac{1}{2}}{12})(-\frac{15}{4}) + (-\frac{3}{2})(-\frac{2}{5})$.

Note: If a pair of signs of aggregation is preceded by a negative sign, change all the signs within the signs of aggregation when they are removed; if the preceding sign is positive, the signs within remain the same.

9. Simplify each of the following:
   (a) $\frac{1}{2} - 2[3 + 5(1 - \frac{1}{2})]$ (b) $3 - 3[\frac{1}{2} - (2 + \frac{1}{4})] - 1$
   (c) $2\{3[1 - \frac{2}{3}] + 1\} - 2$ (d) $3 - 2\{(1 - \frac{1}{2})(2 + \frac{2}{3}) - 1\}$
10. Simplify each of the following:
    (a) $\dfrac{2\{3 + [5 - 2(1 - \frac{1}{2})]\}}{2 + 4[1 - (\frac{1}{2})(2 - \frac{1}{3})]}$ (b) $1 - \dfrac{1}{2 - \dfrac{1}{3 - \frac{1}{2}}}$

    (c) $\dfrac{1}{2 + 3[2 - (\frac{1}{2})(3 - \frac{2}{3})]}$

3. Algebraic Expressions

In elementary algebra the number symbols are merely unknown or unidentified real *numbers*. Hence, operations involving these symbols must obey the same rules as those for the real numbers. In fact, an error in a manipulation of symbols may often be easily detected by noting an arithmetic error that appears when the symbols are replaced by specific real numbers. In particular, the rules of operation pertaining to signed numbers are applicable to these algebraic expressions.

Example

$$3x - 2\{3x - 2[1 - 4(x - 1)] + 2\} = 3x - 2\{3x - 2[1 - 4x + 4] + 2\}$$
$$= 3x - 2\{3x - 2[5 - 4x] + 2\}$$
$$= 3x - 2\{11x - 8\}$$
$$= 3x - 22x + 16$$
$$= 16 - 19x$$

There are a number of special products that should be familiar to the student of algebra and that we now list.

(a) *The product of the sum and difference of two numbers.*

$$(x + y)(x - y) = x^2 - y^2$$

Example

$$(3x + 2y)(3x - 2y) = 9x^2 - 4y^2$$

(b) *Powers of a Binomial*

$(x + y)^2 = x^2 + 2xy + y^2$ $(x + y)^3 = x^3 + 3x^2y + 3xy^2 + y^3$
$(x - y)^2 = x^2 - 2xy + y^2$ $(x - y)^3 = x^3 - 3x^2y + 3xy^2 - y^3$

Example

$$(x - 2y)^2 = x^2 - 4xy + 4y^2$$
$$(2x + y)^3 = 8x^3 + 3(2x)^2y + 3(2x)y^2 + y^3$$
$$= 8x^3 + 12x^2y + 6xy^2 + y^3$$

(c) *The Product of Two Binomials.*

$$(x + a)(x + b) = x^2 + (a + b)x + ab$$
$$(ax + b)(cx + d) = acx^2 + (bc + ad)x + bd$$

Example

$$(x - 2)(x - 3) = x^2 + (-2 - 3)x + 6 = x^2 - 5x + 6$$
$$(2x - 3b)(x + 2b) = 2x^2 + (4b - 3b)x - 6b^2 = 2x^2 + bx - 6b^2$$

Exercises

1. Simplify each of the following: (a) $(-4x)(2x^2)$; (b) $3ab - 2ab + ab$; (c) $(2x)(-3x)(-4x)$; (d) $(-ay)(by)(-3)$; (e) $(-6xy)(2x) + 5x^2y$.
2. Find the sum of the quantities in each of the following collections: (a) $8a$, $-3a$, $9a$, $2a$; (b) $12ab$, $-5ab$, $-2ab$; (c) $2ab$, $-6ab$, $4ac$; (d) $2a^2$, $-3a$, $5b$, $5a$.

3. Subtract $12a - 7c$ from $6a - 7b - 10c$.
4. Subtract $12x^2 - 3x + 1$ from $-2x^2 + 9x - 7$.
5. Subtract (a) $18abc$ from $3abc$; (b) $-5m$ from $-8m^2$; (c) $-6x^2 + 4y$ from $2x^2 - 4y$.
6. Subtract (a) $2a + 3b + 5c$ from $5a - 8b + 11c$; (b) $7x + 5y$ from $-6x + 4y$; (c) $-6x^2 - 8$ from $3x^2 - 2y + 7$.
7. Simplify each of the following: (a) $3xy - 2xy + 9y - 2xy$; (b) $3x^2 - 2x^2 + (9y - 2x^2)$; (c) $7a - 4[(2a + 6b) - b^2 + c] - 4(2 - c)$.
8. Simplify each of the following: (a) $ab - 4b^2 - (2a^2 + b^2) - (-5a^2 - 3b^2)$; (b) $x - \{y - z - [x - (-x + y) - z]\} + (2x - y)$; (c) $-1\{-1 - [-1 - (-1)]\}$.
9. Expand each of the following products: (a) $(2x + 5y)(2x - 5y)$; (b) $(3x^2 + 2y^2)(3x^2 - 2y^2)$; (c) $(2x + y)^2$; (d) $(x - 2y)^3$.
10. Expand each of the following products: (a) $(5x - 2y)(5x + 2y)$; (b) $(x^2y - 3a)(x^2y + 3a)$; (c) $(2x - 6y)(2x + 6y)$; (d) $(3x - y)^3$.
11. Expand each of the following products: (a) $(2a - x)^2$; (b) $(1 + x)^3$; (c) $(2x - 1)^3$; (d) $(x + 2)(x + 3)$; (e) $(3xy - z)(3xy + 7z)$.
12. Expand each of the following products: (a) $(x - 2y)(2x - 2y)$; (b) $(a + 7b)(2a - 3b)$; (c) $(x^2 - 3)(x^2 + 4)$; (d) $(x/2 + 5y)(x/2 - 5y)$; (e) $(x/2 - y/4)^2$.
13. Expand each of the following products: (a) $(6x - \frac{1}{2})^2$; (b) $(2 + 3x)^3$; (c) $(5m^3 - 6s^2)(5m^3 + s^2)$; (d) $(3xy - 7)^2$.
14. Simplify each of the following:

(a) $\dfrac{3m^2 + 2m - 5m^3}{m}$ (b) $\dfrac{4x^3 - 2x^2}{2x}$

(c) $\dfrac{x^4 - 12x^3 + 6x^2}{x^2}$ (d) $\dfrac{a^2b^2 - a^3b^3 + ab^5}{ab^2}$

(e) $\dfrac{15xy^2z}{3xz}$

15. Find the products of the following listed algebraic quantities: (a) $5mn^2$, $-4mn^2$; (b) $3b^2c$, $4bc^2$; (c) $5ty^3$, $-8y^2z$; (d) $2x^2y$, $-4x + 7y$, $-xy$; (e) a, $-a$, $-a$, $-a$.
16. Expand each of the following: (a) $(2x - y + 3z)^2$; (b) $(x - 2y)(1 - x)^2$; (c) $(x^2 - 6)^2(2x + 1)$; (d) $(x - 3y)(2x + y)(x + y)$; (e) $(2x + y - z)^3$.

4. Factoring

The ability to factor a given algebraic expression is largely a matter of identifying it as a member of a certain class of expressions. We list some of the more standard of these factoring types here.

(a) *Trinomials That Are Perfect Squares.*

$$x^2 \pm 2xy + y^2 = (x \pm y)^2$$

Example

$$4a^2 - 4ab + b^2 = (2a - b)^2$$

(b) *Difference of Two Squares.* $x^2 - y^2 = (x + y)(x - y)$.

Example

$$4a^2 - 25b^2 = (2a + 5b)(2a - 5b)$$

(c) *Trinomials with 1 as Leading Coefficient.* $x^2 + (a + b)x + ab = (x + a)(x + b)$.

Example

$$x^2 - 7x + 12 = (x - 4)(x - 3)$$

(d) *Sum or Difference of Two Cubes.*

$$x^3 \pm y^3 = (x \pm y)(x^2 \mp xy + y^2)$$

Example

$$8a^3 - b^3 = (2a - b)(4a^2 + 2ab + b^2)$$

(e) *General Trinomials.* $ax^2 + bx + c = (px + r)(qx + s)$, by inspection.

Example

$$8x^2 - 2x - 3 = (2x + 1)(4x - 3)$$

(f) *Grouping*

Example

$$3ax - 3ay + acx - acy = a[3x - 3y + cx - cy] = a[x(3 + c) - y(3 + c)]$$
$$= a[(3 + c)(x - y)] = a(x - y)(3 + c)$$

Exercises

Factor each of the following expressions completely (allowing only integral coefficients), by first factoring out any common monomial and then using one of the above standard forms.

1. $9x^8 - 4y^6$
2. $225 - a^6$
3. $r^4 - 11r^2 + 30$
4. $16x^2 + 30x + 9$
5. $3y^3 + 24$
6. $6x^2 + 7x - 3$
7. $c^3 + 27d^3$
8. $x^2 - 16x + 48$
9. $y^3 - 27z^3$
10. $4x^2 - 3x - 7$
11. $6 - t - 15t^2$
12. $25t^4 - 1$
13. $36a^2 - 132a + 121$
14. $u^6 + u^3 - 110$
15. $3x^4 - 12$
16. $x^8 - y^8$
17. $x^5 - xy^4 - x^4y + y^5$
18. $x^4 - x^3y - xy^3 + y^4$
19. $x^3 - 3x^2 + 3x - 1$
20. $(x + y)^2 - a^2$

21. $c^2 - (a + b)^2$

22. $x^3y^3 + 1$

23. $8 - 27x^3$

24. $24m^2 + 22mn - 21n^2$

25. $16x^2 - 6x - 27$

26. $9 + 35x - 4x^2$

27. $2x^4 + 11x^2y^2 - 21y^4$

28. $(x - y)^2 - 4z^2$

29. $(5x - 7)^2 - 1$

30. $x^2 - (y - x)^2$

31. $(3y + 5)^2 - (2y - 9)^2$

32. $x^4y^4 - 9y^2$

33. $x^2(2x + 1)^2 - (2y - 9)^2$

34. $(x^2 - 4y^2) + x(x + 2y)$

35. $a^2x + a^2y + abx + aby$

36. $a^2x^3 - 64x^3y^2$

37. $a^2x^2 - a^2y^2 + abx^2 - aby^2$

38. $x^3 + x^2 + x + 1$

39. $2 + 3x - 8x^2 - 12x^3$

40. $56 - 32a + 21a^2 - 12a^3$

41. $x^3 + (y - z)^3$

42. $(m + n)^3 + 8t^3$

43. $27a^3 - (a - b)^3$

44. $(x + y)^2 - x^2y^2$

5. Algebraic Fractions

Algebraic expressions arise because the results of designated operations on symbols must be merely formalized or expressed. For example, we can state that $2 + 3 = 5$, but $x + y$ must be left this way unless x and y are identified. With this understanding, the rules for the simplification of algebraic fractions are precisely the rules associated with arithmetic fractions: Express all fractions with a common denominator for addition; factor and reduce for multiplication. We shall use two examples by way of illustration.

Example

$$\frac{x^2 - 7x + 12}{x^2 + x} \cdot \frac{x^2 - 1}{x^2 - 4x + 3} = \frac{\overset{1}{\cancel{(x - 3)}}(x - 4)}{x\cancel{(x + 1)}} \cdot \frac{\overset{1}{\cancel{(x + 1)}}\overset{1}{\cancel{(x - 1)}}}{\cancel{(x - 3)}(x - 1)} = \frac{x - 4}{x}$$

Example

$$\frac{4x}{x^2 + x - 2} - \frac{3x + 1}{x^2 - 3x + 2} = \frac{4x}{(x - 1)(x + 2)} - \frac{3x + 1}{(x - 1)(x - 2)}$$

$$= \frac{4x(x - 2) - (3x + 1)(x + 2)}{(x - 1)(x - 2)(x + 2)}$$

$$= \frac{4x^2 - 8x - 3x^2 - 7x - 2}{(x - 1)(x - 2)(x + 2)}$$

$$= \frac{x^2 - 15x - 2}{(x - 1)(x - 2)(x + 2)}$$

Exercises

Simplify each of the following expressions as much as possible:

1. $\dfrac{x}{2} + \dfrac{y}{6} + \dfrac{x}{3}$

2. $\dfrac{x}{2} - \dfrac{(x - 4)}{4}$

3. $\dfrac{a-1}{a} - \dfrac{b+4}{b}$

4. $\dfrac{5}{4x} + \dfrac{3}{5x^2} - \dfrac{7}{10x^3}$

5. $\dfrac{x-y}{xy} + \dfrac{y-z}{yz} + \dfrac{z-x}{xz}$

6. $\dfrac{2x+1}{5} - \dfrac{2x-1}{7} - \dfrac{x-3}{10}$

7. $\dfrac{x-2}{x-1} + \dfrac{x+2}{x+1}$

8. $\dfrac{x}{x+1} - \dfrac{2x}{x+2} + \dfrac{x}{x+3}$

9. $\dfrac{2y-3}{y-2} + \dfrac{y+3}{3y-2}$

10. $\dfrac{a}{x+a} - \dfrac{b}{x+b}$

11. $\dfrac{3}{2+a-6a^2} - \dfrac{1}{1+a-2a^2}$

12. $\dfrac{x+2}{x-2} - \dfrac{x^2+4}{x^2-4}$

13. $\dfrac{4a^2+8a+3}{2a^2-5a+3} \cdot \dfrac{6a^2-9a}{4a^2-1}$

14. $x + \dfrac{1}{x-1/x}$

15. $\dfrac{x+2}{x} + \dfrac{x}{x-3} - \dfrac{3}{x+3}$

16. $\dfrac{x-1}{x^2-1} - \dfrac{x-2}{x^2-4}$

17. $\dfrac{1}{3+x} + \dfrac{1}{3-x} + \dfrac{6}{x^2-9}$

18. $\dfrac{2x-5}{x-2} + x - 3$

19. $\left(\dfrac{x}{y} - \dfrac{y}{x}\right) \div \left(x - \dfrac{x^2}{x+y}\right)$

20. $\left(x - \dfrac{1}{x}\right) \div \left(x + \dfrac{1}{x} - 2\right)$

21. $\dfrac{1 - 4/x + 3/x^2}{x - 9/x}$

22. $\dfrac{x}{1 - \dfrac{1-x}{1+x}}$

23. $(x^4 - 1/x^4) \div (x-1)/x$

24. $(x - 1/x) \div (x + 1/x - 2)$

6. Linear and Quadratic Equations

The basic principle underlying the solution of equations is that an equality remains true if both members are transformed in the same way. This usually means adding the same quantity to both members, or multiplying or dividing both members by the same nonzero quantity. The principle of "transposition," whereby a term can be transferred from one member of an equation to the other if its sign is changed, is a natural consequence of this basic principle.

(a) *Linear.* Any linear equation in x can be transformed into one of the form $ax = b$. Hence, $x = b/a$ is the solution if $a \neq 0$.

Example

$$5x + 2 - 2x = x + 8$$
$$5x - 2x - x = 8 - 2$$
$$2x = 6$$
$$x = 3$$

(b) *Quadratic.* Any quadratic equation in x can be transformed into one of the form $ax^2 + bx + c = 0$. From this point, we may proceed in one of three ways.

(1) *Factoring.* The basis for this method is the fact that the product of two real or complex numbers is never 0 unless at least one of the numbers is 0.

Example

$$2x^2 + 3x - 2 = (2x - 1)(x + 2) = 0$$
$$2x - 1 = 0 \quad \text{or} \quad x + 2 = 0$$
$$x = \tfrac{1}{2} \quad \text{or} \quad x = -2$$

(2) *Completing the Square.* An expression $x^2 + ax$ can be transformed into the square of a binomial if the square of half the coefficient of x—that is, $(a/2)^2$—is added.

Example

$$2x^2 - 4x + 1 = 0$$
$$x^2 - 2x = -\tfrac{1}{2}$$
$$x^2 - 2x + 1 = -\tfrac{1}{2} + 1 = \tfrac{1}{2}$$
$$(x - 1)^2 = \tfrac{1}{2}$$
$$x - 1 = \pm \sqrt{\tfrac{1}{2}} = \pm \frac{\sqrt{2}}{2}$$
$$x = 1 \pm \frac{\sqrt{2}}{2}$$

(3) *The Quadratic Formula.* The Quadratic Formula is merely a condensation into a single formula of the operations involved in solving $ax^2 + bx + c = 0$ by completing the square. The result is usually expressed as follows:

$$x = \frac{-b \pm \sqrt{b^2 - 4ac}}{2a}$$

Example. If $2x^2 - 4x + 1 = 0$, then $a = 2$, $b = -4$, $c = 1$. Hence,

$$x = \frac{4 \pm \sqrt{16 - 8}}{4} = \frac{4 \pm \sqrt{8}}{4} = \frac{4 \pm 2\sqrt{2}}{4} = 1 \pm \frac{\sqrt{2}}{2}$$

as in (2).

Example.　If $3x^2 - 2x + 1 = 0$, then $a = 3$, $b = -2$, $c = 1$. Hence,

$$x = \frac{2 \pm \sqrt{4 - 12}}{6} = \frac{2 \pm \sqrt{-8}}{6} = \frac{2 \pm 2\sqrt{2}i}{6} = \frac{1}{3} \pm \frac{\sqrt{2}i}{3}$$

where i is the complex number such that $i^2 = -1$.

Exercises

Solve each of the following equations and check your result.

1. $2x + 2 = 7x - 18$
2. $1 - x = 2 - 3x$
3. $2 - 3x + 5 = -6x - 2$
4. $5x + 6 = -7x$
5. $2x - 7 - (x - 5) = 0$
6. $2(3x - 1) = 9(x - 2) - 7$
7. $(x + 3)^2 - (x + 2)^2 = 1$
8. $3 - (x - 1) = -1 - 2(5 - x)$
9. $2x^2 + 5x - 3 = 0$
10. $6x^2 = x + 35$
11. $x^2 + 5x - 3 = 0$
12. $x^2 - 5x = -4$
13. $3x^2 + 4x = 7$
14. $x^2 + 5x = 36$
15. $8x^2 - 22x - 90 = 0$
16. $x^2 - 105x + 2700 = 0$
17. $\frac{1}{4}x^2 - \frac{3}{2}x + 2 = 0$
18. $s^2 = 5s + 6$
19. $3r^2 - 2r = 40$
20. $u^4 - 29u^2 + 100 = 0$
21. $2y + \frac{5}{2} = 5/4y$
22. $t^2 - 6t = 6$
23. $9y^2 - 12y - 8 = 0$
24. $4x^2 + 4x - 5 = 0$
25. $8y^2 - 8y - 3 = 0$
26. $x^2 = 5 + \frac{4}{3}x$

27. $\dfrac{x}{x - 1} - \dfrac{x - 1}{x} = \dfrac{x^2 + 2x + 1}{x^2 - 1}$
28. $x^2 + 100/x^2 = 29$

29. $\dfrac{1}{x - 1} - \dfrac{1}{x + 1} = \dfrac{1}{24}$
30. $\dfrac{1}{x} + \dfrac{1}{x - 3} - \dfrac{7}{3x - 5} = 0$

31. $(x + 1/x)^2 - \frac{16}{3}(x + 1/x) + 7 = \frac{1}{3}$
32. $x^6 - 12x^3 + 35 = 0$

33. $\frac{1}{5}x^2 - \frac{1}{30}x - \frac{1}{2} = 0$
34. $\dfrac{2x - 7}{x^2 - 4} = \dfrac{10x - 3}{5x(x + 2)}$

35. $6a^2 - 10a + 4 = 0$
36. $1 + 2x - 15x^2 = 0$
37. $18x^2 - 3x - 66 = 0$
38. $1 - 20p - 10p^2 = 0$

39. $t + 1/t = a + 1/a$
40. $\dfrac{x - 3}{x - 2} - \dfrac{x + 4}{x} = \dfrac{3}{2}$

7.　Simultaneous Linear Equations

There are two elementary methods in common use for solving a system of n linear equations in n unknowns, provided $n = 2$ or $n = 3$. These are called "elimination by addition or subtraction" and "elimination by substitution." The idea of the first method is to multiply the members of each of two equations by suitable nonzero numbers, so that at least one unknown disappears when corresponding members of the two equations are added or subtracted. The idea of the second method is to solve one equation for one unknown in terms of the other(s) and then eliminate it from the remaining equations. We shall illustrate both of these methods with examples.

(a) *Elimination by Addition or Subtraction*

Example

$$2x + 3y = -1 \qquad (1)$$
$$3x + 4y = -2 \qquad (2)$$

Multiply (1) by 3 and (2) by 2, and subtract:

$$
\begin{aligned}
6x + 9y &= -3 \\
6x + 8y &= -4 \\
\hline
y &= 1
\end{aligned}
$$

From (1),

$$2x + 3 = -1$$
$$2x = -4$$
$$x = -2$$

The solution of the system is then $x = -2$, $y = 1$.

Example

$$x + y + z = 2 \qquad (1)$$
$$2x - 3y + 2z = 9 \qquad (2)$$
$$3x - 3y - 2z = 2 \qquad (3)$$

Subtract (2) from (3):

$$x - 4z = -7 \qquad (4)$$

Multiply (1) by 3 and add to (2):

$$
\begin{aligned}
3x + 3y + 3z &= 6 \\
2x - 3y + 2z &= 9 \\
\hline
5x + 5z &= 15
\end{aligned}
$$

or

$$x + z = 3 \qquad (5)$$

Subtract (4) from (5):

$$5z = 10$$
$$z = 2$$

From (5),

$$x + 2 = 3, \qquad x = 1$$

From (1),

$$1 + y + 2 = 2$$
$$y = -1$$

Hence, the complete solution is

$$x = 1$$
$$y = -1$$
$$z = 2$$

(b) *Elimination by Substitution.*   We shall use the same two systems, as in (a), in order to illustrate this method.

Example

$$2x + 3y = -1 \qquad\qquad (1)$$
$$3x + 4y = -2 \qquad\qquad (2)$$

From (1),

$$3y = -2x - 1$$
$$y = -\tfrac{2}{3}x - \tfrac{1}{3}$$

Substituting this expression for y in (2), we obtain

$$3x + 4(-\tfrac{2}{3}x - \tfrac{1}{3}) = -2$$
$$3x - \tfrac{8}{3}x - \tfrac{4}{3} = -2$$
$$9x - 8x - 4 = -6$$
$$x = -2$$
$$y = -\tfrac{2}{3}x - \tfrac{1}{3} = \tfrac{4}{3} - \tfrac{1}{3} = 1$$

as before.

Example

$$x + y + z = 2 \qquad\qquad (1)$$
$$2x - 3y + 2z = 9 \qquad\qquad (2)$$
$$3x - 3y - 2z = 2 \qquad\qquad (3)$$

From (1),

$$z = 2 - x - y$$

Hence, from (2) and (3),

$$2x - 3y + 4 - 2x - 2y = 9$$
$$3x - 3y - 4 + 2x + 2y = 2$$

or

$$-5y = 5$$
$$5x - y = 6$$

Hence,

$$y = -1, \; x = 1, \; z = 2 - x - y = 2 - 1 + 1 = 2$$

as before.

Exercises

Solve and check each of the systems of linear equations in Problems 1–16.

1. $2x + 5y = 4$
   $4x - 10y = 48$
2. $x - y = 1$
   $x + y = 9$
3. $y = 2x + 3$
   $x = 2y - 3$
4. $2x - 7y = 5$
   $5x + 2y = 5$
5. $2(x + y) = 16$
   $3(x - y) = 6$
6. $x + y/5 = 17$
   $x - y = 5$
7. $3x + 4y = 24$
   $5x - 3y = 11$
8. $3x - 4y = -6$
   $x + 5y = 17$
9. $7x + 9y = 41$
   $x + 4y = 14$
10. $5x + 3y = 5$
    $9x + 5y = 8$
11. $x - y - z = -6$
    $2x + y + z = 0$
    $3x - 5y + 8z = 13$
12. $x + 2y + z = 7$
    $x + y - z = 2$
    $3x - y + 2z = 12$
13. $2x - y + 3z = 4$
    $x + 3y + 3z = -2$
    $3x + 2y - 6z = 6$
14. $x + 2y + z = 0$
    $2x + y + 2z = 3$
    $4x - 6y + 3z = 14$
15. $x/2 + y/3 = 9$
    $x/3 + z/2 = 8$
    $y/2 + z/3 = 13$
16. $1/x + 1/y + 2/z = 1$
    $2/x + 1/y - 2/z = 1$
    $3/x + 4/y - 4/z = 2$

17. A man can row downstream 3 miles in 20 minutes, but the return trip takes him 1 hour. What is his speed in still water, and what is the speed of the current?
18. Find two integers, the respective sum and difference of which are 95 and 15.

8. Exponents

For the purposes of this section, we shall regard a and b as positive integers.

Definition. *If n is a positive integer, $\sqrt[n]{a}$ is the positive nth root of a, that is, the positive real number such that $(\sqrt[n]{a})^n = a$.*

Definition

If n is a positive integer, $a^n = a \cdot a \cdot a \cdots a$, with n factors.
If n is a positive integer, $a^{1/n} = \sqrt[n]{a}$.
If p and q are relatively prime positive integers, then

$$a^{p/q} = \sqrt[q]{a^p} = (\sqrt[q]{a})^p$$

If n and r are positive integers such that n/r = p/q, with p and q relatively prime, then

$$a^{n/r} = a^{p/q}$$

LAWS OF EXPONENTS (with x and y rational numbers)

$$a^x \cdot a^y = a^{x+y}$$

$$\frac{a^x}{a^y} = \begin{cases} a^{x-y} & \text{if } x > y \\ \dfrac{1}{a^{y-x}} & \text{if } x < y \\ 1 & \text{if } x = y \end{cases}$$

$$(a^x)^y = a^{xy}$$
$$a^x \cdot b^x = (ab)^x$$

Example

$$5^{1/3} \cdot 5^{2/3} \cdot 5^{1/2} = 5^{1/3+2/3+1/2} = 5^{3/2} = \sqrt{125}$$

Example

$$\left(\frac{4a^{2/3}}{a^{1/2}}\right)^{1/2} = \frac{4^{1/2} \cdot a^{1/3}}{a^{1/4}} = 2a^{1/3-1/4} = 2a^{1/12} = 2\sqrt[12]{a}$$

Exercises

1. Write each of the following quantities in exponential form: (a) $\sqrt{a}$; (b) $\sqrt[4]{x^3}$; (c) $\sqrt[5]{a^7}$; (d) $\sqrt{a^3}$; (e) $\sqrt[5]{a+2}$.

2. Write each of the following quantities in exponential form: (a) $\sqrt{3}$; (b) $\sqrt[3]{2^5}$; (c) $\sqrt[5]{4^4}$; (d) $\sqrt{5}$; (e) $\sqrt[3]{2+x}$.

3. Find an integer equal to (a) $9^{1/2}$; (b) $81^{3/2}$; (c) $125^{5/3}$; (d) $64^{5/6}$; (e) $16^{1/4}$.

4. Write each of the following quantities in radical form: (a) $a^{1/3}$; (b) $x^{5/6}$; (c) $b^{n/3}$; (d) $n^{3/4}$; (e) $s^{7/6}$.

5. Write each of the following as a single exponential quantity: (a) $x^2 \cdot x^{n+1}$; (b) $a^{n-2} \cdot a^{3+n}$; (c) $u^{n+r} \cdot u^{n-r}$; (d) $(p^7)^3$; (e) $(a^4)^3$.

6. Write each of the following as a single exponential quantity: (a) x^{3n}/x^n; (b) $10^{2r+1}/10^r$; (c) u^{n+r}/u^{n-r}; (d) $(x^5/x^4)^4$; (e) $(p^3q^3)^s$; (f) $(r^2s^2)^5$; (g) e^{n+5}/e^3.

7. Simplify each of the following expressions: (a) $x^{1/3}x^{7/3}$; (b) $a^{1/4}a^{1/5}$; (c) $a^{3/7}a^{2/3}$; (d) $x^{1/5}x^{3/10}$.

8. Simplify each of the following expressions: (a) $(a^{2/3})^{1/4}$; (b) $(x^{3/5})^{5/6}$; (c) $(a^{5/12})^4$; (d) $(a^2b^{1/2})^{1/2}$.

9. Simplify each of the following expressions: (a) $x^{1/2}/x^{1/2}$; (b) $(x^5/x^{2/3})^{3/5}$; (c) $(9x^{3/4}/4x^{2/5})^{3/2}$; (d) $(8a^{3/8}b^{9/4})^{4/9}$.

10. Find a rational number equal to (a) 2^{-1}; (b) $16^{-3/4}$; (c) 3^{-2}; (d) $7^{-1}/49^{-1/2}$; (e) 1^{-1}.

11. Find a rational number equal to (a) $2/3^{-2}$; (b) $1^{-8}/8^{-1}$; (c) $32^{-1/5}/2^{-1}$; (d) $512^{-1/3}$.

12. Write each of the following quantities in an equivalent form without negative exponents: (a) a^2b^{-2}; (b) $(a + b)^{-3}$; (c) $3x^{-2}y^{-1/2}$; (d) x^4/y^{-5}; (e) $1/x^{-2}$.

13. Write each of the following quantities as an equivalent expression with denominator 1: (a) $1/x^2$; (b) xy^2/c^3d^4; (c) $(2a^3b^{-3})/(4r^{-2}t^5)$; (d) $ab^{1/2}/(x^{-1/3}y^{s/t})$.

14. Simplify each of the following: (a) $(a^{-5}/a^{-4})^{-7}$; (b) $(x^{-4}/x^{-6})^{-2}$; (c) $(a^{-3}b/x^3y^{-2})^{-3}$; (d) $(r^{-3/4})^{-2/3}$.

9. Equations with Radicals

If the equation involves only one radical, this "radical" term should be isolated first on one side of the equation. Then both members should be raised to the same power as the index of the radical, so that the radical is eliminated. It is important to check "solutions" in the original equation, because extraneous "solutions" frequently arise for this type of equation. We must be careful to recall, in addition, that $\sqrt{a}$ is the *positive* square root of a if $a > 0$. If more than one radical is involved, the most complicated one should be eliminated first, by the above process, followed by the successive elimination of any others that remain.

Example

$$\sqrt{x - 1} = x - 3$$
$$x - 1 = x^2 - 6x + 9$$
$$x^2 - 7x + 10 = 0$$
$$(x - 2)(x - 5) = 0$$
$$x = 5 \quad \text{or} \quad x = 2$$

Check: If $x = 5$: $\sqrt{5 - 1} = \sqrt{4} = 2 = 5 - 3$, and so 5 is a solution. If $x = 2$: $\sqrt{2 - 1} = \sqrt{1} = 1 \neq 2 - 3 = -1$, and so 2 is extraneous and must be discarded. The only solution of the given equation is then 5.

Example

$$\sqrt{5x - 1} + \sqrt{x - 1} - 2 = 0$$
$$\sqrt{5x - 1} = 2 - \sqrt{x - 1}$$
$$5x - 1 = 4 - 4\sqrt{x - 1} + x - 1$$
$$4\sqrt{x - 1} = 4 - 4x$$
$$16(x - 1) = 16 - 32x + 16x^2$$
$$16x^2 - 48x + 32 = 0$$
$$x^2 - 3x + 2 = 0$$
$$(x - 1)(x - 2) = 0$$
$$x = 1 \quad \text{or} \quad x = 2$$

Check: If $x = 1$: $\sqrt{5 - 1} + \sqrt{1 - 1} - 2 = 2 + 0 - 2 = 0$, and so 1 is a solution.

If $x = 2$: $\sqrt{10 - 1} + \sqrt{2 - 1} - 2 = 3 + 1 - 2 \neq 0$, and so 2 is extraneous and must be discarded. The only solution to the given equation is then 1.

Exercises

Solve and check each of the following equations.

1. $\sqrt{x + 4} = 3$
2. $\sqrt{3x - 5} - 5 = 0$
3. $\sqrt[3]{x - 1} = 4$
4. $\sqrt{11x - 8} = 6$
5. $\sqrt{x + 11} = 1 - x$
6. $\sqrt{3x - 2} + 3 = 0$
7. $\sqrt{x - 5} + 2 = 0$
8. $\sqrt{4x + 1} - \sqrt{2x - 3} = 2$
9. $\sqrt{x - 7} - \sqrt{5x - 4} = \sqrt{3x + 1}$
10. $\sqrt{3x - 11} = \sqrt{5 - x}$
11. $x - \sqrt{x} - 6 = 0$
12. $\sqrt{10 - x} - \sqrt{10 + x} + 2 = 0$
13. $\sqrt{6x + 4} + \sqrt{2x} - 6 = 0$
14. $\sqrt{2x + 1} - \sqrt{5x - 4} + 1 = 0$
15. $1/\sqrt{x} + 1/\sqrt{4x} = 3$
16. $1/(\sqrt{x} + \sqrt{4x}) = 3$
17. $\sqrt{3x + 4} + \sqrt{5 - x} = 5$
18. $(\sqrt{x} + \sqrt{3})/\sqrt{x + 3} = 1$

10. Ratio, Proportion, and Variation

Definition. *The ratio of a number m to a number n, written m : n, is a measure of relative size of the numbers. Two ratios m : n and r : s are equal, and we write m : n = r : s, if and only if m/n = r/s.*

If we use a ratio to describe the relative size of two quantities, it is important that we use the same unit of measure in each case.

Example. If the radii of two circles are $2''$ and $1'\ 2''$, the ratio of their respective areas is $4\pi : 196\pi$ or, more simply, $1 : 49$.

Definition. *A proportion is a statement of equality of two ratios. Thus, if m : n and r : s are equal ratios, we can express this fact in the form m : n = r : s or m : n :: r : s. For such a proportion, n and r are the means, and m and s are the extremes.*

The following result follows immediately from the definition of equality of two ratios: *In a proportion, the product of the means is equal to the product of the extremes.*

Example. If $3 : x = 5 : 4$, then $5x = 12$. Hence, $x = \frac{12}{5}$.

Definition. *If m : x = x : n, m : n = n : x, or m : n = r : x, then x is known, respectively, as a mean, third, or fourth proportional to the other numbers.*

Example.   Suppose we wish to find a mean proportional to 3 and 8. Then, $3 : x = x : 8$, $x^2 = 24$, and $x = \pm 2\sqrt{6}$. If the third proportional is desired, we solve $3 : 8 = 8 : y$ for y and obtain $3y = 64$ or $y = \frac{64}{3}$.

Example.   The solution of $3 : 5 = 7 : x$ for x is the fourth proportional to the numbers 3, 5, 7. Hence, $3x = 35$ and $x = \frac{35}{3}$.

In view of our definition of the equality of two ratios, it is often convenient not to distinguish between a ratio $a : b$ and the fraction a/b. This is especially so in the case of real variables x and y with y depending on x in such a way that y/x has a constant value. The following definition introduces the terminology that is used for this situation.

Definition.   *If x and y are real variables with y considered dependent on x such that $y = kx$ for some constant $k \neq 0$, then y is said to* vary directly with *or to* be directly proportional to x. *The constant k is called the* constant of proportionality.

Example.   If y varies directly with x and it is known that $y = 5$ when $x = 2$, we may easily find the relationship that connects y with x. For, by assumption, $5 = 2k$ and so $k = \frac{5}{2}$. Hence, $y = \frac{5}{2}x$ or $5x - 2y = 0$. From this equation it is now possible to find any associated pairs of values of x and y.

In the case of direct variation just discussed, the absolute value of y increases or decreases according as the absolute value of x increases or decreases. The opposite situation is described in the next definition.

Definition.   *If x and y are real variables with y considered dependent on x such that $xy = k$ for some constant $k \neq 0$, then y is said to* vary inversely with, *or to* be inversely proportional to, x.

Example.   The time t required to travel a given distance is clearly inversely proportional to the velocity v, so that $vt = k$. If it takes 6 hours to make a certain trip at a speed of 50 miles per hour, we must have $(50)(6) = k$, so that $k = 300$. The relationship between v and t is then given by the equation $vt = 300$. It is now easy to find the time necessary to make the same trip at, say, 60 miles per hour, because $60t = 300$ and so $t = 5$.

It should be clear that problems involving direct variation can also be solved by using proportions, but in many contexts it is more useful to have the *law of variation*—direct or inverse—in the form of an equation. We may point out, as a final comment, that *both* types of variation may be involved in the description of one physical law.

Exercises

1. Simplify each of the following ratios: (a) $4 : 8$, (b) $\frac{5}{2} : \frac{13}{4}$; (c) $\frac{13}{4} : \frac{9}{2}$; (d) $2 : \frac{17}{8}$; (e) $(x^2 - y^2) : (x + y)$.

2. Find the ratio of the first to the second of each of the following pairs of measurements of length: (a) 2 inches, 3 feet; (b) 8 inches, $2\frac{1}{4}$ feet; (c) 4 feet, 2 yards; (d) 5 centimeters, 45 millimeters.

3. Find the ratio of the first to the second of each of the following pairs of measurements of time: (a) 15 minutes, $1\frac{1}{2}$ hours; (b) 8 hours, 2 days; (c) 24 seconds, 10 minutes.

4. Express each of the following ratios in simplified form:
   (a) $(1 + 1/a) : (1 - 1/a^2)$; (b) $1/(x - 1) : 2/(x^2 - 4x + 3)$;
   (c) $1/x : 3/x^2$.

5. Separate 125 into two parts in the ratio $3 : 2$.

6. Two numbers are in the ratio $2 : 5$, but if 1 is added to each, they are in the ratio $3 : 7$. Find the numbers.

7. Solve each of the following proportions for the unknown member: (a) $2 : 5 = x : 8$; (b) $3 : x = 2 : 9$; (c) $4 : 7 = x : 21$; (d) $x : 12 = 3 : 4$.

8. Find the mean proportional to each of the following pairs of numbers: (a) $3, 12$; (b) $8, 2$; (c) $2, 32$; (d) $3, 8$; (e) $5, 12$.

9. Find the third proportional to a and b if (a) $a = 4, b = 9$; (b) $a = 3, b = 10$; (c) $a = 8, b = 24$.

10. Find the fourth proportional to a, b, and c given that (a) $a = 2, b = 3, c = 4$; (b) $a = 7, b = 11, c = 21$; (c) $a = -3, b = 8, c = 10$.

11. Solve the proportion $(2 - x) : (2 + x) = (1 - x) : (1 + x)$ for x.

12. Solve the proportion $x : (x - 2) = 3 : 4$ for x.

13. Express y in terms of x if it is known that y varies directly with x and (a) $y = 6$ when $x = 4$; (b) $y = 12$ when $x = 5$; (c) $y = 15$ when $x = 18$.

14. Express y in terms of x if it is known that y varies inversely with x and (a) $y = 6$ when $x = 4$; (b) $y = 20$ when $x = 5$; (c) $y = -20$ when $x = -3$.

15. The velocity v of a body falling from rest in the vicinity of the earth's surface is directly proportional to the time t of fall. If the body reaches a speed of 48 feet per second after falling for $1\frac{1}{2}$ seconds, find the equation that connects velocity with time of fall. How far will the body fall in 3 seconds (assuming it has not already hit ground)?

16. Examine the situation described in Problem 15 and decide whether the distance traveled by a falling body is directly proportional to its time of fall.

17. An automobile travels 126 miles in 2 hours and 20 minutes at a constant speed. If the same speed is assumed, determine (a) how far the automobile would travel in 3 hours; (b) how much time would be required for a trip of 297 miles?

18. The current flow I in a wire is inversely proportional to the resistance R of the wire if the electric potential at the ends of the wire remains constant. If the current flow in a certain wire is 2.5 amperes when the resistance is 1000 ohms, find (a) the equation connecting I and R; (b) the current flow if $R = 2500$ ohms.

19. The number of complete swings (i.e., the *period*) of a pendulum varies inversely with the square root of its length. If an 8-foot pendulum has an approximate period of 3 seconds, determine the approximate length of a pendulum whose period is 1 second.

20. If y varies directly with the square of x and inversely with the cube of z, express y in terms of x and z. If $y = 16$ when $x = 2$ and $z = 1$, find y when $x = z = 3$.

Test on Review Material

1. Add the numbers in each of the following collections: (a) $\frac{1}{2}$, $-\frac{2}{3}$, $\frac{3}{4}$, -2; (b) $-\frac{5}{6}$, $\frac{3}{5}$, $\frac{2}{15}$, $-\frac{5}{12}$.

2. Divide the first number by the second in each of the following pairs: (a) $-\frac{5}{4}$, $\frac{2}{3}$; (b) $\frac{5}{6}$, $-\frac{3}{7}$; (c) $\frac{3}{5}$, 5; (d) 4, $-\frac{2}{5}$.

3. Simplify each of the following expressions:

    (a) $\dfrac{\dfrac{x}{x-1}-1}{\dfrac{x}{1-x}+1}$ (b) $\dfrac{\dfrac{1}{x+3}+1}{x-\dfrac{12}{x+1}}$

4. (a) From the sum of $x^2/2$, $-5x^2/4$, and $2 - 3x + x^2$, subtract the sum of $2x^2/3$ and $-5x$. (b) Divide $a/b - b/a$ by $1/b - 1/a$, and simplify the result.

5. Factor completely each of the following expressions: (a) $m^2 - 4n^2$; (b) $t^2 + 6t - 55$; (c) $1 - y^6$.

6. Factor completely each of the following expressions: (a) $am + bm + b + a$; (b) $(1 - x)^2 - (x - y)^2$; (c) $12x^2 + 25x - 7$.

7. Factor completely each of the following expressions: (a) $1 - x^2 - 2xy - y^2$; (b) $(x + 1)^3 - 9(x + 1)^2 + 8(x + 1)$.

8. Use the quadratic formula to solve each of the following equations: (a) $2s^2 - 5s + 1 = 0$; (b) $2x^2 + 3x + 1 = 0$.

9. Solve each of the following quadratic equations, by first factoring the left member: (a) $2x^2 - x - 1 = 0$; (b) $6x^2 + 5x - 6 = 0$.

10. Solve each of the following quadratic equations by completing squares in the left members: (a) $4x^2 - x - 5 = 0$; (b) $2y^2 - 4y - 1 = 0$.

11. Solve each of the following systems of linear equations, and check:

    (a) $x + y = 11$ (b) $2y + 5z = 2$
         $2x - 3y = 22$ $4y + z = 13$

12. Solve each of the following systems of equations, and check:

    (a) $x + y = 18$ (b) $1/x + 1/y = 7$
        $y + z = 13$ $1/y + 1/z = \frac{11}{2}$
        $z + x = 5$ $1/z + 1/x = \frac{5}{2}$

13. (a) Write each of the following in radical form: $2^{1/2}$, $3^{2/3}$, $4^{3/2}$, $6^{-1/2}$, $2^{-2/3}$. (b) Write each of the following in exponential form: $\sqrt[5]{5}$, $\sqrt[3]{3^2}$, $1/\sqrt{3}$, $3/\sqrt[3]{5^2}$.

14. Simplify each of the following expressions: (a) $(x^{-2}y^3y^{-2})/(3x^2y^{-5}z)$; (b) $[(12x^3)(4x^{-2})^3(xy)^2]/[(3xy)^3(2x^{-3})^2]$.

15. (a) The heights of two posts are 18 inches and $3\frac{1}{2}$ feet, respectively. What is the ratio of their heights? (b) Solve the proportion $3 : \frac{11}{2} = (x - 1) : (x + 1)$ for x.

16. Solve the equation $\sqrt{3x + 7} + \sqrt{x + 1} - 2 = 0$ for x.

17. Solve the equation $\sqrt{3y - 2} - 2 = 8/\sqrt{3y - 2}$ for y.

18. The force of electrical attraction between two oppositely charged bodies is inversely proportional to the square of the distance separating them. If the force of attraction is 50 dynes when the bodies are 8 centimeters apart, determine how far apart they should be if the force is to be reduced to 40 dynes.

Appendix B
Matrix Inversion

If $A = [a_{ij}]$ and $B = [b_{ij}]$ are two n by n matrices, the *product* $AB = C$ is defined so that $C = [c_{ij}]$, where $c_{ij} = \sum_{k=1}^{n} a_{ik}b_{kj}$. The multiplication of a matrix A by any real number c is also defined by $cA = [a'_{ij}]$ where $a'_{ij} = ca_{ij}$. This latter kind of multiplication is then performed by merely multiplying each entry of the matrix by c.

If $AB = I$, where I is the n by n identity matrix, it can be shown also that $BA = I$, and B is called the *inverse* of A (and likewise A is the inverse of B). The inverse of a matrix—if it exists—can be shown to be unique, and it is customary to denote the inverse of A by A^{-1}. The necessary and sufficient condition for the existence of the inverse of a square matrix A is that $|A| \neq 0$. If $|A| \neq 0$, A is said to be a *nonsingular*, or *invertible*, matrix, and there are two common methods for determining its inverse. The study of matrix inversion properly belongs in a more intensive course in matrix theory, but we shall give a brief presentation of two methods for inverting a nonsingular matrix.

(a) *The Adjoint Method.* If A_{ij} is the cofactor of the element a_{ij} of the nonsingular matrix $A = [a_{ij}]$, $A^{-1} = \dfrac{1}{|A|} [A^*_{ij}]$, where $A^*_{ij} = A_{ji}$. The matrix $A^* = [A^*_{ij}]$ is called the *adjoint* of A. [Note that the element in the (i, j) position in A^* is the cofactor of the element in the (j, i) position in A.] The verification that A^{-1}, defined in this way, is in fact the inverse can be checked by actual multiplication, and we illustrate for the general case of $n = 3$.

$$
\begin{aligned}
A^*A &= \begin{bmatrix} A_{11} & A_{21} & A_{31} \\ A_{12} & A_{22} & A_{32} \\ A_{13} & A_{23} & A_{33} \end{bmatrix} \begin{bmatrix} a_{11} & a_{12} & a_{13} \\ a_{21} & a_{22} & a_{23} \\ a_{31} & a_{32} & a_{33} \end{bmatrix} \\
&= \begin{bmatrix} |A| & 0 & 0 \\ 0 & |A| & 0 \\ 0 & 0 & |A| \end{bmatrix} = |A| \begin{bmatrix} 1 & 0 & 0 \\ 0 & 1 & 0 \\ 0 & 0 & 1 \end{bmatrix} = |A|I
\end{aligned}
$$

and a similar computation shows that $AA^* = |A|I$. In the above multiplication, it should be observed that we have used Theorem 4.1 of Chapter 2, as well as the definition of $|A|$ in §2.3. It then follows that $A^{-1} = (1/|A|)[A_{ij}^*]$, as asserted.

Example 1. As an illustration, let us determine A^{-1}, where

$$A = \begin{bmatrix} 1 & 0 & -1 \\ 0 & 2 & 2 \\ 1 & 1 & -1 \end{bmatrix}$$

Here $|A| = -2$, and

$$A^* = \begin{bmatrix} -4 & -1 & 2 \\ 2 & 0 & -2 \\ -2 & -1 & 2 \end{bmatrix}$$

Hence,

$$A^{-1} = -\tfrac{1}{2}\begin{bmatrix} -4 & -1 & 2 \\ 2 & 0 & -2 \\ -2 & -1 & 2 \end{bmatrix} = \begin{bmatrix} 2 & \tfrac{1}{2} & -1 \\ -1 & 0 & 1 \\ 1 & \tfrac{1}{2} & -1 \end{bmatrix}$$

and it is easy to verify that

$$\begin{bmatrix} 1 & 0 & -1 \\ 0 & 2 & 2 \\ 1 & 1 & -1 \end{bmatrix}\begin{bmatrix} 2 & \tfrac{1}{2} & -1 \\ -1 & 0 & 1 \\ 1 & \tfrac{1}{2} & -1 \end{bmatrix} = \begin{bmatrix} 2 & \tfrac{1}{2} & -1 \\ -1 & 0 & 1 \\ 1 & \tfrac{1}{2} & -1 \end{bmatrix}\begin{bmatrix} 1 & 0 & -1 \\ 0 & 2 & 2 \\ 1 & 1 & -1 \end{bmatrix}$$

$$= \begin{bmatrix} 1 & 0 & 0 \\ 0 & 1 & 0 \\ 0 & 0 & 1 \end{bmatrix} = I$$

(b) *The L-array Method.* If $|A| \neq 0$, it is possible to use a sequence of elementary row operations, as discussed in §2.5, and reduce A to the identity matrix I. We may also define elementary *column* operations as analogues of the elementary row operations, and it is sometimes simpler to reduce A to I by a sequence of elementary row *and* column operations, using operations of both types as convenient. It is shown in courses in matrix theory that any elementary row (column) operation can be effected on a matrix A by a premultiplication (postmultiplication) of A by the matrix that is the result of performing the same operation on the identity matrix I. Hence, the following practical procedure may be adopted:

Place one identity matrix I directly above the given nonsingular matrix A and another beside A on its right, so that we have the resulting array—in the shape of an L:

$$\begin{array}{cc} I & \\ A & I \end{array}$$

Reduce A to I, by any sequence of row or column operations, including the identity matrix on the right as an extension of the rows of A, and the identity matrix above as an extension of the columns of A. When A has been reduced to I, the resulting array has the form

$$C$$
$$I \quad D$$

where C and D are the resulting transforms of the original identity matrices. Then, it can be shown that $A^{-1} = CD$.

We shall not prove this result, but shall illustrate the method by using the matrix of Example 1. It may be pointed out in passing that if only row (or only column) operations are used—and this may be desirable—we obtain at once that $A^{-1} = D$ (or $A^{-1} = C$).

Example 2. If we form the L-array required by this method, for the matrix of Example 1, the result is

$$\begin{bmatrix} 1 & 0 & 0 \\ 0 & 1 & 0 \\ 0 & 0 & 1 \end{bmatrix}$$

$$\begin{bmatrix} 1 & 0 & -1 \\ 0 & 2 & 2 \\ 1 & 1 & -1 \end{bmatrix} \begin{bmatrix} 1 & 0 & 0 \\ 0 & 1 & 0 \\ 0 & 0 & 1 \end{bmatrix}$$

Let us now designate the rows and columns of the *extensions* of A by (1), (2), (3) and (1)′, (2)′, (3)′, respectively. Further we shall use the symbolism of §2.5 to indicate the row and column operations to be performed on the array and abbreviate it somewhat. For example, (3) − (1) will mean that the first row is to be subtracted from the third row; (3)′ + (1)′ will mean that the first column is to be added to the third column (note order); $\frac{1}{2}$(2) will mean that the elements of the second row are to be multiplied by $\frac{1}{2}$; etc. There is nothing unique about the sequence of operations to be used in the reduction of A to I, but if we use the sequence listed below in the order of listing, the result is the L-array shown below.

$(3) - (1), (3)' + (1)', (3)' - (2)', \frac{1}{2}(2), (3) - (2), (-1)(3)$

$$\begin{bmatrix} 1 & 0 & 1 \\ 0 & 1 & -1 \\ 0 & 0 & 1 \end{bmatrix}$$

$$\begin{bmatrix} 1 & 0 & 0 \\ 0 & 1 & 0 \\ 0 & 0 & 1 \end{bmatrix}\begin{bmatrix} 1 & 0 & 0 \\ 0 & \frac{1}{2} & 0 \\ 1 & \frac{1}{2} & -1 \end{bmatrix}$$

It then follows, from the unproved assertion above, that

$$A^{-1} = \begin{bmatrix} 1 & 0 & 1 \\ 0 & 1 & -1 \\ 0 & 0 & 1 \end{bmatrix} \begin{bmatrix} 1 & 0 & 0 \\ 0 & \frac{1}{2} & 0 \\ 1 & \frac{1}{2} & -1 \end{bmatrix} = \begin{bmatrix} 2 & \frac{1}{2} & -1 \\ -1 & 0 & 1 \\ 1 & \frac{1}{2} & -1 \end{bmatrix}$$

as before.

We now consider the method of solving a system of n linear equations in n unknowns by matrix inversion. The name "coefficient matrix" has already been used in Chapter 2 to refer to the ordered array of coefficients of the unknowns of the equations, but at that time we did not consider either the unknowns or right members of the equations as being involved in any of these matrices. However, if we use X to denote the n by 1 (or "column") matrix whose entries in order are the unknowns and B to denote the column matrix of ordered right members, we may replace the system of equations by the simple matrix equation

$$AX = B$$

It is an elementary computation to verify that this matrix equation is in fact equivalent to the original system of n equations. We make the assumption—without proof—that the multiplication of matrices is associative, and assert that *the above matrix equation can be readily solved, provided A is a nonsingular matrix.* In fact, if A^{-1} exists, a multiplication on the left of both members of the above equation yields $A^{-1}(AX) = A^{-1}B$ and this—by associativity of multiplication—is equivalent to $IX = A^{-1}B$ or, even more simply, to

$$X = A^{-1}B$$

Example 3.   Use a matrix inversion method to solve the system of equations

$$\begin{aligned} x \quad\quad - z &= 1 \\ 2y + 2z &= 2 \\ x + y - z &= 1 \end{aligned}$$

SOLUTION.   In this case, the system of equations can be expressed in the form $AX = B$, where

$$A = \begin{bmatrix} 1 & 0 & -1 \\ 0 & 2 & 2 \\ 1 & 1 & -1 \end{bmatrix} \quad X = \begin{bmatrix} x \\ y \\ z \end{bmatrix} \quad B = \begin{bmatrix} 1 \\ 2 \\ 1 \end{bmatrix}$$

We have previously determined A^{-1} (in Example 1 and Example 2), and so

$$X = A^{-1}B = \begin{bmatrix} 2 & \frac{1}{2} & -1 \\ -1 & 0 & 1 \\ 1 & \frac{1}{2} & -1 \end{bmatrix} \begin{bmatrix} 1 \\ 2 \\ 1 \end{bmatrix} = \begin{bmatrix} 2 \\ 0 \\ 1 \end{bmatrix}$$

Hence, $x = 2$, $y = 0$, $z = 1$.

It must be noted, of course, that the methods of this Appendix are not available for solving a linear system *unless* the number of equations is equal to the number of unknowns and the determinant of the coefficient matrix is nonzero. If this determinant is nonzero and one of these methods is to be used, method (b) is to be preferred except for the case $n = 3$, in which case the two methods are of approximately equal merit. The development of skill in these two methods may be acquired by solving some of the linear systems given in the problem sets of Chapter 2.

Tables

TABLE 1   FOUR-PLACE COMMON LOGARITHMS

N	0	1	2	3	4	5	6	7	8	9
10	0000	0043	0086	0128	0170	0212	0253	0294	0334	0374
11	0414	0453	0492	0531	0569	0607	0645	0682	0719	0755
12	0792	0828	0864	0899	0934	0969	1004	1038	1072	1106
13	1139	1173	1206	1239	1271	1303	1335	1367	1399	1430
14	1461	1492	1523	1553	1584	1614	1644	1673	1703	1732
15	1761	1790	1818	1847	1875	1903	1931	1959	1987	2014
16	2041	2068	2095	2122	2148	2175	2201	2227	2253	2279
17	2304	2330	2355	2380	2405	2430	2455	2480	2504	2529
18	2553	2577	2601	2625	2648	2672	2695	2718	2742	2765
19	2788	2810	2833	2856	2878	2900	2923	2945	2967	2989
20	3010	3032	3054	3075	3096	3118	3139	3160	3181	3201
21	3222	3243	3263	3284	3304	3324	3345	3365	3385	3404
22	3424	3444	3464	3483	3502	3522	3541	3560	3579	3598
23	3617	3636	3655	3674	3692	3711	3729	3747	3766	3784
24	3802	3820	3838	3856	3874	3892	3909	3927	3945	3962
25	3979	3997	4014	4031	4048	4065	4082	4099	4116	4133
26	4150	4166	4183	4200	4216	4232	4249	4265	4281	4298
27	4314	4330	4346	4262	4378	4393	4409	4425	4440	4456
28	4472	4487	4502	4518	4533	4548	4564	4579	4594	4609
29	4624	4639	4654	4669	4683	4698	4713	4728	4742	4757
30	4771	4786	4800	4814	4829	4843	4857	4871	4886	4900
31	4914	4928	4942	4955	4969	4983	4997	5011	5024	5038
32	5051	5065	5079	5092	5105	5119	5132	5145	5159	5172
33	5185	5198	5211	5224	5237	5250	5263	5276	5289	5302
34	5315	5328	5340	5353	5366	5378	5391	5403	5416	5428
35	5441	5453	5465	5478	5490	5502	5514	5527	5539	5551
36	5563	5575	5587	5599	5611	5623	5635	5647	5658	5670
37	5682	5694	5705	5717	5729	5740	5752	5763	5775	5786
38	5798	5809	5821	5832	5843	5855	5866	5877	5888	5899
39	5911	5922	5933	5944	5955	5966	5977	5988	5999	6010
40	6021	6031	6042	6053	6064	6075	6085	6096	6107	6117
41	6128	6138	6149	6160	6170	6180	6191	6201	6212	6222
42	6232	6243	6253	6263	6274	6284	6294	6304	6314	6325
43	6335	6345	6355	6365	6375	6385	6395	6405	6415	6425
44	6435	6444	6454	6464	6474	6484	6493	6503	6513	6522
45	6532	6542	6551	6561	6571	6580	6590	6599	6609	6618
46	6628	6637	6646	6656	6665	6675	6684	6693	6702	6712
47	6721	6730	6739	6749	6758	6767	6776	6785	6794	6803
48	6812	6821	6830	6839	6848	6857	6866	6875	6884	6893
49	6902	6911	6920	6928	6937	6946	6955	6964	6972	6981
50	6990	6998	7007	7016	7024	7033	7042	7050	7059	7067
51	7076	7084	7093	7101	7110	7118	7126	7135	7143	7152
52	7160	7168	7177	7185	7193	7202	7210	7218	7226	7235
53	7243	7251	7259	7267	7275	7284	7292	7300	7308	7316
54	7324	7332	7340	7348	7356	7364	7372	7380	7388	7396
N	0	1	2	3	4	5	6	7	8	9

TABLE 1 FOUR-PLACE COMMON LOGARITHMS

N	0	1	2	3	4	5	6	7	8	9
55	7404	7412	7419	7427	7435	7443	7451	7459	7466	7474
56	7482	7490	7497	7505	7513	7520	7528	7536	7543	7551
57	7559	7566	7574	7582	7589	7597	7604	7612	7619	7627
58	7634	7642	7649	7657	7664	7672	7679	7686	7694	7701
59	7709	7716	7723	7731	7738	7745	7752	7760	7767	7774
60	7782	7789	7796	7803	7810	7818	7825	7832	7839	7846
61	7853	7860	7868	7875	7882	7889	7896	7903	7910	7917
62	7924	7931	7938	7945	7952	7959	7966	7973	7980	7987
63	7993	8000	8007	8014	8021	8028	8035	8041	8048	8055
64	8062	8069	8075	8082	8089	8096	8102	8109	8116	8122
65	8129	8136	8142	8149	8156	8162	8169	8176	8182	8189
66	8195	8202	8209	8215	8222	8228	8235	8241	8248	8254
67	8261	8267	8274	8280	8287	8293	8299	8306	8312	8319
68	8325	8331	8338	8344	8351	8357	8363	8370	8376	8382
69	8388	8395	8401	8407	8414	8420	8426	8432	8439	8445
70	8451	8457	8463	8470	8476	8482	8488	8494	8500	8506
71	8513	8519	8525	8531	8537	8543	8549	8555	8561	8567
72	8573	8579	8585	8591	8597	8603	8609	8615	8621	8627
73	8633	8639	8645	8651	8657	8663	8669	8675	8681	8686
74	8692	8698	8704	8710	8716	8722	8727	8733	8739	8745
75	8751	8756	8762	8768	8774	8779	8785	8791	8797	8802
76	8808	8814	8820	8825	8831	8837	8842	8848	8854	8859
77	8865	8871	8876	8882	8887	8893	8899	8904	8910	8915
78	8921	8927	8932	8938	8943	8949	8954	8960	8965	8971
79	8976	8982	8987	8993	8998	9004	9009	9015	9020	9025
80	9031	9036	9042	9047	9053	9058	9063	9069	9074	9079
81	9085	9090	9096	9101	9106	9112	9117	9122	9128	9133
82	9138	9143	9149	9154	9159	9165	9170	9175	9180	9186
83	9191	9196	9201	9206	9212	9217	9222	9227	9232	9238
84	9243	9248	9253	9258	9263	9269	9274	9279	9284	9289
85	9294	9299	9304	9309	9315	9230	9325	9330	9335	9340
86	9345	9350	9355	9360	9365	9370	9375	9380	9385	9390
87	9395	9400	9405	9410	9415	9420	9425	9430	9435	9440
88	9445	9450	9455	9460	9465	9469	9474	9479	9484	9489
89	9494	9499	9504	9509	9513	9518	9523	9528	9533	9538
90	9542	9547	9552	9557	9562	9566	9571	9576	9581	9586
91	9590	9595	9600	9605	9609	9614	9619	9624	9628	9633
92	9638	9643	9647	9652	9657	9661	9666	9671	9675	9680
93	9685	9689	9694	9699	9703	9708	9713	9717	9722	9727
94	9731	9736	9741	9745	9750	9754	9759	9763	9768	9773
95	9777	9782	9786	9791	9795	9800	9805	9809	9814	9818
96	9823	9827	9832	9836	9841	9845	9850	9854	9859	9863
97	9868	9872	9877	9881	9886	9890	9894	9899	9903	9908
98	9912	9917	9921	9926	9930	9934	9939	9943	9948	9952
99	9956	9961	9965	9969	9974	9978	9983	9987	9991	9996
N	0	1	2	3	4	5	6	7	8	9

TABLE 2 FOUR-PLACE VALUES OF THE CIRCULAR FUNCTIONS

x (degrees)	x (numbers or radians)	$\sin x$	$\tan x$	$\sec x$	$\csc x$	$\cot x$	$\cos x$		
0.0	0.0000	0.00000	0.00000	1.0000	—	—	1.0000	1.5708	**90.0**
0.1	0.0017	0.00175	0.00175	1.0000	572.96	573.0	1.0000	1.5691	89.9
0.2	0.0035	0.00349	0.00349	1.0000	286.48	286.5	1.0000	1.5673	89.8
0.3	0.0052	0.00524	0.00524	1.0000	190.99	191.0	1.0000	1.5656	89.7
0.4	0.0070	0.00698	0.00698	1.0000	143.24	143.24	1.0000	1.5638	89.6
0.5	0.0087	0.00873	0.00873	1.0000	114.59	114.59	1.0000	1.5621	**89.5**
0.6	0.0105	0.01047	0.01047	1.0001	95.495	95.49	0.9999	1.5603	89.4
0.7	0.0122	0.01222	0.01222	1.0001	81.753	81.85	0.9999	1.5586	89.3
0.8	0.0140	0.01396	0.02396	1.0001	71.622	71.62	0.9999	1.5568	89.2
0.9	0.0157	0.01571	0.01571	1.0001	63.665	63.66	0.9999	1.5551	89.1
1.0	0.0175	0.01745	0.01746	1.0002	57.299	57.29	0.9998	1.5533	**89.0**
1.1	0.0192	0.01920	0.01920	1.0002	52.090	52.08	0.9998	1.5516	88.9
1.2	0.0209	0.02094	0.02095	1.0002	47.750	47.74	0.9998	1.5499	88.8
1.3	0.0227	0.02269	0.02269	1.0003	44.077	44.07	0.9997	1.5481	88.7
1.4	0.0244	0.02443	0.02444	1.0003	40.930	40.92	0.9997	1.5464	88.6
1.5	0.0262	0.02618	0.02619	1.0003	38.202	38.19	0.9997	1.5446	**88.5**
1.6	0.0279	0.02792	0.02793	1.0004	35.815	35.80	0.9996	1.5429	88.4
1.7	0.0297	0.02967	0.02968	1.0004	33.708	33.69	0.9996	1.5411	88.3
1.8	0.0314	0.03141	0.03143	1.0005	31.836	31.82	0.9995	1.5394	88.2
1.9	0.0332	0.03316	0.03317	1.0006	30.161	30.14	0.9995	1.5376	88.1
2.0	0.0349	0.03490	0.03492	1.0006	28.654	28.64	0.9994	1.5359	**88.0**
2.1	0.0367	0.03664	0.03667	1.0007	27.290	27.27	0.9993	1.5341	87.9
2.2	0.0384	0.03839	0.03842	1.0007	26.050	26.03	0.9993	1.5324	87.8
2.3	0.0401	0.04013	0.04016	1.0008	24.918	24.90	0.9992	1.5307	87.7
2.4	0.0419	0.04188	0.04191	1.0009	23.880	23.86	0.9991	1.5289	87.6
2.5	0.0436	0.04362	0.04366	1.0010	22.926	22.90	0.9990	1.5272	**87.5**
2.6	0.0454	0.04536	0.04541	1.0010	22.044	22.02	0.9990	1.5254	87.4
2.7	0.0471	0.04711	0.04716	1.0011	21.229	21.20	0.9989	1.5237	87.3
2.8	0.0489	0.04885	0.04891	1.0012	20.471	20.45	0.9988	1.5219	87.2
2.9	0.0506	0.05059	0.05066	1.0013	19.766	19.74	0.9987	1.5202	87.1
3.0	0.0524	0.05234	0.05241	1.0014	19.107	19.081	0.9986	1.5184	**87.0**
3.1	0.0541	0.05408	0.05416	1.0015	18.492	18.464	0.9985	1.5167	86.9
3.2	0.0559	0.05582	0.05591	1.0016	17.914	17.886	0.9984	1.5149	86.8
3.3	0.0576	0.05756	0.05766	1.0017	17.372	17.343	0.9983	1.5132	86.7
3.4	0.0593	0.05931	0.05941	1.0018	16.832	16.832	0.9982	1.5115	86.6
3.5	0.0611	0.06105	0.06116	1.0019	16.380	16.350	0.9981	1.5097	**86.5**
3.6	0.0628	0.06279	0.06291	1.0020	15.926	15.895	0.9980	1.5080	86.4
3.7	0.0646	0.06453	0.06467	1.0021	15.496	15.464	0.9979	1.5062	86.3
3.8	0.0663	0.06627	0.06642	1.0022	15.089	15.056	0.9978	1.5045	86.2
3.9	0.0681	0.06802	0.06817	1.0023	14.703	14.669	0.9977	1.5027	86.1
4.0	0.0698	0.06976	0.06993	1.0024	14.336	14.301	0.9976	1.5010	**86.0**
4.1	0.0716	0.07150	0.07168	1.0026	13.987	13.951	0.9974	1.4992	85.9
4.2	0.0733	0.07324	0.07344	1.0027	13.654	13.617	0.9973	1.4975	85.8
4.3	0.0750	0.07498	0.07519	1.0028	13.337	13.300	0.9972	1.4957	85.7
4.4	0.0768	0.07672	0.07695	1.0030	13.035	12.996	0.9971	1.4940	85.6
		$\cos x$	$\cot x$	$\csc x$	$\sec x$	$\tan x$	$\sin x$	x (numbers or radians)	x (degrees)

TABLE 2 FOUR-PLACE VALUES OF THE CIRCULAR FUNCTIONS

x (degrees)	x (numbers or radians)	sin x	tan x	sec x	csc x	cot x	cos x		
4.5	0.0785	0.07846	0.07870	1.0031	12.745	12.706	0.9969	1.4923	**85.5**
4.6	0.0803	0.08020	0.08046	1.0032	12.469	12.429	0.9968	1.4905	85.4
4.7	0.0820	0.08194	0.08221	1.0034	12.204	12.163	0.9966	1.4888	85.3
4.8	0.0838	0.08368	0.08397	1.0035	11.951	11.909	0.9965	1.4870	85.2
4.9	0.0855	0.08542	0.08573	1.0037	11.707	11.664	0.9963	1.4853	85.1
5.0	0.0873	0.08716	0.08749	1.0038	11.474	11.430	0.9962	1.4835	**85.0**
5.1	0.0890	0.08889	0.08925	1.0040	11.249	11.205	0.9960	1.4818	84.9
5.2	0.0908	0.09063	0.09101	1.0041	11.034	10.988	0.9959	1.4800	84.8
5.3	0.0925	0.09237	0.09277	1.0043	10.826	10.780	0.9957	1.4783	84.7
5.4	0.0942	0.09411	0.09453	1.0045	10.626	10.579	0.9956	1.4765	84.6
5.5	0.0960	0.09585	0.09629	1.0046	10.433	10.385	0.9954	1.4748	**84.5**
5.6	0.0977	0.09758	0.09805	1.0048	10.248	10.199	0.9952	1.4731	84.4
5.7	0.0995	0.09932	0.09981	1.0050	10.068	10.019	0.9951	1.4713	84.3
5.8	0.1012	0.10106	0.10158	1.0051	9.8955	9.845	0.9949	1.4696	84.2
5.9	0.1030	0.10279	0.10334	1.0053	9.7283	9.677	0.9947	1.4678	84.1
6.0	0.1047	0.10453	0.10510	1.0055	9.5668	9.514	0.9945	1.4661	**84.0**
6.1	0.1065	0.10626	0.10687	1.0057	9.4105	9.357	0.9943	1.4643	83.9
6.2	0.1082	0.10800	0.10863	1.0059	9.2593	9.205	0.9942	1.4626	83.8
6.3	0.1100	0.10973	0.11040	1.0061	9.1129	9.058	0.9940	1.4608	83.7
6.4	0.1117	0.11147	0.11217	1.0063	8.9711	8.915	0.9938	1.4591	83.6
6.5	0.1134	0.11320	0.11394	1.0065	8.8337	8.777	0.9936	1.4573	**83.5**
6.6	0.1152	0.11494	0.11570	1.0067	8.7004	8.643	0.9934	1.4556	83.4
6.7	0.1169	0.11667	0.11747	1.0069	8.5711	8.513	0.9932	1.4539	83.3
6.8	0.1187	0.11840	0.11924	1.0071	8.4457	8.386	0.9930	1.4521	83.2
6.9	0.1204	0.12014	0.12101	1.0073	8.3238	8.264	0.9928	1.4504	83.1
7.0	0.1222	0.12187	0.12278	1.0075	8.2055	8.144	0.9925	1.4486	**83.0**
7.1	0.1239	0.12360	0.12456	1.0077	8.0905	8.028	0.9923	1.4469	82.9
7.2	0.1257	0.12533	0.12633	1.0079	7.9787	7.916	0.9921	1.4451	82.8
7.3	0.1274	0.12706	0.12810	1.0082	7.8700	7.806	0.9919	1.4434	82.7
7.4	0.1292	0.12880	0.12988	1.0084	7.7642	7.700	0.9917	1.4416	82.6
7.5	0.1309	0.13053	0.13165	1.0086	7.6613	7.596	0.9914	1.4399	**82.5**
7.6	0.1326	0.13226	0.13343	1.0089	7.5611	7.495	0.9912	1.4382	82.4
7.7	0.1344	0.13399	0.13521	1.0091	7.4635	7.396	0.9910	1.4364	82.3
7.8	0.1361	0.13572	0.13698	1.0093	7.3684	7.300	0.9907	1.4347	82.2
7.9	0.1379	0.13744	0.13876	1.0096	7.2757	7.027	0.9905	1.4329	82.1
8.0	0.1396	0.13917	0.14054	1.0098	7.1853	7.115	0.9903	1.4312	**82.0**
8.1	0.1414	0.14090	0.14232	1.0101	7.0972	7.026	0.9900	1.4294	81.9
8.2	0.1431	0.14263	0.14410	1.0103	7.0112	6.940	0.9898	1.4277	81.8
8.3	0.1449	0.14436	0.14588	1.0106	6.9273	6.855	0.9895	1.4259	81.7
8.4	0.1466	0.14608	0.14767	1.0108	6.8454	6.772	0.9893	1.4242	81.6
8.5	0.1484	0.14781	0.14945	1.0111	6.7655	6.691	0.9890	1.4224	**81.5**
8.6	0.1501	0.14954	0.15124	1.0114	6.6874	6.612	0.9888	1.4207	81.4
8.7	0.1518	0.15126	0.15302	1.0116	6.6111	6.535	0.9885	1.4190	81.3
8.8	0.1536	0.15299	0.15481	1.0119	6.5366	6.460	0.9882	1.4172	81.2
8.9	0.1553	0.15471	0.15660	1.0122	6.4637	6.386	0.9880	1.4155	81.1

	cos x	cot x	csc x	sec x	tan x	sin x	x (numbers or radians)	x (degrees)

TABLE 2 FOUR-PLACE VALUES OF THE CIRCULAR FUNCTIONS

x (degrees)	x (numbers or radians)	$\sin x$	$\tan x$	$\sec x$	$\csc x$	$\cot x$	$\cos x$		
9.0	0.1571	0.15643	0.15838	1.0125	6.3925	6.314	0.9877	1.4137	**81.0**
9.1	0.1588	0.15816	0.16017	1.0127	6.3228	6.243	0.9874	1.4120	80.9
9.2	0.1606	0.15988	0.16196	1.0130	6.2546	6.174	0.9871	1.4102	80.8
9.3	0.1623	0.16160	0.61376	1.0133	6.1880	6.107	0.9869	1.4085	80.7
9.4	0.1641	0.16333	0.16555	1.0136	6.1227	6.041	0.9866	1.4067	80.6
9.5	0.1658	0.16505	0.16734	1.0139	6.0589	5.976	0.9863	1.4050	**80.5**
9.6	0.1676	0.16677	0.16914	1.0142	5.9963	5.912	0.9860	1.4032	80.4
9.7	0.1693	0.16849	0.17093	1.0145	5.9351	5.850	0.9857	1.4015	80.3
9.8	0.1710	0.17021	0.17273	1.0148	5.8751	5.789	0.9854	1.3998	80.2
9.9	0.1728	0.17193	0.17453	1.0151	5.8164	5.730	0.9851	1.3980	80.1
10.0	0.1745	0.1736	0.1763	1.0154	5.7588	5.671	0.9848	1.3963	**80.0**
10.1	0.1763	0.1754	0.1781	1.0157	5.7023	5.614	0.9845	1.3945	79.9
10.2	0.1780	0.1771	0.1799	1.0161	5.6470	5.558	0.9842	1.3928	79.8
10.3	0.1798	0.1788	0.1817	1.0164	5.5928	5.503	0.9839	1.3910	79.7
10.4	0.1815	0.1805	0.1835	1.0167	5.5396	5.449	0.9836	1.3893	79.6
10.5	0.1833	0.1822	0.1853	1.0170	5.4874	5.396	0.9833	1.3875	**79.5**
10.6	0.1850	0.1840	0.1871	1.0174	5.4362	5.343	0.9829	1.3858	79.4
10.7	0.1868	0.1857	0.1890	1.0177	5.3860	5.292	0.9826	1.3840	79.3
10.8	0.1885	0.1874	0.1908	1.0180	5.3367	5.242	0.9823	1.3823	79.2
10.9	0.1902	0.1891	0.1926	1.0184	5.2883	5.193	0.9820	1.3806	79.1
11.0	0.1920	0.1908	0.1944	1.0187	5.2408	5.145	0.9816	1.3788	**79.0**
11.1	0.1937	0.1925	0.1962	1.0191	5.1942	5.097	0.9813	1.3771	78.9
11.2	0.1955	0.1942	0.1980	1.0194	5.1484	5.050	0.9810	1.3753	78.8
11.3	0.1972	0.1959	0.1998	1.0198	5.1034	5.005	0.9806	1.3736	78.7
11.4	0.1990	0.1977	0.2016	1.0201	5.0593	4.959	0.9803	1.3718	78.6
11.5	0.2007	0.1994	0.2035	1.0205	5.0159	4.915	0.9799	1.3701	**78.5**
11.6	0.2025	0.2011	0.2053	1.0209	4.9732	4.872	0.9796	1.3683	78.4
11.7	0.2042	0.2028	0.2071	1.0212	4.9313	4.829	0.9792	1.3666	78.3
11.8	0.2059	0.2045	0.2089	1.0216	4.8901	4.787	0.9789	1.3648	78.2
11.9	0.2077	0.2062	0.2107	1.0220	4.8496	4.745	0.9785	1.3631	78.1
12.0	0.2094	0.2079	0.2126	1.0223	4.8097	4.705	0.9781	1.3614	**78.0**
12.1	0.2112	0.2096	0.2144	1.0227	4.7706	4.665	0.9778	1.3596	77.9
12.2	0.2129	0.2113	0.2162	1.0231	4.7321	4.625	0.9774	1.3579	77.8
12.3	0.2147	0.2130	0.2180	1.0235	4.6942	4.586	0.9770	1.3561	77.7
12.4	0.2164	0.2147	0.2199	1.0239	4.6569	4.548	0.9767	1.3544	77.6
12.5	0.2182	0.2164	0.2217	1.0243	4.6202	4.511	0.9763	1.3526	**77.5**
12.6	0.2199	0.2181	0.2235	1.0247	4.5841	4.474	0.9759	1.3509	77.4
12.7	0.2217	0.2198	0.2254	1.0251	4.5486	4.437	0.9755	1.3491	77.3
12.8	0.2234	0.2215	0.2272	1.0255	4.5137	4.402	0.9751	1.3474	77.2
12.9	0.2251	0.2233	0.2290	1.0259	4.4793	4.366	0.9748	1.3456	77.1
13.0	0.2269	0.2250	0.2309	1.0263	4.4454	4.331	0.9744	1.3439	**77.0**
13.1	0.2286	0.2267	0.2327	1.0267	4.4121	4.297	0.9740	1.3422	76.9
13.2	0.2304	0.2284	0.2345	1.0271	4.3792	4.264	0.9736	1.3404	76.8
13.3	0.2321	0.2300	0.2364	1.0276	4.3469	4.230	0.9732	1.3387	76.7
13.4	0.2339	0.2317	0.2382	1.0280	4.3150	4.198	0.9728	1.3369	76.6

		$\cos x$	$\cot x$	$\csc x$	$\sec x$	$\tan x$	$\sin x$	x (numbers or radians)	x (degrees)

TABLE 2 FOUR-PLACE VALUES OF THE CIRCULAR FUNCTIONS

x (degrees)	x (numbers or radians)	$\sin x$	$\tan x$	$\sec x$	$\csc x$	$\cot x$	$\cos x$		
13.5	0.2356	0.2334	0.2401	1.0284	4.2837	4.165	0.9724	1.3352	**76.5**
13.6	0.2374	0.2351	0.2419	1.0288	4.2527	4.134	0.9720	1.3334	76.4
13.7	0.2391	0.2368	0.2438	1.0293	4.2223	4.102	0.9715	1.3317	76.3
13.8	0.2409	0.2385	0.2456	1.0297	4.1923	4.071	0.9711	1.3299	76.2
13.9	0.2426	0.2402	0.2475	1.0302	4.1627	4.041	0.9707	1.3282	76.1
14.0	0.2443	0.2419	0.2493	1.0306	4.1336	4.011	0.9703	1.3265	**76.0**
14.1	0.2461	0.2436	0.2512	1.0311	4.1048	3.981	0.9699	1.3247	75.9
14.2	0.2478	0.2453	0.2530	1.0315	4.0765	3.952	0.9694	1.3230	75.8
14.3	0.2496	0.2470	0.2549	1.0320	4.0486	3.923	0.9690	1.3212	75.7
14.4	0.2513	0.2487	0.2568	1.0324	4.0211	3.895	0.9686	1.3195	75.6
14.5	0.2531	0.2504	0.2586	1.0329	3.9939	3.867	0.9681	1.3177	**75.5**
14.6	0.2548	0.2521	0.2605	1.0334	3.9672	3.839	0.9677	1.3160	75.4
14.7	0.2566	0.2538	0.2623	1.0338	3.9408	3.812	0.9673	1.3142	75.3
14.8	0.2583	0.2554	0.2642	1.0343	3.9147	3.785	0.9668	1.3125	75.2
14.9	0.2601	0.2571	0.2661	1.0348	3.8890	3.758	0.9664	1.3107	75.1
15.0	0.2618	0.2588	0.2679	1.0353	3.8637	3.732	0.9659	1.3090	**75.0**
15.1	0.2635	0.2605	0.2698	1.0358	3.8387	3.706	0.9655	1.3073	74.9
15.2	0.2653	0.2622	0.2717	1.0363	3.8140	3.681	0.9650	1.3055	74.8
15.3	0.2670	0.2639	0.2736	1.0367	3.7897	3.655	0.9646	1.3038	74.7
15.4	0.2688	0.2656	0.2754	1.0372	3.7657	3.630	0.9641	1.3020	74.6
15.5	0.2705	0.2672	0.2773	1.0377	3.7420	3.606	0.9636	1.3003	**74.5**
15.6	0.2723	0.2689	0.2792	1.0382	3.7186	3.582	0.9632	1.2985	74.4
15.7	0.2740	0.2706	0.2811	1.0388	3.6955	3.558	0.9627	1.2968	74.3
15.8	0.2758	0.2723	0.2830	1.0393	3.6727	3.534	0.9622	1.2950	74.2
15.9	0.2775	0.2740	0.2849	1.0398	3.6502	3.511	0.9617	1.2933	74.1
16.0	0.2793	0.2756	0.2867	1.0403	3.6280	3.487	0.9613	1.2915	**74.0**
16.1	0.2810	0.2773	0.2886	1.0408	3.6060	3.465	0.9608	1.2898	73.9
16.2	0.2827	0.2790	0.2905	1.0413	3.5843	3.442	0.9603	1.2881	73.8
16.3	0.2845	0.2807	0.2924	1.0419	3.5629	3.420	0.9598	1.2863	73.7
16.4	0.2862	0.2823	0.2943	1.0424	3.5418	3.398	0.9593	1.2846	73.6
16.5	0.2880	0.2840	0.2962	1.0429	3.5209	3.376	0.9588	1.2828	**73.5**
16.6	0.2897	0.2857	0.2981	1.0435	3.5003	3.354	0.9583	1.2811	73.4
16.7	0.2914	0.2874	0.3000	1.0440	3.4799	3.333	0.9578	1.2793	73.3
16.8	0.2932	0.2890	0.3019	1.0446	3.4598	3.312	0.9573	1.2776	73.2
16.9	0.2950	0.2907	0.3038	1.0451	3.4399	3.291	0.9568	1.2758	73.1
17.0	0.2967	0.2924	0.3057	1.0457	3.4203	3.271	0.9563	1.2741	**73.0**
17.1	0.2985	0.2940	0.3076	1.0463	3.4009	3.251	0.9558	1.2723	72.9
17.2	0.3002	0.2957	0.3096	1.0468	3.3817	3.230	0.9553	1.2706	72.8
17.3	0.3019	0.2974	0.3115	1.0474	3.3628	3.211	0.9548	1.2689	72.7
17.4	0.3037	0.2990	0.3134	1.0480	3.3440	3.191	0.9542	1.2671	72.6
17.5	0.3054	0.3007	0.3153	1.0485	3.3255	3.172	0.9537	1.2654	**72.5**
17.6	0.3072	0.3024	0.3172	1.0491	3.3072	3.152	0.9532	1.2636	72.4
17.7	0.3089	0.3040	0.3191	1.0497	3.2891	3.133	0.9527	1.2619	72.3
17.8	0.3107	0.3057	0.3211	1.0503	3.2712	3.115	0.9521	1.2601	72.2
17.9	0.3124	0.3074	0.3230	1.0509	3.2535	3.096	0.9516	1.2584	72.1
		$\cos x$	$\cot x$	$\csc x$	$\sec x$	$\tan x$	$\sin x$	x (numbers or radians)	x (degrees)

TABLE 2 FOUR-PLACE VALUES OF THE CIRCULAR FUNCTIONS

x (degrees)	x (numbers or radians)	$\sin x$	$\tan x$	$\sec x$	$\csc x$	$\cot x$	$\cos x$		
18.0	0.3142	0.3090	0.3249	1.0515	3.2361	3.078	0.9511	1.2566	**72.0**
18.1	0.3159	0.3107	0.3269	1.0521	3.2188	3.060	0.9505	1.2549	71.9
18.2	0.3176	0.3123	0.3288	1.0527	3.2017	3.042	0.9500	1.2531	71.8
18.3	0.3194	0.3140	0.3307	1.0533	3.1848	3.024	0.9494	1.2514	71.7
18.4	0.3211	0.3156	0.3327	1.0539	3.1681	3.006	0.9489	1.2497	71.6
18.5	0.3229	0.3173	0.3346	1.0545	3.1515	2.989	0.9483	1.2479	**71.5**
18.6	0.3246	0.3190	0.3365	1.0551	3.1352	2.971	0.9478	1.2462	71.4
18.7	0.3264	0.3206	0.3385	1.0557	3.1190	2.954	0.9472	1.2444	71.3
18.8	0.3281	0.3223	0.3404	1.0564	3.1030	2.937	0.9466	1.2427	71.2
18.9	0.3299	0.3239	0.3424	1.0570	3.0872	2.921	0.9461	1.2409	71.1
19.0	0.3316	0.3256	0.3443	1.0576	3.0716	2.904	0.9455	1.2392	**71.0**
19.1	0.3334	0.3272	0.3463	1.0583	3.0561	2.888	0.9449	1.2374	70.9
19.2	0.3351	0.3289	0.3482	1.0589	3.0407	2.872	0.9444	1.2357	70.8
19.3	0.3368	0.3305	0.3502	1.0595	3.0256	2.856	0.9438	1.2339	70.7
19.4	0.3386	0.3322	0.3522	1.0602	3.0106	2.840	0.9432	1.2322	70.6
19.5	0.3403	0.3338	0.3541	1.0608	2.9957	2.824	0.9426	1.2305	**70.5**
19.6	0.3421	0.3355	0.3561	1.0615	2.9811	2.808	0.9421	1.2287	70.4
19.7	0.3438	0.3371	0.3581	1.0622	2.9665	2.793	0.9415	1.2270	70.3
19.8	0.3456	0.3387	0.3600	1.0628	2.9521	2.778	0.9409	1.2252	70.2
19.9	0.3473	0.3404	0.3620	1.0635	2.9379	2.762	0.9403	1.2235	70.1
20.0	0.3491	0.3420	0.3640	1.0642	2.9238	2.747	0.9397	1.2217	**70.0**
20.1	0.3508	0.3437	0.3659	1.0649	2.9099	2.733	0.9391	1.2200	69.9
20.2	0.3526	0.3453	0.3679	1.0655	2.8960	2.718	0.9385	1.2182	69.8
20.3	0.3543	0.3469	0.3699	1.0662	2.8824	2.703	0.9379	1.2165	69.7
20.4	0.3560	0.3486	0.3719	1.0669	2.8688	2.689	0.9373	1.2147	69.6
20.5	0.3578	0.3502	0.3739	1.0676	2.8555	2.675	0.9367	1.2130	**69.5**
20.6	0.3595	0.3518	0.3759	1.0683	2.8422	2.660	0.9361	1.2113	69.4
20.7	0.3613	0.3535	0.3779	1.0690	2.8291	2.646	0.9354	1.2095	69.3
20.8	0.3630	0.3551	0.3799	1.0697	2.8161	2.633	0.9348	1.2078	69.2
20.9	0.3648	0.3567	0.3819	1.0704	2.8032	2.619	0.9342	1.2060	69.1
21.0	0.3665	0.3584	0.3839	1.0711	2.7904	2.605	0.9336	1.2043	**69.0**
21.1	0.3683	0.3600	0.3859	1.0719	2.7778	2.592	0.9330	1.2025	68.9
21.2	0.3700	0.3616	0.3879	1.0726	2.7653	2.578	0.9323	1.2008	68.8
21.3	0.3718	0.3633	0.3899	1.0733	2.7529	2.565	0.9317	1.1990	68.7
21.4	0.3735	0.3649	0.3919	1.0740	2.7407	2.552	0.9311	1.1973	68.6
21.5	0.3752	0.3665	0.3939	1.0748	2.7285	2.539	0.9304	1.1956	**68.5**
21.6	0.3770	0.3681	0.3959	1.0755	2.7165	2.526	0.9298	1.1938	68.4
21.7	0.3787	0.3697	0.3979	1.0763	2.7046	2.513	0.9291	1.1921	68.3
21.8	0.3805	0.3714	0.4000	1.0770	2.6927	2.500	0.9285	1.1903	68.2
21.9	0.3822	0.3730	0.4020	1.0778	2.6811	2.488	0.9278	1.1886	68.1
22.0	0.3840	0.3746	0.4040	1.0785	2.6695	2.475	0.9272	1.1868	**68.0**
22.1	0.3857	0.3762	0.4061	1.0793	2.6580	2.463	0.9265	1.1851	67.9
22.2	0.3875	0.3778	0.4081	1.0801	2.6466	2.450	0.9259	1.1833	67.8
22.3	0.3892	0.3795	0.4101	1.0808	2.6354	2.438	0.9252	1.1816	67.7
22.4	0.3910	0.3811	0.4122	1.0816	2.6242	2.426	0.9245	1.1798	67.6
		$\cos x$	$\cot x$	$\csc x$	$\sec x$	$\tan x$	$\sin x$	x (numbers or radians)	x (degrees)

TABLE 2 FOUR-PLACE VALUES OF THE CIRCULAR FUNCTIONS

x (de-grees)	x (numbers or radians)	sin x	tan x	sec x	csc x	cot x	cos x		
22.5	0.3927	0.3827	0.4142	1.0824	2.6131	2.414	0.9239	1.1781	**67.5**
22.6	0.3944	0.3843	0.4163	1.0832	2.6022	2.402	0.9232	1.1764	67.4
22.7	0.3962	0.3859	0.4183	1.0840	2.5913	2.391	0.9225	1.1746	67.3
22.8	0.3979	0.3875	0.4204	1.0848	2.5805	2.379	0.9219	1.1729	67.2
22.9	0.3997	0.3891	0.4224	1.0856	2.5699	2.367	0.9212	1.1711	67.1
23.0	0.4014	0.3907	0.4245	1.0864	2.5593	2.356	0.9205	1.1694	**67.0**
23.1	0.4032	0.3923	0.4265	1.0872	2.5488	2.344	0.9198	1.1676	66.9
23.2	0.4049	0.3939	0.4286	1.0880	2.5384	2.333	0.9191	1.1659	66.8
23.3	0.4067	0.3955	0.4307	1.0888	2.5282	2.322	0.9184	1.1641	66.7
23.4	0.4084	0.3971	0.4327	1.0896	2.5180	2.311	0.9178	1.1624	66.6
23.5	0.4102	0.3987	0.4348	1.0904	2.5078	2.300	0.9171	1.1606	**66.5**
23.6	0.4119	0.4003	0.4369	1.0913	2.4978	2.289	0.9164	1.1589	66.4
23.7	0.4136	0.4019	0.4390	1.0921	2.4879	2.278	0.9157	1.1572	66.3
23.8	0.4154	0.4035	0.4411	1.0929	2.4780	2.267	0.9150	1.1554	66.2
23.9	0.4171	0.4051	0.4431	1.0938	2.4683	2.257	0.9143	1.1537	66.1
24.0	0.4189	0.4067	0.4452	1.0946	2.4586	2.246	0.9135	1.1519	**66.0**
24.1	0.4206	0.4083	0.4473	1.0955	2.4490	2.236	0.9128	1.1502	65.9
24.2	0.4224	0.4099	0.4494	1.0963	2.4395	2.225	0.9121	1.1484	65.8
24.3	0.4241	0.4115	0.4515	1.0972	2.4300	2.215	0.9114	1.1467	65.7
24.4	0.4259	0.4131	0.4536	1.0981	2.4207	2.204	0.9107	1.1449	65.6
24.5	0.4276	0.4147	0.4557	1.0989	2.4114	2.194	0.9100	1.1432	**65.5**
24.6	0.4294	0.4163	0.4578	1.0998	2.4022	2.184	0.9092	1.1414	65.4
24.7	0.4311	0.4179	0.4599	1.1007	2.3931	2.174	0.9085	1.1397	65.3
24.8	0.4328	0.4195	0.4621	1.1016	2.3841	2.164	0.9078	1.1380	65.2
24.9	0.4346	0.4210	0.4642	1.1025	2.3751	2.154	0.9070	1.1362	65.1
25.0	0.4363	0.4226	0.4663	1.1034	2.3662	2.145	0.9063	1.1345	**65.0**
25.1	0.4381	0.4242	0.4684	1.1043	2.3574	2.135	0.9056	1.1327	64.9
25.2	0.4398	0.4258	0.4706	1.1052	2.3486	2.125	0.9048	1.1310	64.8
25.3	0.4416	0.4274	0.4727	1.1061	2.3400	2.116	0.9041	1.1292	64.7
25.4	0.4433	0.4289	0.4748	1.1070	2.3314	2.106	0.9033	1.1275	64.6
25.5	0.4451	0.4305	0.4770	1.1079	2.3228	2.097	0.9026	1.1257	**64.5**
25.6	0.4468	0.4321	0.4791	1.1089	2.3144	2.087	0.9018	1.1240	64.4
25.7	0.4485	0.4337	0.4813	1.1098	2.3060	2.078	0.9011	1.1222	64.3
25.8	0.4503	0.4352	0.4834	1.1107	2.2976	2.069	0.9003	1.1205	64.2
25.9	0.4520	0.4368	0.4856	1.1117	2.2894	2.059	0.8996	1.1188	64.1
26.0	0.4538	0.4384	0.4877	1.1126	2.2812	2.050	0.8988	1.1170	64.0
26.1	0.4555	0.4399	0.4899	1.1136	2.2730	2.041	0.8980	1.1153	63.9
26.2	0.4573	0.4415	0.4921	1.1145	2.2650	2.032	0.8973	1.1135	63.8
26.3	0.4590	0.4431	0.4942	1.1155	2.2570	2.023	0.8965	1.1118	63.7
26.4	0.4608	0.4446	0.4964	1.1164	2.2490	2.014	0.8957	1.1100	63.6
26.5	0.4625	0.4462	0.4986	1.1174	2.2412	2.006	0.8949	1.1083	**63.5**
26.6	0.4643	0.4478	0.5008	1.1184	2.2333	1.997	0.8942	1.1065	63.4
26.7	0.4660	0.4493	0.5029	1.1194	2.2256	1.988	0.8934	1.1048	63.3
26.8	0.4677	0.4509	0.5051	1.1203	2.2179	1.980	0.8926	1.1030	63.2
26.9	0.4695	0.4524	0.5073	1.1213	2.2103	1.971	0.8918	1.1013	63.1
		cos x	cot x	csc x	sec x	tan x	sin x	x (numbers or radians)	x (de-grees)

TABLE 2 FOUR-PLACE VALUES OF THE CIRCULAR FUNCTIONS

x (degrees)	x (numbers or radians)	$\sin x$	$\tan x$	$\sec x$	$\csc x$	$\cot x$	$\cos x$		
27.0	0.4712	0.4540	0.5095	1.1223	2.2027	1.963	0.8910	1.0996	**63.0**
27.1	0.4730	0.4555	0.5117	1.1233	2.1952	1.954	0.8902	1.0978	62.9
27.2	0.4747	0.4571	0.5139	1.1243	2.1877	1.946	0.8894	1.0961	62.8
27.3	0.4765	0.4586	0.5161	1.1253	2.1803	1.937	0.8886	1.0943	62.7
27.4	0.4782	0.4602	0.5184	1.1264	2.1730	1.929	0.8878	1.0926	62.6
27.5	0.4800	0.4617	0.5206	1.1274	2.1657	1.921	0.8870	1.0908	**62.5**
27.6	0.4817	0.4633	0.5228	1.1284	2.1584	1.913	0.8862	1.0891	62.4
27.7	0.4835	0.4648	0.5250	1.1294	2.1513	1.905	0.8854	1.0873	62.3
27.8	0.4852	0.4664	0.5272	1.1305	2.1441	1.897	0.8846	1.0856	62.2
27.9	0.4869	0.4679	0.5295	1.1315	2.1371	1.889	0.8838	1.0838	62.1
28.0	0.4887	0.4695	0.5317	1.1326	2.1301	1.881	0.8829	1.0821	**62.0**
28.1	0.4904	0.4710	0.5340	1.1336	2.1231	1.873	0.8821	1.0804	61.9
28.2	0.4922	0.4726	0.5362	1.1347	2.1162	1.865	0.8813	1.0786	61.8
28.3	0.4939	0.4741	0.5384	1.1357	2.1093	1.857	0.8805	1.0769	61.7
28.4	0.4957	0.4756	0.5407	1.1368	2.1025	1.849	0.8796	1.0751	61.6
28.5	0.4974	0.4772	0.5430	1.1379	2.0957	1.842	0.8788	1.0734	**61.5**
28.6	0.4992	0.4787	0.5452	1.1390	2.0890	1.834	0.8780	1.0716	61.4
28.7	0.5009	0.4802	0.5475	1.1401	2.0824	1.827	0.8771	1.0699	61.3
28.8	0.5027	0.4818	0.5498	1.1412	2.0757	1.819	0.8763	1.0681	61.2
28.9	0.5044	0.4833	0.5520	1.1423	2.0692	1.811	0.8755	1.0664	61.1
29.0	0.5061	0.4848	0.5543	1.1434	2.0627	1.804	0.8746	1.0647	**61.0**
29.1	0.5079	0.4863	0.5566	1.1445	2.0562	1.797	0.8738	1.0629	60.9
29.2	0.5096	0.4879	0.5589	1.1456	2.0498	1.789	0.8729	1.0612	60.8
29.3	0.5114	0.4894	0.5612	1.1467	2.0434	1.782	0.8721	1.0594	60.7
29.4	0.5131	0.4909	0.5635	1.1478	2.0371	1.775	0.8712	1.0577	60.6
29.5	0.5149	0.4924	0.5658	1.1490	2.0308	1.767	0.8704	1.0559	**60.5**
29.6	0.5166	0.4939	0.5681	1.1501	2.0245	1.760	0.8695	1.0542	60.4
29.7	0.5184	0.4955	0.5704	1.1512	2.0183	1.753	0.8686	1.0524	60.3
29.8	0.5201	0.4970	0.5727	1.1524	2.0122	1.746	0.8678	1.0507	60.2
29.9	0.5219	0.4985	0.5750	1.1535	2.0061	1.739	0.8669	1.0489	60.1
30.0	0.5236	0.5000	0.5774	1.1547	2.0000	1.7321	0.8660	1.0472	**60.0**
30.1	0.5253	0.5015	0.5797	1.1559	1.9940	1.7251	0.8652	1.0455	59.9
30.2	0.5271	0.5030	0.5820	1.1570	1.9880	1.7182	0.8643	1.0437	59.8
30.3	0.5288	0.5045	0.5844	1.1582	1.9821	1.7113	0.8634	1.0420	59.7
30.4	0.5306	0.5060	0.5867	1.1594	1.9762	1.7045	0.8625	1.0402	59.6
30.5	0.5323	0.5075	0.5890	1.1606	1.9703	1.6977	0.8616	1.0385	**59.5**
30.6	0.5341	0.5090	0.5914	1.1618	1.9645	1.6909	0.8607	1.0367	59.4
30.7	0.5358	0.5105	0.5938	1.1630	1.9587	1.6842	0.8599	1.0350	59.3
30.8	0.5376	0.5120	0.5961	1.1642	1.9530	1.6775	0.8590	1.0332	59.2
30.9	0.5393	0.5135	0.5985	1.1654	1.9473	1.6709	0.8581	1.0315	59.1
31.0	0.5411	0.5150	0.6009	1.1666	1.9416	1.6643	0.8572	1.0297	**59.0**
31.1	0.5428	0.5165	0.6032	1.1679	1.9360	1.6577	0.8563	1.0280	58.9
31.2	0.5445	0.5180	0.6056	1.1691	1.9304	1.6512	0.8554	1.0263	58.8
31.3	0.5463	0.5195	0.6080	1.1703	1.9249	1.6447	0.8545	1.0245	58.7
31.4	0.5480	0.5210	0.6104	1.1716	1.9194	1.6383	0.8536	1.0228	58.6
		$\cos x$	$\cot x$	$\csc x$	$\sec x$	$\tan x$	$\sin x$	x (numbers or radians)	x (degrees)

TABLE 2 FOUR-PLACE VALUES OF THE CIRCULAR FUNCTIONS

x (degrees)	x (numbers or radians)	sin x	tan x	sec x	csc x	cot x	cos x		
31.5	0.5498	0.5225	0.6128	1.1728	1.9139	1.6319	0.8526	1.0210	**58.5**
31.6	0.5515	0.5240	0.6152	1.1741	1.9084	1.6255	0.8517	1.0193	58.4
31.7	0.5533	0.5255	0.6176	1.1753	1.9031	1.6191	0.8508	1.0175	58.3
31.8	0.5550	0.5270	0.6200	1.1766	1.8977	1.6128	0.8499	1.0158	58.2
31.9	0.5568	0.5284	0.6224	1.1779	1.8924	1.6066	0.8490	1.0140	58.1
32.0	0.5585	0.5299	0.6249	1.1792	1.8871	1.6003	0.8480	1.0123	**58.0**
32.1	0.5603	0.5314	0.6273	1.1805	1.8818	1.5941	0.8471	1.0105	57.9
32.2	0.5620	0.5329	0.6297	1.1818	1.8766	1.5880	0.8462	1.0088	57.8
32.3	0.5637	0.5344	0.6322	1.1831	1.8714	1.5818	0.8453	1.0071	57.7
32.4	0.5655	0.5358	0.6346	1.1844	1.8663	1.5757	0.8443	1.0053	57.6
32.5	0.5672	0.5373	0.6371	1.1857	1.8612	1.5697	0.8434	1.0036	**57.5**
32.6	0.5690	0.5388	0.6395	1.1870	1.8561	1.5637	0.8425	1.0018	57.4
32.7	0.5707	0.5402	0.6420	1.1883	1.8510	1.5577	0.8415	1.0001	57.3
32.8	0.5725	0.5417	0.6445	1.1897	1.8460	1.5517	0.8406	0.9983	57.2
32.9	0.5742	0.5432	0.6469	1.1910	1.8410	1.5458	0.8396	0.9966	57.1
33.0	0.5760	0.5446	0.6494	1.1924	1.8361	1.5399	0.8387	0.9948	**57.0**
33.1	0.5777	0.5461	0.6519	1.1937	1.8312	1.5340	0.8377	0.9931	56.9
33.2	0.5794	0.5476	0.6544	1.1951	1.8263	1.5282	0.8368	0.9913	56.8
33.3	0.5812	0.5490	0.6569	1.1964	1.8214	1.5224	0.8358	0.9896	56.7
33.4	0.5829	0.5505	0.6594	1.1978	1.8166	1.5166	0.8348	0.9879	56.6
33.5	0.5847	0.5519	0.6619	1.1992	1.8118	1.5108	0.8339	0.9861	**56.5**
33.6	0.5864	0.5534	0.6644	1.2006	1.8070	1.5051	0.8329	0.9844	56.4
33.7	0.5882	0.5548	0.6669	1.2020	1.8023	1.4994	0.8320	0.9826	56.3
33.8	0.5899	0.5563	0.6694	1.2034	1.7976	1.4938	0.8310	0.9809	56.2
33.9	0.5917	0.5577	0.6720	1.2048	1.7929	1.4882	0.8300	0.9791	56.1
34.0	0.5934	0.5592	0.6745	1.2062	1.7883	1.4826	0.8290	0.9774	**56.0**
34.1	0.5952	0.5606	0.6771	1.2076	1.7837	1.4770	0.8281	0.9756	55.9
34.2	0.5969	0.5621	0.6796	1.2091	1.7791	1.4715	0.8271	0.9739	55.8
34.3	0.5986	0.5635	0.6822	1.2105	1.7745	1.4659	0.8261	0.9721	55.7
34.4	0.6004	0.5650	0.6847	1.2120	1.7700	1.4605	0.8251	0.9704	55.6
34.5	0.6021	0.5664	0.6873	1.2134	1.7655	1.4550	0.8241	0.9687	**55.5**
34.6	0.6039	0.5678	0.6899	1.2149	1.7610	1.4496	0.8231	0.9669	55.4
34.7	0.6056	0.5693	0.6924	1.2163	1.7566	1.4442	0.8221	0.9652	55.3
34.8	0.6074	0.5707	0.6950	1.2178	1.7522	1.4388	0.8211	0.9634	55.2
34.9	0.6091	0.5721	0.6976	1.2193	1.7478	1.4335	0.8202	0.9617	55.1
35.0	0.6109	0.5736	0.7002	1.2208	1.7434	1.4281	0.8192	0.9599	**55.0**
35.1	0.6126	0.5750	0.7028	1.2223	1.7391	1.4229	0.8181	0.9582	54.9
35.2	0.6144	0.5764	0.7054	1.2238	1.7348	1.4176	0.8171	0.9564	54.8
35.3	0.6161	0.5779	0.7080	1.2253	1.7305	1.4124	0.8161	0.9547	54.7
35.4	0.6178	0.5793	0.7107	1.2268	1.7263	1.4071	0.8151	0.9529	54.6
35.5	0.6196	0.5807	0.7133	1.2283	1.7221	1.4019	0.8141	0.9512	**54.5**
35.6	0.6213	0.5821	0.7159	1.2299	1.7179	1.3968	0.8131	0.9495	54.4
35.7	0.6231	0.5835	0.7186	1.2314	1.7137	1.3916	0.8121	0.9477	54.3
35.8	0.6248	0.5850	0.7212	1.2329	1.7095	1.3865	0.8111	0.9460	54.2
35.9	0.6266	0.5864	0.7239	1.2345	1.7054	1.3814	0.8100	0.9442	54.1
	cos x	cot x	csc x	sec x	tan x	sin x		x (numbers or radians)	x (degrees)

TABLE 2 FOUR-PLACE VALUES OF THE CIRCULAR FUNCTIONS

x (degrees)	x (numbers or radians)	$\sin x$	$\tan x$	$\sec x$	$\csc x$	$\cot x$	$\cos x$		
36.0	0.6283	0.5878	0.7265	1.2361	1.7013	1.3764	0.8090	0.9425	**54.0**
36.1	0.6301	0.5892	0.7292	1.2376	1.6972	1.3713	0.8080	0.9407	53.9
36.2	0.6318	0.5906	0.7319	1.2392	1.6932	1.3663	0.8070	0.9390	53.8
36.3	0.6336	0.5920	0.7346	1.2408	1.6892	1.3613	0.8059	0.9372	53.7
36.4	0.6353	0.5934	0.7373	1.2424	1.6852	1.3564	0.8049	0.9355	53.6
36.5	0.6370	0.5948	0.7400	1.2440	1.6812	1.3514	0.8039	0.9338	**53.5**
36.6	0.6388	0.5962	0.7427	1.2456	1.6772	1.3465	0.8028	0.9320	53.4
36.7	0.6405	0.5976	0.7454	1.2472	1.6733	1.3416	0.8018	0.9303	53.3
36.8	0.6423	0.5990	0.7481	1.2489	1.6694	1.3367	0.8007	0.9285	53.2
36.9	0.6440	0.6004	0.7508	1.2505	1.6655	1.3319	0.7997	0.9268	53.1
37.0	0.6458	0.6018	0.7536	1.2521	1.6616	1.3270	0.7986	0.9250	**53.0**
37.1	0.6475	0.6032	0.7563	1.2538	1.6578	1.3222	0.7976	0.9233	52.9
37.2	0.6493	0.6046	0.7590	1.2554	1.6540	1.3175	0.7965	0.9215	52.8
37.3	0.6510	0.6060	0.7618	1.2571	1.6502	1.3127	0.7955	0.9198	52.7
37.4	0.6528	0.6074	0.7646	1.2588	1.6464	1.3079	0.7944	0.9180	52.6
37.5	0.6545	0.6088	0.7673	1.2605	1.6427	1.3032	0.7934	0.9163	**52.5**
37.6	0.6562	0.6101	0.7701	1.2622	1.6390	1.2985	0.7923	0.9146	52.4
37.7	0.6580	0.6115	0.7729	1.2639	1.6353	1.2938	0.7912	0.9128	52.3
37.8	0.6597	0.6129	0.7757	1.2656	1.6316	1.2892	0.7902	0.9111	52.2
37.9	0.6615	0.6143	0.7785	1.2673	1.6279	1.2846	0.7891	0.9093	52.1
38.0	0.6632	0.6157	0.7813	1.2690	1.6243	1.2799	0.7880	0.9076	**52.0**
38.1	0.6650	0.6170	0.7841	1.2708	1.6207	1.2753	0.7869	0.9058	51.9
38.2	0.6667	0.6184	0.7869	1.2725	1.6171	1.2708	0.7859	0.9041	51.8
38.3	0.6685	0.6198	0.7898	1.2742	1.6135	1.2662	0.7848	0.9023	51.7
38.4	0.6702	0.6211	0.7926	1.2760	1.6099	1.2617	0.7837	0.9006	51.6
38.5	0.6720	0.6225	0.7954	1.2778	1.6064	1.2572	0.7826	0.8988	**51.5**
38.6	0.6737	0.6239	0.7983	1.2796	1.6029	1.2527	0.7815	0.8971	51.4
38.7	0.6754	0.6252	0.8012	1.2813	1.5994	1.2482	0.7804	0.8954	51.3
38.8	0.6772	0.6266	0.8040	1.2831	1.5959	1.2437	0.7793	0.8936	51.2
38.9	0.6789	0.6280	0.8069	1.2849	1.5925	1.2393	0.7782	0.8919	51.1
39.0	0.6807	0.6293	0.8098	1.2868	1.5890	1.2349	0.7771	0.8901	**51.0**
39.1	0.6824	0.6307	0.8127	1.2886	1.5856	1.2305	0.7760	0.8884	50.9
39.2	0.6842	0.6320	0.8156	1.2904	1.5822	1.2261	0.7749	0.8866	50.8
39.3	0.6859	0.6334	0.8185	1.2923	1.5788	1.2218	0.7738	0.8849	50.7
39.4	0.6877	0.6347	0.8214	1.2941	1.5755	1.2174	0.7727	0.8831	50.6
39.5	0.6894	0.6361	0.8243	1.2960	1.5721	1.2131	0.7716	0.8814	**50.5**
39.6	0.6912	0.6374	0.8273	1.2978	1.5688	1.2088	0.7705	0.8796	50.4
39.7	0.6929	0.6388	0.8302	1.2997	1.5655	1.2045	0.7694	0.8779	50.3
39.8	0.6946	0.6401	0.8332	1.3016	1.5622	1.2002	0.7683	0.8762	50.2
39.9	0.6964	0.6414	0.8361	1.3035	1.5590	1.1960	0.7672	0.8744	50.1
40.0	0.6981	0.6428	0.8391	1.3054	1.5557	1.1918	0.7660	0.8727	**50.0**
40.1	0.6999	0.6441	0.8421	1.3073	1.5525	1.1875	0.7649	0.8709	49.9
40.2	0.7016	0.6455	0.8451	1.3093	1.5493	1.1833	0.7638	0.8692	49.8
40.3	0.7034	0.6468	0.8481	1.3112	1.5461	1.1792	0.7627	0.8674	49.7
40.4	0.7051	0.6481	0.8511	1.3131	1.5429	1.1750	0.7615	0.8657	49.6
		$\cos x$	$\cot x$	$\csc x$	$\sec x$	$\tan x$	$\sin x$	x (numbers or radians)	x (degrees)

TABLE 2 FOUR-PLACE VALUES OF THE CIRCULAR FUNCTIONS

x (degrees)	x (numbers or radians)	sin x	tan x	sec x	csc x	cot x	cos x		
40.5	0.7069	0.6494	0.8541	1.3151	1.5398	1.1708	0.7604	0.8639	**49.5**
40.6	0.7086	0.6508	0.8571	1.3171	1.5366	1.1667	0.7593	0.8622	49.4
40.7	0.7103	0.6521	0.8601	1.3190	1.5335	1.1626	0.7581	0.8604	49.3
40.8	0.7121	0.6534	0.8632	1.3210	1.5304	1.1585	0.7570	0.8587	49.2
40.9	0.7138	0.6547	0.8662	1.3230	1.5273	1.1544	0.7559	0.8570	49.1
41.0	0.7156	0.6561	0.8693	1.3250	1.5243	1.1504	0.7547	0.8552	**49.0**
41.1	0.7173	0.6574	0.8724	1.3270	1.5212	1.1463	0.7536	0.8535	48.9
41.2	0.7191	0.6587	0.8754	1.3291	1.5182	1.1423	0.7524	0.8517	48.8
41.3	0.7208	0.6600	0.8785	1.3311	1.5151	1.1383	0.7513	0.8500	48.7
41.4	0.7226	0.6613	0.8816	1.3331	1.5121	1.1343	0.7501	0.8482	48.6
41.5	0.7243	0.6626	0.8847	1.3352	1.5092	1.1303	0.7490	0.8465	**48.5**
41.6	0.7261	0.6639	0.8878	1.3373	1.5062	1.1263	0.7478	0.8447	48.4
41.7	0.7278	0.6652	0.8910	1.3393	1.5032	1.1224	0.7466	0.8430	48.3
41.8	0.7295	0.6665	0.8941	1.3414	1.5003	1.1184	0.7455	0.8412	48.2
41.9	0.7313	0.6678	0.8972	1.3435	1.4974	1.1145	0.7443	0.8395	48.1
42.0	0.7330	0.6691	0.9004	1.3456	1.4945	1.1106	0.7431	0.8378	**48.0**
42.1	0.7348	0.6704	0.9036	1.3478	1.4916	1.1067	0.7420	0.8360	47.9
42.2	0.7365	0.6717	0.9067	1.3499	1.4887	1.1028	0.7408	0.8343	47.8
42.3	0.7383	0.6730	0.9099	1.3520	1.4859	1.0990	0.7396	0.8325	47.7
42.4	0.7400	0.6743	0.9131	1.3542	1.4830	1.0951	0.7385	0.8308	47.6
42.5	0.7418	0.6756	0.9163	1.3563	1.4802	1.0913	0.7373	0.8290	**47.5**
42.6	0.7435	0.6769	0.9195	1.3585	1.4774	1.0875	0.7361	0.8273	47.4
42.7	0.7453	0.6782	0.9228	1.3607	1.4746	1.0837	0.7349	0.8255	47.3
42.8	0.7470	0.6794	0.9260	1.3629	1.4718	1.0799	0.7337	0.8238	47.2
42.9	0.7487	0.6807	0.9293	1.3651	1.4690	1.0761	0.7325	0.8221	47.1
43.0	0.7505	0.6820	0.9325	1.3673	1.4663	1.0724	0.7314	0.8203	**47.0**
43.1	0.7522	0.6833	0.9358	1.3696	1.4635	1.0686	0.7302	0.8186	46.9
43.2	0.7540	0.6845	0.9391	1.3718	1.4608	1.0649	0.7290	0.8168	46.8
43.3	0.7557	0.6858	0.9424	1.3741	1.4581	1.0612	0.7278	0.8151	46.7
43.4	0.7575	0.6871	0.9457	1.3763	1.4554	1.0575	0.7266	0.8133	46.6
43.5	0.7592	0.6884	0.9490	1.3786	1.4527	1.0538	0.7254	0.8116	**46.5**
43.6	0.7610	0.6896	0.9523	1.3809	1.4501	1.0501	0.7242	0.8098	46.4
43.7	0.7627	0.6909	0.9556	1.3832	1.4474	1.0464	0.7230	0.8081	46.3
43.8	0.7645	0.6921	0.9590	1.3855	1.4448	1.0428	0.7218	0.8063	46.2
43.9	0.7662	0.6934	0.9623	1.3878	1.4422	1.0392	0.7206	0.8046	46.1
44.0	0.7679	0.6947	0.9657	1.3902	1.4396	1.0355	0.7193	0.8029	**46.0**
44.1	0.7697	0.6959	0.9691	1.3925	1.4370	1.0319	0.7181	0.8011	45.9
44.2	0.7714	0.6972	0.9725	1.3949	1.4344	1.0283	0.7169	0.7994	45.8
44.3	0.7732	0.6984	0.9759	1.3972	1.4318	1.0247	0.7157	0.7976	45.7
44.4	0.7749	0.6997	0.9793	1.3996	1.4293	1.0212	0.7145	0.7959	45.6
44.5	0.7767	0.7009	0.9827	1.4020	1.4267	1.0176	0.7133	0.7941	**45.5**
44.6	0.7784	0.7022	0.9861	1.4044	1.4242	1.0141	0.7120	0.7924	45.5
44.7	0.7802	0.7034	0.9896	1.4069	1.4217	1.0105	0.7108	0.7906	45.3
44.8	0.7819	0.7046	0.9930	1.4093	1.4192	1.0070	0.7096	0.7889	45.2
44.9	0.7837	0.7059	0.9965	1.4118	1.4167	1.0035	0.7083	0.7871	45.1
45.0	0.7854	0.7071	1.0000	1.4142	1.4142	1.0000	0.7071	0.7854	**45.0**
		cos x	cot x	csc x	sec x	tan x	sin x	x (numbers or radians)	x (degrees)

399

Answers to
Odd-Numbered Problems

CHAPTER 1

Section 1.1 (page 6)

1. (c), (d), (e). **3.** (a), (d). **5.** In any triangle, the sides opposite equal angles are equal. and conversely. **7.** The set of living plants on the planet Mars is an example. **9.** (a), (b), **11.** (a), (c), (d). **15.** $\varnothing$, $\{a\}$, $\{b\}$, $\{c\}$, $\{d\}$, $\{a,b\}$, $\{a,c\}$, $\{a,d\}$, $\{b,c\}$, $\{b,d\}$, $\{c,d\}$, $\{a,b,c\}$, $\{a,b,d\}$, $\{a,c,d\}$, $\{b,c,d\}$, $\{a,b,c,d\}$. **17.** (a) $B \subset A$; (b) $F \subset E$; (c) $E \subset C$; (d) $E \subset B$; (e) $F \subset D$; (f) $E \subset A$. **21.** (a) All students in your college who are either coeds or majors in mathematics (or both); (b) all coed mathematics majors in your college. **23.** (a) All male football players in your college who are under 5 feet in height; (b) all red-haired male football players in your college who are under 5 feet in height; (c) all male students in your college who are either under 5 feet in height and play football or who are red-haired (or both); (d) all red-haired boys in your college who are under 5 feet in height. **27.** (a) Neither; (b) neither; (c) $\varnothing$; (d) $\varnothing$; (e) $\varnothing$; (f) neither. **29.** (a) E, F, G; (b) H, I, J; (c) C, D.

Section 1.2 (page 16)

1. (a) **N**: $\{2\}$, **Z**: $\{2\}$, **Q**: $\{-\frac{1}{2}, \frac{1}{5}, 0.272727 \cdots, 2\}$, Irrational: $\{\sqrt{3}\}$; (b) **N**: $\varnothing$, **Z**: $\{-6, 0\}$, **Q**: $\{-6, 0, \frac{1}{2}, 1.571571 \cdots\}$, Irrational: $\{-\sqrt{2}/2, \sqrt[3]{5}\}$; (c) **N**: $\{3, \sqrt{2}/\sqrt{2}\}$, **Z**: $\{-2, 3, \sqrt{2}/\sqrt{2}\}$, **Q**: $\{-2, \frac{5}{6}, \sqrt{2}/\sqrt{2}, 3\}$, Irrational: $\{2/\sqrt{5}, \sqrt[3]{2}\}$. **5.** (a) 2.5; (b) 2.15; (c) 0.75; (d) -1.4. **7.** Exhibit a one-to-one correspondence. **9.** (a) Yes; (b) no; (c) yes; (d) no. **13.** (a) Subtraction; (b) division; (c) none. **15.** II, V, VI, X, XIV, XX, L, C, M. **17.** (a) 100; (b) 144; (c) 342. **21.** (a) $\{x \in \mathbf{R} \mid 2 < x \leq 4\}$; (b) $\{x \in \mathbf{R} \mid -1 \leq x < 5\}$; (c) $\{x \in \mathbf{R} \mid x > 1\}$; (d) $\{x \in \mathbf{R} \mid x > -2\}$; (e) $\{x \mid x \in \mathbf{R}\}$. **23.** (a) $\{1, 2, 5\}$; (b) $\{1, 2, 5, 6, 7, 9\}$. **25.** (a) $\{x \in \mathbf{R} \mid 1 \leq x \leq 2\}$; (b) $\{x \in \mathbf{R} \mid -1 \leq x < 0 \text{ or } 1 < x \leq 2\}$; (c) $\{x \in \mathbf{R} \mid 1 < x \leq 3\}$; (d) $\{x \in \mathbf{R} \mid -1 \leq x < 0 \text{ or } 1 \leq x \leq 2\}$. **29.** (a) $\{x \in \mathbf{R} \mid -2 \leq x \leq 5\} = A$; (b) $\{x \in \mathbf{R} \mid x > 5 \text{ or } x < -2\}$; (c) $\mathbf{R}$.

Section 1.3 (page 21)

1. (a) 2; (b) -2; (c) -2. **3.** (a) $-a$; (b) a^2; (c) $(b - c) - a$. **13.** For example, if $a = b = 1$ and $c = 2$, then $(a - b) - c = -2$; whereas $a - (b - c) = 1 - (-1) = 2$. An equality for arbitrary a and b if $c = 0$. No. **15.** A_3, A_4, A_5. **17.** No—impossible to decide the truth of $a \mathcal{R} b$. **19.** If $\odot$ denotes the operation and x, y are real numbers with $x \neq y$, then $(x * y) \odot z = x$ and $(y * x) \odot z = y$ for some $z \in \mathbf{R}$, whereas $x * y = 0 = y * x$ and so $x = y$ (a contradiction). **23.** $x \sim x$; if $x \sim y$ then $y \sim x$; if $x \sim y$ and $y \sim z$, then $x \sim z$. **25.** For example, 12 is divisible by 4 but 4 is not divisible by 12. **29.** (a) 1, 4; (b) 2, 5, 6, 7.

Section 1.4 (page 24)

11. (a) $8x + 4$; (b) $26x + 7$. **13.** (a) $a^3 + 2a^2b + 2ab^2 + b^3$; (b) $a^3 + 6a^2 + 11a + 6$. **15.** 0, if $a \neq 0$; no, if $a = 0$. **17.** (a), (b), (d). **19.** For example: $\frac{4}{2} \neq \frac{2}{4}$; $\frac{8}{4}/2 = 1 \neq$ $8/\frac{4}{2}$. **23.** Check that $(a + b) + (-a - b) = 0$. **25.** Yes, it does. **27.** Only D, except that the restriction on a in M_4 becomes the corresponding restriction in A_4. (In the usual symbolism, 0 and 1 are also interchanged.)

Section 1.5 (page 28)

1. (a) -7; (b) 11. **3.** Yes. For example, let $x = -3$. **5.** (a) $-\frac{3}{10}$; (b) $-\frac{23}{90}$. **7.** (a) $0.01x^2 - 0.04xy + 0.04y^2$; (b) $0.01x^3 - 0.004x^2y + 0.0004xy^2$. **9.** (a) $-3x^2 + 5x - 2$; (b) $x^4 - 16y^4$. **25.** Because an inverse is unique by Theorem 5.3. **27.** $(a + b)/c = (a + b)c^{-1}$; also $a/c = ac^{-1}$ and $b/c = bc^{-1}$.

CHAPTER 2

Section 2.1 (page 35)

1. (a) There exists an integer divisible by 5; (b) every orange is a fruit; (c) there exists a dangerous dog; (d) any student who studies hard will pass his examinations. **3.** (b), (c). **5.** (a) **Q**; (b) $\{6\}$; (c) $\{2, 3\}$; (d) $\varnothing$; (e) **Q**; (f) **Q**. **7.** (a) $(1, 2), (-1, 2), (1, 3), (-1, 3)$; (b) $(1, 0), (a, 0), (-1, 0), (-1, 1), (a, 1), (1, 1)$; (c) $(2, 1)$; (d) there are none. **9.** $(1, 1), (1, -1), (-1, 1), (-1, -1)$. **11.** x does not really "vary," but is rather an unspecified element of some designated set. **13.** (a) $a = 1, b = -1, c = 2$; (b) $a = 2, b = 1, c = -3$. **15.** (a) 4; (b) 5. **17.** 16. **21.** No substitution for x can make an open sentence into a statement which is simultaneously true and false. **23.** The sentence is an absurdity. **25.** (a) $\{-3, 3\}$, (b) $\varnothing$, (c) $\{2\}$. **27.** (a) Tautology; (b) neither; (c) absurdity; (d) absurdity. **29.** (a) $\{x \in \mathbf{R} \mid x \neq 3\}$; (b) **R**; (c) $\{x \in \mathbf{R} \mid x \geq 6\}$; (d) $\{0\}$; (e) $\varnothing$.

Section 2.2 (page 41)

1. (a) Today is warm and it is cloudy; (b) it is cloudy and the air is humid; (c) today is warm, it is cloudy and the air is humid; (d) today is warm, it is cloudy and a breeze is blowing. **3.** In none of the parts is it possible to break up the sentence into two or more complete statements connected with the word "and." **5.** (a) "Jack went up the hill" and "Jill went up the hill"; (b) "It is snowing" and "The streets are slippery"; (c) "My car has snow tires" and "I arrive at work on time"; (d) "The oranges are large" and "The oranges are sweet" and "The oranges are juicy." **7.** (a) For example: "The day is bright," "The air is warm," and "I am going to town"; (b) for example: "There were 12 questions on the examination," "The questions were easy," "I knew all the answers," and "I passed the course." **15.** $\{(1, 2)\}$. **17.** $\{(a, b) \mid a = 2 + 2b\}$. **19.** $\varnothing$. **21.** $\{(2, 15)\}$. **23.** $\{(\frac{1}{2}, 3)\}$. **27.** $1\frac{1}{3}$ gallons of 20 percent solution and $\frac{2}{3}$ gallon of 5 percent solution. **29.** Mike's age is 7; Spike's age is 2.

Section 2.3 (page 46)

1. (a) $m = 3, n = 4$; (b) $a_{21} = 2, a_{11} = 1, a_{32} = 2, a_{34} = 2$. **3.** (a) 4; (b) -1; (c) -4. **5.** (a) = (b) = (c) = -22. **7.** (a) -2; (b) 6; (c) -4. **9.** (a) -147; (b) 41. **11.** (a) -4; (b) 7. **17.** 16. **21.** $2xy$. **23.** (a) $3x^2 - 4xy + 3x + 2y$; (b) $yz^2 + xy^2 + x^2z - x^2y - y^2z - xz^2$.

Section 2.4 (page 50)

1. $2x + y - z = k_1$, $x + 2y + 3z = k_2$, $3x - y = k_3$, with $k_1, k_2, k_3 \in \mathbf{R}$. **3.** $D = 22$, $K_1 = 3k_1 + k_2 + 5k_3$, $K_2 = 9k_1 + 3k_2 - 7k_3$, $K_3 = -7k_1 + 5k_2 + 3k_3$. **5.** $x = -2$, $y = 3$. **7.** $H = \frac{5}{14}$, $V = \frac{20}{7}$. **9.** $x = 1$, $y = -\frac{1}{3}$, $z = \frac{4}{3}$. **11.** $x = \frac{1}{2}$, $y = 1$, $z = -\frac{1}{2}$. **13.** $x = \frac{1}{2}$, $y = 1$, $z = -\frac{1}{16}$. **15.** $x = 9$, $y = -34$, $z = 6$. **17.** $x = \frac{1}{2}$, $y = 1$, $z = -\frac{1}{3}$. **23.** $b(ac - 3) \neq 0$. **25.** Length is 50 centimeters, width is 30 centimeters. **27.** 423. **29.** (a) 8; (b) 48.

Section 2.5 (page 56)

1. $\begin{bmatrix} 1 & 0 & 0 \\ 0 & 1 & 0 \\ 0 & 0 & 1 \end{bmatrix}$. **3.** $\begin{bmatrix} 17 & 0 & 0 & 43 \\ 0 & 1 & 0 & -2 \\ 0 & 0 & 17 & -6 \end{bmatrix}$. **5.** $\begin{bmatrix} 1 & 0 & 0 & 0 \\ 0 & 1 & 0 & 0 \\ 0 & 0 & 1 & 0 \\ 0 & 0 & 0 & 1 \end{bmatrix}$.

7. $\begin{bmatrix} 1 & 0 & 0 & 17 & -39 \\ 0 & 5 & 0 & -36 & 83 \\ 0 & 0 & 1 & -2 & 5 \end{bmatrix}$. **9.** $\begin{bmatrix} 1 & 0 & 0 & 0 \\ 0 & 1 & 0 & 0 \\ 0 & 0 & 1 & 0 \\ 0 & 0 & 0 & 1 \end{bmatrix}$.

Section 2.6 (page 60)

1. (a) $\begin{bmatrix} 3 & 4 & 6 \\ 2 & -5 & -19 \end{bmatrix}$; (b) $\begin{bmatrix} 3 & 2 & 2 \\ 2 & -3 & 36 \end{bmatrix}$.

3. (a) $\begin{bmatrix} 2 & -1 & 0 & 0 \\ 4 & 0 & 16 & 1 \\ 0 & 64 & -16 & 65 \end{bmatrix}$; (b) $\begin{bmatrix} 1 & -2 & 1 & 7 \\ 0 & 1 & 2 & 1 \\ 2 & 0 & 3 & 4 \end{bmatrix}$.

5. (a) $(0, 0, 0, 0)$; (b) $(1, 3, 2, 2)$; (c) $(-3, 3, 0, 2)$. **7.** Both members may be multiplied by the g.c.d. of the denominators of the coefficients. **9.** (a) No solution; (b) $(\frac{7}{2}, -6, c)$, for any

$c \in$ **R**. **11.** $\begin{bmatrix} 1 & 0 & 0 & 1 \\ 0 & 1 & 0 & 2 \\ 0 & 0 & 1 & 3 \end{bmatrix}$. **13.** $\{(-29, 1, 24)\}$. **15.** $\{(-1, 1, 0)\}$. **17.** $\{(1, 2, -1)\}$.

19. $\{(2, 1, -2, 1)\}$. **21.** $\{(x_1, x_2, x_3, x_4, x_5) = (a, 2a, -a, 1 - 3a, a)$, for any $a \in$ **R**$\}$.

25. No. **27.** $\begin{bmatrix} 1 & 0 & 0 & -29 \\ 0 & 1 & 0 & 1 \\ 0 & 0 & 1 & 24 \end{bmatrix}$. **29.** $\begin{bmatrix} 1 & 0 & 0 & -\frac{55}{12} & 0 \\ 0 & 1 & 0 & \frac{9}{4} & 0 \\ 0 & 0 & 1 & -\frac{17}{12} & 0 \end{bmatrix}$.

Section 2.7 (page 65)

1. $(0, 0)$, $(1, 1)$. **3.** $(-3, 2)$, $(2, -3)$. **5.** $(\pm 5, \pm 3)$. **7.** $(3, 4)$, $(-4, 3)$. **9.** $(1 + a, a - 1)$, $(1 - a, -1 - a)$. **11.** $(\pm 3, 0)$. **13.** $(\frac{5}{2}, 1)$, $(-\frac{5}{2}, -1)$. **15.** $(1, 1)$, $(-1, -1)$, $(\sqrt{29}/29,$ $5\sqrt{29}/29)$, $(-\sqrt{29}/29, -5\sqrt{29}/29)$. **17.** (a) A sum of positive numbers is never zero, contrary to what is asserted in the quadratic equation; (b) radicals such as $\sqrt{y}$ and $\sqrt{xy}$ are positive or zero (if they are real) and the argument in (a) applies. **19.** 3, 4. **21.** 16, 30. **23.** 120 miles per hour, 100 miles per hour. **25.** 6 inches by 10 inches.

CHAPTER 3

Section 3.1 (page 70)

1. $-\pi < -1 < 0 < \sqrt{2} < 2 < |-3| < \pi$. **3.** (a) $\frac{5}{12}$; (b) $\frac{1}{6}$. **5.** (a) $-1 \le a \le 1$; (b) $x \ge 5$ or $x \le -5$; (c) $x = \pm 2$. **9.** (a) $-6 \le 6 \le 6$; (b) $-6 \le -6 \le 6$.

Section 3.2 (page 73)

3. (a) $[-1, 2]$; (b) $(2, 5]$; (c) $(0, 10)$; (d) $[0, 10]$; (e) $(-\infty, -2)$; (f) $(-2, \infty)$. **7.** (a) $0, \frac{3}{2}$; (b) $-\frac{7}{3}, \frac{1}{7}$. **9.** $[-\frac{9}{2}, \infty)$. **11.** $[-\frac{3}{2}, \frac{5}{2}]$. **13.** (a) $\{x \in$ **Z**$| x \le 0$ or $x \ge 4\}$; (b) $(-\infty, 0] \cup [4, \infty)$. **15.** $(-\infty, -\frac{1}{3}) \cup (\frac{1}{3}, \infty)$. **17.** $\{x \in$ **R**$| x \ne 1\}$. **19.** (a) $\{x \in$ **Z**$| x \le 1$ or $x \ge 2\}$; (b) $(-\infty, 1] \cup [2, \infty)$. **21.** $(-\infty, \frac{1}{3}) \cup (1, \infty)$. **23.** $[-\frac{7}{2}, \frac{5}{2}]$. **25.** $\varnothing$. **27.** $(1/(k + 1), \infty)$. **29.** $[2, 7]$.

Section 3.3 (page 78)

1. $(-\frac{3}{2}, \frac{1}{2})$. **3.** $(-\infty, \frac{2}{3}) \cup (2, \infty)$. **5.** $(-\infty, -\frac{1}{2}) \cup (3. \infty)$. **7.** $[1, 3)$. **9.** $(-\infty, -\frac{1}{2})$. **11.** $(-\infty, -3) \cup [-1, \infty)$. **13.** $(2, 3)$. **15.** $\{0\} \cup [4, 6]$. **17.** $(-\infty, 0)$. **19.** $(-\infty, -1) \cup (1, 2)$. **21.** $(-\infty, -3) \cup (-2, -1)$. **23.** $(0, 1) \cup (-\infty, -1)$. **25.** $\{0\} \cup [\frac{1}{2}, \infty)$. **27.** $\emptyset$. **29.** If a, b, c have the same sign, then $1/c < 1/b < 1/a$; if $a < 0$, $b > 0$, $c > 0$, then $1/a < 1/c < 1/b$; if $a < 0$, $b < 0$, $c > 0$, then $1/b < 1/a < 1/c$.

Section 3.4 (page 79)

1. (a) 5, -3; (b) 10, -2; (c) 1, $-\frac{2}{3}$. **3.** (a) $5, 2$; (b) 3, -2; (c) 1, -1; (d) $7, 0$. **5.** (a) 4, -2; (b) $\sqrt{5}$, $-\sqrt{5}$; (c) 8, -2; (d) 5, -3; (e) neither exists. **7.** For example, $[0, \infty)$, $(0, \infty)$.

Section 3.5 (page 84)

3. (a) For example, $x = y = 0$; (b) $x = y = 1$; (c) $x = 1$, $y = 2$. **5.** The triangular region with vertices at $(2, \frac{4}{3})$, $(2, 5)$, $(\frac{15}{2}, 5)$. **7.** The rectangular region with vertices at $(3, 2)$, $(3, -2)$, $(-3, -2)$, $(-3, 2)$. **9.** The polygonal region with vertices at $(\frac{1}{2}, \frac{1}{2})$, $(\frac{6}{5}, \frac{6}{5})$, $(3, 0)$, $(1, 0)$. **23.** (a) Half plane above $2x - 3y + 2 = 0$; (b) half plane below $3x - 2y - 7 = 0$; (c) half plane below $x + 3y + 3 = 0$; half plane above $2x + 5y - 8 = 0$. **25.** (a) max. $= 2$, min. $= -\frac{4}{3}$; (b) max. $= 11$, min. $= -\frac{7}{3}$; (c) max. $= 6$, min. $= 0$. **27.** \$8. **29.** 12 tables, 36 chairs.

CHAPTER 4

Section 4.1 (page 90)

1. (a) $0, 1$; (b) domain: $1, 2, 3, 4, 5$; range: $-1, 0, 1, 2, 3$. **3.** $5, 10, 26, 37$. **5.** (a) 0; (b) 9; (c) $\frac{1}{4}$; (d) 1. **9.** Provided no two dissimilar items have different prices. **11.** (a) The function f defined on $\mathbf{R}$ by $f(x) = x^2$; (b) the function f, defined on the subset of nonzero real numbers by $f(x) = 1/x$; (c) the function f, defined on the interval $[-1, 1]$ by $f(x) = \sqrt{1 - x^2}$. **13.** (a) domain of f is $\{x \in \mathbf{Z} \mid x > 0\}$, range is $\{0\}$, $f(x) = 0$; (b) domain of f is $\{x \in \mathbf{Z} \mid x > 0\}$, range of f is $\{x \in \mathbf{Z} \mid x > 1\}$, $f(x) = x + 1$; (c) domain is $\mathbf{R}$, range is $[-\frac{1}{4}, \infty)$, $f(x) = x^2 + x$; (d) domain = range = $[0, \infty)$, $f(x) = x + \sqrt{x}$; (e) domain of f is $(0, \infty)$, range of f is $(-\infty, -2] \cup [2, \infty)$, $f(x) = x + 1/x$. **15.** (a) 3; (b) -9; (c) $2|a| - 1$; (d) $2y^2 - 1$; (e) 0. **17.** $\{x \in \mathbf{R} \mid x \neq \pm 1\}$, 0, $-\frac{4}{3}$. **19.** No; only the symbolism is different. **21.** (a) $\{x \in \mathbf{R} \mid x \neq 0\}$; (b) $(0, \infty)$; (c) $(-\infty, 1 - \sqrt{7}] \cup [1 + \sqrt{7}, \infty)$; (d) $\{x \in \mathbf{R} \mid x \neq 0\}$. **23.** $g(n) = [10^n \pi] - 10[10^{n-1}\pi]$. **25.** None. **27.** 3, 20, 23; domain = $\{x \in \mathbf{Z} \mid x > 0\}$, range = $\{x \in \mathbf{Z} \mid x \geq 0\}$. **29.** $V = f(r)$, where $f(r) = 28\pi r^3/3$.

Section 4.2 (page 95)

7. Include either $(3, 0)$ or $(3, 1)$ in f. **9.** $S \cup T = \{(1, 2), (1, 3), (2, 5), (3, 6), (3, 7), (7, 1), (4, 5)\}$ and $S \cap T = \{(1, 3), (3, 6)\}$; $S \cap T$ is a function but S, T, and $S \cup T$ are not. **11.** (a) n^m; (b) m^m; $\{(0, 0), (1, 0),\}$ $\{(0, 1), (1, 0)\}$, $\{(0, 1), (1, 1)\}$, $\{(0, 0), (1, 1)\}$. **29.** For example, "is similar to" in a set of plane triangles.

Section 4.3 (page 101)

15. (a) mx; (b) $x + b$; (c) b. **17.** (a) $x - 1$; (b) 1; (c) $2x$. **19.** $x^2 - 2x + 1$. **21.** (b, a), $(-a, -b)$, $(-b, -a)$.

Section 4.4 (page 106)

1. No; their domains may differ. **3.** $(f + g)(x) = 3x^2 + 2x + 8$. **5.** $(f/g)(x) =$ $(3x^2 + 1)/(2x + 7)$. **7.** $(1/g)(x) = 1/(2x + 7)$. **9.** $(g/f + g \cdot f)(x) = (2x + 7)/(3x^2 + 1)$ $+ (3x^2 + 1)(2x + 7)$. **11.** $\{x \in \mathbf{R}| \ x \neq 1, 2\}$; $(f \cdot g)(x) = 1/(x - 1)(x - 2)^2$. **13.** $\{x \in \mathbf{R}| \ x \neq 1, 2\}, (f - g)(x) = (x^2 - 5x + 5)/(x - 1)(x - 2)^2$; $\{x \in \mathbf{R}| \ x \neq 1, 2\}$, $(f/g)(x) = (x - 2)^2/(x - 1)$. **17.** The *function* 1 in both cases. **19.** A subset of points of a horizontal line. No. **21.** $f(x) = 1$. **23.** (a) 5, -4, 11; (b) -1, 2, -1; (c) 6, 3, 30; (d) $\frac{2}{3}, \frac{1}{3}, \frac{5}{6}$. **25.** (a) 6, -3, 15; (b) 12, -9, 27; (c) 16, 4, 100; (d) 12, -12, 27; (e) 40, 31, 157. **27.** $(f \cdot g)(x) = 2[x]$; $(f - g)(x) = 2 - [x]$. **29.** Either remove 0 from the common domain, or define g so that $g(0) \neq 0$.

Section 4.5 (page 113)

1. No fixed domain is understood for I. **3.** $(fg)(x) = 9x^3 - 2$, $(gf)(x) = 3(3x - 2)^3$, $(g^2)(x) = 81x^9$. **5.** $(gf)(x) = 6/x - 1$, for $x \in [2, 4]$; No, because $(fg)(x)$ is defined only when $g(x) \in [2, 4]$. **7.** (a), (d). **9.** I. No, because it is not a one-to-one mapping. **13.** For example, let the domain be $[0, \infty)$. **15.** (a) $fI = f = f \cdot 1$, with our usual assumptions concerning the domain of I; (b) $If = f = 1 \cdot f$, as in (a). **17.** $(fg)(x) = (2x - 1)^2 + 1$; $(f \cdot g)(x) = (x^2 + 1)(2x - 1)$. **19.** $g(\mathbf{R})$ coincides with the domain of f, and $(fg)(x) = (1 - x)^2$; f and g have the same domain $\mathbf{R}$, and $(f \cdot g)(x) = x^2(1 - x)$; $f(\mathbf{R})$ is in the domain of f, and $f^2(x) = x^4$; $g(\mathbf{R})$ is in the domain of g, and $g^2(x) = x$. **21.** Because then a reverse mapping is possible. No, because the domain of an invertible function is not required to be $\mathbf{R}$. **23.** (a) $g^{-1}(x) = (3x - 2)/(1 - x)$ for $x \in [0, 1)$; (b) $g^2(x) = (8 + 3x)/(11 + 4x)$ for $x \in \mathbf{R}$. **25.** $(fg)(x) = |[x]|$ and $(gf)(x) = [|x|]$, the domain of both functions being $\mathbf{R}$; f and f^2 are the same function; g^2 is quite different from g, because g^2 is the identity function I on $\mathbf{Z}$. **27.** Yes; yes.

CHAPTER 5

Section 5.1 (page 119)

1. (a) 16; (b) $-2\sqrt[3]{2}$; (c) 3; (d) $4\sqrt[3]{4}$; (e) 4. **3.** (a) $\sqrt[3]{16}$; (b) $\sqrt[4]{216}$; (c) $\sqrt[6]{16}$; (d) $-1/\sqrt[5]{125}$. **5.** (a) 6561; (b) $\frac{8}{27}$; (c) $1/\sqrt[4]{4}$; (d) $4/\sqrt[3]{6561}$; (e) 64. **7.** $1/(2x^0) (= \frac{1}{2}) < (2x)^0 (= 1) < 2x^0 (= 2)$. **9.** (a) $2x$, $\sqrt[3]{3}\,x$; (b) $2|x|$, $\sqrt[3]{3}\,x$. **11.** (a) a^5b^8; (b) a^3; (c) $2^5 3^7$; (d) xy^4; (e) $xy/(x + y)$. **13.** (a) $27/x^6$; (b) xy^2; (c) $1/(ab^7c)$; (d) $1/x^4y^6$. **15.** (a) a^r, where $r = |m|/|n|$; (b) a^r, where $r = -|m/n|$. **17.** (a) y^6/x^2; (b) $1/(3x^2y^3z)$; (c) $(1/x)\sqrt{2/x}$. **19.** (a) $1/\sqrt[6]{x}$; (b) $\sqrt[6]{108a^{11}b^7}$; (c) $\sqrt[12]{512x^{11}y^6/3}$; (d) $\sqrt[8]{3^7}$. **21.** $-4, 6$. **23.** 2 and 3. **25.** (a) No; (b) Yes. 512 **27.** Yes.

Section 5.2 (page 124)

1. Any horizontal line above the x-axis intersects the graph of the basic exponential function defined by $y = b^k$ in exactly one point. No. **3.** (a) 1.73, 3.14; (b) 1.732, 3.141; (c) 1.7321, 3.1416. **5.** (a) 4.7; (b) 32; (c) 1.4. **9.** (a) 2; (b) 2; (c) π. **11.** $y = 3^{2x/3+1}$. **13.** The special case when the base is 1; $(0, \infty)$. **19.** (a) one; (b) one; (c) none. **23.** No; $f(x_1 + x_2) = ca^{x_1+x_2} \neq [f(x_1)][f(x_2)]$. **25.** approx. 15.6 milligrams. **27.** 3. **29.** $0.8/\sqrt{3.2} \approx$ 0.45 amperes.

Section 5.3 (page 129)

1. (a) $\log_2 16 = 4$; (b) $\log_{10} 1000 = 3$; (c) $\log_{10} 1 = 0$; (d) $\log_3 27 = 3$; (e) $\log_{25} 5 = \frac{1}{2}$. **3.** (a) $\log_x 12 = 5$; (b) $\log_5 7 = x$; (c) $\log_6 x = 7$; (d) $\log_{10} 55 = x$. **5.** Because $1^x = 1$ for any real number x. **7.** (a) Because $a^0 = 1$; (b) definition of a logarithm; (c) because $a^1 = a$. **13.** (a) 2; (b) -1; (c) $\frac{1}{2}$. **15.** (a) 2; (b) 2.5; (c) 3.2 **17.** (a) $\pm\frac{1}{9}$; (b) ± 5; (c) ± 1. **19.** (a) 7; (b) 3; (c) -2; (d) any positive real number. **21.** 4. **23.** (a) -3; (b) $\frac{3}{2}$; (c) -3. **27.** $\log_a x_1 x_2 = \log_a x_1 + \log_a x_2$. **29.** 10^{10} inches or over 157,800 miles!!

Section 5.4 (page 133)

1. (a) 1.792; (b) 2.995; (c) 3.584; (d) 5.010; (e) 1.700; (f) 2.389; (g) 3.250.   **3.** (a) -0.203; (b) -0.418; (c) 1.555; (d) -0.819; (e) -0.680.   **5.** (a) -2.485; (b) -2.708; (c) -1.700; (d) -2.409; (e) -0.541; (f) -0.530.   **7.** (a) 0.6990; (b) 1.3010; (c) 1.6532; (d) 0.9771; (e) -0.8673.   **9.** (a) 9, $\frac{1}{9}$; (b) 1080.   **11.** (a) $\log_a (y/x^{13/2})$; (b) $\log_a [2(2 - x^2)/(2 + x)^3]$; (c) $\log_a (3/\sqrt[3]{x})$.   **13.** (a) $\log_a |x^2 + xy + y^2|$; (b) $\log_a [(x^2 + y^2)/|x + y|]$.   **15.** (a) $(x + y)\log_3 2 + 1$; (b) $4(x + y)$; (c) $(x + y)^4$.   **17.** $P_2/P_1 = 10^{N/10}$.   **19.** 4.27; if $b = c$ or $bc = 1$.   **23.** $x = 2$, $y = 4$.   **25.** $\log_a y = p \log_a x + \log_a k$; linear.   **27.** No; their domains are different.

Section 5.5 (page 138)

1. (a) 2; (b) -4; (c) 4; (d) -3.   **3.** (a) 0.4082; (b) 0.0294; (c) 0.9143; (d) 0.7300; (e) 0.6580.   **5.** (a) 1.3711; (b) -0.1169; (c) 1.1072; (d) -2.3665; (e) 4.5378;   **7.** (a) 2^4; (b) 2^c where $c = 4\log_2 5 + 3\log_2 3 - 3\log_2 17 + 6$.   **9.** (a) $3 + 0.1010$; (b) $-4 + 0.854$; (c) $-2 + 0.5608$; (d) $-6 + 0.799$.   **11.** (a) -0.2219, -0.2218; (b) -0.1761, -0.1761; (c) -0.2430, -0.2431. Discrepancies due to inaccuracy of Table 1.   **13.** (a) 4; (b) 2.5; (c) -1.76; (d) -0.01.   **15.** (a) 100,000; (b) 0.01; (c) 0.001; (d) 10,000.   **17.** (a) 706; (b) 6560; (c) 85.0; (d) 5500.   **19.** (a) 335.7; (b) 23.42; (c) 0.000472; (d) 0.00513.   **21.** $10^{0.7424}$.   **23.** (a) 0.3986; (b) -0.6109; (c) 0.2914; (d) -3.7198.   **25.** (a) 352; (b) 29.6; (c) 0.00546; (d) 0.000208.   **27.** (a) 2.262; (b) 1.827; (c) 1.838; (d) 4.130.   **29.** (a) 1.853; (b) -3.407; (c) -1.277.

Section 5.6 (page 143)

1. (a) $3.54 \approx$ the principal thousandth root of 10^{549}; (b) $5.18 \approx$ the principal ten-thousandth root of 10^{7143}; (c) $8.42 \approx$ the principal ten-thousandth root of 10^{9253}.   **3.** (a) $7.3548 - 10$; (b) $4.2984 - 10$; (c) $6.0105 - 10$; (d) $9.7722 - 10$.   **5.** 0.9355 (for both); 0.1203, 0.1206.   **7.** $16^{4/5}$; (b) $27^{3/5}$; (c) $3\sqrt{2}$.   **9.** (a) 802.6; (b) 35,170; (c) 0.005682.   **11.** (a) 351.6; (b) 0.2828; (c) 4.789.   **13.** (a) 95,000; (b) 2.34; (c) 254.   **15.** 0.8242.   **17.** $6.12(10^6)$.   **19.** -0.0101.   **21.** 2.25 seconds.   **23.** \$670.   **25.** $2.6(10^{11})$ cubic miles.

Section 5.7 (page 148)

1. (a) 0.683; (b) -0.281; (c) -0.292; (d) -0.693.   **3.** (a) -0.369; (b) -0.0693; (c) -0.843; (d) ± 1.61.   **5.** (a) $e^{1.238}$; (b) $e^{-0.844}$; (c) $e^{2.595}$; (d) $e^{-6.46}$.   **7.** e^π.   **9.** 0.450.   **11.** -5, -1.   **13.** ± 1.34.   **15.** (a) 10^{10}; (b) e^e; (c) e^{e^e}.   **17.** 78.9.   **19.** $10 \leq |x| \leq 100$.   **21.** $p = p_0 10^{-0.0838h}$.   **23.** 13.   **25.** No.   **27.** \$35,500.   **29.** 7.9 amperes.

CHAPTER 6

Section 6.1 (page 164)

1. (a) (1, 0); (b) $(-1, 0)$; (c) (1, 0); (d) $(-1, 0)$.   **3.** (a) 0; (b) π; (c) $\frac{5}{4}\pi$; (d) $\frac{7}{4}\pi$.   **7.** (a) (0, 1), $(0, -1)$; (b) (0, 1), $(0, -1)$; (c) $(-1, 0)$, $(-1, 0)$; (d) (0, 1), $(0, -1)$.   **9.** (a) 3π; (b) $\frac{15}{4}\pi$; (c) 2π; (d) $\frac{5}{2}\pi$.   **11.** (a) $\frac{1}{2}\pi$, $\frac{5}{2}\pi$, $\frac{9}{2}\pi$, $-\frac{3}{2}\pi$, $-\frac{7}{2}\pi$; (b) $\frac{3}{2}\pi$, $\frac{7}{2}\pi$, $\frac{11}{2}\pi$, $-\frac{1}{2}\pi$, $-\frac{5}{2}\pi$.   **13.** (a) 0; (b) 0; (c) -1.   **15.** (a) -2; (b) $-2/\sqrt{3}$; (c) $\sqrt{3}$.   **17.** (a) -2.2; (b) -0.16; (c) -0.27.   **19.** tan: $\{\theta \in \mathbf{R}\mid \theta \neq \frac{1}{2}(2k + 1)\pi, \ k \in \mathbf{Z}\}$, cot: $\{\theta \in \mathbf{R}\mid \theta \neq 2k\pi, \ k \in \mathbf{Z}\}$, sec: $\{\theta \in \mathbf{R}\mid \theta \neq \frac{1}{2}(2k + 1)\pi, k \in \mathbf{Z}\}$, csc: $\{\theta \in \mathbf{R}\mid \theta \neq k\pi, k \in \mathbf{Z}\}$.   **21.** $-2\sqrt{2}/3$.   **23.** $(-2/\sqrt{5}, -1/\sqrt{5})$; (a) $-1/\sqrt{5}$, (b) $\frac{1}{2}$, (c) 2.   **25.** (a) 5; (b) 0.

Section 6.2 (page 169)

1. (a) 1; (b) 1; (c) 0; (d) 1; (e) 0; (f) 1; (g) $-\sqrt{3}/2$; (h) $2/\sqrt{3}$; (i) $-\frac{1}{2}$.   **3.** (a) $-\sqrt{3}/2$; (b) $2/\sqrt{3}$; (c) -1; (d) 1; (e) 0; (f) 0; (g) -1; (h) 1; (i) -1.   **5.** $(\frac{1}{3}, 2\sqrt{2}/3)$.   **7.** $(\frac{1}{4}, \sqrt{15}/4)$,

$(-\frac{1}{4}, -\sqrt{15}/4)$, $(-\frac{1}{4}, \sqrt{15}/4)$. **9.** (a) $\frac{2}{3}\pi$; (b) $\frac{4}{3}\pi$; (c) $\frac{2}{3}\pi$. **11.** (a) $\frac{1}{4}\pi$; (b) $\frac{4}{3}\pi$; (c) $\frac{4}{3}\pi$. **13.** (a) $-\frac{1}{6}\pi$; (b) $\pm\frac{1}{4}\pi$; (c) $-\frac{1}{4}\pi$; (d) $-\frac{1}{3}\pi$; (e) $\frac{1}{3}\pi$. **15.** $\sin(\pi - \theta_1) = 0.5736$, $\sin(\pi + \theta_1) = -0.5736$, $\sin(2\pi - \theta_1) = -0.5736$. **17.** Neither the abscissa nor the ordinate of any point on the unit circle exceeds the radius. No. **19.** (a) $(0, \pi)$; (b) $(0, \frac{1}{2}\pi) \cup (\frac{3}{2}\pi, 2\pi)$; (c) $(0, \frac{1}{2}\pi) \cup (\pi, \frac{3}{2}\pi)$. **21.** The ordinate of a point on the unit circle in quadrant II is positive but not so for the abscissa. **23.** (a) $\frac{1}{3}, \frac{4}{3}$; $1, 2$; $3, 4$. (b) $3, 4$; $1, 2$; $\frac{1}{3}, \frac{4}{3}$ $(\sec\theta)^2 - (\tan\theta)^2 = 1$; $(\csc\theta)^2 - (\cot\theta)^2 = 1$. **27.** $\frac{3}{2}\pi$. **29.** (a) $(5\sqrt{3} - 3\sqrt{2})/3$; (b) $2/(2\sqrt{3} + 1)$.

Section 6.3 (page 176)

1. (a) 0.66; (b) -0.80; (c) 1.6; (d) 0.43. **5.** (a) -0.76; (b) -2.2; (c) 0.65; (d) 0.46. **7.** (a) $(0.94, 0.33)$; (b) $(0.85, 0.53)$; (c) $(0.78, 0.62)$. **9.** (a) $(-0.34, 0.94)$; (b) $(-0.34, -0.94)$; (c) $(0.63, -0.77)$. **11.** (a) Increasing; (b) neither; (c) neither; (d) increasing; (e) decreasing. **13.** (a) $[0, 0.34]$, approx.; (b) $[0, 0.23]$, approx. **27.** cosine, secant.

Section 6.4 (page 184)

1. (a) $\frac{1}{6}\pi$; (b) $\frac{2}{3}\pi$; (c) $-\frac{1}{4}\pi$; (d) $\frac{1}{4}\pi$. **3.** (a) 0; (b) $\frac{3}{4}\pi$; (c) π; (d) $-\frac{1}{2}\pi$. **5.** (a) -0.5061; (b) 0.6405; (c) 2.5011; (d) -0.7069. **7.** 5, -1, 4.2, -2, $-\frac{5}{8}\pi$. **9.** (a) $1/\sqrt{2}$; (b) $\sqrt{3}$; (c) 1; (d) 0; (e) $1/\sqrt{3}$. **11.** (a) 0; (b) $1/\sqrt{2}$; (c) $-1/\sqrt{3}$; (d) $2/\sqrt{3}$. **15.** $(2\pi + \sqrt{3} - 3)/3$ **17.** (a) $(\sin y)/2$; (b) $\cos\frac{1}{4}(\pi - 2y)$; (c) $\frac{1}{2}[\cos\frac{1}{12}(\pi - 24y) - 1]$ **27.** (a) Arcsin b; (b) Arccos a; (c) Arcsin $(b - a)$; (d) Arccos $(a - b)$.

Section 6.5 (page 191)

9. (a) 3, π, $-\frac{3}{2}$; (b) $\frac{1}{2}$, 2π, 2; (c) 3, 4π, $\frac{3}{2}$; (d) 2, 2, $2/\pi$. **11.** (a) No; (b) yes, 2π; (c) no; (d) yes, π. **13.** $(e^2 - 1)/2e$, 2π. **15.** $a = a' = \frac{1}{3}$; $b' = 3b = -5$.

Section 6.6 (page 195)

1. $-\frac{1}{2}, -2\sqrt{3}/3$. **3.** $\sqrt{7}/3, -4/\sqrt{7}$. **5.** $2\sqrt{2}, -3$. **7.** $-7/\sqrt{58}, 3/\sqrt{58}, -\frac{3}{7}$. **9.** (1): $\{x \in \mathbf{R} \mid x \neq n\pi, n \in \mathbf{Z}\}$; (2): $\{x \in \mathbf{R} \mid x \neq \frac{1}{2}(2n + 1)\pi, n \in \mathbf{Z}\}$; (3): $\{x \in \mathbf{R} \mid x \neq n\pi, n \in \mathbf{Z}\}$; (4): $\{x \in \mathbf{R} \mid x \neq \frac{1}{2}(2n + 1)\pi, n \in \mathbf{Z}\}$; (5): $\{x \in \mathbf{R} \mid x \neq n\pi, n \in \mathbf{Z}\}$; (6): $\mathbf{R}$; (7): $\{x \in \mathbf{R} \mid x \neq \frac{1}{2}(2n + 1)\pi, n \in \mathbf{Z}\}$; (8): $\{x \in \mathbf{R} \mid x \neq n\pi, n \in \mathbf{Z}\}$. **11.** $-\frac{15}{8}$. **13.** (a) $\sqrt{1 - \cos^2 x}$; (b) $\sqrt{1 - \cos^2 x}/\cos x$; (c) $1/\cos x$; (d) $1/\sqrt{1 - \cos^2 x}$; (e) $(\cos x)/\sqrt{1 - \cos^2 x}$; **31.** $-\tan x$. **33.** $2\cot x$.

Section 6.7 (page 203)

13. (a) $-\frac{1}{2}$; (b) $\sqrt{2} + \sqrt{6}$; (c) $2 - \sqrt{3}$; (d) $2 + \sqrt{3}$; (e) $-(\sqrt{2} + \sqrt{6})$; (f) $(\sqrt{6} - \sqrt{2})/4$. **15.** (a) $-(3\sqrt{3} + 4)/10$, $(4\sqrt{3} - 3)/10$; (b) $-(\sqrt{10} + 2\sqrt{2})/6$, $(2\sqrt{2} - \sqrt{10})6$. **17.** (a) $\sin\frac{7}{12}\pi + \sin\frac{1}{12}\pi$; (b) $\cos\frac{5}{6}\pi + \cos\frac{1}{2}\pi$; (c) $\frac{1}{2}(\sin\frac{7}{24}\pi - \sin\frac{1}{24}\pi)$; (d) $\frac{1}{2}(\cos\frac{1}{6}\pi - \cos\frac{3}{2}\pi)$. **25.** $(a + b)/(1 - ab)$. **27.** (a) $y = 2\sin x$; (b) $y = 3\sin(2x + \pi - 3)$; (c) $y = 3\sin(\pi - 3x)$; (d) $y = 4\sin(\frac{3}{2}\pi - 2x)$. **29.** Let $C = \sqrt{A^2 + B^2}$, $A/C = \cos b$, and $B/C = \sin b$.

Section 6.8 (page 207)

1. $\sin\frac{1}{8}\pi = \sqrt{2 - \sqrt{2}}/2$, $\cos\frac{1}{8}\pi = \sqrt{2 + \sqrt{2}}/2$, $\tan\frac{1}{8}\pi = \sqrt{2} - 1$, etc. **5.** $\cot\frac{1}{2}x = (\sin x)/(1 - \cos x) = (1 + \cos x)/\sin x$. **7.** (a) $(\sin x)/\sqrt{1 - \sin^2 x}$; (b) $1/\sqrt{1 - \sin^2 x}$; (c) $1 - 2\sin^2 x$; (d) $\sqrt{2(1 + \sqrt{1 - \sin^2 x})}/\sin x$; (e) $\sqrt{1 - \sin^2 x}/\sin x$; (f) $-\frac{1}{2}\sqrt{2(1 + \sqrt{1 - \sin^2 x})}$. **11.** $\sin 3x = 3\sin x - 4\sin^3 x$. **13.** (a) 0.42; (b) 1.70; (c) -1.28; (d) 0. **17.** $\sin(\ln x)\cos(\ln y) + \cos(\ln x)\sin(\ln y)$. **19.** No; for example, $x = \frac{1}{8}\pi$. **21.** No; for example, $x = \frac{1}{6}\pi$. **23.** Yes. **25.** Yes. **27.** Yes. **29.** Yes. **35.** $\sqrt{17}\cos(2t - 0.24)$.

Section 6.9 (page 212)

1. $\frac{1}{2}\pi$, π, $\frac{3}{2}\pi$. **3.** 0, $\frac{1}{3}\pi$, $\frac{5}{3}\pi$, 2π. **5.** No solutions. **7.** $\frac{1}{8}\pi$, $\frac{5}{8}\pi$, $\frac{9}{8}\pi$, $\frac{13}{8}\pi$. **9.** $\pm$Arccos $\frac{2}{3} \approx$ ± 0.841. **11.** $\frac{1}{6}\pi$, $\frac{1}{4}\pi$, $\frac{3}{4}\pi$, $\frac{5}{6}\pi$. **13.** $\frac{7}{4}\pi$. **15.** $\frac{1}{6}\pi$, $\frac{5}{6}\pi$. **17.** $\frac{1}{3}\pi$. **19.** $r = \frac{1}{2}$, $\theta = \frac{1}{3}\pi$; $r = \frac{1}{2}$, $\theta = \frac{5}{3}\pi$. **21.** (a) $x = 0, \pi, 2\pi$; $y = 0, 2\pi$. (b) $x = \frac{3}{8}\pi + \frac{1}{2}$, $y = \frac{3}{8}\pi - \frac{1}{2}$. **23.** (a) $\frac{1}{4}\pi$, $\frac{3}{4}\pi$; (b) $\frac{3}{2}\pi$. **25.** (a) $0.104, 0.104$; (b) $0.99, 0.99$; (c) $0.10, 0.105$. **29.** (a) $\sqrt{3} + 1$; (b) $(2 \pm \sqrt{2})/2$. **31.** (a) $(2 \pm \sqrt{2})/2$; (b) $\sqrt{3} - 1$; (c) 0.

CHAPTER 7

Section 7.1 (page 221)

1. (a) $\frac{2}{3}\pi$, 2; (b) $\frac{1}{2}\pi$, 3; (c) $\frac{1}{5}\pi$, 3. **3.** (a) $3/2\pi$, 0; (b) $2/\pi$, 0; (c) $5/\pi$, $-\frac{1}{3}\pi$. **5.** Phase difference is $\frac{1}{4}\pi$. **7.** The first differs from the second in amplitude and from the third in phase; the second differs from the third in both phase and amplitude. **9.** Same period but differ in amplitude and phase. **11.** $x = 3 \cos \pi t$. **13.** 4.

Section 7.2 (page 226)

1. (a) 2, $\frac{2}{3}$; (b) 10, $\frac{3}{2}$; (c) 50, 15. **3.** (a) $\frac{2}{3}\pi$, $\frac{2}{3}\pi$; (b) 6π, 4π; (c) 15, 1. **5.** $y = 3 \sin \frac{2}{75}\pi(5x - 22t)$, with x, y in feet and t in seconds. **7.** $y = (\cos 300\pi t)(\sin \frac{1}{10}\pi x)$. **9.** (a) A stationary wave of amplitude 20, wave length 2, and period $\frac{2}{3}$; (b) a stationary wave of amplitude 2, wave length 12π, and period 10π. **11.** $y = 8 \cos \frac{1}{5}\pi t \sin \frac{1}{100}\pi x$, with t in seconds, x in meters, and y in centimeters. **13.** (a) $y = 5 \sin \frac{1}{3}(x + 12t - 10)$; (b) $y = 5 \sin \frac{1}{3}(x + 12t + 5)$.

Section 7.3 (page 232)

1. (a) $143°$; (b) $92°$; (c) $286°$; (d) $-183°$; (e) $-344°$. **3.** (a) $\frac{1}{6}\pi$; (b) $-\frac{5}{4}\pi$; (c) $\frac{3}{4}\pi$; (d) $-\frac{3}{2}\pi$; (e) $\frac{4}{3}\pi$; (f) $-\frac{7}{4}\pi$. **9.** (a) 2; (b) 3; (c) $\frac{7}{2}$; (d) π. **11.** (a) π; (b) 5π; (c) $\frac{4.9}{4}\pi$; (d) $\frac{2}{3}\pi$. **13.** (a) $\frac{5}{6}\pi$; (b) $\frac{10}{3}\pi$; (c) $\frac{25}{6}\pi$. **17.** (a) $\frac{1}{6}\pi$; (b) $\frac{5}{4}\pi$; (c) $\frac{5}{3}\pi$. **19.** $\frac{2000}{3}\pi$. **21.** $865{,}000$ miles. **23.** (a) $\frac{5}{6}\pi$; (b) $\frac{25}{3}\pi$. **25.** $32\frac{8}{11}° \approx 32.7°$. **29.** $\frac{25}{3}\pi$. **31.** $16(10^5)$ miles.

Section 7.4 (page 239)

1. (a) 0.4114 radian; (b) 0.8426 radian; (c) 0.6971 radian; (d) 0.3206 radian; (e) 1.4043 radians. **3.** (a) $77.62°$; (b) $36.64°$; (c) $83.82°$; (d) $11.21°$; (e) $58.08°$. **5.** (a) 1.1681; (b) 0.5723; (c) 0.5198; (d) 0.3203; (e) 0.5715. **7.** $\sin 90°$. **9.** (a) 0.5604; (b) 0.03110; (c) -1.4173; (d) -2.0836. **11.** (a) -0.3101; (b) 0.4646; (c) 3.920; (d) 1.5207; **13.** (a) -0.5089; (b) 16.537; (c) -1.9687; (d) 0.6541. **15.** (a) 0.6606; (b) -0.5036; (c) 1.0002; (d) 41.55. **17.** (a) -0.5498; (b) -0.9997; (c) -1.4613; (d) -1.778. **19.** (a) 0.6993; (b) -0.7899; (c) 1.993; (d) -3.0530. **25.** (a) $-180°$, $0°$, $30°$, $150°$, $180°$; (b) $-112.5°$, $-22.5°$, $67.5°$, $157.5°$. **29.** (a) $\{\pm 45°,$ $\pm 135°$, $\pm 225°$, $\pm 315°\}$; (b) $\{A|\ -315° < A < -270°$, $-135° < A < -90°$, $45° <$ $A < 90°$, $225° < A < 270°\}$.

Section 7.5 (page 247)

3. (a) $\sqrt{13}$; (b) $\sqrt{37}$; (c) $4\sqrt{2}$. **5.** (a) $c \approx 21$, $A \approx 28°$, $B \approx 112°$; (b) $a \approx 3.6$, $B \approx 30°$, $C \approx 121°$; (c) $b \approx 37.2$, $A \approx 24°$, $C \approx 86°$. **7.** 65 miles. **9.** 9.1 miles. **13.** $48\ 2°$, $58.4°$, $73.4°$. **19.** 3600 feet. **29.** $5r^2 \tan 18°$.

Section 7.6 (page 254)

1. (a) 0.58; (b) 2.3; (c) 1.2; (d) 11. **3.** (a) $\sin 25°46'$; (b) $\csc 3°30'$; (c) $\sec 15°7'$; (d) $\tan 6°5'$; (e) $\cot 1°5'$. **5.** (a) $\cos 24°$; (b) $\sin 35°10'$; (c) $\cot 52°15'$; (d) $\tan 50°$. **7.** 67 feet. **9.** 3700 feet. **11.** 1.02 inches. **13.** 164 feet. **15.** No. **17.** $\sqrt{3} : 1$. **19.** 667 feet. **21.** 10.5 feet.

CHAPTER 8

Section 8.1 (page 260)

1. (a) $(-3, 7)$; (b) $(-1, 7)$; (c) $(7, 1)$.   **3.** (a) $(3, 6)$; (b) $(2, 6)$; (c) $(-4, 0)$; (d) $(1, -9)$.
5. (a) $x = 3$, $y = 0$; (b) $x = 5$, $y = -7$; (c) $x = 2$, $y = \frac{1}{2}$; (d) $x = c - b$, $y = d - a$.
7. (a) $(-\frac{1}{3}, -\frac{2}{3})$; (b) $(\frac{1}{5}, -\frac{2}{5})$.   **9.** (a) $(-\frac{7}{2}, \frac{21}{2})$; (b) $(-\frac{2}{15}, \frac{9}{8})$.   **11.** $(\frac{1}{2}, \frac{1}{2})$.   **13.** $(4, -7)$.
15. That $(0, 1)$ is a number whose square is -1.   **17.** Yes.   **21.** $a - b$ would not be a
natural number.   **23.** (a) $(0, 5)$; (b) $(3, -7)$; (c) $(-16, -15)$.   **25.** (a) $(1, -1)$, $(-1, 1)$;
(b) $(1, 1)$, $(-1, -1)$; (c) $(-3, 0)$, $(-2, 0)$; (d) $(-3, 0)$, $(2, 0)$.

Section 8.2 (page 266)

1. (a) $-3 + 5i$; (b) $3 - 2i$; (c) $2 + 6i$; (d) i; (e) 0; (f) $-1 - i$.   **3.** (a) $11 - 16i$; (b) $20 -
20i$; (c) $-23 + 9i$; (d) $-10 + 5i$; (e) -24; (f) $12i$.   **5.** (a) $-26 - 13i$; (b) $-\frac{64}{5} + \frac{83}{5}i$;
(c) $\frac{3}{5} - \frac{2}{5}i$; (d) $1 - i$.   **9.** (a) $x = -5$, $y = -3$; (b) $x = \frac{3}{2}$, $y = -\frac{5}{2}$; (c) $x = 3$, $y = -\frac{3}{4}$;
(d) $x = 1$, $y = -2$.   **19.** The complex (nonreal) solutions of a real polynomial equation
occur in conjugate pairs.   **23.** (a) $-\frac{2}{3}i$; (b) $-1 + i$; (c) $(1 - 3i)/5$; (d) $1 - i$; (e) $\pm 2i$;
(f) $4i$.   **25.** $x = e - \ln 3$, $y = \ln 3$.   **27.** (a) $-1 + 2i$; (b) $-1 - 4i$; (c) $1 - 2i$.   **29. R.**

Section 8.3 (page 276)

1. (a) $\sqrt{2}\,\text{cis}\,(-\frac{1}{4}\pi)$; (b) $2\sqrt{2}\,\text{cis}\,\frac{1}{4}\pi$; (c) $\text{cis}\,\frac{2}{3}\pi$; (d) $\text{cis}\,\frac{1}{6}\pi$; (e) $2\,\text{cis}\,(-\frac{1}{2}\pi)$.   **3.** (a) 1, $\frac{1}{2}\pi$;
(b) 1, $-\frac{1}{2}\pi$; (c) $2\sqrt{2}$, $-\frac{1}{4}\pi$; (d) 2, $-\frac{2}{3}\pi$.   **5.** (a) $-\sqrt{3} + i$; (b) -3; (c) $\frac{5}{2} + \frac{5}{2}\sqrt{3}i$; (d)
$\sqrt{3} + i$; (e) $-2 + 2\sqrt{3}i$; (f) $(3 + 3\sqrt{3}i)/2$.   **7.** (a) $\sqrt{13}\,\text{cis}\,(-0.983)$; (b) $\sqrt{13}\,\text{cis}\,(-2.159)$;
(c) $\sqrt{10}\,\text{cis}\,1.250$; (d) $\sqrt{10}\,\text{cis}\,(-1.892)$; (e) $5\,\text{cis}\,0.927$; (f) $5\,\text{cis}\,(-2.215)$.   **9.** (a) $27\,\text{cis}\,6$
or $27\,\text{cis}\,(-0.2832)$; (b) $16\,\text{cis}\,12$ or $16\,\text{cis}\,(-0.5664)$.   **11.** $(-1 + i)/2$.   **13.** $-\sqrt{3} + i$.
15. $2^{10}\,\text{cis}\,100° \approx 2^{10}(-0.1736 + 0.9848i)$.   **19.** (a) $1000\,\text{cis}\,(-1.9)$; (b) $169\sqrt{13}\,\text{cis}\,(-1.4)$;
(c) $26^5\,\text{cis}\,(-1.2)$.   **27.** (a) Points inside or on the circle with center at origin and radius $\frac{3}{2}$;
(b) points whose abscissas are less than $\frac{1}{2}$; (c) points whose abscissas exceed $\frac{1}{2}$; (d) points
whose ordinates are 1.

Section 8.5 (page 283)

3. $\sqrt{2}/2 + \sqrt{2}i/2$, $-\sqrt{2}/2 + \sqrt{2}i/2$, $-\sqrt{2}/2 - \sqrt{2}i/2$, $\sqrt{2}/2 - \sqrt{2}i/2$.   **5.** $\sqrt[3]{2}\,\text{cis}\,\frac{1}{18}\pi$,
$\sqrt[3]{2}\,\text{cis}\,\frac{13}{18}\pi$, $\sqrt[3]{2}\,\text{cis}\,\frac{25}{18}\pi$.   **7.** $\sqrt[6]{13}(0.95 - 0.32i) \approx 1.47 - 0.50i$, $\sqrt[6]{13}(-0.19 + 0.98i) \approx
-0.29 + 1.52i$, $\sqrt[6]{13}(-0.75 - 0.66i) \approx -1.16 - 1.02i$.   **9.** 1, $\text{cis}\,\frac{2}{5}\pi$, $\text{cis}\,\frac{4}{5}\pi$, $\text{cis}\,\frac{6}{5}\pi$, $\text{cis}\,\frac{8}{5}\pi$.
11. (a) $4i$; (b) $6i$; (c) $2\sqrt{3}i$.   **13.** (a) True; (b) true.   **15.** (a) $\{\text{cis}\,75° \approx 0.2588 + 0.9659i$,
$\text{cis}\,165° \approx -0.9659 + 0.2588i$, $\text{cis}\,255° \approx -0.2588 - 0.9659i$, $\text{cis}\,345° \approx 0.9659 - 0.2588i\}$;
(b) $\{3, -i\}$.   **17.** $1 + 2i$, $-1 - 2i$.   **19.** (a) 2; (b) 3; (c) 5.   **21.** $(x - 4)(x + 2 + 2\sqrt{3}i)(x +
2 - 2\sqrt{3}i)$.   **23.** The sum of the five complex fifth roots of unity is 0.   **31.** No, YOU
answer it!

CHAPTER 9

Section 9.1 (page 289)

1. (a) $6x^5 + 5x^4 + 4x^3 + 3x^2 + 2x + 1$; (b) $13x^7 + 11x^6 + 9x^5 + 7x^4 + 5x^3 + 3x^2 +
x$; (c) $\frac{2}{3}x^5 + \frac{3}{2}x^4 + \frac{1}{2}x^3 + \frac{1}{2}x^2$.   **3.** For example, the number 5—regarded as a polyno-
mial—has degree 0; the number 0 has no real number assigned as its degree.   **5.** (a) $x^3 - 1$;
(b) $3x^4 + 3x^3 - 2x^2 - x - 4$; (c) $x^3 - 2x^2 + 7x + 5$.   **7.** (a) $2x^4 - 4x^3 - 4x^2 +
14x - 12$; (b) $9x^7 - 9x^6 + 6x^5 - 24x^4 + 10x^3 - 10x^2 + 11x - 5$; (c) $2x^4 - x^3 +
4x^2 + 19x + 6$.   **9.** (a) $(1 - i)x^3 + 2x^2 - (1 - 4i)x - 3$; (b) $(1 - i)x^3 - 2x^2 +
(1 + 2i)x - 5$; (c) $2(1 - i)x^5 + 2ix^4 + (1 + 5i)x^3 - (11 + 3i)x^2 + (4 - i)x - 4$.

11. (a) 4; (b) 3; (c) 2; (d) 5. **13.** (a) Algebraic; (b) algebraic; (c) nonalgebraic; (d) non-algebraic; (e) algebraic; (f) algebraic; (g) algebraic. **15.** (a) 10; (b) 4; (c) 6. **17.** (a) $q(x) = 2x^2 + x - \frac{1}{2}, r(x) = \frac{1}{2}$; (b) $q(x) = x^4 + 2x^2 - 7$, $r(x) = 20$; (c) $q(x) = 3x^3 + 7x^2 + 22x + 67$, $r(x) = 199$. **19.** (a) 0; (b) $1 - 5i$; (c) $-7 + 4i$; (d) $\frac{3}{8}$; (e) $\frac{49}{8} - \frac{11}{4}i$. **21.** Left member is positive for any $x \in \mathbf{R}$. **23.** 1. **25.** For example, $x^2 + x = x(x + 1)$. **27.** (a) $\{2\}$; (b) $\{\frac{1}{2}, 2\}$; (c) $\{\frac{1}{2}, 2\}$; (d) $\{\pm i, \frac{1}{2}, 2\}$. **29.** -3.5.

Section 9.2 (page 294)

1. (a) $\frac{2}{3}$; (b) $-\frac{3}{4}$; (c) $-t/k$; (d) t/s; (e) $\frac{7}{2}$; (f) $\frac{3}{2}$; (g) $\frac{21}{4}$; (h) $\frac{10}{9}$. **3.** (a) $1, \frac{1}{2}$; (b) $(-1 \pm \sqrt{37})/6$; (c) $(-1 \pm \sqrt{11}i)/4$; (d) $(5 \pm \sqrt{21}i)/2$. **5.** (a) $\frac{2}{3}, \frac{1}{3}$; (b) $-\frac{1}{4}, \frac{3}{4}$; (c) $\frac{3}{2}, \frac{1}{2}$; (d) 3, 9; (e) $-p/3$, $q/3$; (f) $2/r, t/r$. **7.** (a) $-\frac{21}{2}$; (b) $(t^2 - a^2)/(c + b)$; (c) $(y + 3 + 3i)/(y + i)$. **9.** (a) -1.8, 0.3; (b) 1.4, 3.6; (c) $-2.6, -0.4$. **11.** (a) None; (b) two; (c) none. **13.** (a) $|k| \geq 4\sqrt{2}$; (b) $|k| \geq 2\sqrt{3}/3$; (c) $k \leq \frac{1}{9}$. **15.** (a) $\pm\frac{1}{2}\sqrt{10}i$; (b) $\pm\sqrt{3}t/2$; (c) $\pm kti$. **17.** (a) $\pm\sqrt{3}$, $\pm\sqrt{2}i$; (b) $\pm 2, \pm\sqrt{2}i$; (c) 1, 2, $-1 - \sqrt{3}i$, $-1 + \sqrt{3}i$, $(-1 - \sqrt{3}i)/2$, $(-1 + \sqrt{3}i)/2$. **19.** (a) $(a - S)/r + S$; (b) $2S/n - a$; (c) $R/t - gt/2$; (d) $2\sin\alpha/(\sin\beta - \sin\alpha)$. **21.** (a) ± 1; (b) $\pm\sqrt{3}, \pm\sqrt{5}i$; (c) 1. **23.** $\frac{1}{8}\pi, \frac{3}{8}\pi, \frac{5}{8}\pi, \frac{7}{8}\pi, \frac{9}{8}\pi, \frac{11}{8}\pi, \frac{13}{8}\pi, \frac{15}{8}\pi$. **25.** (a) 4; (b) 0; (c) 12. **27.** (a) $\pm\frac{1}{2}$; (b) -2; (c) $[-3, -2)$. **29.** $1\frac{5}{7}$ hours. **31.** 150 miles per hour.

Section 9.3 (page 298)

1. $p(x) = (x + 3)(x^4 - 3x^3 + 9x^2 - 27x + 83) - 248$. **3.** $p(x) = (2x - 5)(x^2 + x + \frac{5}{2}) + \frac{29}{2}$. **5.** $(x + 1)(x - 1)(x - 2)$. **7.** $(x + 2)(x + 1)(x - 1)(x - 2)$. **11.** (a) $x^4 - 3x^3 + 3x^2 - 3x + 2$; (b) $x^4 - 7x^3 + 18x^2 - 22x + 12$; (c) $x^4 - 4x^3 + 14x^2 - 4x + 13$; (d) $x^3 - \frac{5}{3}x^2 + \frac{23}{12}x - \frac{5}{6}$. **13.** (a) $x^5 - 5x^4 + 6x^3 + 4x^2 - 8x$; (b) $x^3 - 3x^2 + 4$; (c) $x^6 - (1 + 3i)x^5 - (4 - 3i)x^4 + (4 + 4i)x^3 + (3 - 4i)x^2 - (3 + i)x + i$; (d) $x^3 - ix^2 - 2x + 2i$. **15.** (a) $1 - i$; (b) $-17 + 43i$; (c) $-\frac{1}{8} - i$. **17.** (a) $\{-5, 2, 3\}$; (b) $\{\pm i, (-1 \pm \sqrt{3}i)/2\}$; (c) $\{-2, \pm 1, 3, \pm 2i\}$. **19.** (a) $(i \pm \alpha)/3$ where $\alpha^2 = -10 - 3i$; (b) $-i(3 \pm \alpha)/4$, where $\alpha^2 = 1 - 16i$; (c) $(1 \pm \alpha - i)/2$, where $\alpha^2 = 4 - 2i$; (d) $(-i \pm \alpha)/2$, where $\alpha^2 = -1 + 4i$. **23.** (a) -2; (b) $\pm\sqrt{33}i/2$; (c) $(-3 \pm \sqrt{183}i)/12$. **25.** (a) $a = -4, b = 2$; (b) $a = 1$, $b = -3$. **27.** $x^6 + 3x^5 - 3x^4 - 11x^3 + 6x^2 + 12x - 8$. **29.** 1, $(-1 \pm \sqrt{2}i)/2$; $(x - 1)(2x + 1 + \sqrt{2}i)(2x + 1 - \sqrt{2}i)$.

Section 9.4 (page 304)

1. (a) $2x^2 + x + 6$, $R = -4$; (b) $2x^2 - 3x + 8$, $R = -18$; (c) $2x^2 + 3x + 11$, $R = 12$; (d) $2x^2 - 5x + 15$, $R = -40$. **3.** (a) $3x^2 + x/2 + \frac{9}{4}$, $R = \frac{49}{8}$; (b) $3x^2 - 5x/2 + \frac{13}{4}$, $R = \frac{27}{8}$; (c) $3x^2 + x + \frac{8}{3}$, $R = \frac{61}{9}$; (d) $3x^2 - 3x + 4$, $R = \frac{7}{3}$. **5.** (a) -2; (b) -8; (c) 13; (d) -62. **7.** (a) 4; (b) 10; (c) 31; (d) $\frac{53}{8}$. **11.** $-\frac{1}{2}, 2$. **13.** (a) $-\frac{17}{2}$; (b) 8; (c) 2. **15.** 61, -18, -17, -8, -15, -14, 67. **17.** 3. **21.** $3x^3 + (1 - 3i)x^2 - (1 + i)x + i$; the two quotients should be complex conjugates. **23.** $2x^3 + (6 + 2\sqrt{2})x^2 + (10 + 6\sqrt{2})x + 10\sqrt{2}$. **25.** $4i$.

Section 9.5 (page 308)

1. Those for which at least one member of the equation becomes meaningless. **3.** Coefficients of the same power of the variable are the same in every case. **5.** For example: $(x - 1)(x - 2)(x - 3) = x^3 - 6x^2 + 11x - 6$; $2(x - 1)(x - 2)(x - 3) = 2x^3 - 12x^2 + 22x - 12$. **7.** Complex zeros of a real polynomial occur in pairs. **9.** (a) $x^4 - 6x^3 + 22x^2 - 30x + 13 = 0$; (b) $x^4 - 4x^3 - x^2 + 14x + 10 = 0$; (c) $x^5 - 6x^4 + 15x^3 - 18x^2 + 10x = 0$; (d) $x^6 - 2x^5 + 7x^4 - 10x^3 + 14x^2 - 8x + 8 = 0$. **11.** (a) $(x - 1)(x^2 - 4x + 5)$; (b) $(x - 1)(2x - 1)(x^2 + 1)$. **15.** $-1, 2, -1 + i, -1 - i$. **17.** This would imply that a polynomial of degree n may have more than n (real) zeros. **19.** (a) $A = B = 2$; (b) $A = -\frac{1}{4}, B = \frac{5}{4}$. **25.** Both members of the equation have meaning for every real number, but the right member has an infinite number of real zeros—which is impossible for the left member.

Section 9.6 (page 316)

1. (a) $15x^5 + 18x^3 - 30x^2 + 15x - 10 = 0$; (b) $3x^6 - 6x^4 + 4x^2 + 12 = 0$; (c) $36x^3 - 40x^2 + 15x - 20 = 0$. **5.** (a) $-1, 2$; (b) $-2, 3$; (c) $-1, 2$. **7.** (a) 1 or 3 positive, no negative; (b) 0, 2, or 4 positive, no negative; (c) none; (d) 0 or 2 positive, no negative. **11.** (a) $\{\pm 1, \pm 3, \pm 9, \pm \frac{1}{3}\}$; (b) $\varnothing$; (c) $\{\pm 1, \pm 2, \pm 4, \pm 8, \pm \frac{1}{5}, \pm \frac{2}{5}, \pm \frac{4}{5}, \pm \frac{8}{5}\}$; (d) $\{-1, -\frac{1}{2}\}$. **15.** (a) $\{\frac{1}{2}, 2, \pm i\}$; (b) $\{-1, 1, -\frac{1}{2}, \frac{2}{3}\}$; (c) $\{-1, 1, 1 + i, 1 - i\}$; (d) $\{-1, 0, 2, \frac{1}{3}, 2 - i, 2 + i\}$. **17.** (a) $\pm \frac{2}{3}$; (b) $-1, \frac{1}{2}$; (c) 0. **19.** Consider the Factor Theorem. **21.** (a) $[-2, -1]$, $[0, 1]$, $[1, 2]$; (b) $[-4, -3], [0, 1]$, $[1, 2]$; (c) $[-4, -3]$, $[1, 2]$, $[3, 4]$. **23.** 6, 1. **27.** $3x^4 - \sqrt{2}x^3 + \pi x + 1 - i = 0$.

Section 9.7 (page 324)

1. (a) $[-1, 0]$, $[0, 1]$; (b) $[-1, 0]$, $[0, 1]$, $[9, 10]$; (c) $[-4, -3]$, $[-1, 0]$, $[0, 1]$; (d) $[0, 1]$. **5.** 0.35. **7.** 0.61. **9.** -1.33. **11.** 3.37. **13.** $-0.37, 5.37$. **15.** $-4.13, -0.51, 0.31$. **17.** -3.55, 1.19, 0.86. **19.** -6.03, 0.61, 5.41. **21.** The values of the functions are the same at each point of intersection of their graphs. **23.** (a) Two; (b) infinitely many negative solutions; (c) infinitely many negative solutions. **25.** Two solutions; 0.36. **27.** Infinitely many real solutions; 0.60.

CHAPTER 10

Section 10.1 (page 321)

1. (a) 6; (b) 12. **3.** 24. **11.** 14. **13.** 28. **15.** 18. **17.** 86,400. **19.** 18. **21.** 720. **23.** (a) 24; (b) 256. **25.** 343. **27.** 16, 256. **29.** $\frac{1}{4}$, 2, $3\frac{1}{4}$, 4, 8, $12\frac{1}{4}$.

Section 10.2 (page 335)

1. (a) 6; (b) 40,320; (c) 120; (d) 1; (e) 3,628,800. **3.** (a) 20; (b) 30,240; (c) 210; (d) 11,404,800. **5.** (a) 28; (b) 120; (c) 15,504. **7.** (a) 10; (b) 35; (c) 210; (d) 1140. **9.** 5005. **11.** 10. **13.** 40,320. **15.** (a) $\binom{52}{13}\binom{39}{13}\binom{26}{13}$; (b) $40\binom{39}{13}\binom{26}{13}$. **17.** $\binom{40}{3}\binom{50}{3}\binom{30}{3}$. **19.** 3003. **21.** 7. **23.** 6.

Section 10.3 (page 340)

1. (a) 140; (b) 360; (c) 495. **3.** 120. **5.** (a) 14,400; (b) 57,600; (c) $\binom{12}{6}(5!)^2 = 13,305,600$. **7.** (a) 511; (b) 315. **9.** 154. **11.** 63. **13.** $8^5 = 32,768$. **15.** (a) 22; (b) 286. **17.** 7875. **19.** 756,756. **21.** 9. **23.** $\binom{47}{5} = \frac{47!}{42!5!}$. **27.** $\binom{6}{4}\frac{9!}{2!3!4!} = 18,900$.

Section 10.4 (page 344)

1. $27x^3 + 135x^2 + 225x + 125$. **3.** $\frac{1}{16} - x + 6x^2 - 16x + 16x^4$. **5.** $1 + 12x^2 + 60x^4 + 160x^6 + 240x^8 + 192x^{10} + 64x^{12}$. **7.** $1 - 8x + 28x^2 - 56x^3 + 70x^4 - 56x^5 + 28x^6 - 8x^7 + x^8$. **9.** $-769,824x^7y^5$. **11.** $63\sqrt{2}x^8/2$, $63x^{10}/4$. **13.** $12!6^6/6!6!$. **15.** (a) $1 - 5i + 10i^2 - 10i^3 + 5i^4 + i^5 = -4 + 6i$; (b) $1 + 8i + 24i^2 + 32i^3 + 16i^4 = -7 - 24i$. **17.** $512x^{27} - 1152x^{47/2} + 1152x^{20} - 672x^{33/2} + 252x^{13} - 63x^{19/2} + 21x^6/2 - \frac{9}{8}x^{5/2} + 9/128x - 1/512x^{9/2}$. **23.** (a) $1 + 3x - 3y + 3x^2 - 6xy + 3y^2 + x^3 - 3x^2y + 3xy^2 - y^3$; (b) $x^2 - 2xy + y^2 + 2xz - 2yz + z^2$; (c) $2(1 + \sin x + \cos x + \sin x \cos x)$. **29.** (a) -2; (b) -1.

Section 10.5 (page 348)

1. $1 + 3x/2 - 9x^2/8 + 27x^3/16$, $|x| < \frac{1}{3}$. **3.** $\sqrt[3]{2}(1 + 5x^2/6 - 25x^4/36 + 625x^6/648)$, $x^2 < \frac{4}{5}$. **5.** $1 + 2x + 4x^2 + 8x^3$, $|x| < \frac{1}{2}$. **7.** $\sqrt[3]{4}(1 + 5a/12 - 25a^2/144 + 625a^3/5184)$, $|a| < \frac{4}{5}$. **9.** $3 < 1$. **11.** $1 + 3a - 3b + 3a^2 - 6ab + 3b^2 + a^3 - 3a^2b + 3ab^2 - b^3$. **13.** 0.980. **15.** 0.674. **17.** 4.932. **21.** 0.004 second. **23.** $\sqrt{6h}/2$ miles.

Section 10.6 (page 351)

1. (a) 3, 5, 7, 9, 11; (b) 4, 2, 4, 2, 4; (c) 1, $\frac{1}{2}$, $\frac{1}{4}$, $\frac{1}{8}$, $\frac{1}{16}$; (d) -1, 1, -1, 1, -1. **3.** (a) 2, 2, 2, 2, 2; (b) 3, 3, 3, 3, 3; (c) 1, $\frac{1}{3}$, $\frac{1}{15}$, $\frac{1}{105}$, $\frac{1}{945}$. **5.** (a) $(-1)^{n+1}$; (b) $[1 + (-1)^{n+1}]/2$; (c) $\sin\frac{1}{2}n\pi$; (d) $3^{2^{1-n}}$. No. **7.** (a) 3, 3, $\frac{9}{2}$, 9, $\frac{45}{2}$; (b) 0, 2, 6, 38, 1446. **9.** (a) 1, 2, 2, 4, 8; (b) 1, -2, 3, -4, 5. **11.** 1, 1, 2, 3, 5, 8, 13, 21, 34, 55. **13.** (a) 1, 3, 5, $6^{1/3}$; (b) -2, 8, -14, 68. **15.** 4, 2, 8; 4, 6, 14. **17.** 4, 16, 36, 64, 100. **25.** n; n^2; 2^n.

Section 10.7 (page 355)

3. 35; 222. **5.** -59. **7.** (a) -63; (b) 54. **9.** $S_n = n^2$. **11.** (a) 275; (b) 783; (c) 1425; (d) -1530. **13.** 5, 8, 11, 14, 17, 20. **15.** \$480. $[a_1 + (n-1)d$, where $a_1 = 300$, $n = 11$, $d = 18$.] **17.** $a_1 = 16$, $a_8 = 2$. **21.** 10. **23.** 322 feet per second. **25.** \$1260.

Section 10.8 (page 359)

3. (a) 162; (b) -0.000001; (c) 0.0001024. **5.** 116,050/19,683. **7.** 6, 2, $\frac{2}{3}$. **9.** ± 4. **11.** (a) 6; (b) $\frac{3}{2}$; (c) $\frac{8}{9}$. **13.** 12. **15.** (a) 2; (b) $\frac{3}{4}$. **17.** 200 feet. **19.** $4\sqrt{3}/3$ square feet. **21.** $2^{21}/5^9$ gallons. **23.** (a, a, a) for any $a(\neq 0) \in \mathbf{R}$; arithmetic with $d = 0$, geometric with $r = 1$.

ANSWERS TO PROBLEMS IN APPENDIX A

Section 1 (page 362)

1. Divide numerator and denominator by the number "canceled." **2.** (a) 2^6; (b) $2^2 \cdot 3^2$; (c) $2^3 \cdot 3^2$; (d) $2^5 \cdot 5$; (e) $2 \cdot 3 \cdot 7$; (f) $2 \cdot 3^2$; (g) 5^3; (h) $2^2 \cdot 3 \cdot 5$; (i) $2^4 \cdot 5$; (j) $2 \cdot 3^2 \cdot 5$; (k) $2 \cdot 3 \cdot 17$. **3.** (a) 1; (b) 3; (c) 2; (d) 15; (e) 1. **4.** (a) $\frac{1}{3}$; (b) $\frac{2}{3}$; (c) $\frac{1}{3}$; (d) $\frac{10}{3}$; (e) $\frac{15}{4}$; (f) $\frac{6}{13}$. **5.** (a) $\frac{10}{45}$; (b) $\frac{15}{20}$; (c) $\frac{25}{15}$; (d) $\frac{20}{30}$; (e) $\frac{20}{45}$. **6.** (a) $\frac{40}{30}$; (b) $\frac{20}{70}$; (c) $\frac{50}{60}$; (d) $\frac{50}{60}$; (e) $\frac{30}{40}$. **7.** (a) $2\frac{13}{24}$; (b) $2\frac{43}{60}$; (c) $1\frac{9}{70}$. **8.** (a) $4\frac{1}{3}$; (b) $\frac{7}{12}$; (c) $1\frac{5}{18}$; (d) $3\frac{1}{4}$; (e) $\frac{2}{5}$. **9.** (a) $1\frac{19}{24}$; (b) $1\frac{7}{120}$; (c) $2\frac{226}{315}$. **10.** (a) $\frac{1}{12}$; (b) $\frac{8}{25}$; (c) $1\frac{7}{18}$. **11.** (a) $\frac{9}{8}$; (b) $\frac{5}{8}$; (c) $\frac{15}{32}$; (d) $\frac{1}{14}$; (e) 32; (f) $\frac{2}{9}$. **12.** (a) $1\frac{1}{2}$; (b) $\frac{49}{72}$; (c) $\frac{83}{240}$; (d) $5\frac{5}{6}$; (e) $3\frac{3}{5}$. **13.** $4\frac{37}{40}$. **14.** $10\frac{7}{8}$; $12\frac{1}{3}$. **15.** $4\frac{1}{4}$ feet. **16.** 42 cents. **17.** 16 cents **18.** $2\frac{9}{10}$; $3\frac{31}{33}$.

Section 2 (page 364)

1. (a) 6; (b) 7; (c) 4; (d) $\frac{3}{5}$; (e) $\frac{5}{7}$. **2.** (a) 17; (b) -21; (c) $-2\frac{3}{8}$; (d) $1\frac{77}{120}$. **3.** (a) -3; (b) -17; (c) 1; (d) -2. **4.** (a) $\frac{5}{12}$; (b) $2\frac{1}{28}$; (c) $2\frac{13}{280}$. **5.** (a) $1\frac{1}{28}$; (b) $-2\frac{1}{15}$; (c) $5\frac{3}{4}$; (d) $-3\frac{5}{7}$; (e) $-\frac{14}{15}$; (f) $4\frac{3}{5}$; (g) $\frac{1}{4}$. **6** (a) $\frac{2}{5}$; (b) -8; (c) $-3\frac{6}{7}$. **7.** (a) $-\frac{3}{5}$; (b) $\frac{5}{9}$; (c) $-6\frac{1}{4}$; (d) $-\frac{3}{10}$. **8.** (a) $-7\frac{1}{2}$; (b) $\frac{128}{245}$; (c) $-18\frac{37}{80}$. **9.** (a) $-10\frac{1}{2}$; (b) $7\frac{1}{4}$; (c) 2; (d) $2\frac{1}{3}$. **10.** (a) $5\frac{1}{4}$; (b) $\frac{3}{8}$; (c) $\frac{2}{9}$.

Section 3 (page 365)

1. (a) $-8x^3$; (b) $2ab$; (c) $24x^3$; (d) $3aby^2$; (e) $-7x^2y$. **2.** (a) $16a$; (b) $5ab$; (c) $4ac - 4ab$; (d) $2a^2 + 2a + 5b$. **3.** $-6a - 7b - 3c$. **4.** $-14x^2 + 12x - 8$. **5.** (a) $-15abc$; (b) $5m - 8m^2$; (c) $8x^2 - 8y$. **6.** (a) $3a - 11b + 6c$; (b) $-13x - y$; (c) $9x^2 - 2y + 15$. **7.** (a) $9y - xy$; (b) $9y - x^2$; (c) $4b^2 - 24b - a - 8$. **8.** (a) $3a^2 + ab - 2b^2$; (b) $5x - 3y$; (c) 1. **9.** (a) $4x^2 - 25y^2$; (b) $9x^4 - 4y^4$; (c) $4x^2 + 4xy + y^2$; (d) $x^3 - 6x^2y + 12xy^2 -$

$8y^3$. **10.** (a) $25x^2 - 4y^2$; (b) $x^4y^2 - 9a^2$; (c) $4x^2 - 36y^2$; (d) $27x^3 - 27x^2y + 9xy^3 - y^3$. **11.** (a) $4a^2 - 4ax + x^2$; (b) $1 + 3x + 3x^2 + x^3$; (c) $8x^3 - 12x^2 + 6x - 1$; (d) $x^2 + 5x + 6$; (e) $9x^2y^2 + 18xyz - 7z^2$. **12.** (a) $2x^2 - 6xy + 4y^2$; (b) $2a^2 + 11ab - 21b^2$; (c) $x^4 + x^2 - 12$; (d) $x^2/4 - 25y^2$; (e) $x^2/4 - xy/4 + y^2/16$. **13.** (a) $36x^2 - 6x + \frac{1}{4}$; (b) $8 + 36x + 54x^2 + 27x^3$; (c) $25m^6 - 25m^3s^2 - 6s^4$, (d) $9x^2y^2 - 42xy + 49$. **14.** (a) $3m + 2 - 5m^2$; (b) $2x^2 - x$; (c) $x^2 - 12x + 6$; (d) $a - a^2b + b^3$; (e) $5y^2$. **15.** (a) $-20m^2n^4$; (b) $12b^3c^3$; (c) $-40ty^5z$; (d) $8x^4y^2 - 14x^3y^3$; (e) $-a^4$. **16.** (a) $4x^2 + y^2 + 9z^2 - 4xy + 12xz - 6yz$; (b) $x - 2x^2 + x^3 - 2y + 4xy - 2x^2y$; (c) $2x^5 + x^4 - 24x^3 - 12x^2 + 72x + 36$; (d) $2x^3 - 3x^2y - 8xy^2 - 3y^3$; (e) $8x^3 + y^3 - z^3 - 12xyz - 12x^2z + 12x^2y + 6xz^2 + 6xy^2 - 3y^2z + 3yz^2$.

Section 4 (page 367)

1. $(3x^4 - 2y^3)(3x^4 + 2y^3)$. **2.** $(15 - a^3)(15 + a^3)$. **3.** $(r^2 - 5)(r^2 - 6)$. **4.** $(8x + 3)(2x + 3)$. **5.** $3(y + 2)(y^2 - 2y + 4)$. **6.** $(3x - 1)(2x + 3)$. **7.** $(c + 3d)(c^2 - 3cd + 9d^2)$. **8.** $(x - 12)(x - 4)$. **9.** $(y - 3z)(y^2 + 3yz + 9z^2)$. **10.** $(x + 1)(4x - 7)$. **11.** $(3 - 5t)(2 + 3t)$. **12.** $(5t^2 - 1)(5t^2 + 1)$. **13.** $(6a - 11)^2$. **14.** $(u^3 - 10)(u^3 + 11)$. **15.** $3(x^2 - 2)(x^2 + 2)$. **16.** $(x^4 + y^4)(x^2 + y^2)(x + y)(x - y)$. **17.** $(x^2 + y^2)(x - y)^2(x + y)$. **18.** $(x - y)^2 (x^2 + xy + y^2)$. **19.** $(x - 1)^3$. **20.** $(x + y - a)(x + y + a)$. **21.** $(c + a + b)(c - a - b)$. **22.** $(xy + 1)(x^2y^2 - xy + 1)$. **23.** $(2 - 3x)(4 + 6x + 9x^2)$. **24.** $(2m + 3n)(12m - 7n)$. **25.** $(8x + 9)(2x - 3)$. **26.** $(1 + 4x)(9 - x)$. **27.** $(2x^2 - 3y^2)(x^2 + 7y^2)$. **28.** $(x - y - 2z)(x - y + 2z)$. **29.** $(5x - 6)(5x - 8)$. **30.** $y(2x - y)$. **31.** $(5y - 4)(y + 14)$. **32.** $y^4(x^2 - 3)(x^2 + 3)$. **33.** $(2x^2 + 2y + x - 9)(2x^2 + x - 2y + 9)$. **34.** $2(x + 2y)(x - y)$. **35.** $a(a + b)(x + y)$. **36.** $x^3(a - 8y)(a + 8y)$. **37.** $a(x - y)(x + y)(a + b)$. **38.** $(x^2 + 1)(x + 1)$. **39.** $(1 - 2x)(1 + 2x)(2 + 3x)$. **40.** $(7 - 4a)(8 + 3a^2)$. **41.** $(x + y - z)(x^2 + y^2 + z^2 - xy + xz - 2yz)$. **42.** $(m + n + 2t)(m^2 + n^2 + 4t^2 + 2mn - 2mt - 2nt)$. **43.** $(2a + b)(13a^2 - 5ab + b^2)$. **44.** $(x + y - xy)(x + y + xy)$.

Section 5 (page 368)

1. $(5x + y)/6$. **2.** $(x + 4)/4$. **3.** $-(4a + b)/ab$. **4.** $(25x^2 + 12x - 14)/20x^3$. **5.** 0. **6.** $(x + 45)/70$. **7.** $2(x^2 - 2)/(x^2 - 1)$. **8.** $2x/(x + 1)(x + 2)(x + 3)$. **9.** $y(7y - 12)/(y - 2)(3y - 2)$. **10.** $x(a - b)/(x + a)(x + b)$. **11.** $1/(1 - a)(1 + 2a)(2 - 3a)$. **12.** $4x/(x^2 - 4)$. **13.** $3a(2a + 3)/(2a - 1)(a - 1)$. **14.** $x^3/(x^2 - 1)$. **15.** $2(x^3 + x^2 - 9)/x(x - 3)(x + 3)$. **16.** $1/(x + 1)(x + 2)$. **17.** 0. **18.** $(x^2 - 3x + 1)/(x - 2)$. **19.** $(x - y)(x + y)^2/x^2y^2$. **20.** $(x + 1)/(x - 1)$. **21.** $(x - 1)/x(x + 3)$. **22.** $(x + 1)/2$. **23.** $(x + 1)(x^2 + 1)(x^4 + 1)/x^3$. **24.** $(x + 1)/(x - 1)$.

Section 6 (page 371)

1. 4. **2.** $\frac{1}{2}$. **3.** -3. **4.** $-\frac{1}{2}$. **5.** 2. **6.** $7\frac{2}{3}$. **7.** -2. **8.** 5. **9.** $\frac{1}{2}, -3$. **10.** $-\frac{7}{3}, \frac{5}{2}$. **11.** $(-5 \pm \sqrt{37})/2$. **12.** $4, 1$. **13.** $-\frac{7}{3}, 1$. **14.** $-9, 4$. **15.** $-\frac{9}{4}, 5$. **16.** $60, 45$. **17.** $4, 2$. **18.** $6, -1$. **19.** $4, -\frac{10}{3}$. **20.** $\pm 2, \pm 5$. **21.** $(-5 \pm \sqrt{65})/8$. **22.** $3 \pm \sqrt{15}$. **23.** $(2 \pm 2\sqrt{3})/3$. **24.** $(-1 \pm \sqrt{6})/2$. **25.** $(2 \pm \sqrt{10})/4$. **26.** $3, -\frac{5}{3}$. **27.** No real solution. **28.** $\pm 5, \pm 2$. **29.** ± 7. **30.** $5, -3$. **31.** $\frac{1}{3}, 3, 1$. **32.** $\sqrt[3]{7}, \sqrt[3]{5}$. **33.** $\frac{5}{3}, -\frac{3}{2}$. **34.** $-\frac{1}{2}$. **35.** $\frac{2}{3}, 1$. **36.** $-\frac{1}{5}, \frac{1}{3}$. **37.** $-\frac{11}{6}, 2$. **38.** $(-10 \pm \sqrt{110})/10$. **39.** $a, 1/a$. **40.** $(-2 \pm 2\sqrt{13})/3$.

Section 7 (page 374)

1. $x = 7, y = -2$. **2.** $x = 5, y = 4$. **3.** $x = -1, y = 1$. **4.** $x = \frac{15}{13}, y = -\frac{5}{13}$. **5.** $x = 5, y = 3$. **6.** $x = 15, y = 10$. **7.** $x = 4, y = 3$. **8.** $x = 2, y = 3$. **9.** $x = 2, y = 3$. **10.** $x = -\frac{1}{2}, y = \frac{5}{2}$. **11.** $x = -2, y = 1, z = 3$. **12.** $x = 3, y = 1, z = 2$. **13.** $x = 2, y = -1, z = -\frac{1}{3}$. **14.** $x = 2, y = -1, z = 0$. **15.** $x = 6, y = 18, z = 12$. **16.** $x = 2, y = 4, z = 8$. **17.** 6 miles per hour, 3 miles per hour. **18.** $55, 40$.

Section 8 (page 375)

1. (a) $a^{1/2}$; (b) $x^{3/4}$; (c) $a^{7/5}$; (d) $a^{3/2}$; (e) $(a+2)^{1/5}$. 2. (a) $3^{1/2}$; (b) $2^{5/3}$; (c) $4^{4/5}$; (d) $5^{/12}$; (e) $(2+x)^{1/3}$. 3. (a) 3; (b) 729; (c) 3125; (d) 32; (e) 2. 4. (a) $\sqrt[3]{a}$; (b) $\sqrt[6]{x^5}$; (c) $\sqrt[3]{b^n}$; (d) $\sqrt[4]{n^3}$; (e) $\sqrt[6]{s^7}$. 5. (a) x^{n+3}; (b) a^{2n+1}; (c) u^{2n}; (d) p^{21}; (e) a^{12}. 6. (a) x^{2n}; (b) 10^{r+1}; (c) u^{2r}; (d) x^4; (e) $(pq)^{3s}$; (f) $(rs)^{10}$; (g) e^{n+2}. 7. (a) $x^{8/3}$; (b) $a^{9/20}$; (c) $a^{23/21}$; (d) $x^{1/2}$. 8. (a) $a^{1/6}$; (b) $x^{1/2}$; (c) $a^{5/3}$; (d) $ab^{1/4}$. 9. (a) 1; (b) $x^{13/5}$; (c) $\frac{27}{8}x^{21/40}$; (d) $2^{4/3}a^{1/6}b$. 10. (a) $\frac{1}{2}$; (b) $\frac{1}{8}$; (c) $\frac{1}{9}$; (d) 1; (e) 1. 11. (a) 18; (b) 8; (c) 1; (d) $\frac{1}{8}$. 12. (a) a^2/b^2; (b) $1/(a+b)^3$; (c) $3/x^2y^{1/2}$; (d) x^4y^5; (e) x^2. 13. (a) x^{-2}; (b) $xy^2c^{-3}d^{-4}$; (c) $2^{-1}a^3b^{-3}r^2t^{-5}$; (d) $ab^{1/2}x^{1/3}y^{-s/t}$. 14. (a) a^7; (b) $1/x^4$; (c) a^9x^9/b^3y^6; (d) $r^{1/2}$.

Section 9 (page 377)

1. 5. 2. 10. 3. 65. 4. 4. 5. -2. 6. No solution. 7. No solution. 8. 2, 6. 9. No solution. 10. 4. 11. 9. 12. 6. 13. 2. 14. 4. 15. $\frac{1}{4}$ 16. $\frac{1}{81}$. 17. 4. 18. 0.

Section 10 (page 379)

1. (a) 1:2; (b) 10:13; (c) 13:18; (d) 16:17; (e) $(x-y):1$. 2. (a) 1:18; (b) 8:27; (c) 2:3; (d) 10:9. 3. (a) 1:6; (b) 1:6; (c) 1:25. 4. (a) $a:(a-1)$; (b) $(x-3):2$; (c) $x:3$. 5. 75, 50. 6. 8, 20. 7. (a) $\frac{16}{5}$; (b) $\frac{27}{2}$; (c) 12; (d) 9. 8. (a) 6; (b) 4; (c) 8; (d) $2\sqrt{6}$; (e) $2\sqrt{15}$. 9. (a) $\frac{81}{4}$; (b) $\frac{100}{3}$; (c) 72. 10. (a) 6; (b) 33; (c) $-\frac{80}{3}$. 11. $x = 0$. 12. $x = -6$. 13. (a) $y = 3x/2$; (b) $y = 12x/5$; (c) $y = 5x/6$. 14. (a) $y = 24/x$; (b) $y = 100/x$; (c) $y = 60/x$. 15. $v = 32t$, 96 feet. 16. No—proportional to the square of time of fall. 17. (a) 162 miles; (b) $5\frac{1}{2}$ hours. 18. (a) $IR = 2500$; (b) 1 ampere. 19. 72 feet. 20. $\frac{4}{3}$.

Test (page 380)

1. (a) $-1\frac{5}{12}$; (b) $-\frac{31}{60}$. 2. (a) $-1\frac{7}{8}$; (b) $-1\frac{17}{18}$; (c) $\frac{3}{25}$; (d) -10. 3. (a) -1; (b) $(x+1)/(x^2-9)$. 4. (a) $2+2x-5x^2/12$; (b) $a+b$. 5. (a) $(m-2n)(m+2n)$; (b) $(t+11)(t-5)$; (c) $(1+y)(1-y)(1+y+y^2)(1-y+y^2)$. 6. (a) $(a+b)(m+1)$; (b) $(1-y)(1-2x+y)$; (c) $(4x-1)(3x+7)$. 7. (a) $(1-x-y)(1+x+y)$; (b) $x(x+1)(x-7)$. 8. (a) $(5 \pm \sqrt{17})/4$; (b) $-\frac{1}{2}$, -1. 9. (a) $-\frac{1}{2}$, 1; (b) $\frac{2}{3}$, $-\frac{3}{2}$. 10. (a) -1, $\frac{5}{4}$; (b) $(2 \pm \sqrt{6})/2$. 11. (a) $x = 11$, $y = 0$; (b) $y = \frac{7}{2}$, $z = -1$. 12. (a) $x = 5$, $y = 13$, $z = 0$; (b) $x = \frac{1}{2}$, $y = \frac{1}{5}$, $z = 2$. 13. (a) $\sqrt{2}$, $\sqrt[3]{9}$, $\sqrt{64}$, $1/\sqrt{6}$, $1/\sqrt[3]{4}$; (b) $5^{1/5}$, $3^{2/3}$, $3^{-1/2}$, $3(5^{-2/3})$. 14. (a) $y^6/3x^4z$; (b) $64x^2/9y$. 15. (a) 3:7; (b) $x = 3\frac{2}{5}$. 16. $x = -1$. 17. $x = 6$. 18. $4\sqrt{5}$ centimeters.

Index

Bold face numbers refer to chapters; all other numbers refer to pages.